Pearson New International Edition

Quantum Mechanics
McIntyre Manogue Tate
First Edition

Pearson Education Limited
Edinburgh Gate
Harlow
Essex CM20 2JE
England and Associated Companies throughout the world

Visit us on the World Wide Web at: www.pearsoned.co.uk

© Pearson Education Limited 2014

ISBN 10: 1-292-02083-0
ISBN 13: 978-1-292-02083-9

British Library Cataloguing-in-Publication Data
A catalogue record for this book is available from the British Library

Printed in the United States of America

Table of Contents

1. Stern-Gerlach Experiments
David H. McIntyre
1

Problem Set (1/e): Stern-Gerlach Experiments
David H. McIntyre
31

2. Operators and Measurement
David H. McIntyre
35

Problem Set (1/e): Operators and Measurement
David H. McIntyre
67

3. Schrödinger Time Evolution
David H. McIntyre
71

Problem Set (1/e): Schrödinger Time Evolution
David H. McIntyre
99

4. Quantized Energies: Particle in a Box
David H. McIntyre
103

Problem Set (1/e): Quantized Energies: Particle in a Box
David H. McIntyre
155

5. Quantum Spookiness
David H. McIntyre
161

Problem Set (1/e): Quantum Spookiness
David H. McIntyre
171

6. Unbound States
David H. McIntyre
173

Problem Set (1/e): Unbound States
David H. McIntyre
211

7. Angular Momentum
David H. McIntyre
217

Problem Set (1/e): Angular Momentum
David H. McIntyre
263

8. Hydrogen Atom
David H. McIntyre
269

Problem Set (1/e): Hydrogen Atom
David H. McIntyre
293

9. Harmonic Oscillator
David H. McIntyre
297

Problem Set (1/e): Harmonic Oscillator
David H. McIntyre
331

10. Perturbation Theory
David H. McIntyre
335

Problem Set (1/e): Perturbation Theory
David H. McIntyre
377

11. Hyperfine Structure and the Addition of Angular Momenta
David H. McIntyre
383

Problem Set (1/e): Hyperfine Structure and the Addition of Angular Momenta
David H. McIntyre
409

12. Perturbation of Hydrogen
David H. McIntyre
413

Problem Set (1/e): Perturbation of Hydrogen
David H. McIntyre
441

13. Identical Particles
David H. McIntyre
445

Problem Set (1/e): Identical Particles
David H. McIntyre
479

14. Time-Dependent Perturbation Theory
David H. McIntyre
483

Problem Set (1/e): Time-Dependent Perturbation Theory
David H. McIntyre
507

15. Periodic Systems
David H. McIntyre
511

Problem Set (1/e): Periodic Systems
David H. McIntyre
543

16. Modern Applications of Quantum Mechanics
David H. McIntyre
545

Problem Set (1/e): Modern Applications of Quantum Mechanics
David H. McIntyre
573

17. Appendix: Physical Constants
David H. McIntyre
575

18. Appendix: Integrals
David H. McIntyre
577

19. Appendix: Matrices
David H. McIntyre
579

20. Appendix: Waves and Fourier Analysis
David H. McIntyre
583

21. Appendix: Separation of Variables
David H. McIntyre
589

22. Appendix: Complex Numbers
David H. McIntyre
591

23. Appendix: Probability
David H. McIntyre
595

24. Useful Definitions and Equations
David H. McIntyre
599

25. Spin and Angular Momentum Relations; Bound State Systems; Fundamental Constants
David H. McIntyre
601

26. Preface
David H. McIntyre
603

Index
609

Stern-Gerlach Experiments

It was not a dark and stormy night when Otto Stern and Walther Gerlach performed their now famous experiment in 1922. The Stern-Gerlach experiment demonstrated that measurements on microscopic or quantum particles are not always as certain as we might expect. Quantum particles behave as mysteriously as Erwin's socks—sometimes forgetting what we have already measured. Erwin's adventure with the mystery socks is farfetched because you know that everyday objects do not behave like his socks. If you observe a sock to be black, it remains black no matter what other properties of the sock you observe. However, the Stern-Gerlach experiment goes against these ideas. Microscopic or quantum particles do not behave like the classical objects of your everyday experience. The act of observing a quantum particle affects its measurable properties in a way that is foreign to our classical experience.

We focus on the Stern-Gerlach experiment because it is a conceptually simple experiment that demonstrates many basic principles of quantum mechanics. The mathematical formalism of quantum mechanics is based upon six postulates. (A complete list of these postulates is in Section 5.) We use the Stern-Gerlach experiment to learn about quantum mechanics theory for two primary reasons: (1) It demonstrates how quantum mechanics works in principle by illustrating the postulates of quantum mechanics, and (2) it demonstrates how quantum mechanics works in practice through the use of Dirac notation and matrix mechanics to solve problems. By using a simple example, we can focus on the principles and the new mathematics, rather than having the complexity of the physics obscure these new aspects.

1 ■ STERN-GERLACH EXPERIMENT

In 1922 Otto Stern and Walther Gerlach performed a seminal experiment in the history of quantum mechanics. In its simplest form, the experiment consisted of an oven that produced a beam of neutral atoms, a region of space with an inhomogeneous magnetic field, and a detector for the atoms, as depicted in Fig. 1. Stern and Gerlach used a beam of silver atoms and found that the beam was split into two in its passage through the magnetic field. One beam was deflected upwards and one downwards in relation to the direction of the magnetic field gradient.

To understand why this result is so at odds with our classical expectations, we must first analyze the experiment classically. The results of the experiment suggest an interaction between a neutral particle and a magnetic field. We expect such an interaction if the particle possesses a magnetic moment $\boldsymbol{\mu}$. The potential energy of this interaction is $E = -\boldsymbol{\mu}\cdot\mathbf{B}$, which results in a force $\mathbf{F} = \nabla(\boldsymbol{\mu}\cdot\mathbf{B})$. In the

The companion websites for this text are http://physics.oregonstate.edu/portfolioswiki and http://physics.oregonstate.edu/qmactivities.

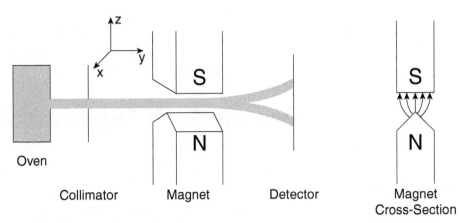

FIGURE 1   Stern-Gerlach experiment to measure the spin component of neutral particles along the z-axis. The magnet cross section at right shows the inhomogeneous field used in the experiment.

Stern-Gerlach experiment, the magnetic field gradient is primarily in the z-direction, and the resulting z-component of the force is

$$F_z = \frac{\partial}{\partial z}(\boldsymbol{\mu} \cdot \mathbf{B})$$

$$\cong \mu_z \frac{\partial B_z}{\partial z}. \tag{1}$$

This force is perpendicular to the direction of motion and deflects the beam in proportion to the component of the magnetic moment in the direction of the magnetic field gradient.

Now consider how to understand the origin of the atom's magnetic moment from a classical viewpoint. The atom consists of charged particles, which, if in motion, can produce loops of current that give rise to magnetic moments. A loop of area A and current I produces a magnetic moment

$$\mu = IA \tag{2}$$

in MKS units. If this loop of current arises from a charge q traveling at speed v in a circle of radius r, then

$$\mu = \frac{q}{2\pi r / v} \pi r^2$$

$$= \frac{qrv}{2} \tag{3}$$

$$= \frac{q}{2m} L,$$

where $L = mrv$ is the orbital angular momentum of the particle. In the same way that the earth revolves around the sun and rotates around its own axis, we can also imagine a charged particle in an atom having **orbital angular momentum L** and a new property, the **intrinsic angular momentum**, which we label **S** and call **spin**. The intrinsic angular momentum also creates current loops, so we expect a similar relation between the magnetic moment $\boldsymbol{\mu}$ and **S**. The exact calculation involves an integral over the charge distribution, which we will not do. We simply assume that we can relate the magnetic moment to the intrinsic angular momentum in the same fashion as Eq. (3), giving

$$\boldsymbol{\mu} = g\frac{q}{2m}\mathbf{S},\tag{4}$$

where the dimensionless **gyroscopic ratio** g contains the details of that integral.

A silver atom has 47 electrons, 47 protons, and 60 or 62 neutrons (for the most common isotopes). The magnetic moments depend on the inverse of the particle mass, so we expect the heavy protons and neutrons ($\approx 2000\, m_e$) to have little effect on the magnetic moment of the atom and so we neglect them. From your study of the periodic table in chemistry, you recall that silver has an electronic configuration $1s^2 2s^2 2p^6 3s^2 3p^6 4s^2 3d^{10} 4p^6 4d^{10} 5s^1$, which means that there is only the lone $5s$ electron outside of the closed shells. The electrons in the closed shells can be represented by a spherically symmetric cloud with no orbital or intrinsic angular momentum (unfortunately we are injecting some quantum mechanical knowledge of atomic physics into this classical discussion). That leaves the lone $5s$ electron as a contributor to the magnetic moment of the atom as a whole. An electron in an s state has no orbital angular momentum, but it does have spin. Hence the magnetic moment of this electron, and therefore of the entire neutral silver atom, is

$$\boldsymbol{\mu} = -g\frac{e}{2m_e}\mathbf{S},\tag{5}$$

where e is the magnitude of the electron charge. The classical force on the atom can now be written as

$$F_z \cong -g\frac{e}{2m_e}S_z\frac{\partial B_z}{\partial z}.\tag{6}$$

The deflection of the beam in the Stern-Gerlach experiment is thus a measure of the component (or projection) S_z of the spin along the z-axis, which is the orientation of the magnetic field gradient.

If we assume that the $5s$ electron of each atom has the same magnitude $|\mathbf{S}|$ of the intrinsic angular momentum or spin, then classically we would write the z-component as $S_z = |\mathbf{S}|\cos\theta$, where θ is the angle between the z-axis and the direction of the spin $\mathbf{S}$. In the thermal environment of the oven, we expect a random distribution of spin directions and hence all possible angles θ. Thus we expect some continuous distribution (the details are not important) of spin components from $S_z = -|\mathbf{S}|$ to $S_z = +|\mathbf{S}|$, which would yield a continuous spread in deflections of the silver atomic beam. Rather, the experimental result that Stern and Gerlach observed was that there are only two deflections, indicating that there are only two possible values of the z-component of the electron spin. The magnitudes of these deflections are consistent with values of the spin component of

$$S_z = \pm\frac{\hbar}{2},\tag{7}$$

where $\hbar$ is Planck's constant h divided by 2π and has the numerical value

$$\begin{aligned}\hbar &= 1.0546 \times 10^{-34} \text{ J·s}\\ &= 6.5821 \times 10^{-16} \text{ eV·s}.\end{aligned}\tag{8}$$

This result of the Stern-Gerlach experiment is evidence of the **quantization** of the electron's spin angular momentum component along an axis. This quantization is at odds with our classical expectations for this measurement. The factor of 1/2 in Eq. (7) leads us to refer to this as a **spin-1/2** system.

In this example, we have chosen the z-axis along which to measure the spin component, but there is nothing special about this direction in space. We could have chosen any other axis and we would have obtained the same results.

Now that we know the fine details of the Stern-Gerlach experiment, we simplify the experiment for the rest of our discussions by focusing on the essential features. A simplified schematic representation of the experiment is shown in Fig. 2, which depicts an oven that produces the beam of atoms, a Stern-Gerlach device with two output ports for the two possible values of the spin component, and two counters to detect the atoms leaving the output ports of the Stern-Gerlach device. The Stern-Gerlach device is labeled with the axis along which the magnetic field is oriented. The up and down arrows indicate the two possible measurement results for the device; they correspond respectively to the results $S_z = \pm \hbar/2$ in the case where the field is oriented along the z-axis. There are only two possible results in this case, so they are generally referred to as **spin up** and **spin down**. The physical quantity that is measured, S_z in this case, is called an **observable**. In our detailed discussion of the experiment above, we chose the field gradient in such a manner that the spin up states were deflected upwards. In this new simplification, the deflection itself is not an important issue. We simply label the output port with the desired state and count the particles leaving that port. The Stern-Gerlach device sorts (or filters, selects or analyzes) the incoming particles into the two possible outputs $S_z = \pm \hbar/2$ in the same way that Erwin sorted his socks according to color or length. We follow convention and refer to a Stern-Gerlach device as an **analyzer**.

In Fig. 2, the input and output beams are labeled with a new symbol called a **ket**. We use the ket $|+\rangle$ as a mathematical representation of the quantum state of the atoms that exit the upper port corresponding to $S_z = +\hbar/2$. The lower output beam is labeled with the ket $|-\rangle$, which corresponds to $S_z = -\hbar/2$, and the input beam is labeled with the more generic ket $|\psi\rangle$. The kets are representations of the quantum states. They are used in mathematical expressions and they represent all the information that we can know about the state. This ket notation was developed by Paul A. M. Dirac and is central to the approach to quantum mechanics that we take in this text. We will discuss the mathematics of these kets in full detail later. With regard to notation, you will find many different ways of writing the same ket. The symbol within the ket brackets is any simple label to distinguish the ket from other different kets. For example, the kets $|+\rangle$, $|+\hbar/2\rangle$, $|S_z = +\hbar/2\rangle$, $|+\hat{\mathbf{z}}\rangle$, and $|\uparrow\rangle$ are all equivalent ways of writing the same thing, which in this case signifies that we have measured the z-component of the spin and found it to be $+\hbar/2$ or spin up. Though we may label these kets in different ways, they all refer to the same physical state and so they all behave the same mathematically. The symbol $|\pm\rangle$ refers to both the $|+\rangle$ and $|-\rangle$ kets. The first postulate of quantum mechanics tells us that kets in general describe the quantum state mathematically and that they contain all the information that we can know about the state. We denote a general ket as $|\psi\rangle$.

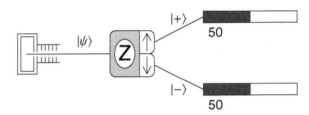

FIGURE 2 Simplified schematic of the Stern-Gerlach experiment, depicting a source of atoms, a Stern-Gerlach analyzer, and two counters.

Postulate 1

The state of a quantum mechanical system, including all the information you can know about it, is represented mathematically by a normalized ket $|\psi\rangle$.

We have chosen the particular simplified schematic representation of the Stern-Gerlach experiment shown in Fig. 2, because it is the same representation used in the SPINS software program that you may use to simulate these experiments. The SPINS program allows you to perform all the experiments described in this text. This software is freely available, as detailed in Resources at the end of the chapter. In the SPINS program, the components are connected with simple lines to represent the paths the atoms take. The directions and magnitudes of deflections of the beams in the program are not relevant. That is, whether the spin up output beam is drawn as deflected upwards, downwards, or not at all, is not relevant. The labeling on the output port is enough to tell us what that state is. Thus the extra ket label $|+\rangle$ on the spin up output beam in Fig. 2 is redundant and will be dropped soon.

The SPINS program permits alignment of Stern-Gerlach analyzing devices along all three axes and also at any angle ϕ measured from the x-axis in the x-y plane. This would appear to be difficult, if not impossible, given that the atomic beam in Fig. 1 is directed along the y-axis, making it unclear how to align the magnet in the y-direction and measure a deflection. In our depiction and discussion of Stern-Gerlach experiments, we ignore this technical complication.

In the SPINS program, as in real Stern-Gerlach experiments, the numbers of atoms detected in particular states can be predicted by probability rules that we will discuss later. To simplify our schematic depictions of Stern-Gerlach experiments, the numbers shown for detected atoms are those obtained by using the calculated probabilities without any regard to possible statistical uncertainties. That is, if the theoretically predicted probabilities of two measurement possibilities are each 50%, then our schematics will display equal numbers for those two possibilities, whereas in a real experiment, statistical uncertainties might yield a 55%/45% split in one experiment and a 47%/53% split in another, etc. The SPINS program simulations are designed to give statistical uncertainties, so you will need to perform enough experiments to convince yourself that you have a sufficiently good estimate of the probability (see SPINS Lab 1 for more information on statistics).

Now let's consider a series of simple Stern-Gerlach experiments with slight variations that help to illustrate the main features of quantum mechanics. We first describe the experiments and their results and draw some qualitative conclusions about the nature of quantum mechanics. Then we introduce the formal mathematics of the ket notation and show how it can be used to predict the results of each of the experiments.

1.1 ■ Experiment 1

The first experiment is shown in Fig. 3 and consists of a source of atoms, two Stern-Gerlach analyzers both aligned along the z-axis, and counters for the output ports of the analyzers. The atomic beam coming into the first Stern-Gerlach analyzer is split into two beams at the output, just like the original experiment. Now instead of counting the atoms in the upper output beam, the spin component is measured again by directing those atoms into the second Stern-Gerlach analyzer. The result of this experiment is that no atoms are ever detected coming out of the lower output port of the second Stern-Gerlach analyzer. All atoms that are output from the upper port of the first analyzer also pass

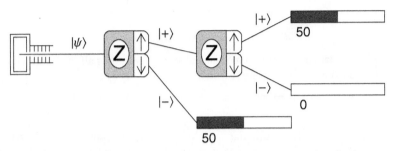

FIGURE 3 Experiment 1 measures the spin component along the z-axis twice in succession.

through the upper port of the second analyzer. Thus we say that when the first Stern-Gerlach analyzer measures an atom to have a z-component of spin $S_z = +\hbar/2$, then the second analyzer also measures $S_z = +\hbar/2$ for that atom. This result is not surprising, but it sets the stage for results of experiments to follow.

Though both Stern-Gerlach analyzers in Experiment 1 are identical, they play different roles in this experiment. The first analyzer *prepares* the beam in a particular quantum state $(|+\rangle)$ and the second analyzer *measures* the resultant beam, so we often refer to the first analyzer as a **state preparation device**. By preparing the state with the first analyzer, the details of the source of atoms can be ignored. Thus our main focus in Experiment 1 is what happens at the second analyzer because we know that any atom entering the second analyzer is represented by the $|+\rangle$ ket prepared by the first analyzer. All the experiments we will describe employ a first analyzer as a state preparation device, though the SPINS program has a feature where the state of the atoms coming from the oven is determined but unknown, and the user can perform experiments to determine the unknown state using only one analyzer in the experiment.

1.2 ■ Experiment 2

The second experiment is shown in Fig. 4 and is identical to Experiment 1 except that the second Stern-Gerlach analyzer has been rotated by 90° to be aligned with the x-axis. Now the second analyzer measures the spin component along the x-axis rather the z-axis. Atoms input to the second analyzer are still represented by the ket $|+\rangle$ because the first analyzer is unchanged. The result of this experiment is that atoms appear at both possible output ports of the second analyzer. Atoms leaving the upper port of the second analyzer have been measured to have $S_x = +\hbar/2$, and atoms leaving

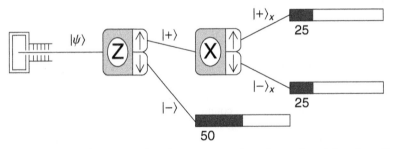

FIGURE 4 Experiment 2 measures the spin component along the z-axis and then along the x-axis.

the lower port have $S_x = -\hbar/2$. On average, each of these ports has 50% of the atoms that left the upper port of the first analyzer. As shown in Fig. 4, the output states of the second analyzer have new labels $|+\rangle_x$ and $|-\rangle_x$, where the x subscript denotes that the spin component has been measured along the x-axis. We assume that if no subscript is present on the quantum ket (e.g., $|+\rangle$), then the spin component is along the z-axis. This use of the z-axis as the default is a common convention throughout our work and also in much of physics.

A few items are noteworthy about this experiment. First, we notice that there are still only two possible outputs of the second Stern-Gerlach analyzer. The fact that it is aligned along a different axis doesn't affect the fact that we get only two possible results for the case of a spin-1/2 particle. Second, it turns out that the results of this experiment would be unchanged if we used the lower port of the first analyzer. That is, atoms entering the second analyzer in state $|-\rangle$ would also result in half the atoms in each of the $|\pm\rangle_x$ output ports. Finally, we cannot predict which of the second analyzer output ports any particular atom will come out. This can be demonstrated in actual experiments by recording the individual counts out of each port. The arrival sequences at any counter are completely random. We can say only that there is a 50% probability that an atom from the second analyzer will exit the upper analyzer port and a 50% probability that it will exit the lower port. The random arrival of atoms at the detectors can be seen clearly in the SPINS program simulations.

This probabilistic nature is at the heart of quantum mechanics. One might be tempted to say that we just don't know enough about the system to predict which port the atom will exit. That is to say, there may be some other variables, of which we are ignorant, that would allow us to predict the results. Such a viewpoint is known as a **local hidden variable theory**. John Bell proved that such theories are not compatible with the experimental results of quantum mechanics. The conclusion to draw from this is that even though quantum mechanics is a probabilistic theory, it is a complete description of reality.

Note that the 50% probability referred to above is the probability that an atom input to the second analyzer exits one particular output port. It is not the probability for an atom to pass through the whole system of Stern-Gerlach analyzers. It turns out that the results of this experiment (the 50/50 split at the second analyzer) are the same for any combination of two orthogonal axes of the first and second analyzers.

1.3 ■ Experiment 3

Experiment 3, shown in Fig. 5, extends Experiment 2 by adding a third Stern-Gerlach analyzer aligned along the z-axis. Atoms entering the third analyzer have been measured by the first Stern-Gerlach analyzer to have spin component up along the z-axis, and by the second analyzer to have spin component up along the x-axis. The third analyzer then measures how many atoms have spin component up or down

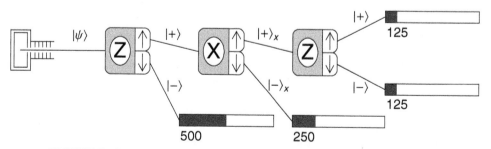

FIGURE 5 Experiment 3 measures the spin component three times in succession.

along the z-axis. Classically, one would expect that the final measurement would yield the result spin up along the z-axis, because that was measured at the first analyzer. That is to say: classically the first two analyzers tell us that the atoms have $S_z = +\hbar/2$ and $S_x = +\hbar/2$, so the third measurement must yield $S_z = +\hbar/2$. But that doesn't happen, as Erwin learned with his quantum socks in the Prologue. The quantum mechanical result is that the atoms are split with 50% probability into each output port at the third analyzer. Thus the last two analyzers behave like the two analyzers of Experiment 2 (except with the order reversed), and the fact that there was an initial measurement that yielded $S_z = +\hbar/2$ is somehow forgotten or erased.

This result demonstrates another key feature of quantum mechanics: a measurement disturbs the system. The second analyzer has disturbed the system such that the spin component along the z-axis does not have a unique value, even though we measured it with the first analyzer. Erwin saw this when he sorted, or measured, his socks by color and then by length. When he looked, or measured, a third time, he found that the color he had measured originally was now random—the socks had forgotten about the first measurement. One might ask: Can I be more clever in designing the experiment such that I don't disturb the system? The short answer is no. There is a fundamental incompatibility in trying to measure the spin component of the atom along two different directions. So we say that S_x and S_z are **incompatible observables**. We cannot know the measured values of both simultaneously. The state of the system can be represented by the ket $|+\rangle = |S_z = +\hbar/2\rangle$ or by the ket $|+\rangle_x = |S_x = +\hbar/2\rangle$, but it cannot be represented by a ket $|S_z = +\hbar/2, S_x = +\hbar/2\rangle$ that specifies values of both components. Having said this, it should be said that not all pairs of quantum mechanical observables are incompatible. It is possible to do some experiments without disturbing some of the other aspects of the system. Whether two observables are compatible or not is very important in how we analyze a quantum mechanical system.

Not being able to measure both the S_z and S_x spin components is clearly distinct from the classical case where we can measure all three components of the spin vector, which tells us which direction the spin is pointing. In quantum mechanics, the incompatibility of the spin components means that we cannot know which direction the spin is pointing. So when we say "the spin is up," we really mean only that the spin component along that one axis is up (vs. down). The quantum mechanical spin vector cannot be said to be pointing in any given direction. As is often the case, we must check our classical intuition at the door of quantum mechanics.

1.4 ■ Experiment 4

Experiment 4 is depicted in Fig. 6 and is a slight variation on Experiment 3. Before we get into the details, note a few changes in the schematic drawings. As promised, we have dropped the ket labels on the beams because they are redundant. We have deleted the counters on all but the last analyzer and instead simply blocked the unwanted beams and given the average number of atoms passing from one analyzer to the next. The beam blocks are shown explicitly in Fig. 6 but will not be shown after this to be consistent with the SPINS program. Note also that in Experiment 4c two output beams are combined as input to the following analyzer. This is simple in principle and in the SPINS program but can be difficult in practice. The recombination of the beams must be done properly so as to avoid "disturbing" the beams. If you care to read more about this problem, see Feynman's *Lectures on Physics*, volume 3. For now we simply assume that the beams can be recombined in the proper manner.

Experiment 4a is identical to Experiment 3. In Experiment 4b, the upper beam of the second analyzer is blocked and the lower beam is sent to the third analyzer. In Experiment 4c, both beams are combined with our new method and sent to the third analyzer. It should be clear from our previous experiments that Experiment 4b has the same results as Experiment 4a. We now ask about the results of

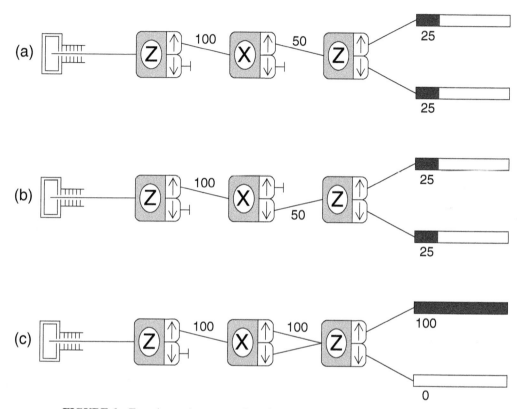

FIGURE 6 Experiment 4 measures the spin component three times in succession and uses (a and b) one or (c) two beams from the second analyzer.

Experiment 4c. If we were to use classical probability analysis, then Experiment 4a would indicate that the probability for an atom leaving the first analyzer to take the upper path through the second analyzer and then exit through the upper port of the third analyzer is 25%, where we are now referring to the total probability for those two steps. Likewise, Experiment 4b would indicate that the total probability to take the lower path through the second analyzer and exit through the upper port of the third analyzer is also 25%. Hence the total probability to exit from the upper port of the third analyzer when both paths are available, which is Experiment 4c, would be 50%, and likewise for the exit from the lower port.

However, the quantum mechanical result in Experiment 4c is that all the atoms exit the upper port of the third analyzer and none exits the lower port. The atoms now appear to "remember" that they were initially measured to have spin up along the z-axis. By combining the two beams from the second analyzer, we have avoided the quantum mechanical disturbance that was evident in Experiments 3, 4a, and 4b. The result is now the same as Experiment 1, which means it is as if the second analyzer is not there.

To see how odd this is, look carefully at what happens at the lower port of the third analyzer. In this discussion, we refer to percentages of atoms leaving the first analyzer, because that analyzer is the same in all three experiments. In Experiments 4a and 4b, 50% of the atoms are blocked after the middle analyzer and 25% of the atoms exit the lower port of the third analyzer. In Experiment 4c, 100% of the atoms pass from the second analyzer to the third analyzer, yet fewer atoms come out of the lower port. In fact, no atoms make it through the lower port! So we have a situation where

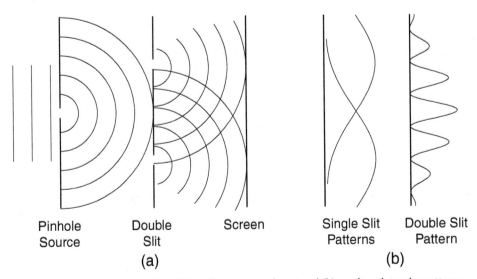

FIGURE 7 (a) Young's double-slit interference experiment and (b) resultant intensity patterns observed on the screen, demonstrating single-slit diffraction and double-slit interference.

allowing more ways or paths to reach a counter results in fewer counts. Classical probability theory cannot explain this aspect of quantum mechanics. It is as if you opened a second window in a room to get more sunlight and the room went dark!

However, you may already know of a way to explain this effect. Imagine a procedure whereby combining two effects leads to cancellation rather than enhancement. The concept of wave interference, especially in optics, comes to mind. In the Young's double-slit experiment, light waves pass through two narrow slits and create an interference pattern on a distant screen, as shown in Fig. 7. Either slit by itself produces a nearly uniform illumination of the screen, but the two slits combined produce bright and dark interference fringes, as shown in Fig. 7(b). We explain this by adding together the electric field vectors of the light from the two slits, then squaring the resultant vector to find the light intensity. We say that we add the amplitudes and then square the total amplitude to find the resultant intensity. See an optics textbook for more details about this experiment.

We follow a similar prescription in quantum mechanics. We add together amplitudes and then take the square to find the resultant probability, which opens the door to interference effects. Before we discuss quantum mechanical interference, we must explain what we mean by an amplitude in quantum mechanics and how we calculate it.

2 ■ QUANTUM STATE VECTORS

Postulate 1 of quantum mechanics stipulates that kets are to be used for a mathematical description of a quantum mechanical system. These kets are abstract entities that obey many of the rules you know about ordinary spatial vectors. Hence they are called **quantum state vectors**. As we will show in Example 3, these vectors must employ complex numbers in order to properly describe quantum mechanical systems. Quantum state vectors are part of a vector space that we call a **Hilbert space**. The dimensionality of the Hilbert space is determined by the physics of the system at hand. In the Stern-Gerlach example, the two possible results for a spin component measurement dictate that the vector space has only two dimensions. That makes this problem mathematically as simple as it can be, which is why we have chosen to study it. Because the quantum state vectors are abstract, it is hard to say much about what they are, other than how they behave mathematically and how they lead to physical predictions.

In the two-dimensional vector space of a spin-1/2 system, the two kets $|\pm\rangle$ form a basis, just like the **unit vectors** $\hat{\mathbf{i}}$, $\hat{\mathbf{j}}$, and $\hat{\mathbf{k}}$ form a basis for describing vectors in three-dimensional space. However, the analogy we want to make with these spatial vectors is only mathematical, not physical. The spatial unit vectors have three important mathematical properties that are characteristic of a basis: the basis vectors $\hat{\mathbf{i}}$, $\hat{\mathbf{j}}$, and $\hat{\mathbf{k}}$ are **normalized**, **orthogonal**, and **complete**. Spatial vectors are normalized if their magnitudes are unity, and they are orthogonal if they are geometrically perpendicular to each other. The basis is complete if any general vector in the space can be written as a linear superposition of the basis vectors. These properties of spatial basis vectors can be summarized as follows:

$$\hat{\mathbf{i}}\cdot\hat{\mathbf{i}} = \hat{\mathbf{j}}\cdot\hat{\mathbf{j}} = \hat{\mathbf{k}}\cdot\hat{\mathbf{k}} = 1 \qquad normalization$$

$$\hat{\mathbf{i}}\cdot\hat{\mathbf{j}} = \hat{\mathbf{i}}\cdot\hat{\mathbf{k}} = \hat{\mathbf{j}}\cdot\hat{\mathbf{k}} = 0 \qquad orthogonality \qquad (9)$$

$$\mathbf{A} = a_x\hat{\mathbf{i}} + a_y\hat{\mathbf{j}} + a_z\hat{\mathbf{k}} \qquad completeness,$$

where $\mathbf{A}$ is a general vector. Note that the **dot product**, also called the **scalar product**, is central to the description of these properties.

Continuing the mathematical analogy between spatial vectors and abstract vectors, we require that these same properties (at least conceptually) apply to quantum mechanical basis vectors. For the S_z measurement, there are only two possible results, corresponding to the states $|+\rangle$ and $|-\rangle$, so these two states comprise a complete set of basis vectors. This basis is known as the S_z **basis**. We focus on this basis for now and refer to other possible basis sets later. The completeness of the basis kets $|\pm\rangle$ implies that a general quantum state vector $|\psi\rangle$ is a linear combination of the two basis kets:

$$|\psi\rangle = a|+\rangle + b|-\rangle, \qquad (10)$$

where a and b are complex scalar numbers multiplying each ket. This addition of two kets yields another ket in the same abstract space. The complex scalar can appear either before or after the ket without affecting the mathematical properties of the ket (i.e., $a|+\rangle = |+\rangle a$). It is customary to use the Greek letter ψ (psi) for a general quantum state. You may have seen $\psi(x)$ used before as a quantum mechanical wave function. However, the state vector or ket $|\psi\rangle$ is not a wave function. Kets do not have any spatial dependence as wave functions do.

To discuss orthogonality and normalization (known together as **orthonormality**) we must first define scalar products as they apply to these new kets. As we said above, the machinery of quantum mechanics requires the use of complex numbers. You may have seen other fields of physics use complex numbers. For example, sinusoidal oscillations can be described using the complex exponential $e^{i\omega t}$ rather than $\cos(\omega t)$. However, in such cases, the complex numbers are not required, but are rather a convenience to make the mathematics easier. When using complex notation to describe classical vectors like electric and magnetic fields, the definition of the dot product is generalized slightly, such that one of the vectors is complex conjugated. A similar approach is taken in quantum mechanics. The analog to the complex conjugated vector of classical physics is called a **bra** in the Dirac notation of quantum mechanics. Thus corresponding to a general ket $|\psi\rangle$, there is a bra, or bra vector, which is written as $\langle\psi|$. If a general ket $|\psi\rangle$ is specified as $|\psi\rangle = a|+\rangle + b|-\rangle$, then the corresponding bra $\langle\psi|$ is defined as

$$\langle\psi| = a^*\langle+| + b^*\langle-|, \qquad (11)$$

where the basis bras $\langle +|$ and $\langle -|$ correspond to the basis kets $|+\rangle$ and $|-\rangle$, respectively, and the coefficients a and b have been complex conjugated.

The scalar product in quantum mechanics is defined as the product of a bra and a ket taken in the proper order—bra first, then ket second:

$$(\langle bra|)(|ket\rangle). \tag{12}$$

When the bra and ket are combined together in this manner, we get a bracket (*bra ket*)—*a little physics humor*—that is written in shorthand as

$$\langle bra|ket\rangle. \tag{13}$$

Thus, given the basis kets $|+\rangle$ and $|-\rangle$, one inner product, for example, is written as

$$(\langle +|)(|-\rangle) = \langle +|-\rangle \tag{14}$$

and so on. Note that we have eliminated the extra vertical bar in the middle. The scalar product in quantum mechanics is generally referred to as an **inner product** or a **projection**.

So how do we calculate the inner product $\langle +|+\rangle$? We do it the same way we calculate the dot product $\hat{\mathbf{i}} \cdot \hat{\mathbf{i}}$. We define it to be unity because we like basis vectors to be unit vectors. There is a little more to it than that, because in quantum mechanics (as we will see shortly) using normalized basis vectors is more rooted in physics than in our personal preferences for mathematical cleanliness. But for all practical purposes, if someone presents a set of basis vectors to you, you can probably assume that they are normalized. So the normalization of the spin-1/2 basis vectors is expressed in this new notation as $\langle +|+\rangle = 1$ and $\langle -|-\rangle = 1$.

Now, what about orthogonality? The spatial unit vectors $\hat{\mathbf{i}}$, $\hat{\mathbf{j}}$, and $\hat{\mathbf{k}}$ used for spatial vectors are orthogonal to each other because they are at $90°$ with respect to each other. That orthogonality is expressed mathematically in the dot products $\hat{\mathbf{i}} \cdot \hat{\mathbf{j}} = \hat{\mathbf{i}} \cdot \hat{\mathbf{k}} = \hat{\mathbf{j}} \cdot \hat{\mathbf{k}} = 0$. For the spin basis kets $|+\rangle$ and $|-\rangle$, there is no spatial geometry involved. Rather, the spin basis kets $|+\rangle$ and $|-\rangle$ are orthogonal in the mathematical sense, which we express with the inner product as $\langle +|-\rangle = 0$. Again, we do not prove to you that these basis vectors are orthogonal, but we assume that a well-behaved basis set obeys orthogonality. Though there is no geometry in this property for quantum mechanical basis vectors, the fundamental idea of orthogonality is the same, so we use the same language—if a general vector "points" in the direction of a basis vector, then there is no component in the "direction" of the other unit vectors.

In summary, the properties of normalization, orthogonality, and completeness can be expressed in the case of a two-state spin-1/2 quantum system as:

$$\left. \begin{array}{l} \langle +|+\rangle = 1 \\ \langle -|-\rangle = 1 \end{array} \right\} \quad normalization$$

$$\left. \begin{array}{l} \langle +|-\rangle = 0 \\ \langle -|+\rangle = 0 \end{array} \right\} \quad orthogonality \tag{15}$$

$$|\psi\rangle = a|+\rangle + b|-\rangle \quad completeness \quad .$$

Note that a product of kets (e.g., $|+\rangle|+\rangle$) or a similar product of bras (e.g., $\langle +|\langle +|$) is meaningless in this new notation, while a product of a ket and a bra in the "wrong" order (e.g., $|+\rangle\langle +|$) has a meaning. Equations (15) are sufficient to define how the basis kets behave mathematically.

Note that the inner product is defined using a bra and a ket, though it is common to refer to the inner product of two kets, where it is understood that one is converted to a bra first. The order does matter, as we will see shortly.

Using this new notation, we can learn a little more about general quantum states and derive some expressions that will be useful later. Consider the general state vector $|\psi\rangle = a|+\rangle + b|-\rangle$. Take the inner product of this ket with the bra $\langle+|$ and obtain

$$
\begin{aligned}
\langle+|\psi\rangle &= \langle+|\,(a|+\rangle + b|-\rangle) \\
&= \langle+|a|+\rangle + \langle+|b|-\rangle \\
&= a\langle+|+\rangle + b\langle+|-\rangle \\
&= a,
\end{aligned}
\tag{16}
$$

using the properties that inner products are distributive and that scalars can be moved freely through bras or kets. Likewise, you can show that $\langle-|\psi\rangle = b$. Hence the coefficients multiplying the basis kets are simply the inner products or projections of the general state $|\psi\rangle$ along each basis ket, albeit in an abstract complex vector space rather than the concrete three-dimensional space of normal vectors. Using these results, we rewrite the general state as

$$
\begin{aligned}
|\psi\rangle &= a|+\rangle + b|-\rangle \\
&= |+\rangle a + |-\rangle b \\
&= |+\rangle\{\langle+|\psi\rangle\} + |-\rangle\{\langle-|\psi\rangle\},
\end{aligned}
\tag{17}
$$

where the rearrangement of the second equation again uses the property that scalars (e.g., $a = \langle+|\psi\rangle$) can be moved through bras or kets.

For a general state vector $|\psi\rangle = a|+\rangle + b|-\rangle$, we defined the corresponding bra to be $\langle\psi| = a^*\langle+|+b^*\langle-|$. Thus, the inner product of the state $|\psi\rangle$ with the basis ket $|+\rangle$ taken in the reverse order compared to Eq. (16) yields

$$
\begin{aligned}
\langle\psi|+\rangle &= \langle+|a^*|+\rangle + \langle-|b^*|+\rangle \\
&= a^*\langle+|+\rangle + b^*\langle-|+\rangle \\
&= a^*.
\end{aligned}
\tag{18}
$$

Thus, we see that an inner product with the states reversed results in a complex conjugation of the inner product:

$$
\langle+|\psi\rangle = \langle\psi|+\rangle^*.
\tag{19}
$$

This important property holds for any inner product. For example, the inner product of two general states is

$$
\boxed{\langle\phi|\psi\rangle = \langle\psi|\phi\rangle^*}.
\tag{20}
$$

Now we come to a new mathematical aspect of quantum vectors that differs from the use of vectors in classical mechanics. The rules of quantum mechanics (postulate 1) require that all state vectors describing a quantum system be normalized, not just the basis kets. This is clearly different from ordinary spatial vectors, where the length or magnitude of a vector means something and only the unit vectors $\hat{\mathbf{i}}$, $\hat{\mathbf{j}}$, and $\hat{\mathbf{k}}$ are normalized to unity. This new rule means that in the quantum mechanical state space only the direction—in an abstract sense—is important. If we apply this normalization requirement to a general state $|\psi\rangle$, then we obtain

$$
\begin{aligned}
\langle\psi|\psi\rangle &= \{a^*\langle+| + b^*\langle-|\}\{a|+\rangle + b|-\rangle\} = 1 \\
&\Rightarrow a^*a\langle+|+\rangle + a^*b\langle+|-\rangle + b^*a\langle-|+\rangle + b^*b\langle-|-\rangle = 1 \\
&\Rightarrow a^*a + b^*b = 1 \\
&\Rightarrow |a|^2 + |b|^2 = 1,
\end{aligned} \tag{21}
$$

or using the expressions for the coefficients obtained above,

$$
_{\circ}|\langle+|\psi\rangle|^2 + |\langle-|\psi\rangle|^2 = 1. \tag{22}
$$

Example 1 Normalize the vector $|\psi\rangle = C(1|+\rangle + 2i|-\rangle)$. The complex constant C is often referred to as the **normalization constant**.

To normalize $|\psi\rangle$, we set the inner product of the vector with itself equal to unity and then solve for C—note the requisite complex conjugations

$$
\begin{aligned}
1 &= \langle\psi|\psi\rangle \\
&= C^*\{1\langle+| - 2i\langle-|\}C\{1|+\rangle + 2i|-\rangle\} \\
&= C^*C\{1\langle+|+\rangle + 2i\langle+|-\rangle - 2i\langle-|+\rangle + 4\langle-|-\rangle\} \\
&= 5|C|^2 \\
&\Rightarrow |C| = \frac{1}{\sqrt{5}}.
\end{aligned} \tag{23}
$$

The overall phase of the normalization constant is not physically meaningful (Problem 3), so we follow the standard convention and choose it to be real and positive. This yields $C = 1/\sqrt{5}$. The normalized quantum state vector is then

$$
|\psi\rangle = \frac{1}{\sqrt{5}}(1|+\rangle + 2i|-\rangle). \tag{24}
$$

Now comes the crucial element of quantum mechanics. We postulate that each term in the sum of Eq. (22) is equal to the **probability** that the quantum state described by the ket $|\psi\rangle$ is measured to be in the corresponding basis state. Thus

$$
\mathcal{P}_{S_z=+\hbar/2} = |\langle+|\psi\rangle|^2 \tag{25}
$$

is the probability that the state $|\psi\rangle$ is found to be in the state $|+\rangle$ when a measurement of S_z is made, meaning that the result $S_z = +\hbar/2$ is obtained. Likewise,

$$
\mathcal{P}_{S_z=-\hbar/2} = |\langle-|\psi\rangle|^2 \tag{26}
$$

is the probability that the measurement yields the result $S_z = -\hbar/2$. The subscript on the probability indicates the measured value. For the spin component measurements, we will usually abbreviate this to, for example, $\mathcal{P}_+$ for an $S_z = +\hbar/2$ result or $\mathcal{P}_{-y}$ for an $S_y = -\hbar/2$ measurement.

We now have a prescription for predicting the outcomes of the experiments we have been discussing. For example, the experiment shown in Fig. 8 has the state $|\psi\rangle = |+\rangle$ prepared by the first Stern-Gerlach device and then input to the second Stern-Gerlach device aligned along the z-axis. Therefore the probabilities of measuring the input state $|\psi\rangle = |+\rangle$ to have the two output values are as shown. Because the spin-1/2 system has only two possible measurement results, these two probabilities must sum to unity—there is a 100% probability of recording some value in the experiment. This basic rule of probabilities is why the rules of quantum mechanics require that all state vectors be properly normalized before they are used in any calculation of probabilities. The experimental predictions shown in Fig. 8 are an example of the fourth postulate of quantum mechanics, which is presented below.

Postulate 4 (Spin-1/2 system)

The probability of obtaining the value $\pm\hbar/2$ in a measurement of the observable S_z on a system in the state $|\psi\rangle$ is

$$\mathcal{P}_\pm = |\langle\pm|\psi\rangle|^2,$$

where $|\pm\rangle$ is the basis ket of S_z corresponding to the result $\pm\hbar/2$.

This is labeled as the fourth postulate because we have written this postulate using the language of the spin-1/2 system, while the general statement of the fourth postulate presented in Section 5 requires the second and third postulates (not included in this chapter). A general spin component measurement is shown in Fig. 9, along with a histogram that compactly summarizes the measurement results.

Because the quantum mechanical probability is found by squaring an inner product, we refer to an inner product, $\langle+|\psi\rangle$ for example, as a **probability amplitude** or sometimes just an **amplitude**; much like a classical wave intensity is found by squaring the wave amplitude. Note that the convention is to put the input or initial state on the right and the output or final state on the left: $\langle out|in\rangle$, so one would read from right to left in describing a problem. Because the probability involves the complex square of the amplitude, and $\langle out|in\rangle = \langle in|out\rangle^*$, this convention is not critical for calculating probabilities. Nonetheless, it is the accepted practice and is important in situations where several amplitudes are combined.

Armed with these new quantum mechanical rules and tools, let's continue to analyze the experiments discussed earlier. Using the experimental results and the new rules we have introduced, we can learn more about the mathematical behavior of the kets and the relationships among them. We will focus on the first two experiments in this chapter.

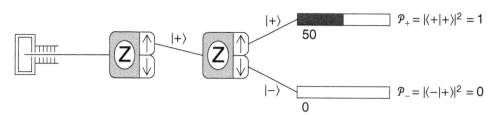

FIGURE 8 Probabilities of spin component measurements.

(a) (b)

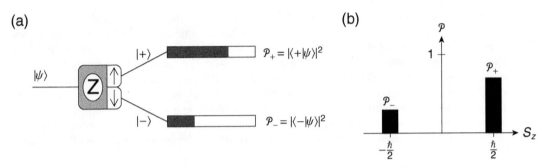

FIGURE 9 (a) Spin component measurement for a general input state and (b) histogram of measurement results.

2.1 ■ Analysis of Experiment 1

In Experiment 1, the first Stern-Gerlach analyzer prepared the system in the $|+\rangle$ state and the second analyzer later measured this state to be in the $|+\rangle$ state and not in the $|-\rangle$ state. The results of the experiment are summarized in the histogram in Fig. 10. We can use the fourth postulate to predict the results of this experiment. We take the inner product of the input state $|+\rangle$ with each of the possible output basis states $|+\rangle$ and $|-\rangle$. Because we know that the basis states are normalized and orthogonal, we calculate the probabilities to be

$$\begin{aligned} \mathcal{P}_+ &= \left| \langle + | + \rangle \right|^2 = 1 \\ \mathcal{P}_- &= \left| \langle - | + \rangle \right|^2 = 0. \end{aligned} \tag{27}$$

These predictions agree exactly with the histogram of experimental results shown in Fig. 10. A $|+\rangle$ state is always measured to have $S_z = +\hbar/2$.

2.2 ■ Analysis of Experiment 2

In Experiment 2, the first Stern-Gerlach analyzer prepared the system in the $|+\rangle$ state and the second analyzer performed a measurement of the spin component along the x-axis, finding 50% probabilities for each of the two possible states $|+\rangle_x$ and $|-\rangle_x$, as shown in the histogram in Fig. 11(a). For this experiment, we cannot predict the results of the measurements, because we do not yet have

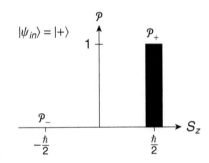

FIGURE 10 Histogram of S_z spin component measurements for Experiment 1 with $|\psi_{in}\rangle = |+\rangle$.

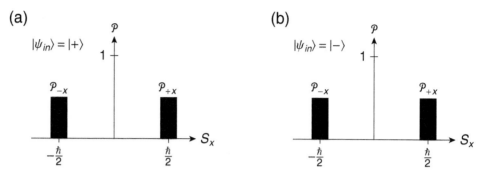

FIGURE 11 Histograms of S_x spin component measurements for Experiment 2 for different input states (a) $|\psi_{in}\rangle = |+\rangle$ and (b) $|\psi_{in}\rangle = |-\rangle$.

enough information about how the states $|+\rangle_x$ and $|-\rangle_x$ behave mathematically. Rather, we will use the results of the experiment to determine these states. Recalling that the experimental results would be the same if the first analyzer prepared the system to be in the $|-\rangle$ state [see Fig. 11(b)], we have four results for the two experiments:

$$
\begin{aligned}
\mathcal{P}_{1,+x} &= \left|{}_x\langle+|+\rangle\right|^2 = \tfrac{1}{2} \\
\mathcal{P}_{1,-x} &= \left|{}_x\langle-|+\rangle\right|^2 = \tfrac{1}{2} \\
\mathcal{P}_{2,+x} &= \left|{}_x\langle+|-\rangle\right|^2 = \tfrac{1}{2} \\
\mathcal{P}_{2,-x} &= \left|{}_x\langle-|-\rangle\right|^2 = \tfrac{1}{2}.
\end{aligned}
\tag{28}
$$

Because the kets $|+\rangle$ and $|-\rangle$ form a complete basis, the kets describing the S_x measurement, $|+\rangle_x$ and $|-\rangle_x$, can be written in terms of them. We do not yet know the specific coefficients of the $|\pm\rangle_x$ states, so we use general expressions

$$
\begin{aligned}
|+\rangle_x &= a|+\rangle + b|-\rangle \\
|-\rangle_x &= c|+\rangle + d|-\rangle,
\end{aligned}
\tag{29}
$$

and now our task is to use the results of Experiment 2 to determine the coefficients a, b, c, and d. The first measured probability in Eq. (28) is

$$
\mathcal{P}_{1,+x} = \left|{}_x\langle+|+\rangle\right|^2 = \tfrac{1}{2}.
\tag{30}
$$

Using the general expression for $|+\rangle_x$ in Eq. (29), we calculate the probability that the $|+\rangle$ input state is measured to be in the $|+\rangle_x$ output state, that is, to have $S_x = +\hbar/2$:

$$
\begin{aligned}
\mathcal{P}_{1,+x} &= \left|{}_x\langle+|+\rangle\right|^2 \\
&= \left|\{a^*\langle+| + b^*\langle-|\}|+\rangle\right|^2 \\
&= \left|a^*\right|^2 = |a|^2,
\end{aligned}
\tag{31}
$$

where we convert the $|+\rangle_x$ ket to a bra ${}_x\langle+|$ in order to calculate the inner product. Equating the experimental result in Eq. (30) and the prediction in Eq. (31), we find

$$
|a|^2 = \tfrac{1}{2}.
\tag{32}
$$

Similarly, one can calculate the other three probabilities to arrive at $|b|^2 = |c|^2 = |d|^2 = \frac{1}{2}$. (Problem 4) Because each coefficient is complex, each has an amplitude and phase. However, the overall phase of a quantum state vector is not physically meaningful (see Problem 3). Only the relative phase between different components of the state vector is physically measurable. Hence, we are free to choose *one* coefficient of each vector to be real and positive without any loss of generality. This allows us to write the desired states as

$$|+\rangle_x = \tfrac{1}{\sqrt{2}}\big[|+\rangle + e^{i\alpha}|-\rangle\big]$$
$$|-\rangle_x = \tfrac{1}{\sqrt{2}}\big[|+\rangle + e^{i\beta}|-\rangle\big],$$

(33)

where α and β are relative phases that we have yet to determine. Note that these states are already normalized because we used all of the experimental results, which reflect the fact that the probability for all possible results of an experiment must sum to unity.

We have used all the experimental results from Experiment 2, but the $|\pm\rangle_x$ kets are still not determined. We need some more information. If we perform Experiment 1 with both analyzers aligned along the x-axis, the results will be as you expect—all $|+\rangle_x$ states from the first analyzer will be measured to have $S_x = +\hbar/2$ at the second analyzer, that is, all atoms exit in the $|+\rangle_x$ state and none in the $|-\rangle_x$. The probability calculations for this experiment are

$$\mathcal{P}_{+x} = \big|_x\langle+|+\rangle_x\big|^2 = 1$$
$$\mathcal{P}_{-x} = \big|_x\langle-|+\rangle_x\big|^2 = 0,$$

(34)

which tell us mathematically that the $|\pm\rangle_x$ states are orthonormal to each other, just like the $|\pm\rangle$ states. This also implies that the $|\pm\rangle_x$ kets form a basis, the S_x basis, which you might expect because they correspond to the distinct results of a different spin component measurement. The general expressions we used for the $|\pm\rangle_x$ kets are already normalized but are not yet orthogonal. That is the new piece of information we need. The orthogonality condition leads to

$$_x\langle-|+\rangle_x = 0$$
$$\tfrac{1}{\sqrt{2}}\big[\langle+| + e^{-i\beta}\langle-|\big]\tfrac{1}{\sqrt{2}}\big[|+\rangle + e^{i\alpha}|-\rangle\big] = 0$$
$$\tfrac{1}{2}\big[1 + e^{i(\alpha-\beta)}\big] = 0$$
$$e^{i(\alpha-\beta)} = -1$$
$$e^{i\alpha} = -e^{i\beta},$$

(35)

where the complex conjugation of the second coefficient of the $_x\langle-|$ bra should be noted.

We now have an equation relating the remaining coefficients α and β, but we need some more information to determine their values. Unfortunately, there is no more information to be obtained, so we are free to choose the value of the phase α. This freedom comes from the fact that we have required only that the x-axis be perpendicular to the z-axis, which limits the x-axis only to a plane rather than to a unique direction. We follow convention here and choose the phase $\alpha = 0$. Thus we can express the S_x basis kets in terms of the S_z basis kets as

$$|+\rangle_x = \tfrac{1}{\sqrt{2}}\big[|+\rangle + |-\rangle\big]$$
$$|-\rangle_x = \tfrac{1}{\sqrt{2}}\big[|+\rangle - |-\rangle\big].$$

(36)

We generally use the S_z basis as the preferred basis for writing general states, but we could use any basis we choose. If we were to use the S_x basis, then we could write the $|\pm\rangle$ kets as general states in terms of the $|\pm\rangle_x$ kets. This can be done by solving Eq. (36) for the $|\pm\rangle$ kets, yielding

$$|+\rangle = \tfrac{1}{\sqrt{2}}[|+\rangle_x + |-\rangle_x]$$
$$|-\rangle = \tfrac{1}{\sqrt{2}}[|+\rangle_x - |-\rangle_x]. \tag{37}$$

With respect to the measurements performed in Experiment 2, Eq. (37) tells us that the $|+\rangle$ state is a combination of the states $|+\rangle_x$ and $|-\rangle_x$. The coefficients tell us that there is a 50% probability for measuring the spin component to be up along the x-axis, and likewise for the down possibility, which is in agreement with the histogram of measurements shown in Fig. 11(a). We must now take a moment to describe carefully what a combination of states, such as in Eqs. (36) and (37), is and what it is not.

2.3 ■ Superposition States

A general spin-1/2 state vector $|\psi\rangle$ can be expressed as a combination of the basis kets $|+\rangle$ and $|-\rangle$

$$|\psi\rangle = a|+\rangle + b|-\rangle. \tag{38}$$

We refer to such a combination of states as a **superposition state**. To understand the importance of a quantum mechanical superposition state, consider the particular state

$$|\psi\rangle = \tfrac{1}{\sqrt{2}}(|+\rangle + |-\rangle) \tag{39}$$

and measurements on this state, as shown in Fig. 12(a). Note that the state $|\psi\rangle$ is none other than the state $|+\rangle_x$ that we found in Eq. (36), so we already know what the measurement results are. If we measure the spin component along the x-axis for this state, then we record the result $S_x = +\hbar/2$ with 100% probability (Experiment 1 with both analyzers along the x-axis). If we measure the spin component along the orthogonal z-axis, then we record the two results $S_z = \pm\hbar/2$ with 50% probability each (Experiment 2 with the first and second analyzers along the x- and z-axes, respectively). Based upon this second set of results, one might be tempted to consider the state $|\psi\rangle$ as describing a beam that contains a mixture of atoms with 50% of the atoms in the $|+\rangle$ state and 50% in the $|-\rangle$ state. Such a state is called a **mixed state** and is very different from a superposition state.

To clarify the difference between a mixed state and a superposition state, let's carefully examine the results of experiments on the proposed mixed-state beam, as shown in Fig. 12(b). If we measure the spin component along the z-axis, then each atom in the $|+\rangle$ state yields the result $S_z = +\hbar/2$ with 100% certainty and each atom in the $|-\rangle$ state yields the result $S_z = -\hbar/2$ with 100% certainty. The net result is that 50% of the atoms yield $S_z = +\hbar/2$ and 50% yield $S_z = -\hbar/2$. This is exactly the same result as that obtained with all atoms in the $|+\rangle_x$ state, as seen in Fig. 12(a). If we instead measure the spin component along the x-axis, then each atom in the $|+\rangle$ state yields the two results $S_x = \pm\hbar/2$ with 50% probability each (Experiment 2 with the first and second analyzers along the z- and x-axes, respectively). The atoms in the $|-\rangle$ state yield the same results. The net result is that 50% of the atoms yield $S_x = +\hbar/2$ and 50% yield $S_x = -\hbar/2$. This is in stark contrast to the results of Experiment 1, which tell us that once we have prepared the state to be $|+\rangle_x$, then subsequent measurements yield $S_x = +\hbar/2$ with certainty, as seen in Fig. 12(a).

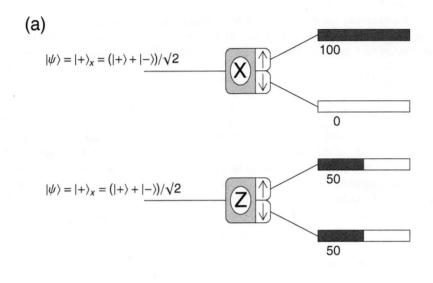

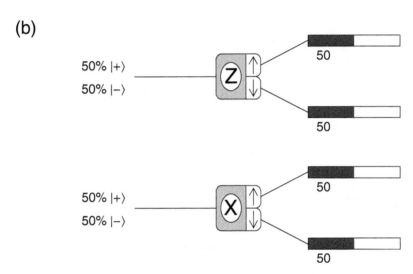

FIGURE 12   (a) Superposition state measurements and (b) mixed state measurements.

Hence we must conclude that the system described by the $|\psi\rangle = |+\rangle_x$ state is not a mixed state with some atoms in the $|+\rangle$ state and some in the $|-\rangle$ state. Rather, each atom in the $|+\rangle_x$ beam is in a state that itself is a superposition of the $|+\rangle$ and $|-\rangle$ states. A superposition state is often called a **coherent superposition** because the relative phase of the two terms is important. For example, if the input beam were in the $|-\rangle_x$ state, then there would be a relative minus sign between the two coefficients, which would result in an $S_x = -\hbar/2$ measurement but would not affect the S_z measurement.

We will not have any further need to speak of mixed states, so any combination of states we use is a superposition state. Note that we cannot even write down a ket describing a mixed state. So if someone gives you a quantum state written as a ket, then it must be a superposition state and not a mixed state. The random option in the SPINS program produces a mixed state, while the unknown states are all superposition states.

Example 2 Consider the input state

$$|\psi_{in}\rangle = 3|+\rangle + 4|-\rangle. \tag{40}$$

Normalize this state vector and find the probabilities of measuring the spin component along the z-axis to be $S_z = \pm\hbar/2$.

To normalize this state, introduce an overall complex multiplicative factor and solve for this factor by imposing the normalization condition:

$$
\begin{aligned}
|\psi_{in}\rangle &= C[3|+\rangle + 4|-\rangle] \\
\langle\psi_{in}|\psi_{in}\rangle &= 1 \\
\{C^*[3\langle+| + 4\langle-|]\}\{C[3|+\rangle + 4|-\rangle]\} &= 1 \\
C^*C[9\langle+|+\rangle + 12\langle+|-\rangle + 12\langle-|+\rangle + 16\langle-|-\rangle] &= 1 \\
C^*C[25] &= 1 \\
|C|^2 &= \frac{1}{25}.
\end{aligned} \tag{41}
$$

Because an overall phase is physically meaningless, we choose C to be real and positive: $C = 1/5$. Hence the normalized input state is

$$|\psi_{in}\rangle = \tfrac{3}{5}|+\rangle + \tfrac{4}{5}|-\rangle. \tag{42}$$

The probability of measuring $S_z = +\hbar/2$ is

$$
\begin{aligned}
\mathcal{P}_+ &= \left|\langle+|\psi_{in}\rangle\right|^2 \\
&= \left|\langle+|[\tfrac{3}{5}|+\rangle + \tfrac{4}{5}|-\rangle]\right|^2 \\
&= \left|\tfrac{3}{5}\langle+|+\rangle + \tfrac{4}{5}\langle+|-\rangle\right|^2 \\
&= \left|\tfrac{3}{5}\right|^2 = \tfrac{9}{25}.
\end{aligned} \tag{43}
$$

The probability of measuring $S_z = -\hbar/2$ is

$$
\begin{aligned}
\mathcal{P}_- &= \left|\langle-|\psi_{in}\rangle\right|^2 \\
&= \left|\langle-|[\tfrac{3}{5}|+\rangle + \tfrac{4}{5}|-\rangle]\right|^2 \\
&= \left|\tfrac{3}{5}\langle-|+\rangle + \tfrac{4}{5}\langle-|-\rangle\right|^2 \\
&= \left|\tfrac{4}{5}\right|^2 = \tfrac{16}{25}.
\end{aligned} \tag{44}
$$

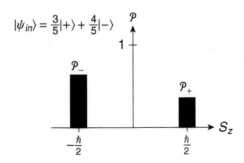

FIGURE 13 Histogram of S_z spin component measurements.

Note that the two probabilities add to unity, which indicates that we normalized the input state properly. A histogram of the predicted measurement results is shown in Fig. 13.

3 ■ MATRIX NOTATION

Up to this point, we have defined kets mathematically in terms of their inner products with other kets. Thus, in the general case we write a ket as

$$|\psi\rangle = \langle+|\psi\rangle|+\rangle + \langle-|\psi\rangle|-\rangle, \tag{45}$$

or in a specific case, we write

$$\begin{aligned}
|+\rangle_x &= \langle+|+\rangle_x|+\rangle + \langle-|+\rangle_x|-\rangle \\
&= \tfrac{1}{\sqrt{2}}|+\rangle + \tfrac{1}{\sqrt{2}}|-\rangle.
\end{aligned} \tag{46}$$

In both of these cases, we have chosen to write the kets in terms of the $|+\rangle$ and $|-\rangle$ basis kets. If we agree on that choice of basis as a convention, then the two coefficients $\langle+|+\rangle_x$ and $\langle-|+\rangle_x$ uniquely specify the quantum state, and we can simplify the notation by using just those numbers. Thus, we represent a ket as a **column vector** containing the two coefficients that multiply each basis ket. For example, we represent $|+\rangle_x$ as

$$|+\rangle_x \doteq \frac{1}{\sqrt{2}}\begin{pmatrix} 1 \\ 1 \end{pmatrix}, \tag{47}$$

where we have used the new symbol $\doteq$ to signify "is represented by," and it is understood that we are using the $|+\rangle$ and $|-\rangle$ basis or the S_z basis. We cannot say that the ket *equals* the column vector, because the ket is an abstract vector in the state space and the column vector is just two complex numbers. If we were to choose a different basis for representing the vector, then the complex coefficients would be different even though the vector is unchanged. We need to have a convention for the ordering of the amplitudes in the column vector. The standard convention is to put the spin up amplitude first (at the top). Thus, the representation of the $|-\rangle_x$ state in Eq. (36) is

$$|-\rangle_x \doteq \frac{1}{\sqrt{2}}\begin{pmatrix} 1 \\ -1 \end{pmatrix} \begin{matrix} \leftarrow |+\rangle \\ \leftarrow |-\rangle \end{matrix}, \tag{48}$$

where we have explicitly labeled the rows according to their corresponding basis kets. Using this convention, it should be clear that the basis kets themselves are written as

$$|+\rangle \doteq \begin{pmatrix} 1 \\ 0 \end{pmatrix}$$
$$|-\rangle \doteq \begin{pmatrix} 0 \\ 1 \end{pmatrix}. \tag{49}$$

This demonstrates the important feature that *basis kets are unit vectors when written in their own basis.*

This new way of expressing a ket simply as the collection of coefficients that multiply the basis kets is referred to as a **representation**. Because we have assumed the S_z kets as the basis kets, this is called the S_z representation. It is always true that basis kets have the simple form shown in Eq. (49) when written in their own representation. A general ket $|\psi\rangle$ is written as

$$|\psi\rangle \doteq \begin{pmatrix} \langle+|\psi\rangle \\ \langle-|\psi\rangle \end{pmatrix}. \tag{50}$$

This use of matrix notation simplifies the mathematics of bras and kets. The advantage is not so evident for the simple two-dimensional state space of spin-1/2 systems, but it is very evident for larger dimensional problems. This notation is indispensable when using computers to calculate quantum mechanical results. For example, the SPINS program employs matrix calculations coded in the Java computer language to simulate the Stern-Gerlach experiments using the same probability rules you are learning here.

We saw earlier [Eq. (11)] that the coefficients of a bra are the complex conjugates of the coefficients of the corresponding ket. We also know that an inner product of a bra and a ket yields a single complex number. In order for the matrix rules of multiplication to be used, a bra must be represented by a **row vector**, with the entries being the coefficients ordered in the same sense as for the ket. For example, if we use the general ket

$$|\psi\rangle = a|+\rangle + b|-\rangle, \tag{51}$$

which is represented as

$$|\psi\rangle \doteq \begin{pmatrix} a \\ b \end{pmatrix}, \tag{52}$$

then the corresponding bra

$$\langle\psi| = a^*\langle+| + b^*\langle-| \tag{53}$$

is represented by a row vector as

$$\langle\psi| \doteq \begin{pmatrix} a^* & b^* \end{pmatrix}. \tag{54}$$

The rules of matrix algebra can then be applied to find an inner product. For example,

$$\langle\psi|\psi\rangle = \begin{pmatrix} a^* & b^* \end{pmatrix}\begin{pmatrix} a \\ b \end{pmatrix}$$
$$= |a|^2 + |b|^2. \tag{55}$$

So a bra is represented by a row vector that is the complex conjugate and transpose of the column vector representing the corresponding ket.

Example 3   To get some practice using this new matrix notation, and to learn some more about the spin-1/2 system, use the results of Experiment 2 to determine the S_y basis kets using the matrix approach instead of the Dirac bra-ket approach.

Consider Experiment 2 in the case where the second Stern-Gerlach analyzer is aligned along the y-axis. We said before that the results are the same as in the case shown in Fig. 4. Thus, we have

$$\mathcal{P}_{1,+y} = \left|{}_y\langle+|+\rangle\right|^2 = \tfrac{1}{2}$$
$$\mathcal{P}_{1,-y} = \left|{}_y\langle-|+\rangle\right|^2 = \tfrac{1}{2}$$
$$\mathcal{P}_{2,+y} = \left|{}_y\langle+|-\rangle\right|^2 = \tfrac{1}{2}$$
$$\mathcal{P}_{2,-y} = \left|{}_y\langle-|-\rangle\right|^2 = \tfrac{1}{2},$$

(56)

as depicted in the histograms of Fig. 14.

These results allow us to determine the kets $|\pm\rangle_y$ corresponding to the spin component up and down along the y-axis. The argument and calculation proceeds exactly as it did earlier for the $|\pm\rangle_x$ states up until the point [Eq. (35)] where we arbitrarily chose the phase α to be zero. Having done that for the $|\pm\rangle_x$ states, we are no longer free to make that same choice for the $|\pm\rangle_y$ states. Thus we use Eq. (35) to write the $|\pm\rangle_y$ states as

$$|+\rangle_y = \frac{1}{\sqrt{2}}\left[|+\rangle + e^{i\alpha}|-\rangle\right] \doteq \frac{1}{\sqrt{2}}\begin{pmatrix} 1 \\ e^{i\alpha} \end{pmatrix}$$
$$|-\rangle_y = \frac{1}{\sqrt{2}}\left[|+\rangle - e^{i\alpha}|-\rangle\right] \doteq \frac{1}{\sqrt{2}}\begin{pmatrix} 1 \\ -e^{i\alpha} \end{pmatrix}.$$

(57)

To determine the phase α, we use some more information at our disposal. Experiment 2 could be performed with the first Stern-Gerlach analyzer aligned along the x-axis and the second analyzer along the y-axis. Again the results would be identical (50% at each output port), yielding

$$\mathcal{P}_{+y} = \left|{}_y\langle+|+\rangle_x\right|^2 = \tfrac{1}{2}$$

(58)

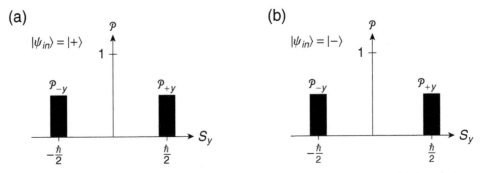

FIGURE 14   Histograms of S_y spin component measurements for input states (a) $|\psi_{in}\rangle = |+\rangle$ and (b) $|\psi_{in}\rangle = |-\rangle$.

as one of the measured quantities. Now use matrix algebra to calculate this:

$$_y\langle+|+\rangle_x = \tfrac{1}{\sqrt{2}}\begin{pmatrix}1 & e^{-i\alpha}\end{pmatrix}\tfrac{1}{\sqrt{2}}\begin{pmatrix}1\\1\end{pmatrix}$$
$$= \tfrac{1}{2}(1 + e^{-i\alpha})$$
$$\left|_y\langle+|+\rangle_x\right|^2 = \tfrac{1}{2}(1 + e^{-i\alpha})\tfrac{1}{2}(1 + e^{i\alpha}) \qquad (59)$$
$$= \tfrac{1}{4}(1 + e^{i\alpha} + e^{-i\alpha} + 1)$$
$$= \tfrac{1}{2}(1 + \cos\alpha) = \tfrac{1}{2}.$$

This result requires that $\cos\alpha = 0$, or that $\alpha = \pm\pi/2$. The two choices for the phase correspond to the two possibilities for the direction of the y-axis relative to the already determined x- and z-axes. The choice $\alpha = +\pi/2$ can be shown to correspond to a right-handed coordinate system, which is the standard convention, so we choose that phase. We thus represent the $|\pm\rangle_y$ kets as

$$|+\rangle_y \doteq \frac{1}{\sqrt{2}}\begin{pmatrix}1\\i\end{pmatrix}$$
$$|-\rangle_y \doteq \frac{1}{\sqrt{2}}\begin{pmatrix}1\\-i\end{pmatrix}. \qquad (60)$$

Note that the imaginary components of these kets are required. They are not merely a mathematical convenience as one sees in classical mechanics. In general, quantum mechanical state vectors have complex coefficients. But this does not mean that the results of physical measurements are complex. On the contrary, we always calculate a measurement probability using a complex square, so all quantum mechanics predictions of probabilities are real.

---

4 ■ GENERAL QUANTUM SYSTEMS

The machinery we have developed for spin-1/2 systems can be generalized to other quantum systems. For example, if an observable A yields quantized measurement results a_n for some finite range of n, then we generalize the schematic depiction of a Stern-Gerlach measurement to a measurement of the

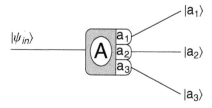

FIGURE 15   Generic depiction of the quantum mechanical measurement of observable A.

observable A, as shown in Fig. 15. The observable A labels the measurement device and the possible results a_1, a_2, a_3, etc. label the output ports. The basis kets corresponding to the results a_n are then $|a_n\rangle$. The mathematical rules about kets in this general case are

$$\langle a_i | a_j \rangle = \delta_{ij} \qquad \qquad \textit{orthonormality}$$
$$|\psi\rangle = \sum_i \langle a_i | \psi \rangle |a_i\rangle \qquad \textit{completeness}, \tag{61}$$

where we use the **Kronecker delta**

$$\delta_{ij} = \begin{cases} 0 & i \neq j \\ 1 & i = j \end{cases} \tag{62}$$

to express the orthonormality condition compactly. In this case, the generalization of postulate 4 says that the probability of a measurement of one of the possible results a_n is

$$\mathcal{P}_{a_n} = |\langle a_n | \psi_{in} \rangle|^2. \tag{63}$$

Example 4 Imagine a quantum system with an observable A that has three possible measurement results: a_1, a_2, and a_3. The three kets $|a_1\rangle$, $|a_2\rangle$, and $|a_3\rangle$ corresponding to these possible results form a complete orthonormal basis. The system is prepared in the state

$$|\psi\rangle = 2|a_1\rangle - 3|a_2\rangle + 4i|a_3\rangle. \tag{64}$$

Calculate the probabilities of all possible measurement results of the observable A.

The state vector in Eq. (64) is not normalized, so we must normalize it before calculating probabilities. Introducing a complex normalization constant C, we find

$$\begin{aligned} 1 &= \langle \psi | \psi \rangle \\ &= C^*(2\langle a_1| - 3\langle a_2| - 4i\langle a_3|)C(2|a_1\rangle - 3|a_2\rangle + 4i|a_3\rangle) \\ &= |C|^2\{4\langle a_1|a_1\rangle - 6\langle a_1|a_2\rangle + 8i\langle a_1|a_3\rangle \\ &\quad - 6\langle a_2|a_1\rangle + 9\langle a_2|a_2\rangle - 12i\langle a_2|a_3\rangle \\ &\quad - 8i\langle a_3|a_1\rangle + 12i\langle a_3|a_2\rangle + 16\langle a_3|a_3\rangle\} \\ &= |C|^2\{4 + 9 + 16\} = |C|^2 29 \\ &\Rightarrow C = \tfrac{1}{\sqrt{29}}. \end{aligned} \tag{65}$$

The normalized state is

$$|\psi\rangle = \tfrac{1}{\sqrt{29}}(2|a_1\rangle - 3|a_2\rangle + 4i|a_3\rangle). \tag{66}$$

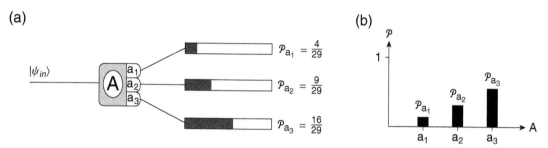

FIGURE 16 (a) Schematic diagram of the measurement of observable A and (b) histogram of the predicted measurement probabilities.

The probabilities of measuring the results a_1, a_2, and a_3 are

$$\mathcal{P}_{a_1} = \left|\langle a_1|\psi\rangle\right|^2$$
$$= \left|\langle a_1|\tfrac{1}{\sqrt{29}}\{2|a_1\rangle - 3|a_2\rangle + 4i|a_3\rangle\}\right|^2$$
$$= \tfrac{1}{29}\left|2\langle a_1|a_1\rangle - 3\langle a_1|a_2\rangle + 4i\langle a_1|a_3\rangle\right|^2 = \tfrac{4}{29}$$

$$\mathcal{P}_{a_2} = \left|\langle a_2|\psi\rangle\right|^2 = \left|\langle a_2|\tfrac{1}{\sqrt{29}}\{2|a_1\rangle - 3|a_2\rangle + 4i|a_3\rangle\}\right|^2 = \tfrac{9}{29}$$

$$\mathcal{P}_{a_3} = \left|\langle a_3|\psi\rangle\right|^2 = \left|\langle a_3|\tfrac{1}{\sqrt{29}}\{2|a_1\rangle - 3|a_2\rangle + 4i|a_3\rangle\}\right|^2 = \tfrac{16}{29}.$$

(67)

A schematic of this experiment is shown in Fig. 16(a) and a histogram of the predicted probabilities is shown in Fig. 16(b).

5 ◾ POSTULATES

We have introduced two of the postulates of quantum mechanics in this chapter. The postulates of quantum mechanics dictate how to treat a quantum mechanical system mathematically and how to interpret the mathematics to learn about the physical system in question. These postulates cannot be proven, but they have been successfully tested by many experiments, and so we accept them as an accurate way to describe quantum mechanical systems. New results could force us to reevaluate these postulates at some later time. All six postulates are listed below to give you an idea where we are headed and a framework into which you can place the new concepts as we confront them.

Postulates of Quantum Mechanics

1. The state of a quantum mechanical system, including all the information you can know about it, is represented mathematically by a normalized ket $|\psi\rangle$.

2. A physical observable is represented mathematically by an operator A that acts on kets.

3. The only possible result of a measurement of an observable is one of the eigenvalues a_n of the corresponding operator A.

4. The probability of obtaining the eigenvalue a_n in a measurement of the observable A on the system in the state $|\psi\rangle$ is

$$\mathcal{P}_{a_n} = |\langle a_n|\psi\rangle|^2,$$

where $|a_n\rangle$ is the normalized eigenvector of A corresponding to the eigenvalue a_n.

5. After a measurement of A that yields the result a_n, the quantum system is in a new state that is the normalized projection of the original system ket onto the ket (or kets) corresponding to the result of the measurement:

$$|\psi'\rangle = \frac{P_n|\psi\rangle}{\sqrt{\langle\psi|P_n|\psi\rangle}}.$$

6. The time evolution of a quantum system is determined by the Hamiltonian or total energy operator $H(t)$ through the Schrödinger equation

$$i\hbar\frac{d}{dt}|\psi(t)\rangle = H(t)|\psi(t)\rangle.$$

As you read these postulates for the first time, you will undoubtedly encounter new terms and concepts. We have chosen this example because it is inherently quantum mechanical and forces us to break away from reliance on classical intuition or concepts. Moreover, this simple example is a paradigm for many other quantum mechanical systems. By studying it in detail, we can appreciate much of the richness of quantum mechanics.

SUMMARY

Through the Stern-Gerlach experiment we have learned several key concepts about quantum mechanics in this chapter.

- Quantum mechanics is probabilistic.
  We cannot predict the results of experiments precisely. We can predict only the probability that a certain result is obtained in a measurement.

- Spin measurements are quantized.
  The possible results of a spin component measurement are quantized. Only these discrete values are measured.

- Quantum measurements disturb the system.
  Measuring one physical observable can "destroy" information about other observables.

We have learned how to describe the state of a quantum mechanical system mathematically using a ket, which represents all the information we can know about that state. The kets $|+\rangle$ and $|-\rangle$ result when the spin component S_z along the z-axis is measured to be up or down, respectively. These kets form an orthonormal basis, which we denote by the inner products

$$\begin{aligned}
\langle+|+\rangle &= 1 \\
\langle-|-\rangle &= 1 \\
\langle+|-\rangle &= 0.
\end{aligned} \tag{68}$$

The basis is also complete, which means that it can be used to express all possible kets as superposition states

$$|\psi\rangle = a|+\rangle + b|-\rangle. \tag{69}$$

For spin component measurements, the kets corresponding to spin up or down along the three Cartesian axes are

$$
\begin{aligned}
|+\rangle && |+\rangle_x = \tfrac{1}{\sqrt{2}}\big[|+\rangle + |-\rangle\big] && |+\rangle_y = \tfrac{1}{\sqrt{2}}\big[|+\rangle + i|-\rangle\big] \\
|-\rangle && |-\rangle_x = \tfrac{1}{\sqrt{2}}\big[|+\rangle - |-\rangle\big] && |-\rangle_y = \tfrac{1}{\sqrt{2}}\big[|+\rangle - i|-\rangle\big].
\end{aligned}
\tag{70}
$$

We also found it useful to introduce a matrix notation for calculations. In this matrix language the kets in Eq. (70) are represented by

$$
\begin{aligned}
|+\rangle \doteq \begin{pmatrix} 1 \\ 0 \end{pmatrix} && |+\rangle_x \doteq \frac{1}{\sqrt{2}}\begin{pmatrix} 1 \\ 1 \end{pmatrix} && |+\rangle_y \doteq \frac{1}{\sqrt{2}}\begin{pmatrix} 1 \\ i \end{pmatrix} \\
|-\rangle \doteq \begin{pmatrix} 0 \\ 1 \end{pmatrix} && |-\rangle_x \doteq \frac{1}{\sqrt{2}}\begin{pmatrix} 1 \\ -1 \end{pmatrix} && |-\rangle_y \doteq \frac{1}{\sqrt{2}}\begin{pmatrix} 1 \\ -i \end{pmatrix}.
\end{aligned}
\tag{71}
$$

The most important tool we have learned so far is the probability postulate (postulate 4). To calculate the probability that a measurement on an input state $|\psi_{in}\rangle$ will yield a particular result, for example $S_z = \hbar/2$, we complex square the inner product of the input state with the ket corresponding to the measured result, $|+\rangle$ in this case:

$$\mathcal{P}_+ = \big|\langle +|\psi_{in}\rangle\big|^2. \tag{72}$$

This is generalized to other systems where a measurement yields a particular result a_n corresponding to the ket $|a_n\rangle$ as:

$$\mathcal{P}_{a_n} = \big|\langle a_n|\psi_{in}\rangle\big|^2. \tag{73}$$

RESOURCES

Activities

SPINS: A software program to simulate Stern-Gerlach spin experiments. The Java software runs on all platforms and can be downloaded in two forms:

Open Source Physics framework

> www.physics.oregonstate.edu/~mcintyre/ph425/spins/index_SPINS_OSP.html

or

Standalone Java

> www.physics.oregonstate.edu/~mcintyre/ph425/spins

The bulleted activities are available at

www.physics.oregonstate.edu/qmactivities

- **SPINS Lab 1:** An introduction to successive Stern-Gerlach spin-1/2 measurements. The randomness of measurements is demonstrated and students use statistical analysis to deduce probabilities from measurements.

- **SPINS Lab 2:** Students deduce unknown quantum state vectors from measurements of spin projections (part 3 requires material not included in this chapter to do the calculations).

Stern-Gerlach simulation: A different simulation of the Stern-Gerlach experiment from the PHET group at the University of Colorado (somewhat Flashier version):

http://phet.colorado.edu/en/simulation/stern-gerlach

Further Reading

The history of the Stern-Gerlach experiment and how a bad cigar helped are chronicled in a *Physics Today* article:

B. Friedrich and D. Herschbach, "Stern and Gerlach: How a Bad Cigar Helped Reorient Atomic Physics," *Phys. Today* **56**(12), 53–59 (2003).
http://dx.doi.org/10.1063/1.1650229

A different spin on the quantum mechanics of socks is discussed by John S. Bell in this article:

J. S. Bell, "Bertlmann's socks and the nature of reality, " *J. Phys. Colloq.* **42**, C22 C2.41-C2.62 (1981).
http://cdsweb.cern.ch/record/142461

Nature has published a supplement on the milestones in spin physics. An extensive timeline of historical events, review articles, and links to original articles are included.

Nature Phys. 4, S1–S43 (2008).
www.nature.com/milestones/spin

The SPINS lab software is described in this pedagogical article:

D. V. Schroeder and T. A. Moore, "A computer-simulated Stern-Gerlach laboratory," *Am. J. Phys.* **61**, 798–805 (1993).
http://dx.doi.org/10.1119/1.17172

Some other textbooks that take a spins-first approach or have an extensive treatment of Stern-Gerlach experiments:

R. P. Feynman, R. B. Leighton, and M. Sands, *The Feynman Lectures on Physics, Volume 3, Quantum Mechanics,* Reading, MA: Addison-Wesley Publishing Company, Inc., 1965.

J. J. Sakurai, *Modern Quantum Mechanics*, Redwood City, CA: Addison-Wesley Publishing Company, Inc., 1985.

J. S. Townsend, *A Modern Approach to Quantum Mechanics*, New York: McGraw Hill, Inc., 1992.

C. Cohen-Tannoudji, B. Diu, and F. Laloë, *Quantum Mechanics*, New York: John Wiley & Sons, 1977.

D. F. Styer, *The Strange World of Quantum Mechanics*, Cambridge: Cambridge University Press, 2000.

Stern-Gerlach Experiments: Problem Set

1 Consider the following state vectors:

$$|\psi_1\rangle = 3|+\rangle + 4|-\rangle$$
$$|\psi_2\rangle = |+\rangle + 2i|-\rangle$$
$$|\psi_3\rangle = 3|+\rangle - e^{i\pi/3}|-\rangle.$$

a) Normalize each state vector.

b) For each state vector, calculate the probability that the spin component is up or down along each of the three Cartesian axes. Use bra-ket notation for the entire calculation.

c) Write each normalized state in matrix notation.

d) Repeat part (b) using matrix notation for the entire calculation.

2 Consider the three quantum states:

$$|\psi_1\rangle = \tfrac{1}{\sqrt{3}}|+\rangle + i\tfrac{\sqrt{2}}{\sqrt{3}}|-\rangle$$
$$|\psi_2\rangle = \tfrac{1}{\sqrt{5}}|+\rangle - \tfrac{2}{\sqrt{5}}|-\rangle$$
$$|\psi_3\rangle = \tfrac{1}{\sqrt{2}}|+\rangle + e^{i\pi/4}\tfrac{1}{\sqrt{2}}|-\rangle.$$

Use bra-ket notation (not matrix notation) to solve the following problems. Note that $\langle+|+\rangle = 1$, $\langle-|-\rangle = 1$, and $\langle+|-\rangle = 0$.

a) For each of the $|\psi_i\rangle$ above, find the normalized vector $|\phi_i\rangle$ that is orthogonal to it.

b) Calculate the inner products $\langle\psi_i|\psi_j\rangle$ for i and $j = 1, 2, 3$.

3 Show that a change in the overall phase of a quantum state vector does not change the probability of obtaining a particular result in a measurement. To do this, consider how the probability is affected by changing the state $|\psi\rangle$ to the state $e^{i\delta}|\psi\rangle$.

4 Show by explicit bra-ket calculations using the states in Eq. (29)

$$|+\rangle_x = a|+\rangle + b|-\rangle$$
$$|-\rangle_x = c|+\rangle + d|-\rangle,$$

(29)

that the four experimental results in Eq. (28)

$$\mathcal{P}_{1,+x} = |_x\langle+|+\rangle|^2 = \tfrac{1}{2}$$
$$\mathcal{P}_{1,-x} = |_x\langle-|+\rangle|^2 = \tfrac{1}{2}$$
$$\mathcal{P}_{2,+x} = |_x\langle+|-\rangle|^2 = \tfrac{1}{2}$$
$$\mathcal{P}_{2,-x} = |_x\langle-|-\rangle|^2 = \tfrac{1}{2}.$$

(28)

lead to the results $|b|^2 = |c|^2 = |d|^2 = \tfrac{1}{2}$.

From Chapter 1 of *Quantum Mechanics: A Paradigms Approach*, First Edition. David H. McIntyre. Copyright © 2012 by Pearson Education, Inc. Published by Pearson Addison-Wesley. All rights reserved.

The companion websites for this text are http://physics.oregonstate.edu/portfolioswiki and http://physics.oregonstate.edu/qmactivities.

5 A beam of spin-1/2 particles is prepared in the state

$$|\psi\rangle = \frac{2}{\sqrt{13}}|+\rangle + i\frac{3}{\sqrt{13}}|-\rangle.$$

a) What are the possible results of a measurement of the spin component S_z, and with what probabilities would they occur?

b) What are the possible results of a measurement of the spin component S_x, and with what probabilities would they occur?

c) Plot histograms of the predicted measurement results from parts (a) and (b).

6 A beam of spin-1/2 particles is prepared in the state

$$|\psi\rangle = \frac{2}{\sqrt{13}}|+\rangle_x + i\frac{3}{\sqrt{13}}|-\rangle_x.$$

a) What are the possible results of a measurement of the spin component S_z, and with what probabilities would they occur?

b) What are the possible results of a measurement of the spin component S_x, and with what probabilities would they occur?

c) Plot histograms of the predicted measurement results from parts (a) and (b).

7 A classical coin is thrown in the air and lands on the ground, where a measurement is made of its state.

a) What are the possible results of this measurement?

b) What are the predicted probabilities for these possible outcomes?

c) Plot a histogram of the predicted measurement results.

8 A classical cubical die is thrown onto a table and comes to rest, where a measurement is made of its state.

a) What are the possible results of this measurement?

b) What are the predicted probabilities for these possible outcomes?

c) Plot a histogram of the predicted measurement results.

9 A pair of dice (classical cubes) are thrown onto a table and come to rest, where a measurement is made of the state of the system (i.e., the sum of the two dice).

a) What are the possible results of this measurement?

b) What are the predicted probabilities for these possible outcomes?

c) Plot a histogram of the predicted measurement results.

10 Consider the three quantum states:

$$|\psi_1\rangle = \frac{4}{5}|+\rangle + i\frac{3}{5}|-\rangle$$
$$|\psi_2\rangle = \frac{4}{5}|+\rangle - i\frac{3}{5}|-\rangle$$
$$|\psi_3\rangle = -\frac{4}{5}|+\rangle + i\frac{3}{5}|-\rangle.$$

a) For each of the $|\psi_i\rangle$ above, calculate the probabilities of spin component measurements along the x-, y-, and z-axes.

b) Use your results from (a) to comment on the importance of the overall phase and of the relative phases of the quantum state vector.

11 A beam of spin-1/2 particles is prepared in the state

$$|\psi\rangle = \tfrac{3}{\sqrt{34}}|+\rangle + i\tfrac{5}{\sqrt{34}}|-\rangle.$$

a) What are the possible results of a measurement of the spin component S_z, and with what probabilities would they occur?

b) Suppose that the S_z measurement yields the result $S_z = -\hbar/2$. Subsequent to that result a second measurement is performed to measure the spin component S_x. What are the possible results of that measurement, and with what probabilities would they occur?

c) Draw a schematic diagram depicting the successive measurements in parts (a) and (b).

12 Consider a quantum system with an observable A that has three possible measurement results: a_1, a_2, and a_3. Write down the orthogonality, normalization, and completeness relations for the three kets comprising the basis corresponding to the possible results of the A measurement.

13 Consider a quantum system with an observable A that has three possible measurement results: a_1, a_2, and a_3.

a) Write down the three kets $|a_1\rangle$, $|a_2\rangle$, and $|a_3\rangle$ corresponding to these possible results using matrix notation.

b) The system is prepared in the state

$$|\psi\rangle = 1|a_1\rangle - 2|a_2\rangle + 5|a_3\rangle.$$

Write this state in matrix notation and calculate the probabilities of all possible measurement results of the observable A. Plot a histogram of the predicted measurement results.

c) In a different experiment, the system is prepared in the state

$$|\psi\rangle = 2|a_1\rangle + 3i|a_2\rangle.$$

Write this state in matrix notation and calculate the probabilities of all possible measurement results of the observable A. Plot a histogram of the predicted measurement results.

14 Consider a quantum system in which the energy E is measured and there are four possible measurement results: 2 eV, 4 eV, 7 eV, and 9 eV. The system is prepared in the state

$$|\psi\rangle = \tfrac{1}{\sqrt{39}}\{3|2\text{ eV}\rangle - i|4\text{ eV}\rangle + 2e^{i\pi/7}|7\text{ eV}\rangle + 5|9\text{ eV}\rangle\}.$$

Calculate the probabilities of all possible measurement results of the energy E. Plot a histogram of the predicted measurement results.

15 Consider a quantum system described by a basis $|a_1\rangle$, $|a_2\rangle$, and $|a_3\rangle$. The system is initially in a state

$$|\psi_i\rangle = \tfrac{i}{\sqrt{3}}|a_1\rangle + \sqrt{\tfrac{2}{3}}|a_2\rangle.$$

Find the probability that the system is measured to be in the final state

$$|\psi_f\rangle = \tfrac{1+i}{\sqrt{3}}|a_1\rangle + \tfrac{1}{\sqrt{6}}|a_2\rangle + \tfrac{1}{\sqrt{6}}|a_3\rangle.$$

16 The spin components of a beam of atoms prepared in the state $|\psi_{in}\rangle$ are measured and the following experimental probabilities are obtained:

$$\mathcal{P}_+ = \tfrac{1}{2} \qquad \mathcal{P}_{+x} = \tfrac{3}{4} \qquad \mathcal{P}_{+y} = 0.067$$

$$\mathcal{P}_- = \tfrac{1}{2} \qquad \mathcal{P}_{-x} = \tfrac{1}{4} \qquad \mathcal{P}_{-y} = 0.933.$$

From the experimental data, determine the input state.

17 In part (1) of SPINS Lab #2, you measured the probabilities of all the possible spin components for each of the unknown initial states $|\psi_i\rangle$ ($i = 1, 2, 3, 4$). Using your data from that lab, find the unknown states $|\psi_1\rangle$, $|\psi_2\rangle$, $|\psi_3\rangle$, and $|\psi_4\rangle$. Express each of the unknown states as a linear superposition of the S_z basis states $|+\rangle$ and $|-\rangle$. For each state, use your result to calculate the theoretical values of the probabilities for each component measurement and compare these theoretical predictions with your experimental results.

Operators and Measurement

From Chapter 2 of *Quantum Mechanics: A Paradigms Approach*, First Edition. David H. McIntyre. Copyright © 2012 by Pearson Education, Inc. Published by Pearson Addison-Wesley. All rights reserved.

The companion websites for this text are http://physics.oregonstate.edu/portfolioswiki and http://physics.oregonstate.edu/qmactivities.

Operators and Measurement

Consider the results of experiments to deduce a mathematical description of the spin-1/2 system. The Stern-Gerlach experiments demonstrate that spin component measurements along the x-, y-, or z-axes yield only $\pm\hbar/2$ as possible results. We can predict the probabilities of these measurements using the basis kets of the spin component observables S_x, S_y, and S_z, and these predictions agree with the experiments. However, the real power of a theory is its ability to predict results of experiments that you haven't yet done. For example, what are the possible results of a measurement of the spin component S_n along an arbitrary direction $\hat{\mathbf{n}}$ and what are the predicted probabilities? To make these predictions, we need to learn about the operators of quantum mechanics.

1 ■ OPERATORS, EIGENVALUES, AND EIGENVECTORS

Given the mathematical theory using only quantum state vectors, the state vector represents all the information we can know about the system and we use the state vectors to calculate probabilities. With each observable S_x, S_y, and S_z we associate a pair of kets corresponding to the possible measurement results of that observable. The observables themselves are not yet included in this mathematical theory, but the distinct association between an observable and its measurable kets provides the means to do so.

The role of physical observables in the mathematics of quantum theory is described by the two postulates listed below. Postulate 2 states that physical observables are represented by mathematical operators, in the same sense that physical states are represented by mathematical vectors or kets (postulate 1). An **operator** is a mathematical object that acts or operates on a ket and transforms it into a new ket, for example $A|\psi\rangle = |\phi\rangle$. However, there are special kets that are not changed by the operation of a particular operator, except for a possible multiplicative constant, which we know does not change anything measurable about the state. An example of a ket that is not changed by an operator would be $A|\psi\rangle = a|\psi\rangle$. Such kets are known as **eigenvectors** of the operator A and the multiplicative constants are known as the **eigenvalues** of the operator. These are important because postulate 3 states that the only possible result of a measurement of a physical observable is one of the eigenvalues of the corresponding operator.

Postulate 2

A physical observable is represented mathematically by an operator A that acts on kets.

Postulate 3

The only possible result of a measurement of an observable is one of the eigenvalues a_n of the corresponding operator A.

We now have a mathematical description of that special relationship between a physical observable, S_z say, the possible results $\pm \hbar/2$, and the kets $|\pm\rangle$ corresponding to those results. This relationship is known as the **eigenvalue equation** and is depicted in Fig. 1 for the case of the spin up state in the z-direction. In the eigenvalue equation, the observable is represented by an operator, the eigenvalue is one of the possible measurement results of the observable, and the eigenvector is the ket corresponding to the chosen eigenvalue of the operator. The eigenvector appears on both sides of the equation because it is unchanged by the operator.

The eigenvalue equations for the S_z operator in a spin-1/2 system are:

$$S_z|+\rangle = +\frac{\hbar}{2}|+\rangle$$
$$S_z|-\rangle = -\frac{\hbar}{2}|-\rangle. \tag{1}$$

These equations tell us that $+\hbar/2$ is the eigenvalue of S_z corresponding to the eigenvector $|+\rangle$ and $-\hbar/2$ is the eigenvalue of S_z corresponding to the eigenvector $|-\rangle$. Equations (1) are sufficient to define how the S_z operator acts mathematically on kets. However, it is useful to use matrix notation to represent operators in the same sense that we use column vectors and row vectors to represent bras and kets, respectively. For Eqs. (1) to be satisfied using matrix algebra with the kets represented as column vectors of size 1×2, the operator S_z must be represented by a 2×2 matrix. The eigenvalue equations (1) provide sufficient information to determine this matrix.

To determine the matrix representing the operator S_z, assume the most general form for a 2×2 matrix

$$S_z \doteq \begin{pmatrix} a & b \\ c & d \end{pmatrix}, \tag{2}$$

where we are again using the $\doteq$ symbol to mean "is represented by." Now write the eigenvalue equations in matrix form:

$$\begin{pmatrix} a & b \\ c & d \end{pmatrix}\begin{pmatrix} 1 \\ 0 \end{pmatrix} = +\frac{\hbar}{2}\begin{pmatrix} 1 \\ 0 \end{pmatrix}$$
$$\begin{pmatrix} a & b \\ c & d \end{pmatrix}\begin{pmatrix} 0 \\ 1 \end{pmatrix} = -\frac{\hbar}{2}\begin{pmatrix} 0 \\ 1 \end{pmatrix}. \tag{3}$$

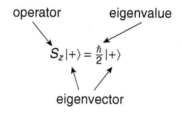

FIGURE 1   Eigenvalue equation for the spin up state.

Note that we are still using the convention that the $|\pm\rangle$ kets are used as the basis for the representation. It is crucial that the rows and columns of the operator matrix are ordered in the same manner as used for the ket column vectors; anything else would amount to nonsense. An explicit labeling of the rows and columns of the operator and the basis kets makes this clear:

$$
\begin{array}{c|cc}
S_z & |+\rangle & |-\rangle \\
\hline
\langle+| & a & b \\
\langle-| & c & d
\end{array}
\qquad
\begin{array}{c|c}
|+\rangle & \\
\hline
\langle+| & 1 \\
\langle-| & 0
\end{array}
\qquad
\begin{array}{c|c}
|-\rangle & \\
\hline
\langle+| & 0 \\
\langle-| & 1
\end{array}
\;. \tag{4}
$$

Carrying through the multiplication in Eqs. (3) yields

$$
\begin{pmatrix} a \\ c \end{pmatrix} = +\frac{\hbar}{2}\begin{pmatrix} 1 \\ 0 \end{pmatrix}
$$
$$
\begin{pmatrix} b \\ d \end{pmatrix} = -\frac{\hbar}{2}\begin{pmatrix} 0 \\ 1 \end{pmatrix}, \tag{5}
$$

which results in

$$
a = +\frac{\hbar}{2} \qquad b = 0
$$
$$
c = 0 \qquad d = -\frac{\hbar}{2}. \tag{6}
$$

Thus the matrix representation of the operator S_z is

$$
S_z \doteq \begin{pmatrix} \hbar/2 & 0 \\ 0 & -\hbar/2 \end{pmatrix}
$$
$$
\doteq \frac{\hbar}{2}\begin{pmatrix} 1 & 0 \\ 0 & -1 \end{pmatrix}. \tag{7}
$$

Note two important features of this matrix: (1) it is a **diagonal matrix**—it has only diagonal elements— and (2) the diagonal elements are the eigenvalues of the operator, ordered in the same manner as the corresponding eigenvectors. In this example, the basis used for the matrix representation is that formed by the eigenvectors $|\pm\rangle$ of the operator S_z. That the matrix representation of the operator in this case is a diagonal matrix is a necessary and general result of linear algebra that will prove valuable as we study quantum mechanics. In simple terms, we say that *an operator is always diagonal in its own basis*. This special form of the matrix representing the operator is similar to the special form that the eigenvectors $|\pm\rangle$ take in this same representation—the *eigenvectors are unit vectors in their own basis*. These ideas cannot be overemphasized, so we repeat them:

> **An operator is always diagonal in its own basis.**
> **Eigenvectors are unit vectors in their own basis.**

Let's also summarize the matrix representations of the S_z operator and its eigenvectors:

$$
S_z \doteq \frac{\hbar}{2}\begin{pmatrix} 1 & 0 \\ 0 & -1 \end{pmatrix} \qquad |+\rangle \doteq \begin{pmatrix} 1 \\ 0 \end{pmatrix} \qquad |-\rangle \doteq \begin{pmatrix} 0 \\ 1 \end{pmatrix}. \tag{8}
$$

Operators and Measurement

1.1 ■ Matrix Representation of Operators

Now consider how matrix representation works in general. Consider a general operator A describing a physical observable (still in the two-dimensional spin-1/2 system), which we represent by the general matrix

$$A \doteq \begin{pmatrix} a & b \\ c & d \end{pmatrix} \tag{9}$$

in the S_z basis. The operation of A on the basis ket $|+\rangle$ yields

$$A|+\rangle \doteq \begin{pmatrix} a & b \\ c & d \end{pmatrix}\begin{pmatrix} 1 \\ 0 \end{pmatrix} = \begin{pmatrix} a \\ c \end{pmatrix}. \tag{10}$$

The inner product of this new ket $A|+\rangle$ with the ket $|+\rangle$ (converted to a bra following the rules) results in

$$\langle +|A|+\rangle = \begin{pmatrix} 1 & 0 \end{pmatrix}\begin{pmatrix} a \\ c \end{pmatrix} = a, \tag{11}$$

which serves to isolate one of the elements of the matrix. Hence an individual element such as $\langle +|A|+\rangle$ or $\langle +|A|-\rangle$ is generally referred to as a **matrix element**. This "sandwich" of a bra, an operator, and a ket

$$\langle bra|OPERATOR|ket\rangle \tag{12}$$

plays an important role in many quantum mechanical calculations. Even in cases where the bra and ket are not basis kets, such as in $\langle \psi|A|\phi\rangle$, we still refer to this as a matrix element. A schematic diagram of a generic matrix element is depicted in Fig. 2(a).

All four elements of the matrix representation of A can be determined in the same manner as Eq. (11), with the final result

$$A \doteq \begin{pmatrix} \langle +|A|+\rangle & \langle +|A|-\rangle \\ \langle -|A|+\rangle & \langle -|A|-\rangle \end{pmatrix}. \tag{13}$$

To emphasize the structure of the matrix, let's write it with explicit labeling of the rows and columns:

$$\begin{array}{c|cc} A & |+\rangle & |-\rangle \\ \hline \langle +| & \langle +|A|+\rangle & \langle +|A|-\rangle \\ \langle -| & \langle -|A|+\rangle & \langle -|A|-\rangle \end{array}. \tag{14}$$

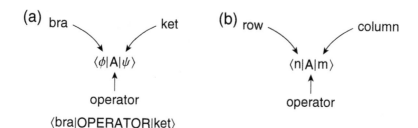

FIGURE 2 (a) Schematic diagram of a generic matrix element. (b) Schematic diagram of the row and column labeling convention for matrix elements.

Operators and Measurement

In a more general problem with more than two dimensions in the complex vector space, the matrix representation of an operator is

$$A \doteq \begin{pmatrix} A_{11} & A_{12} & A_{13} & \cdots \\ A_{21} & A_{22} & A_{23} & \cdots \\ A_{31} & A_{32} & A_{33} & \cdots \\ \vdots & \vdots & \vdots & \ddots \end{pmatrix}, \tag{15}$$

where the matrix elements are

$$A_{ij} = \langle i|A|j \rangle \tag{16}$$

and the basis is assumed to be the states labeled $|i\rangle$, with the subscripts i and j labeling the rows and columns respectively, as depicted in Fig. 2(b). Using this matrix representation, the action of this operator on a general ket $|\psi\rangle = \sum_i c_i|i\rangle$ is

$$A|\psi\rangle \doteq \begin{pmatrix} A_{11} & A_{12} & A_{13} & \cdots \\ A_{21} & A_{22} & A_{23} & \cdots \\ A_{31} & A_{32} & A_{33} & \cdots \\ \vdots & \vdots & \vdots & \ddots \end{pmatrix} \begin{pmatrix} c_1 \\ c_2 \\ c_3 \\ \vdots \end{pmatrix} = \begin{pmatrix} A_{11}c_1 + A_{12}c_2 + A_{13}c_3 + \cdots \\ A_{21}c_1 + A_{22}c_2 + A_{23}c_3 + \cdots \\ A_{31}c_1 + A_{32}c_2 + A_{33}c_3 + \cdots \\ \vdots \end{pmatrix}. \tag{17}$$

If we write the new ket $|\phi\rangle = A|\psi\rangle$ as $|\phi\rangle = \sum_i b_i|i\rangle$, then from Eq. (17) the coefficients b_i are

$$b_i = \sum_j A_{ij}c_j \tag{18}$$

in summation notation.

1.2 ■ Diagonalization of Operators

In the case of the operator S_z above, we used the experimental results and the eigenvalue equations to find the matrix representation of the operator in Eq. (7). It is more common to work the other way. That is, one is given the matrix representation of an operator and is asked to find the possible results of a measurement of the corresponding observable. According to the third postulate, the possible results are the eigenvalues of the operator, and the eigenvectors are the quantum states representing them. In the case of a general operator A in a two-state system, the eigenvalue equation is

$$A|a_n\rangle = a_n|a_n\rangle, \tag{19}$$

where we have labeled the eigenvalues a_n and we have labeled the eigenvectors with the corresponding eigenvalues. In matrix notation, the eigenvalue equation is

$$\begin{pmatrix} A_{11} & A_{12} \\ A_{21} & A_{22} \end{pmatrix} \begin{pmatrix} c_{n1} \\ c_{n2} \end{pmatrix} = a_n \begin{pmatrix} c_{n1} \\ c_{n2} \end{pmatrix}, \tag{20}$$

where c_{n1} and c_{n2} are the unknown coefficients of the eigenvector $|a_n\rangle$ corresponding to the eigenvalue a_n. This matrix equation yields the set of homogeneous equations

$$\begin{aligned} (A_{11} - a_n)c_{n1} + A_{12}c_{n2} &= 0 \\ A_{21}c_{n1} + (A_{22} - a_n)c_{n2} &= 0. \end{aligned} \tag{21}$$

The rules of linear algebra dictate that a set of homogeneous equations has solutions for the unknowns c_{n1} and c_{n2} only if the determinant of the coefficients vanishes:

$$\begin{vmatrix} A_{11} - a_n & A_{12} \\ A_{21} & A_{22} - a_n \end{vmatrix} = 0. \tag{22}$$

It is common notation to use the symbol λ for the eigenvalues, in which case this equation is

$$\det(A - \lambda I) = 0, \tag{23}$$

where I is the identity matrix

$$I = \begin{pmatrix} 1 & 0 \\ 0 & 1 \end{pmatrix}. \tag{24}$$

Equation (23) is known as the **secular** or **characteristic** equation. It is a second order equation in the parameter λ and the two roots are identified as the two eigenvalues a_1 and a_2 that we are trying to find. Once these eigenvalues are found, they are then individually substituted back into Eqs. (21), which are solved to find the coefficients of the corresponding eigenvector.

Example 1   Assume that we know (e.g., from Problem 1) that the matrix representation for the operator S_y is

$$S_y \doteq \frac{\hbar}{2} \begin{pmatrix} 0 & -i \\ i & 0 \end{pmatrix}. \tag{25}$$

Find the eigenvalues and eigenvectors of the operator S_y.
   The general eigenvalue equation is

$$S_y |\lambda\rangle = \lambda |\lambda\rangle, \tag{26}$$

and the possible eigenvalues λ are found using the secular equation

$$\det|S_y - \lambda I| = 0. \tag{27}$$

The secular equation is

$$\begin{vmatrix} -\lambda & -i\dfrac{\hbar}{2} \\ i\dfrac{\hbar}{2} & -\lambda \end{vmatrix} = 0, \tag{28}$$

and solving yields the eigenvalues

$$\lambda^2 + i^2 \left(\frac{\hbar}{2}\right)^2 = 0$$

$$\lambda^2 - \left(\frac{\hbar}{2}\right)^2 = 0$$

$$\lambda^2 = \left(\frac{\hbar}{2}\right)^2 \tag{29}$$

$$\lambda = \pm\frac{\hbar}{2},$$

which was to be expected, because we know that the only possible results of a measurement of any spin component are $\pm\hbar/2$.

As before, we label the eigenvectors $|\pm\rangle_y$. The eigenvalue equation for the positive eigenvalue is

$$S_y|+\rangle_y = +\frac{\hbar}{2}|+\rangle_y, \tag{30}$$

or in matrix notation

$$\frac{\hbar}{2}\begin{pmatrix} 0 & -i \\ i & 0 \end{pmatrix}\begin{pmatrix} a \\ b \end{pmatrix} = +\frac{\hbar}{2}\begin{pmatrix} a \\ b \end{pmatrix}, \tag{31}$$

where we must solve for a and b to determine the eigenvector. Multiplying through and canceling the common factor yields

$$\begin{pmatrix} -ib \\ ia \end{pmatrix} = \begin{pmatrix} a \\ b \end{pmatrix}. \tag{32}$$

This results in two equations, but they are not linearly independent, so we need some more information. The normalization condition provides what we need. Thus we have two equations that determine the eigenvector coefficients:

$$b = ia$$
$$|a|^2 + |b|^2 = 1. \tag{33}$$

Solving these yields

$$|a|^2 + |ia|^2 = 1$$
$$|a|^2 = \tfrac{1}{2}. \tag{34}$$

Again we follow the convention of choosing the first coefficient to be real and positive, resulting in

$$a = \tfrac{1}{\sqrt{2}}$$
$$b = i\tfrac{1}{\sqrt{2}}. \tag{35}$$

Thus the eigenvector corresponding to the positive eigenvalue is

$$|+\rangle_y \doteq \frac{1}{\sqrt{2}}\begin{pmatrix} 1 \\ i \end{pmatrix}. \tag{36}$$

Likewise, one can find the eigenvector for the negative eigenvalue to be

$$|-\rangle_y \doteq \frac{1}{\sqrt{2}}\begin{pmatrix} 1 \\ -i \end{pmatrix}. \tag{37}$$

This procedure of finding the eigenvalues and eigenvectors of a matrix is known as **diagonalization** of the matrix and is the key step in many quantum mechanics problems. Generally, if we find a new operator, the first thing we do is diagonalize it to find its eigenvalues and eigenvectors. However, we stop short of the mathematical exercise of finding the matrix that transforms the original matrix to its new diagonal form. This would amount to a change of basis from the original basis to a new basis of the eigenvectors we have just found, much like a rotation in three dimensions changes from one coordinate system to another. We don't want to make this change of basis. In the example above, the S_y matrix is not diagonal, whereas the S_z matrix is diagonal, because we are using the S_z basis. It is common practice to use the S_z basis as the default basis, so you can assume that is the case unless you are told otherwise.

In summary, we now know three operators and their eigenvalues and eigenvectors. The spin component operators S_x, S_y, and S_z all have eigenvalues $\pm \hbar/2$. The matrix representations of the operators and eigenvectors are (see Problem 1)

$$
\begin{aligned}
S_x &\doteq \frac{\hbar}{2}\begin{pmatrix} 0 & 1 \\ 1 & 0 \end{pmatrix} & |+\rangle_x &\doteq \frac{1}{\sqrt{2}}\begin{pmatrix} 1 \\ 1 \end{pmatrix} & |-\rangle_x &\doteq \frac{1}{\sqrt{2}}\begin{pmatrix} 1 \\ -1 \end{pmatrix} \\
S_y &\doteq \frac{\hbar}{2}\begin{pmatrix} 0 & -i \\ i & 0 \end{pmatrix} & |+\rangle_y &\doteq \frac{1}{\sqrt{2}}\begin{pmatrix} 1 \\ i \end{pmatrix} & |-\rangle_y &\doteq \frac{1}{\sqrt{2}}\begin{pmatrix} 1 \\ -i \end{pmatrix} \\
S_z &\doteq \frac{\hbar}{2}\begin{pmatrix} 1 & 0 \\ 0 & -1 \end{pmatrix} & |+\rangle &\doteq \begin{pmatrix} 1 \\ 0 \end{pmatrix} & |-\rangle &\doteq \begin{pmatrix} 0 \\ 1 \end{pmatrix}
\end{aligned}
\tag{38}
$$

2 ■ NEW OPERATORS

2.1 ■ Spin Component in a General Direction

Now that we know the three operators corresponding to the spin components along the three Cartesian axes, we can use them to find the operator S_n for the spin component along a general direction $\hat{\mathbf{n}}$. This new operator will allow us to predict results of experiments we have not yet performed. The direction $\hat{\mathbf{n}}$ is specified by the polar and azimuthal angles θ and ϕ as shown in Fig. 3. The unit vector $\hat{\mathbf{n}}$ is

$$
\hat{\mathbf{n}} = \hat{\mathbf{i}}\sin\theta\cos\phi + \hat{\mathbf{j}}\sin\theta\sin\phi + \hat{\mathbf{k}}\cos\theta.
\tag{39}
$$

The spin component along this direction is obtained by projecting the spin vector $\mathbf{S}$ onto this new unit vector

$$
\begin{aligned}
S_n &= \mathbf{S}\cdot\hat{\mathbf{n}} \\
&= S_x \sin\theta\cos\phi + S_y \sin\theta\sin\phi + S_z \cos\theta.
\end{aligned}
\tag{40}
$$

The matrix representations we found for S_x, S_y, and S_z lead to the matrix representation of the spin component operator S_n (Problem 6):

$$
S_n \doteq \frac{\hbar}{2}\begin{pmatrix} \cos\theta & \sin\theta\, e^{-i\phi} \\ \sin\theta\, e^{i\phi} & -\cos\theta \end{pmatrix}.
\tag{41}
$$

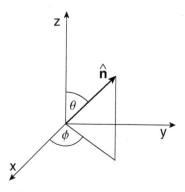

FIGURE 3 General direction along which to measure the spin component.

We have found a new operator, so to learn about its properties, we diagonalize it. Following the diagonalization procedure outlined in Section 1.2, we find that the eigenvalues of S_n are $\pm\hbar/2$ (Problem 7). So if we measure the spin component along any direction, we get only two possible results. The eigenvectors for these two possible measurements are (Problem 7):

$$|+\rangle_n = \cos\frac{\theta}{2}|+\rangle + \sin\frac{\theta}{2}e^{i\phi}|-\rangle$$

$$|-\rangle_n = \sin\frac{\theta}{2}|+\rangle - \cos\frac{\theta}{2}e^{i\phi}|-\rangle,$$

(42)

where we again use the convention of choosing the first coefficient to be real and positive. It is important to point out that the $|+\rangle_n$ eigenstate (or equivalently the $|-\rangle_n$ eigenstate) can be used to represent any possible ket in a spin-1/2 system, if one allows for all possible angles $0 \leq \theta < \pi$ and $0 \leq \phi < 2\pi$. We generally write the most general state as $|\psi\rangle = a|+\rangle + b|-\rangle$, where a and b are complex. Requiring that the state be normalized and using the freedom to choose the first coefficient real and positive reduces this to

$$|\psi\rangle = |a||+\rangle + \sqrt{1-|a|^2}e^{i\phi}|-\rangle.$$

(43)

If we change the parametrization of $|a|$ to $\cos(\theta/2)$, we see that $|+\rangle_n$ is equivalent to the most general state $|\psi\rangle$. This correspondence between the $|+\rangle_n$ eigenstate and the most general state is only valid in a two-state system such as spin 1/2. In systems with more dimensionality, it does not hold because more parameters are needed to specify the most general state than are afforded by the two angles θ and ϕ.

Example 2 Find the probabilities of the measurements shown in Fig. 4, assuming that the first Stern-Gerlach analyzer is aligned along the direction $\hat{n}$ defined by the angles $\theta = 2\pi/3$ and $\phi = \pi/4$.

The measurement by the first Stern-Gerlach analyzer prepares the system in the spin up state $|+\rangle_n$ along the direction $\hat{n}$. This state is then the input state to the second Stern-Gerlach analyzer. The input state is

$$|\psi_{in}\rangle = |+\rangle_n = \cos\frac{\theta}{2}|+\rangle + \sin\frac{\theta}{2}e^{i\phi}|-\rangle$$

$$= \cos\frac{\pi}{3}|+\rangle + \sin\frac{\pi}{3}e^{i\pi/4}|-\rangle$$

(44)

$$= \frac{1}{2}|+\rangle + \frac{\sqrt{3}}{2}e^{i\pi/4}|-\rangle.$$

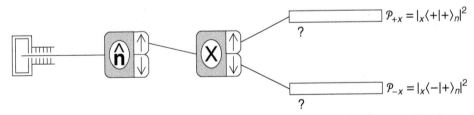

FIGURE 4 Measurement of the spin component after state preparation in a new direction.

Operators and Measurement

The second analyzer is aligned along the x-axis, so the probabilities are

$$\mathcal{P}_{+x} = |_x\langle +|\psi_{in}\rangle|^2 = |_x\langle +|+\rangle_n|^2$$
$$\mathcal{P}_{-x} = |_x\langle -|\psi_{in}\rangle|^2 = |_x\langle -|+\rangle_n|^2.$$

(45)

Let's calculate the first probability using bra-ket notation, recalling that $|+\rangle_x = \frac{1}{\sqrt{2}}[|+\rangle + |-\rangle]$:

$$
\begin{aligned}
\mathcal{P}_{+x} &= |_x\langle +|+\rangle_n|^2 \\
&= \left|\frac{1}{\sqrt{2}}[\langle +| + \langle -|]\frac{1}{2}[|+\rangle + \sqrt{3}e^{i\pi/4}|-\rangle]\right|^2 \\
&= \left|\frac{1}{2\sqrt{2}}[1 + \sqrt{3}e^{i\pi/4}]\right|^2 \\
&= \frac{1}{8}[1 + \sqrt{3}e^{i\pi/4}][1 + \sqrt{3}e^{-i\pi/4}] \\
&= \frac{1}{8}[1 + \sqrt{3}(e^{i\pi/4} + e^{-i\pi/4}) + 3] \\
&= \frac{1}{8}[4 + 2\sqrt{3}\cos(\pi/4)] \\
&= \frac{1}{8}[4 + 2\sqrt{3}/\sqrt{2}] \cong 0.806.
\end{aligned}
$$

(46)

Let's calculate the second probability using matrix notation, recalling that $|-\rangle_x = \frac{1}{\sqrt{2}}[|+\rangle - |-\rangle]$:

$$
\begin{aligned}
\mathcal{P}_{-x} &= |_x\langle -|+\rangle_n|^2 \\
&= \left|\frac{1}{\sqrt{2}}(1 \quad -1)\frac{1}{2}\begin{pmatrix} 1 \\ \sqrt{3}e^{i\pi/4} \end{pmatrix}\right|^2 \\
&= \left|\frac{1}{2\sqrt{2}}[1 - \sqrt{3}e^{i\pi/4}]\right|^2 \\
&= \frac{1}{8}[4 - 2\sqrt{3}\cos(\pi/4)] \\
&= \frac{1}{8}[4 - 2\sqrt{3}/\sqrt{2}] \cong 0.194.
\end{aligned}
$$

(47)

The two results sum to unity as they must. A histogram of the measured results is shown in Fig. 5.

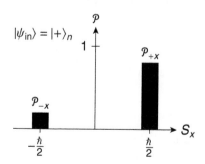

FIGURE 5 Histogram of spin component S_x measurement.

2.2 ■ Hermitian Operators

So far we have defined how operators act upon kets. For example, an operator A acts on a ket $|\psi\rangle$ to produce a new ket $|\phi\rangle = A|\psi\rangle$. The operator acts on the ket from the left; if the operator is on the right of the ket, the result is not defined, which is clear if you try to use matrix representation. Similarly, an operator acting on a bra must be on the right side of the bra

$$\langle \xi | = \langle \psi | A \tag{48}$$

and the result is another bra. However, the bra $\langle \xi | = \langle \psi | A$ is *not* the bra $\langle \phi |$ that corresponds to the ket $|\phi\rangle = A|\psi\rangle$. Rather the bra $\langle \phi |$ is found by defining a new operator $A^\dagger$ that obeys

$$\langle \phi | = \langle \psi | A^\dagger. \tag{49}$$

This new operator $A^\dagger$ is called the **Hermitian adjoint** of the operator A. We can learn something about the Hermitian adjoint by taking the inner product of the state $|\phi\rangle = A|\psi\rangle$ with another (unspecified) state $|\beta\rangle$

$$\langle \phi | \beta \rangle = \langle \beta | \phi \rangle^*$$
$$[\langle \psi | A^\dagger] | \beta \rangle = \{\langle \beta | [A | \psi \rangle]\}^* \tag{50}$$
$$\langle \psi | A^\dagger | \beta \rangle = \langle \beta | A | \psi \rangle^*,$$

which relates the matrix elements of A and $A^\dagger$. Equation (50) tells us that the matrix representing the Hermitian adjoint $A^\dagger$ is found by transposing and complex conjugating the matrix representing A. This is consistent with the definition of Hermitian adjoint used in matrix algebra.

An operator A is said to be **Hermitian** if it is equal to its Hermitian adjoint $A^\dagger$. If an operator is Hermitian, then the bra $\langle \psi | A$ is equal to the bra $\langle \phi |$ that corresponds to the ket $|\phi\rangle = A|\psi\rangle$. That is, a Hermitian operator can act to the right on a ket or to the left on a bra with the same result. In quantum mechanics, all operators that correspond to physical observables are Hermitian. This includes spin operators as well as energy, position, and momentum operators. The Hermiticity of physical observables is important in light of two features of Hermitian matrices: (1) Hermitian matrices have real eigenvalues, which ensures that results of measurements are always real; and (2) the eigenvectors of a Hermitian matrix comprise a complete set of basis states, which ensures that we can use the eigenvectors of any observable as a valid basis.

2.3 ■ Projection Operators

For the spin-1/2 system, we now know four operators: S_x, S_y, S_z, and S_n. Let's look for some other operators. Consider the ket $|\psi\rangle$ written in terms of its coefficients in the S_z basis

$$|\psi\rangle = a|+\rangle + b|-\rangle$$
$$= ((\langle +|\psi\rangle)|+\rangle + ((\langle -|\psi\rangle)|-\rangle. \tag{51}$$

Looking for the moment only at the first term, we can write it as a number times a ket, or as a ket times a number:

$$((\langle +|\psi\rangle)|+\rangle = |+\rangle((\langle +|\psi\rangle) \tag{52}$$

without changing its meaning. Using the second form, we can separate the bra and ket that form the inner product and obtain

$$|+\rangle((\langle +|\psi\rangle) = (|+\rangle\langle +|)|\psi\rangle. \tag{53}$$

Operators and Measurement

The new term in parentheses is a product of a ket and a bra but in the opposite order compared to the inner product defined earlier. This new object must be an operator because it acts on the ket $|\psi\rangle$ and produces another ket: $((\langle+|\psi\rangle)|+\rangle$. This new type of operator is known as an **outer product**.

Returning now to Eq. (51), we write $|\psi\rangle$ using these new operators:

$$
\begin{aligned}
|\psi\rangle &= \langle+|\psi\rangle|+\rangle + \langle-|\psi\rangle|-\rangle \\
&= |+\rangle\langle+|\psi\rangle + |-\rangle\langle-|\psi\rangle \\
&= (|+\rangle\langle+| + |-\rangle\langle-|)|\psi\rangle.
\end{aligned}
\tag{54}
$$

The term in parentheses is a sum of two outer products and is clearly an operator because it acts on a ket to produce another ket. In this special case, the result is the same as the original ket, so the operator must be the **identity operator 1**. This relationship is often written as

$$
|+\rangle\langle+| + |-\rangle\langle-| = \mathbf{1}
\tag{55}
$$

and is known as the **completeness relation** or **closure**. It expresses the fact that the basis states $|\pm\rangle$ comprise a complete set of states, meaning any arbitrary ket can be written in terms of them. To make it obvious that outer products are operators, it is useful to express Eq. (55) in matrix notation using the standard rules of matrix multiplication:

$$
\begin{aligned}
|+\rangle\langle+| + |-\rangle\langle-| &\doteq \begin{pmatrix} 1 \\ 0 \end{pmatrix}(1 \quad 0) + \begin{pmatrix} 0 \\ 1 \end{pmatrix}(0 \quad 1) \\
&\doteq \begin{pmatrix} 1 & 0 \\ 0 & 0 \end{pmatrix} + \begin{pmatrix} 0 & 0 \\ 0 & 1 \end{pmatrix} \\
&\doteq \begin{pmatrix} 1 & 0 \\ 0 & 1 \end{pmatrix}.
\end{aligned}
\tag{56}
$$

Each outer product is represented by a matrix, as we expect for operators, and the sum of these two outer products is represented by the identity matrix, which we expected from Eq. (54).

Now consider the individual operators $|+\rangle\langle+|$ and $|-\rangle\langle-|$. These operators are called **projection** operators, and for spin 1/2 they are given by

$$
\begin{aligned}
P_+ &= |+\rangle\langle+| \doteq \begin{pmatrix} 1 & 0 \\ 0 & 0 \end{pmatrix} \\
P_- &= |-\rangle\langle-| \doteq \begin{pmatrix} 0 & 0 \\ 0 & 1 \end{pmatrix}.
\end{aligned}
\tag{57}
$$

In terms of these new operators the completeness relation can also be written as

$$
P_+ + P_- = \mathbf{1}.
\tag{58}
$$

When a projection operator for a particular eigenstate acts on a state $|\psi\rangle$, it produces a new ket that is aligned along the eigenstate and has a magnitude equal to the amplitude (including the phase) for the state $|\psi\rangle$ to be in that eigenstate. For example,

$$
\begin{aligned}
P_+|\psi\rangle &= |+\rangle\langle+|\psi\rangle = (\langle+|\psi\rangle)|+\rangle \\
P_-|\psi\rangle &= |-\rangle\langle-|\psi\rangle = (\langle-|\psi\rangle)|-\rangle.
\end{aligned}
\tag{59}
$$

Note also that a projector acting on its corresponding eigenstate results in that eigenstate, and a projector acting on an orthogonal state results in zero:

$$
\begin{aligned}
P_+|+\rangle &= |+\rangle\langle+|+\rangle = |+\rangle \\
P_-|+\rangle &= |-\rangle\langle-|+\rangle = 0.
\end{aligned}
\tag{60}
$$

Because the projection operator produces the probability amplitude, we expect that it must be intimately tied to measurement in quantum mechanics.

The probability of a measurement is given by the square of the inner product of initial and final states (Postulate 4). Using the new projection operators, we rewrite the probability as

$$
\begin{aligned}
\mathcal{P}_+ &= |\langle+|\psi\rangle|^2 \\
&= \langle+|\psi\rangle^*\langle+|\psi\rangle \\
&= \langle\psi|+\rangle\langle+|\psi\rangle \\
&= \langle\psi|P_+|\psi\rangle.
\end{aligned}
\tag{61}
$$

Thus we say that the probability of the measurement $S_z = \hbar/2$ can be calculated as a matrix element of the projection operator, using the input state $|\psi\rangle$ and the projector P_+ corresponding to the result.

Another important aspect of quantum measurement is that a measurement disturbs the system. That is, if an input state $|\psi\rangle$ is measured to have $S_z = +\hbar/2$, then the output state is no longer $|\psi\rangle$ but is changed to $|+\rangle$. We saw above that the projection operator does this operation for us, with a multiplicative constant of the probability amplitude. Thus, if we divide by this amplitude, which is the square root of the probability, then we can describe the abrupt change of the input state as

$$
|\psi'\rangle = \frac{P_+|\psi\rangle}{\sqrt{\langle\psi|P_+|\psi\rangle}} = |+\rangle,
\tag{62}
$$

where $|\psi'\rangle$ is the output state. This effect is described by the fifth postulate, which is presented below and is often referred to as the **projection postulate**.

Postulate 5

After a measurement of A that yields the result a_n, the quantum system is in a new state that is the normalized projection of the original system ket onto the ket (or kets) corresponding to the result of the measurement:

$$
|\psi'\rangle = \frac{P_n|\psi\rangle}{\sqrt{\langle\psi|P_n|\psi\rangle}}.
$$

The projection postulate is at the heart of quantum measurement. This effect is often referred to as the **collapse** (or **reduction** or **projection**) of the quantum state vector. The projection postulate clearly states that quantum measurements cannot be made without disturbing the system (except in the case where the input state is the same as the output state), in sharp contrast to classical measurements. The collapse of the quantum state makes quantum mechanics irreversible, again in contrast to classical mechanics.

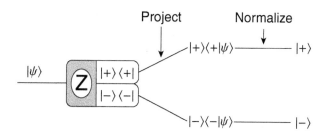

FIGURE 6   Schematic diagram of the role of the projection operator in a Stern-Gerlach spin measurement.

We can use the projection postulate to make a model of quantum measurement, as shown in the revised depiction of a Stern-Gerlach measurement system in Fig. 6. The projection operators act on the input state to produce output states with probabilities given by the squares of the amplitudes that the projection operations yield. For example, the input state $|\psi_{in}\rangle$ is acted on the projection operator $P_+ = |+\rangle\langle+|$, producing an output ket $|\psi_{out}\rangle = |+\rangle(\langle+|\psi_{in}\rangle)$ with probability $\mathcal{P}_+ = |\langle+|\psi_{in}\rangle|^2$. The output ket $|\psi_{out}\rangle = |+\rangle(\langle+|\psi_{in}\rangle)$ is really just a $|+\rangle$ ket that is not properly normalized, so we normalize it for use in any further calculations. We do not really know what is going on in the measurement process, so we cannot explain the mechanism of the collapse of the quantum state vector. This lack of understanding makes some people uncomfortable with this aspect of quantum mechanics and has been the source of much controversy surrounding quantum mechanics. Trying to better understand the measurement process in quantum mechanics is an ongoing research problem. However, despite our lack of understanding, the theory for predicting the results of experiments has been proven with very high accuracy.

2.4 ■ Analysis of Experiments 3 and 4

We now turn to Experiments 3 and 4 from the chapter *Stern-Gerlach Experiments* and analyze them with these new tools. Recall that Experiment 3 is the same as Experiment 4a, and Experiments 4a and 4b are similar in that they each use only one of the output ports of the second Stern-Gerlach analyzer as input to the third analyzer. Figure 7 depicts these experiments again, with Fig. 7(a) showing a hybrid experiment that is essentially Experiment 4a in its upper half and Experiment 4b in its lower half, and Fig. 7(b) showing Experiment 4c. In this problem, we discuss the probability that an atom leaving the first analyzer in the $|+\rangle$ state is detected in one of the counters connected to the output ports of the third analyzer. Such a probability involves two measurements at the second and third analyzers. The total probability is the product of the individual probabilities of each measurement.

For the hybrid experiment shown in Fig. 7(a), the probability of measuring an atom at the topmost counter is the probability of measuring $S_x = +\hbar/2$ at the second analyzer, $|_x\langle+|+\rangle|^2$, times the probability of measuring $S_z = +\hbar/2$ at the third analyzer, $|\langle+|+\rangle_x|^2$, giving

$$\mathcal{P}_{upper,+} = |\langle+|+\rangle_x|^2 |_x\langle+|+\rangle|^2. \tag{63}$$

Likewise the probability of measuring the atom to have $S_x = +\hbar/2$ and then $S_z = -\hbar/2$ is

$$\mathcal{P}_{upper,-} = |\langle-|+\rangle_x|^2 |_x\langle+|+\rangle|^2, \tag{64}$$

where we have written the product so as to be read from right to left as is the usual practice with quantum mechanical amplitudes and probabilities. For atoms that take the lower path from the second analyzer, the final probabilities are

$$\mathcal{P}_{\text{lower},+} = |\langle +|-\rangle_x|^2 |_x\langle -|+\rangle|^2$$
$$\mathcal{P}_{\text{lower},-} = |\langle -|-\rangle_x|^2 |_x\langle -|+\rangle|^2. \tag{65}$$

For Experiment 4c, shown in Fig. 7(b), we have a new situation at the second analyzer. Both output ports are connected to the third analyzer, which means that the probability of an atom from the first analyzer being input to the third analyzer is 100%. So we need only calculate the probability of passage through the third analyzer. The crucial step is determining the input state, for which we use the projection postulate. Because both states are used, the relevant projection operator is the sum of the two projection operators for each port, $P_{+x} + P_{-x}$, where $P_{+x} = |+\rangle_{x\,x}\langle +|$ and $P_{-x} = |-\rangle_{x\,x}\langle -|$. Thus the state after the second analyzer is

$$
\begin{aligned}
|\psi_2\rangle &= \frac{(P_{+x} + P_{-x})|\psi_1\rangle}{\sqrt{\langle \psi_1|(P_{+x} + P_{-x})|\psi_1\rangle}} \\
&= \frac{(P_{+x} + P_{-x})|+\rangle}{\sqrt{\langle +|(P_{+x} + P_{-x})|+\rangle}}.
\end{aligned}
\tag{66}
$$

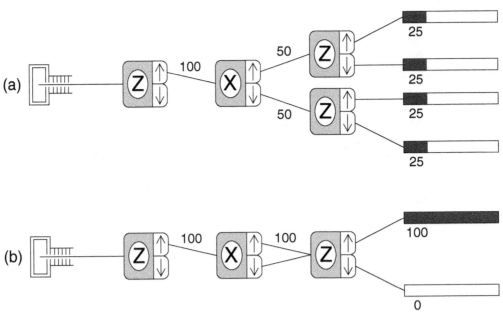

FIGURE 7   (a) Hybrid Experiment 4a and 4b, and (b) Experiment 4c.

In this simple example, the projector $P_{+x} + P_{-x}$ is equal to the identity operator because the two states form a complete basis. This clearly simplifies the calculation, giving $|\psi_2\rangle = |+\rangle$, but to illustrate our point, let's simplify only the denominator (which equals one), giving

$$\begin{aligned} |\psi_2\rangle &= (|+\rangle_x {}_x\langle+| + |-\rangle_x {}_x\langle-|)|+\rangle \\ &= |+\rangle_x {}_x\langle+|+\rangle + |-\rangle_x {}_x\langle-|+\rangle. \end{aligned} \tag{67}$$

Thus the beam entering the third analyzer can be viewed as a coherent superposition of the eigenstates of the second analyzer. Now calculate the probability of measuring spin up at the third analyzer:

$$\begin{aligned} \mathcal{P}_+ &= |\langle+|\psi_2\rangle|^2 \\ &= |\langle+|+\rangle_x {}_x\langle+|+\rangle + \langle+|-\rangle_x {}_x\langle-|+\rangle|^2. \end{aligned} \tag{68}$$

The probability of measuring spin down at the third analyzer is similarly

$$\begin{aligned} \mathcal{P}_- &= |\langle-|\psi_2\rangle|^2 \\ &= |\langle-|+\rangle_x {}_x\langle+|+\rangle + \langle-|-\rangle_x {}_x\langle-|+\rangle|^2. \end{aligned} \tag{69}$$

In each case, the probability is a square of a sum of amplitudes, each amplitude being the amplitude for a successive pair of measurements. For example, in $\mathcal{P}_-$ the amplitude $\langle-|+\rangle_x {}_x\langle+|+\rangle$ refers to the upper path that the initial $|+\rangle$ state takes as it is first measured to be in the $|+\rangle_x$ state and then measured to be in the $|-\rangle$ state (read from right to left). This amplitude is added to the amplitude for the lower path because the beams of the second analyzer are combined, in the proper fashion, to create the input beam to the third analyzer. When the sum of amplitudes is squared, four terms are obtained, two squares and two cross terms, giving

$$\begin{aligned} \mathcal{P}_- &= |\langle-|+\rangle_x {}_x\langle+|+\rangle|^2 + |\langle-|-\rangle_x {}_x\langle-|+\rangle|^2 \\ &\quad + \langle-|+\rangle_x^* {}_x\langle+|+\rangle^* \langle-|-\rangle_x {}_x\langle-|+\rangle \\ &\quad + \langle-|+\rangle_x {}_x\langle+|+\rangle \langle-|-\rangle_x^* {}_x\langle-|+\rangle^* \\ &= \mathcal{P}_{\text{upper},-} + \mathcal{P}_{\text{lower},-} + \text{interference terms}. \end{aligned} \tag{70}$$

This tells us that the probability of detecting an atom to have spin down when both paths are used is the sum of the probabilities for detecting a spin down atom when either the upper path or the lower path is used alone *plus* additional cross terms involving both amplitudes, which are commonly called interference terms. It is these additional terms, which are not complex squares and so could be positive or negative, that allow the total probability to become zero in this case, illustrating the phenomenon of interference.

This interference arises from the nature of the superposition of states that enters the third analyzer. To illustrate, consider what happens if we change the superposition state to a mixed state. Recall that a superposition state implies a beam with each atom in the same state, which is a combination of states, while a mixed state implies that the beam consists of atoms in separate states. As we have described it so far, Experiment 4c involves a superposition state as the input to the third analyzer. We can change this to a mixed state by "watching" to see which of the two output ports of the second analyzer each atom travels through. There are a variety of ways to imagine doing this experimentally. The usual idea proposed is to illuminate the paths with light and watch for the scattered light from the atoms. With proper design of the optics, the light can be localized sufficiently to determine which path the atom takes. Hence, such experiments are generally referred to as "**Which Path**" or "**Welcher Weg**" experiments. Such experiments can be performed in the SPINS program by selecting the "Watch" feature. Once we know which path the atom takes, the state is not the superposition $|\psi_2\rangle$ described above, but is either $|+\rangle_x$ or $|-\rangle_x$, depending on which path produces the light signal. To find the probability that atoms are detected at the spin down counter of the third analyzer, we add the probabilities for atoms to follow the path $|+\rangle \rightarrow |+\rangle_x \rightarrow |-\rangle$ to the probability for other atoms to follow the path $|+\rangle \rightarrow |-\rangle_x \rightarrow |-\rangle$ because these are independent events, giving

$$\mathcal{P}_{\text{watch},-} = |\langle-|+\rangle_x {}_x\langle+|+\rangle|^2 + |\langle-|-\rangle_x {}_x\langle-|+\rangle|^2$$
$$= \mathcal{P}_{\text{upper},-} + \mathcal{P}_{\text{lower},-}, \tag{71}$$

in which no interference terms are present.

This interference example illustrates again the important distinction between a coherent superposition state and a statistical mixed state. In a coherent superposition, there is a definite relative phase between the different states, which gives rise to interference effects that are dependent on that phase. In a statistical mixed state, the phase relationship between the states has been destroyed and the interference is washed out. Now we can understand what it takes to have the beams "properly" combined after the second analyzer of Experiment 4c. The relative phases of the two paths must be preserved. Anything that randomizes the phase is equivalent to destroying the superposition and leaving only a statistical mixture. If the beams are properly combined to leave the superposition intact, the results of Experiment 4c are the same as if no measurement were made at the second analyzer. So even though we have used a measuring device in the middle of Experiment 4c, we generally say that no measurement was made there. We can summarize our conclusions by saying that if no measurement is made on the intermediate state, then we add amplitudes and then square to find the probability, while if an intermediate measurement is performed (i.e., watching), then we square the amplitudes first and then add to find the probability. One is the square of a sum and the other is the sum of squares, and only the former exhibits interference.

2.3 ■ MEASUREMENT

Let's discuss how the probabilistic nature of quantum mechanics affects the way experiments are performed and compared with theory. In classical physics, a theoretical prediction can be reliably compared to a single experimental result. For example, a prediction of the range of a projectile can be tested by doing an experiment. The experiment may be repeated several times in order to understand and possibly reduce any systematic errors (e.g., wind) and measurement errors (e.g., misreading the tape measure). In quantum mechanics, a single measurement is meaningless. If we measure an atom to have spin up in a Stern-Gerlach analyzer, we cannot discern whether the original state was $|+\rangle$ or $|-\rangle_x$ or any arbitrary state $|\psi\rangle$ (except $|-\rangle$). Moreover, we cannot repeat the measurement on the same atom, because the original measurement changed the state, per the projection postulate.

Thus, one must, by necessity, perform identical measurements on identically prepared systems. In the spin-1/2 example, an initial Stern-Gerlach analyzer is used to prepare atoms in a particular state $|\psi\rangle$. Then a second Stern-Gerlach analyzer is used to perform the same experiment on each identically prepared atom. Consider performing a measurement of S_z on N identically prepared atoms. Let N_+ be the number of times the result $+\hbar/2$ is recorded and N_- be the number of times the result $-\hbar/2$ is recorded. Because there are only two possible results for each measurement, we must have $N = N_+ + N_-$. The probability postulate (postulate 4) predicts that the probability of measuring $+\hbar/2$ is

$$\mathcal{P}_+ = |\langle+|\psi\rangle|^2. \tag{72}$$

For a finite number N of atoms, we expect that N_+ is only approximately equal to $\mathcal{P}_+ N$ due to the statistical fluctuations inherent in a random process. Only in the limit of an infinite number N do we expect exact agreement:

$$\lim_{N \to \infty} \frac{N_+}{N} = \mathcal{P}_+ = |\langle + | \psi \rangle|^2. \tag{73}$$

It is useful to characterize a data set in terms of the **mean** and **standard deviation** (see Appendix A for further information on probability). The mean value of a data set is the average of all the measurements. The expected or predicted mean value of a measurement is the sum of the products of each possible result and its probability, which for this spin-1/2 measurement is

$$\boxed{\langle S_z \rangle = \left(+\frac{\hbar}{2} \right) \mathcal{P}_+ + \left(-\frac{\hbar}{2} \right) \mathcal{P}_-,} \tag{74}$$

where the angle brackets signify average or mean value. Using the rules of quantum mechanics we rewrite this mean value as

$$
\begin{aligned}
\langle S_z \rangle &= +\frac{\hbar}{2} |\langle + | \psi \rangle|^2 + \left(-\frac{\hbar}{2} \right) |\langle - | \psi \rangle|^2 \\
&= +\frac{\hbar}{2} \langle \psi | + \rangle \langle + | \psi \rangle + \left(-\frac{\hbar}{2} \right) \langle \psi | - \rangle \langle - | \psi \rangle \\
&= \langle \psi | \left[+\frac{\hbar}{2} | + \rangle \langle + | \psi \rangle + \left(-\frac{\hbar}{2} \right) | - \rangle \langle - | \psi \rangle \right] \\
&= \langle \psi | \left[S_z | + \rangle \langle + | \psi \rangle + S_z | - \rangle \langle - | \psi \rangle \right] \\
&= \langle \psi | S_z [| + \rangle \langle + | + | - \rangle \langle - |] | \psi \rangle.
\end{aligned} \tag{75}
$$

According to the completeness relation, the term in square brackets in the last line is unity, so we obtain

$$\boxed{\langle S_z \rangle = \langle \psi | S_z | \psi \rangle.} \tag{76}$$

We now have two ways to calculate the predicted mean value, Eq. (74) and Eq. (76). Which you use generally depends on what quantities you have readily available. The matrix element version in Eq. (76) is more common and is especially useful in systems that are more complicated than the 2-level spin-1/2 system. This predicted mean value is commonly called the **expectation value**, but it is *not* the expected value of any single experiment. Rather it is the expected mean value of a large number of experiments. It is *not* a time average, but an average over many identical experiments. For a general quantum mechanical observable, the expectation value is

$$\boxed{\langle A \rangle = \langle \psi | A | \psi \rangle = \sum_n a_n \mathcal{P}_{a_n},} \tag{77}$$

where a_n are the eigenvalues of the operator A.

To see how the concept of expectation values applies to our study of spin-1/2 systems, consider two examples. First consider a system prepared in the state $| + \rangle$. The expectation value of S_z is

$$\langle S_z \rangle = \langle + | S_z | + \rangle, \tag{78}$$

which we calculate with bra-ket notation

$$\begin{aligned}
\langle S_z \rangle &= \langle + | S_z | + \rangle \\
&= \langle + | \frac{\hbar}{2} | + \rangle \\
&= \frac{\hbar}{2} \langle + | + \rangle \\
&= \frac{\hbar}{2}.
\end{aligned} \tag{79}$$

This result should seem obvious because $+\hbar/2$ is the only possible result of a measurement of S_z for the $|+\rangle$ state, so it must be the expectation value.

Next consider a system prepared in the state $|+\rangle_x$. In this case, the expectation value of S_z is

$$\langle S_z \rangle = {}_x\langle + | S_z | + \rangle_x. \tag{80}$$

Using matrix notation, we obtain

$$\begin{aligned}
\langle S_z \rangle &= \frac{1}{\sqrt{2}} (1 \quad 1) \frac{\hbar}{2} \begin{pmatrix} 1 & 0 \\ 0 & -1 \end{pmatrix} \frac{1}{\sqrt{2}} \begin{pmatrix} 1 \\ 1 \end{pmatrix} \\
&= \frac{\hbar}{4} (1 \quad 1) \begin{pmatrix} 1 \\ -1 \end{pmatrix} = 0\hbar.
\end{aligned} \tag{81}$$

Again this is what you expect, because the two possible measurement results $\pm\hbar/2$ each have 50% probability, so the average value is zero. Note that the value of zero is never measured, so it is not the value "expected" for any given measurement, but rather the expected mean value of an ensemble of measurements.

In addition to the mean value, it is common to characterize a measurement by the standard deviation, which quantifies the spread of measurements about the mean or expectation value. The standard deviation is defined as the *square root* of the *mean* of the *square* of the deviations from the mean, and for an observable A is given by

$$\Delta A = \sqrt{\langle (A - \langle A \rangle)^2 \rangle}, \tag{82}$$

where the angle brackets signify average value as used in the definition of an expectation value. This result is also often called the **root-mean-square deviation**, or r.m.s. deviation. We need to square the deviations, because the deviations from the mean are equally distributed above and below the mean in such a way that the average of the deviations themselves is zero. This expression can be simplified by expanding the square and performing the averages, resulting in

$$\begin{aligned}
\Delta A &= \sqrt{\langle (A^2 - 2A\langle A \rangle + \langle A \rangle^2) \rangle} \\
&= \sqrt{\langle A^2 \rangle - 2\langle A \rangle \langle A \rangle + \langle A \rangle^2} \\
&= \sqrt{\langle A^2 \rangle - \langle A \rangle^2},
\end{aligned} \tag{83}$$

Operators and Measurement

where one must be clear to distinguish between the square of the mean $\langle A \rangle^2$ and the mean of the square $\langle A^2 \rangle$. While the mean of the square of an observable may not be a common experimental quantity, it can be calculated using the definition of the expectation value

$$\langle A^2 \rangle = \langle \psi | A^2 | \psi \rangle. \tag{84}$$

The square of an operator means that the operator acts twice in succession:

$$A^2 | \psi \rangle = AA | \psi \rangle = A(A | \psi \rangle). \tag{85}$$

To gain experience with the standard deviation, return to the two examples used above. To calculate the standard deviation, we need to find the mean of the square of the operator S_z. In the first case ($|+\rangle$ initial state), we get

$$\langle S_z^2 \rangle = \langle + | S_z^2 | + \rangle = \langle + | S_z S_z | + \rangle = \langle + | S_z \frac{\hbar}{2} | + \rangle$$

$$= \langle + | \left(\frac{\hbar}{2} \right)^2 | + \rangle \tag{86}$$

$$= \left(\frac{\hbar}{2} \right)^2.$$

We already have the mean of the operator S_z in Eq. (79) so the standard deviation is

$$\Delta S_z = \sqrt{\langle S_z^2 \rangle - \langle S_z \rangle^2}$$

$$= \sqrt{\left(\frac{\hbar}{2} \right)^2 - \left(\frac{\hbar}{2} \right)^2} \tag{87}$$

$$= 0\hbar,$$

which is to be expected because there is only one possible result, and hence no spread in the results of the measurement, as shown in the histogram in Fig. 8(a).

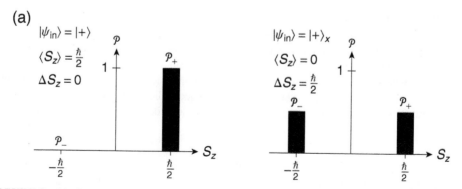

FIGURE 8 Idealized measurements of S_z with (a) a $|+\rangle$ input state and (b) with a $|+\rangle_x$ input state.

In the second case ($|+\rangle_x$ initial state), the mean of the square of the operator S_z is

$$\langle S_z^2 \rangle = {}_x\langle+|S_z^2|+\rangle_x$$
$$= \tfrac{1}{\sqrt{2}}(1 \quad 1)\frac{\hbar}{2}\begin{pmatrix}1 & 0\\0 & -1\end{pmatrix}\frac{\hbar}{2}\begin{pmatrix}1 & 0\\0 & -1\end{pmatrix}\tfrac{1}{\sqrt{2}}\begin{pmatrix}1\\1\end{pmatrix}$$
$$= \tfrac{1}{2}\left(\frac{\hbar}{2}\right)^2(1 \quad 1)\begin{pmatrix}1 & 0\\0 & -1\end{pmatrix}\begin{pmatrix}1\\-1\end{pmatrix} \tag{88}$$
$$= \tfrac{1}{2}\left(\frac{\hbar}{2}\right)^2(1 \quad 1)\begin{pmatrix}1\\1\end{pmatrix}$$
$$= \left(\frac{\hbar}{2}\right)^2.$$

The mean of the operator S_z is in Eq. (81), giving a standard deviation of

$$\Delta S_z = \sqrt{\langle S_z^2\rangle - \langle S_z\rangle^2}$$
$$= \sqrt{\left(\frac{\hbar}{2}\right)^2 - 0\hbar^2} \tag{89}$$
$$= \frac{\hbar}{2}.$$

Again this makes sense because each measurement deviates from the mean ($0\hbar$) by the same value of $\hbar/2$, as shown in the histogram in Fig. 8(b).

The standard deviation ΔA represents the uncertainty in the results of an experiment. In quantum mechanics, this uncertainty is inherent and fundamental, meaning that you cannot design the experiment any better to improve the result. What we have calculated then is the minimum uncertainty allowed by quantum mechanics. Any actual uncertainty may be larger due to experimental error. This is another ramification of the probabilistic nature of quantum mechanics and will lead us to the Heisenberg uncertainty relation in Section 5.

4 ■ COMMUTING OBSERVABLES

We found in Experiment 3 that two incompatible observables could not be known or measured simultaneously, because measurement of one somehow erased knowledge of the other. Let us now explore further what it means for two observables to be incompatible and how incompatibility affects the results of measurements. First we need to define a new object called a **commutator**. The commutator of two operators is defined as the difference between the products of the two operators taken in alternate orders:

$$[A,B] = AB - BA. \tag{90}$$

If the commutator is equal to zero, we say that the operators or observables **commute**; if it is not zero, we say they don't commute. Whether or not two operators commute has important ramifications in analyzing a quantum system and in making measurements of the two observables represented by those operators.

Operators and Measurement

Consider what happens when two operators A and B do commute:

$$[A, B] = 0$$
$$AB - BA = 0 \tag{91}$$
$$AB = BA.$$

Thus, for commuting operators the order of operation does not matter, whereas it does for noncommuting operators. Now let $|a\rangle$ be an eigenstate of the operator A with eigenvalue a:

$$A|a\rangle = a|a\rangle. \tag{92}$$

Operate on both sides of this equation with the operator B and use the fact that A and B commute:

$$BA|a\rangle = Ba|a\rangle$$
$$AB|a\rangle = aB|a\rangle \tag{93}$$
$$A(B|a\rangle) = a(B|a\rangle).$$

The last equation says that the state $B|a\rangle$ is also an eigenstate of the operator A with the same eigenvalue a. Assuming that each eigenvalue has a unique eigenstate (which is true if there is no degeneracy, but we haven't discussed degeneracy yet), the state $B|a\rangle$ must be some scalar multiple of the state $|a\rangle$. If we call this multiple b, then we can write

$$B|a\rangle = b|a\rangle, \tag{94}$$

which is just an eigenvalue equation for the operator B. Thus, we must conclude that the state $|a\rangle$ is also an eigenstate of the operator B, with the eigenvalue b. The assumption that the operators A and B commute has led us to the result that A and B have common or **simultaneous sets of eigenstates**. This result bears repeating:

> **Commuting operators share common eigenstates.**

The ramifications of this result for experiments are very important. Recall that a measurement of the observable A projects the initial state $|\psi\rangle$ onto an eigenstate of A: $|a\rangle$. A subsequent measurement of the observable B then projects the input state $|a\rangle$ onto an eigenstate of B. But the eigenstates of the commuting operators A and B are the same, so the second measurement does not change the state $|a\rangle$. Thus, another measurement of A following the measurement of B yields the same result as the initial measurement of A, as illustrated in Fig. 9. Thus we say that we can know the eigenvalues of these two observables **simultaneously**. It is common to extend this language and say that these two observables can be measured simultaneously, although, as illustrated in Fig. 9, we do not really measure them simultaneously. What we mean is that we can measure one observable without erasing our knowledge of the previous results of the other observable. Observables A and B are said to be **compatible**.

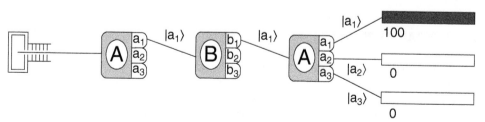

FIGURE 9 Successive measurements of commuting observables.

57

Conversely, if two operators do not commute, then they are incompatible observables and cannot be measured or known simultaneously. This is the case for Experiment 3 *(in the chapter Stern-Gerlach Experiments)*, where the two observables were S_x and S_z. Let's take a look at their commutator to show that they are not compatible:

$$
\begin{aligned}
[S_z, S_x] &\doteq \frac{\hbar}{2}\begin{pmatrix} 1 & 0 \\ 0 & -1 \end{pmatrix}\frac{\hbar}{2}\begin{pmatrix} 0 & 1 \\ 1 & 0 \end{pmatrix} - \frac{\hbar}{2}\begin{pmatrix} 0 & 1 \\ 1 & 0 \end{pmatrix}\frac{\hbar}{2}\begin{pmatrix} 1 & 0 \\ 0 & -1 \end{pmatrix} \\
&\doteq \left(\frac{\hbar}{2}\right)^2\left[\begin{pmatrix} 0 & 1 \\ -1 & 0 \end{pmatrix} - \begin{pmatrix} 0 & -1 \\ 1 & 0 \end{pmatrix}\right] \\
&\doteq \left(\frac{\hbar}{2}\right)^2\begin{pmatrix} 0 & 2 \\ -2 & 0 \end{pmatrix} \\
&= i\hbar S_y.
\end{aligned}
\tag{95}
$$

As expected, these two operators do not commute. In fact, none of the spin component operators commute with each other. The complete commutation relations are

$$
\boxed{
\begin{aligned}
[S_x, S_y] &= i\hbar S_z \\
[S_y, S_z] &= i\hbar S_x \\
[S_z, S_x] &= i\hbar S_y
\end{aligned}
},
\tag{96}
$$

so written to make the cyclic relations clear.

When we represent operators as matrices, we can often decide whether two operators commute by inspection of the matrices. Recall the important statement: *An operator is always diagonal in its own basis.* If you are presented with two matrices that are both diagonal, they must share a common basis, and so they commute with each other. To be explicit, the product of two diagonal matrices

$$
\begin{aligned}
AB &\doteq \begin{pmatrix} a_1 & 0 & 0 & \cdots \\ 0 & a_2 & 0 & \cdots \\ 0 & 0 & a_3 & \cdots \\ \vdots & \vdots & \vdots & \ddots \end{pmatrix}\begin{pmatrix} b_1 & 0 & 0 & \cdots \\ 0 & b_2 & 0 & \cdots \\ 0 & 0 & b_3 & \cdots \\ \vdots & \vdots & \vdots & \ddots \end{pmatrix} \\
&\doteq \begin{pmatrix} a_1 b_1 & 0 & 0 & \cdots \\ 0 & a_2 b_2 & 0 & \cdots \\ 0 & 0 & a_3 b_3 & \cdots \\ \vdots & \vdots & \vdots & \ddots \end{pmatrix},
\end{aligned}
\tag{97}
$$

is clearly independent of the order of the product. Note, however, that you may *not* conclude that two operators do not commute if one is diagonal and one is not, nor if both are not diagonal.

5 ■ UNCERTAINTY PRINCIPLE

The intimate connection between the commutator of two observables and the possible precision of measurements of the two corresponding observables is reflected in an important relation that we simply state here (see more advanced texts for a derivation). The product of the uncertainties or standard deviations of two observables is related to the commutator of the two observables:

$$
\boxed{\Delta A \Delta B \geq \tfrac{1}{2}|\langle [A, B] \rangle|}.
\tag{98}
$$

This is the **uncertainty principle** of quantum mechanics. Consider what it says about a simple Stern-Gerlach experiment. The uncertainty principle for the S_x and S_y spin components is

$$\Delta S_x \Delta S_y \geq \tfrac{1}{2} |\langle [S_x, S_y] \rangle|$$
$$\geq \tfrac{1}{2} |\langle i\hbar S_z \rangle|$$
$$\geq \frac{\hbar}{2} |\langle S_z \rangle|. \tag{99}$$

These uncertainties are the minimal quantum mechanical uncertainties that would arise in any experiment. Any experimental uncertainties due to experimenter error, apparatus errors, and statistical limitations would be additional.

Let's now apply the uncertainty principle to Experiment 3 where we first learned of the impact of measurements in quantum mechanics. If the initial state is $|+\rangle$, then a measurement of S_z results in an expectation value $\langle S_z \rangle = \hbar/2$ with an uncertainty $\Delta S_z = 0$, as illustrated in Fig. 8(a). Thus the uncertainty principle dictates that the product of the other uncertainties for measurements of the $|+\rangle$ state is

$$\Delta S_x \Delta S_y \geq \left(\frac{\hbar}{2} \right)^2, \tag{100}$$

or simply

$$\Delta S_x \Delta S_y \neq 0. \tag{101}$$

This implies that

$$\Delta S_x \neq 0$$
$$\Delta S_y \neq 0. \tag{102}$$

The conclusion to draw from this is that while we can know one spin component absolutely ($\Delta S_z = 0$), we can never know all three, nor even two, simultaneously. This is in agreement with our results from Experiment 3. This lack of ability to measure all spin components simultaneously implies that the spin does not really point in a given direction, as a classical spin or angular momentum does. So when we say that we have measured "spin up," we really mean only that the spin component along that axis is up, as opposed to down, and not that the complete spin angular momentum vector points up along that axis.

6 ■ S² OPERATOR

Another indication that the spin does not point along the axis along which you measure the spin component is obtained by considering a new operator that represents the magnitude of the spin vector but has no information about the direction. It is common to use the square of the spin vector for this task. This new operator is

$$\mathbf{S}^2 = S_x^2 + S_y^2 + S_z^2, \tag{103}$$

and it is calculated in the S_z representation as

$$\mathbf{S}^2 \doteq \left(\frac{\hbar}{2} \right)^2 \left[\begin{pmatrix} 0 & 1 \\ 1 & 0 \end{pmatrix} \begin{pmatrix} 0 & 1 \\ 1 & 0 \end{pmatrix} + \begin{pmatrix} 0 & -i \\ i & 0 \end{pmatrix} \begin{pmatrix} 0 & -i \\ i & 0 \end{pmatrix} + \begin{pmatrix} 1 & 0 \\ 0 & -1 \end{pmatrix} \begin{pmatrix} 1 & 0 \\ 0 & -1 \end{pmatrix} \right]$$
$$\doteq \left(\frac{\hbar}{2} \right)^2 \left[\begin{pmatrix} 1 & 0 \\ 0 & 1 \end{pmatrix} + \begin{pmatrix} 1 & 0 \\ 0 & 1 \end{pmatrix} + \begin{pmatrix} 1 & 0 \\ 0 & 1 \end{pmatrix} \right] \tag{104}$$
$$\doteq \tfrac{3}{4} \hbar^2 \begin{pmatrix} 1 & 0 \\ 0 & 1 \end{pmatrix}.$$

Thus the $\mathbf{S}^2$ operator is proportional to the identity operator, which means it must commute with all the other operators S_x, S_y, and S_z. It also means that all states are eigenstates of the $\mathbf{S}^2$ operator. Thus, we can write

$$\mathbf{S}^2|\psi\rangle = \tfrac{3}{4}\hbar^2|\psi\rangle \tag{105}$$

for any state $|\psi\rangle$ in the spin-1/2 system.

For the case of spin 1/2, note that the expectation value of the operator $\mathbf{S}^2$ is

$$\langle \mathbf{S}^2\rangle = \tfrac{3}{4}\hbar^2, \tag{106}$$

which would imply that the "length" of the spin vector is

$$|\mathbf{S}| = \sqrt{\langle \mathbf{S}^2\rangle} = \sqrt{3}\frac{\hbar}{2}. \tag{107}$$

This is appreciably longer than the measured component of $\hbar/2$, implying that the spin vector can never be fully aligned along any axis. A useful mental model of the spin vector and its component is shown in Fig. 10. In this **vector model**, one can imagine the total spin vector $\mathbf{S}$ precessing around the z-axis at a constant angle to form a cone, with a constant spin component S_z. For a spin-1/2 system in the "spin up" state $|+\rangle$, this classical model yields the same expectation values and uncertainties as the quantum model (Problem 9)

$$\begin{aligned}
\langle S_z\rangle &= \frac{\hbar}{2} & \Delta S_z &= 0 \\
\langle S_x\rangle &= 0 & \Delta S_x &\neq 0 \\
\langle S_y\rangle &= 0 & \Delta S_y &\neq 0.
\end{aligned} \tag{108}$$

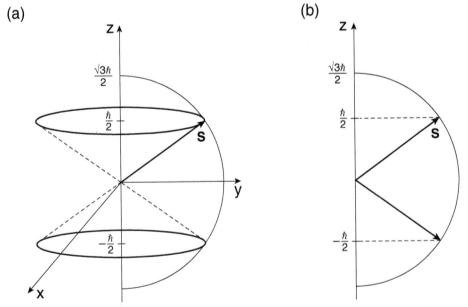

FIGURE 10 (a) Vector model illustrating the classical precision of a spin vector and the allowed quantum mechanical components. (b) Two-dimensional version of the vector model with constant spin vector length and two possible components.

However, a quantum mechanical experiment on a spin component eigenstate does not yield the time dependence of the precession implied by the picture in Fig. 10(a). Rather, the quantum mechanical spin vector is more accurately thought of as smeared out over the whole cone in a uniform random sense. This randomness is often termed **quantum fuzziness** and will be evident in other systems we will study later. To avoid the inaccurate precession part of the vector model, it is often illustrated as in Fig. 10(b).

7 ■ SPIN-1 SYSTEM

The Stern-Gerlach experiment to measure the spin component of neutral particles along the z-axis can be performed on a variety of atoms or particles. Such experiments always result in a finite number of discrete beams exiting the analyzer. For spin-1/2 particles, there are two output beams. For the case of three output beams, the deflections are consistent with magnetic moments arising from spin angular momentum components of $1\hbar$, $0\hbar$, and $-1\hbar$. For an analyzer aligned along the z-axis, the three output states are labeled $|1\rangle$, $|0\rangle$, and $|-1\rangle$, as shown in Fig. 11. This is what we call a **spin-1** system. (Note that the SPINS software and our Stern-Gerlach schematics use arrows for the $|1\rangle$ and $|-1\rangle$ output beams, but these outputs are not the same as the spin-1/2 states that are also denoted with arrows.)

The three eigenvalue equations for the spin component operator S_z of a spin-1 system are

$$S_z|1\rangle = \hbar|1\rangle$$
$$S_z|0\rangle = 0\hbar|0\rangle \tag{109}$$
$$S_z|-1\rangle = -\hbar|-1\rangle.$$

As with the spin-1/2 case, we choose the S_z basis as the standard basis in which to express kets and operators using matrix representation. In Section 1, we found that *eigenvectors are unit vectors in their own basis* and *an operator is always diagonal in its own basis*. Using the first rule, we can immediately write down the eigenvectors of the S_z operator:

$$|1\rangle \doteq \begin{pmatrix} 1 \\ 0 \\ 0 \end{pmatrix} \qquad |0\rangle \doteq \begin{pmatrix} 0 \\ 1 \\ 0 \end{pmatrix} \qquad |-1\rangle \doteq \begin{pmatrix} 0 \\ 0 \\ 1 \end{pmatrix}, \tag{110}$$

where we again use the convention that the ordering of the rows follows the eigenvalues in descending order. Using the second rule, we write down the S_z operator

$$S_z \doteq \begin{pmatrix} 1\hbar & 0 & 0 \\ 0 & 0\hbar & 0 \\ 0 & 0 & -1\hbar \end{pmatrix} = \hbar \begin{pmatrix} 1 & 0 & 0 \\ 0 & 0 & 0 \\ 0 & 0 & -1 \end{pmatrix} \tag{111}$$

with the eigenvalues $1\hbar$, $0\hbar$, and $-1\hbar$ ordered along the diagonal. The value zero is a perfectly valid eigenvalue in some systems.

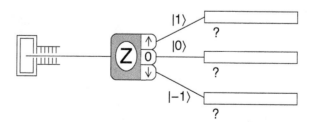

FIGURE 11 Spin-1 Stern-Gerlach experiment.

Operators and Measurement

The same four experiments performed on the spin-1/2 system can be performed on a spin-1 system. Conceptually the results are the same. One important difference occurs in Experiment 2 *(in the chapter Stern-Gerlach Experiments)*, where a measurement of S_z is first performed to prepare a particular state, and then a subsequent measurement of S_x (or S_y) is performed. Based upon the results of the spin-1/2 experiment, one might expect each of the possible components to have one-third probability. Such is not the case. Rather, one set of results is

$$\mathcal{P}_{1x} = |_x\langle 1|1\rangle|^2 = \tfrac{1}{4}$$
$$\mathcal{P}_{0x} = |_x\langle 0|1\rangle|^2 = \tfrac{1}{2} \qquad (112)$$
$$\mathcal{P}_{-1x} = |_x\langle -1|1\rangle|^2 = \tfrac{1}{4},$$

as illustrated in Fig. 12. These experimental results can be used to determine the S_x eigenstates in terms of the S_z basis

$$|1\rangle_x = \tfrac{1}{2}|1\rangle + \tfrac{1}{\sqrt{2}}|0\rangle + \tfrac{1}{2}|-1\rangle$$
$$|0\rangle_x = \tfrac{1}{\sqrt{2}}|1\rangle - \tfrac{1}{\sqrt{2}}|-1\rangle \qquad (113)$$
$$|-1\rangle_x = \tfrac{1}{2}|1\rangle - \tfrac{1}{\sqrt{2}}|0\rangle + \tfrac{1}{2}|-1\rangle.$$

Likewise, we can find the S_y eigenstates:

$$|1\rangle_y = \tfrac{1}{2}|1\rangle + i\tfrac{1}{\sqrt{2}}|0\rangle - \tfrac{1}{2}|-1\rangle$$
$$|0\rangle_y = \tfrac{1}{\sqrt{2}}|1\rangle + \tfrac{1}{\sqrt{2}}|-1\rangle \qquad (114)$$
$$|-1\rangle_y = \tfrac{1}{2}|1\rangle - i\tfrac{1}{\sqrt{2}}|0\rangle - \tfrac{1}{2}|-1\rangle.$$

The matrix representations of the S_x and S_y operators are

$$S_x \doteq \frac{\hbar}{\sqrt{2}}\begin{pmatrix} 0 & 1 & 0 \\ 1 & 0 & 1 \\ 0 & 1 & 0 \end{pmatrix} \qquad S_y \doteq \frac{\hbar}{\sqrt{2}}\begin{pmatrix} 0 & -i & 0 \\ i & 0 & -i \\ 0 & i & 0 \end{pmatrix}. \qquad (115)$$

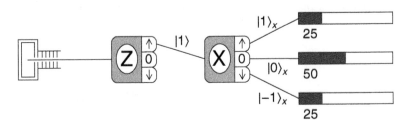

FIGURE 12 Experiment 2 in the spin-1 case.

Example 3 A spin-1 system is prepared in the state

$$|\psi_{in}\rangle = \tfrac{2}{\sqrt{6}}|1\rangle - \tfrac{i}{\sqrt{6}}|0\rangle + \tfrac{i}{\sqrt{6}}|-1\rangle. \tag{116}$$

Find the probabilities of measuring each of the possible spin components along the z-axis.

The probability of measuring $S_z = +1\hbar$ is

$$
\begin{aligned}
\mathcal{P}_1 &= |\langle 1|\psi_{in}\rangle|^2 \\
&= \left|\langle 1|\left[\tfrac{2}{\sqrt{6}}|1\rangle - \tfrac{i}{\sqrt{6}}|0\rangle + \tfrac{i}{\sqrt{6}}|-1\rangle\right]\right|^2 \\
&= \left|\tfrac{2}{\sqrt{6}}\langle 1|1\rangle - \tfrac{i}{\sqrt{6}}\langle 1|0\rangle + \tfrac{i}{\sqrt{6}}\langle 1|-1\rangle\right|^2 \\
&= \left|\tfrac{2}{\sqrt{6}}\right|^2 = \tfrac{2}{3}.
\end{aligned}
\tag{117}
$$

The probability of measuring $S_z = 0\hbar$ is

$$
\begin{aligned}
\mathcal{P}_0 &= |\langle 0|\psi_{in}\rangle|^2 \\
&= \left|\langle 0|\left[\tfrac{2}{\sqrt{6}}|1\rangle - \tfrac{i}{\sqrt{6}}|0\rangle + \tfrac{i}{\sqrt{6}}|-1\rangle\right]\right|^2 \\
&= \left|\tfrac{-i}{\sqrt{6}}\right|^2 = \tfrac{1}{6}.
\end{aligned}
\tag{118}
$$

The probability of measuring $S_z = -1\hbar$ is

$$
\begin{aligned}
\mathcal{P}_{-1} &= |\langle -1|\psi_{in}\rangle|^2 \\
&= \left|\langle -1|\left[\tfrac{2}{\sqrt{6}}|1\rangle - \tfrac{i}{\sqrt{6}}|0\rangle + \tfrac{i}{\sqrt{6}}|-1\rangle\right]\right|^2 \\
&= \left|\tfrac{i}{\sqrt{6}}\right|^2 = \tfrac{1}{6}.
\end{aligned}
\tag{119}
$$

The three probabilities add to unity, as they must. A histogram of the predicted measurement results is shown in Fig. 13.

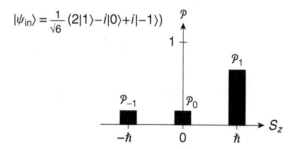

FIGURE 13 Histogram of measurements of z-component of spin for spin-1 particle.

To generalize to other possible spin systems, we need to introduce new labels. We use the label s to denote the spin of the system, such as spin 1/2, spin 1, spin 3/2. The number of beams exiting a Stern-Gerlach analyzer is $2s + 1$. In each of these cases, a measurement of a spin component along any axis yields results ranging from a maximum value of $s\hbar$ to a minimum value of $-s\hbar$, in unit steps of the value $\hbar$. We denote the possible values of the spin component along the z-axis by the label m, the integer or half-integer multiplying $\hbar$. A quantum state with specific values of s and m is denoted as $|sm\rangle$, yielding the eigenvalue equations

$$\mathbf{S}^2|sm\rangle = s(s+1)\hbar^2|sm\rangle$$
$$S_z|sm\rangle = m\hbar|sm\rangle. \tag{120}$$

The label s is referred to as the **spin angular momentum quantum number** or the **spin quantum number** for short. The label m is referred to as the **spin component quantum number** or the **magnetic quantum number** because of its role in magnetic field experiments like the Stern-Gerlach experiment. The connection between this new $|sm\rangle$ notation and the spin-1/2 $|\pm\rangle$ notation is

$$\left|\tfrac{1}{2}\tfrac{1}{2}\right\rangle = |+\rangle$$
$$\left|\tfrac{1}{2},-\tfrac{1}{2}\right\rangle = |-\rangle. \tag{121}$$

For the spin-1 case, the connection to this new notation is

$$|11\rangle = |1\rangle$$
$$|10\rangle = |0\rangle$$
$$|1,-1\rangle = |-1\rangle. \tag{122}$$

We will continue to use the $|\pm\rangle$ notation, but we will find the new notation useful in later study.

8 ■ GENERAL QUANTUM SYSTEMS

Let's extend the important results of this chapter to general quantum mechanical systems. For a general observable A with quantized measurement results a_n, the eigenvalue equation is

$$A|a_n\rangle = a_n|a_n\rangle. \tag{123}$$

In the basis formed by the eigenstates $|a_n\rangle$, the operator A is represented by a matrix with the eigenvalues along the diagonal

$$A \doteq \begin{pmatrix} a_1 & 0 & 0 & \cdots \\ 0 & a_2 & 0 & \cdots \\ 0 & 0 & a_3 & \cdots \\ \vdots & \vdots & \vdots & \ddots \end{pmatrix}, \tag{124}$$

whose size depends on the dimensionality of the system. In this same basis, the eigenstates are represented by the column vectors

$$|a_1\rangle \doteq \begin{pmatrix} 1 \\ 0 \\ 0 \\ \vdots \end{pmatrix}, \ |a_2\rangle \doteq \begin{pmatrix} 0 \\ 1 \\ 0 \\ \vdots \end{pmatrix}, \ |a_3\rangle \doteq \begin{pmatrix} 0 \\ 0 \\ 1 \\ \vdots \end{pmatrix}, \dots. \tag{125}$$

The projection operators corresponding to measurement of the eigenvalues a_n are

$$P_{a_n} = |a_n\rangle\langle a_n|. \tag{126}$$

The completeness of the basis states is expressed by saying that the sum of the projection operators is the identity operator

$$\sum_n P_{a_n} = \sum_n |a_n\rangle\langle a_n| = \mathbf{1}. \tag{127}$$

SUMMARY

In this chapter we have extended the mathematical description of quantum mechanics by using operators to represent physical observables. The only possible results of measurements are the eigenvalues of operators. The eigenvectors of the operator are the basis states corresponding to each possible eigenvalue. We find the eigenvalues and eigenvectors by diagonalizing the matrix representing the operator, which allows us to predict the results of measurements. The eigenvalue equations for the spin-1/2 component operator S_z are

$$S_z|+\rangle = +\frac{\hbar}{2}|+\rangle$$
$$S_z|-\rangle = -\frac{\hbar}{2}|-\rangle. \tag{128}$$

The matrices representing the spin-1/2 operators are

$$S_x \doteq \frac{\hbar}{2}\begin{pmatrix} 0 & 1 \\ 1 & 0 \end{pmatrix} \qquad S_y \doteq \frac{\hbar}{2}\begin{pmatrix} 0 & -i \\ i & 0 \end{pmatrix}$$
$$S_z \doteq \frac{\hbar}{2}\begin{pmatrix} 1 & 0 \\ 0 & -1 \end{pmatrix} \qquad \mathbf{S}^2 \doteq \frac{3\hbar^2}{4}\begin{pmatrix} 1 & 0 \\ 0 & 1 \end{pmatrix}. \tag{129}$$

We characterized quantum mechanical measurements of an observable A by the expectation value

$$\langle A \rangle = \langle \psi|A|\psi \rangle = \sum_n a_n \mathcal{P}_{a_n} \tag{130}$$

and the uncertainty

$$\Delta A = \sqrt{\langle A^2 \rangle - \langle A \rangle^2}. \tag{131}$$

We made a connection between the commutator $[A, B] = AB - BA$ of two operators and the ability to measure the two observables. If two operators commute, then we can measure both observables simultaneously, but if they do not commute, then we cannot measure them simultaneously. We quantified this disturbance that measurement inflicts on quantum systems through the quantum mechanical uncertainty principle

$$\Delta A \Delta B \geq \tfrac{1}{2}\left|\langle [A, B] \rangle\right|. \tag{132}$$

We also introduced the projection postulate, which states how the quantum state vector is changed after a measurement.

RESOURCES

Activities

This activity is available at

www.physics.oregonstate.edu/qmactivities

Spins Lab 3: Stern-Gerlach measurements of a spin-1 system.

Operators and Measurement: Problem Set

1 Given the following information:

$$S_x|\pm\rangle_x = \pm\frac{\hbar}{2}|\pm\rangle_x \qquad\qquad S_y|\pm\rangle_y = \pm\frac{\hbar}{2}|\pm\rangle_y$$

$$|\pm\rangle_x = \tfrac{1}{\sqrt{2}}[|+\rangle \pm |-\rangle] \qquad\qquad |\pm\rangle_y = \tfrac{1}{\sqrt{2}}[|+\rangle \pm i|-\rangle]$$

    find the matrix representations of S_x and S_y in the S_z basis.

2 From the previous problem we know that the matrix representation of S_x in the S_z basis is

$$S_x \doteq \frac{\hbar}{2}\begin{pmatrix} 0 & 1 \\ 1 & 0 \end{pmatrix}.$$

    Diagonalize this matrix to find the eigenvalues and the eigenvectors of S_x.

3 Find the matrix representation of S_z in the S_x basis for spin 1/2. Diagonalize this matrix to find the eigenvalues and the eigenvectors in this basis. Show that the eigenvalue equations for S_z are satisfied in this new representation.

4 Show by explicit matrix calculation that the matrix elements of a general operator A (within a spin-1/2 system) are as shown in Eq. (13),

$$A \doteq \begin{pmatrix} \langle+|A|+\rangle & \langle+|A|-\rangle \\ \langle-|A|+\rangle & \langle-|A|-\rangle \end{pmatrix}. \tag{13}$$

5 Calculate the commutators of the spin-1/2 operators S_x, S_y, and S_z, thus verifying Eqs. (96),

$$\boxed{\begin{aligned} [S_x, S_y] &= i\hbar S_z \\ [S_y, S_z] &= i\hbar S_x \\ [S_z, S_x] &= i\hbar S_y \end{aligned}} \tag{96}$$

6 Verify that the spin component operator S_n along the direction $\hat{\mathbf{n}}$ has the matrix representation shown in Eq. (41),

$$S_n \doteq \frac{\hbar}{2}\begin{pmatrix} \cos\theta & \sin\theta\, e^{-i\phi} \\ \sin\theta\, e^{i\phi} & -\cos\theta \end{pmatrix}. \tag{41}$$

7 Diagonalize the spin component operator S_n along the direction $\hat{\mathbf{n}}$ to find its eigenvalues and the eigenvectors.

8 Find the probabilities of the measurements shown in Fig. 14. The first Stern-Gerlach analyzer is aligned along the direction $\hat{\mathbf{n}}$ defined by the angles $\theta = \pi/4$ and $\phi = 5\pi/3$.

The companion websites for this text are http://physics.oregonstate.edu/portfolioswiki and http://physics.oregonstate.edu/qmactivities.

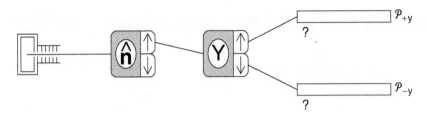

FIGURE 14 Measurement of spin components (Prob. 8).

9 For the state $|+\rangle$, calculate the expectation values and uncertainties for measurements of S_x, S_y, and S_z in order to verify Eq. (108),

$$\langle S_z \rangle = \frac{\hbar}{2} \qquad \Delta S_z = 0$$

$$\langle S_x \rangle = 0 \qquad \Delta S_x \neq 0 \tag{108}$$

$$\langle S_y \rangle = 0 \qquad \Delta S_y \neq 0.$$

10 For the state $|+\rangle_y$, calculate the expectation values and uncertainties for measurements of S_x, S_y, and S_z. Draw a diagram of the vector model applied to this state and reconcile your quantum mechanical calculations with the classical results.

11 Show that the $\mathbf{S}^2$ operator commutes with each of the spin component operators of S_x, S_y, and S_z. Do this once with matrix notation for a spin-1/2 system and a second time using only the component commutation relations in Eqs. (96),

$$\boxed{\begin{aligned} \left[S_x, S_y \right] &= i\hbar S_z \\ \left[S_y, S_z \right] &= i\hbar S_x \\ \left[S_z, S_x \right] &= i\hbar S_y \end{aligned}} \tag{96}$$

and the definition of $\mathbf{S}^2$ in Eq. (103),

$$\mathbf{S}^2 = S_x^2 + S_y^2 + S_z^2. \tag{103}$$

12 Diagonalize the S_x and S_y operators in the spin-1 case to find the eigenvalues and the eigenvectors of both operators.

13 For a spin-1 system, show by explicit matrix calculation that the spin component operators obey the commutation relations in Eqs. (96).

14 Find the matrix representation of the $\mathbf{S}^2$ operator for a spin-1 system. Do this once by explicit matrix calculation and a second time by inspection of the $\mathbf{S}^2$ eigenvalue equation (120),

$$\mathbf{S}^2|sm\rangle = s(s + 1)\hbar^2|sm\rangle$$

$$S_z|sm\rangle = m\hbar|sm\rangle. \tag{120}$$

15 A beam of spin-1 particles is prepared in the state

$$|\psi\rangle = \tfrac{2}{\sqrt{29}}|1\rangle + i\tfrac{3}{\sqrt{29}}|0\rangle - \tfrac{4}{\sqrt{29}}|-1\rangle.$$

a) What are the possible results of a measurement of the spin component S_z, and with what probabilities would they occur?

b) What are the possible results of a measurement of the spin component S_x, and with what probabilities would they occur?

c) Plot histograms of the predicted measurement results from parts (a) and (b), and calculate the expectation values for both measurements.

16 A beam of spin-1 particles is prepared in the state

$$|\psi\rangle = \tfrac{2}{\sqrt{29}}|1\rangle_y + i\tfrac{3}{\sqrt{29}}|0\rangle_y - \tfrac{4}{\sqrt{29}}|-1\rangle_y.$$

a) What are the possible results of a measurement of the spin component S_z, and with what probabilities would they occur?

b) What are the possible results of a measurement of the spin component S_y, and with what probabilities would they occur?

c) Plot histograms of the predicted measurement results from parts (a) and (b), and calculate the expectation values for both measurements.

17 A spin-1 particle is in the state

$$|\psi\rangle \doteq \frac{1}{\sqrt{30}}\begin{pmatrix} 1 \\ 2 \\ 5i \end{pmatrix}.$$

a) What are the possible results of a measurement of the spin component S_z, and with what probabilities would they occur? Calculate the expectation value of the spin component S_z.

b) Calculate the expectation value of the spin component S_x. *Suggestion*: Use matrix mechanics to evaluate the expectation value.

18 A spin-1 particle is prepared in the state

$$|\psi\rangle = \tfrac{1}{\sqrt{14}}|1\rangle - \tfrac{3}{\sqrt{14}}|0\rangle + i\tfrac{2}{\sqrt{14}}|-1\rangle.$$

a) What are the possible results of a measurement of the spin component S_z, and with what probabilities would they occur?

b) Suppose that the S_z measurement on the particle yields the result $S_z = -\hbar$. Subsequent to that result a second measurement is performed to measure the spin component S_x. What are the possible results of that measurement, and with what probabilities would they occur?

c) Draw a schematic diagram depicting the successive measurements in parts (a) and (b).

19 A spin-1 particle is prepared in the state

$$|\psi_i\rangle = \sqrt{\tfrac{1}{6}}|1\rangle - \sqrt{\tfrac{2}{6}}|0\rangle + i\sqrt{\tfrac{3}{6}}|-1\rangle.$$

Find the probability that the system is measured to be in the final state

$$|\psi_f\rangle = \tfrac{1+i}{\sqrt{7}}|1\rangle_y + \tfrac{2}{\sqrt{7}}|0\rangle_y - i\tfrac{1}{\sqrt{7}}|-1\rangle_y.$$

20 In part (2) of SPINS Lab #3, you measured the spin components of the unknown (spin 1) initial states $|\psi_i\rangle$ ($i = 1, 2, 3, 4$) along the three axes. Using your measured values, deduce the unknown initial states.

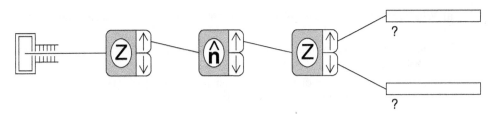

FIGURE 15 Measurement of spin components (Prob. 22).

21 In part (3) of SPINS Lab #3, you built a spin-1 interferometer and measured the relative probabilities after the final Stern-Gerlach analyzer for the seven possible cases where one beam, a pair of beams, or all three beams from the second Stern-Gerlach analyzer were used. Show how you used the projection postulate to calculate the theoretical probabilities.

22 A beam of spin-1/2 particles is sent through a series of three Stern-Gerlach analyzers, as shown in Fig. 15. The second Stern-Gerlach analyzer is aligned along the $\hat{n}$ direction, which makes an angle θ in the x-z plane with respect to the z-axis.

a) Find the probability that particles transmitted through the first Stern-Gerlach analyzer are measured to have spin down at the third Stern-Gerlach analyzer?

b) How must the angle θ of the second Stern-Gerlach analyzer be oriented so as to maximize the probability that particles are measured to have spin down at the third Stern-Gerlach analyzer? What is this maximum fraction?

c) What is the probability that particles have spin down at the third Stern-Gerlach analyzer if the second Stern-Gerlach analyzer is removed from the experiment?

23 Consider a three-dimensional ket space. In the basis defined by three orthogonal kets $|1\rangle$, $|2\rangle$, and $|3\rangle$, the operators A and B are represented by

$$
A \doteq \begin{pmatrix} a_1 & 0 & 0 \\ 0 & a_2 & 0 \\ 0 & 0 & a_3 \end{pmatrix} \qquad B \doteq \begin{pmatrix} b_1 & 0 & 0 \\ 0 & 0 & b_2 \\ 0 & b_2 & 0 \end{pmatrix},
$$

where all the quantities are real.

a) Do the operators A and B commute?

b) Find the eigenvalues and normalized eigenvectors of both operators.

c) Assume the system is initially in the state $|2\rangle$. Then the observable corresponding to the operator B is measured. What are the possible results of this measurement and the probabilities of each result? After this measurement, the observable corresponding to the operator A is measured. What are the possible results of this measurement and the probabilities of each result?

d) How are questions (a) and (c) above related?

24 If a beam of spin-3/2 particles is input to a Stern-Gerlach analyzer, there are four output beams whose deflections are consistent with magnetic moments arising from spin angular momentum components of $\frac{3}{2}\hbar$, $\frac{1}{2}\hbar$, $-\frac{1}{2}\hbar$, and $-\frac{3}{2}\hbar$. For a spin-3/2 system:

a) Write down the eigenvalue equations for the S_z operator.

b) Write down the matrix representation of the S_z eigenstates.

c) Write down the matrix representation of the S_z operator.

d) Write down the eigenvalue equations for the S^2 operator.

e) Write down the matrix representation of the S^2 operator.

25 Are the projection operators P_+ and P_- Hermitian? Explain.

Schrödinger Time Evolution

From Chapter 3 of *Quantum Mechanics: A Paradigms Approach*, First Edition. David H. McIntyre. Copyright © 2012 by Pearson Education, Inc. Published by Pearson Addison-Wesley. All rights reserved.

The companion websites for this text are http://physics.oregonstate.edu/portfolioswiki and http://physics.oregonstate.edu/qmactivities.

Schrödinger Time Evolution

This chapter marks the final step in developing the mathematical basis of a quantum theory. Recall how to use kets to describe quantum states and how to predict the probabilities of results of measurements. Also recall how to use operators to represent physical observables and how to determine the possible measurement results. The key missing aspect is the ability to predict the future. Physics theories are judged on their predictive power. Classical mechanics relies on Newton's second law $\mathbf{F} = m\mathbf{a}$ to predict the future of a particle's motion. The ability to predict the quantum future started with Erwin Schrödinger and bears his name.

1 ■ SCHRÖDINGER EQUATION

The sixth postulate of quantum mechanics says that the time evolution of a quantum system is governed by the differential equation

$$i\hbar \frac{d}{dt}|\psi(t)\rangle = H(t)|\psi(t)\rangle, \tag{1}$$

where the operator H corresponds to the total energy of the system and is called the **Hamiltonian** operator of the system because it is derived from the classical Hamiltonian. This equation is known as the **Schrödinger equation**.

Postulate 6

The time evolution of a quantum system is determined by the Hamiltonian or total energy operator $H(t)$ through the Schrödinger equation

$$i\hbar \frac{d}{dt}|\psi(t)\rangle = H(t)|\psi(t)\rangle.$$

The Hamiltonian may be a new operator, but you can use ideas you're already developed to understand its basic properties. The Hamiltonian H is an observable, so it is a Hermitian operator. The eigenvalues of the Hamiltonian are the allowed energies of the quantum system, and the eigenstates of H are the energy eigenstates of the system. If we label the allowed energies as E_n, then the **energy eigenvalue equation** is

$$\boxed{H|E_n\rangle = E_n|E_n\rangle}. \tag{2}$$

If we have the Hamiltonian H in a matrix representation, then we diagonalize the matrix to find the eigenvalues E_n and the eigenvectors $|E_n\rangle$ just as we do with the spin operators. For the moment, let's assume that we have already diagonalized the Hamiltonian [i.e., solved Eq. (2)] so that we know the eigenvalues E_n and the eigenvectors $|E_n\rangle$, and let's see what we can learn about quantum time evolution in general by solving the Schrödinger equation.

The eigenvectors of the Hamiltonian form a complete basis because the Hamiltonian is an observable, and therefore a Hermitian operator. Because H is the only operator appearing in the Schrödinger equation, it would seem reasonable (and will prove invaluable) to consider the energy eigenstates as the basis of choice for expanding general state vectors:

$$|\psi(t)\rangle = \sum_n c_n(t)|E_n\rangle. \tag{3}$$

The basis of eigenvectors of the Hamiltonian is also orthonormal, so

$$\langle E_k|E_n\rangle = \delta_{kn}. \tag{4}$$

We refer to this basis as the **energy basis**.

For now, we assume that the Hamiltonian is time independent (we will do the time-dependent case $H(t)$ in Section 4). The eigenvectors of a time-independent Hamiltonian come from diagonalization procedure, so there is no reason to expect the eigenvectors themselves to carry any time dependence. Thus if a general state $|\psi\rangle$ is to be time dependent, as the Schrödinger equation implies, then the time dependence must reside in the expansion coefficients $c_n(t)$, as expressed in Eq. (3). Substitute this general state into the Schrödinger equation (1)

$$i\hbar\frac{d}{dt}\sum_n c_n(t)|E_n\rangle = H\sum_n c_n(t)|E_n\rangle \tag{5}$$

and use the energy eigenvalue equation (2) to obtain

$$i\hbar\sum_n \frac{dc_n(t)}{dt}|E_n\rangle = \sum_n c_n(t)E_n|E_n\rangle. \tag{6}$$

Each side of this equation is a sum over all the energy states of the system. To simplify this equation, we isolate single terms in these two sums by taking the inner product of the ket on each side with one particular ket $|E_k\rangle$ (this ket can have any label k, but must not have the label n that is already used in the summation). The orthonormality condition $\langle E_k|E_n\rangle = \delta_{kn}$ then collapses the sums:

$$\langle E_k|i\hbar\sum_n \frac{dc_n(t)}{dt}|E_n\rangle = \langle E_k|\sum_n c_n(t)E_n|E_n\rangle$$

$$i\hbar\sum_n \frac{dc_n(t)}{dt}\langle E_k|E_n\rangle = \sum_n c_n(t)E_n\langle E_k|E_n\rangle$$

$$i\hbar\sum_n \frac{dc_n(t)}{dt}\delta_{kn} = \sum_n c_n(t)E_n\delta_{kn} \tag{7}$$

$$i\hbar\frac{dc_k(t)}{dt} = c_k(t)E_k.$$

We are left with a single differential equation for each of the possible energy states of the systems $k = 1, 2, 3, \ldots$. This first-order differential equation can be rewritten as

$$\frac{dc_k(t)}{dt} = -i\frac{E_k}{\hbar}c_k(t). \tag{8}$$

The solution to Eq. (8) is a complex exponential

$$c_k(t) = c_k(0)e^{-iE_k t/\hbar}. \tag{9}$$

In Eq. (9), we have denoted the initial condition as $c_k(0)$, but we denote it simply as c_k hereafter. Each coefficient in the energy basis expansion of the state obeys the *same* form of the time dependence in Eq. (9), but with a *different* exponent due to the different energies. The time-dependent solution for the full state vector is summarized by saying that if the initial state of the system at time $t = 0$ is

$$|\psi(0)\rangle = \sum_n c_n |E_n\rangle, \tag{10}$$

then the time evolution of this state under the action of the time-independent Hamiltonian H is

$$\boxed{|\psi(t)\rangle = \sum_n c_n e^{-iE_n t/\hbar} |E_n\rangle}. \tag{11}$$

So the time dependence of the original state vector is found by multiplying *each* energy eigenstate coefficient by its own phase factor $e^{-iE_n t/\hbar}$ that depends on the energy of *that* eigenstate. Note that the factor $E/\hbar$ is an angular frequency, so that the time dependence is of the form $e^{-i\omega t}$, a form commonly found in many areas of physics. It is important to remember that one must use the *energy* eigenstates for the expansion in Eq. (10) in order to use the simple phase factor multiplication in Eq. (11) to account for the Schrödinger time evolution of the state. This key role of the energy basis accounts for the importance of the Hamiltonian operator and for the common practice of finding the energy eigenstates to use as the preferred basis.

A few examples help to illustrate some of the important consequences of this time evolution of the quantum mechanical state vector. First, consider the simplest possible situation where the system is initially in one particular energy eigenstate:

$$|\psi(0)\rangle = |E_1\rangle, \tag{12}$$

for example. The prescription for time evolution tells us that after some time t the system is in the state

$$|\psi(t)\rangle = e^{-iE_1 t/\hbar} |E_1\rangle. \tag{13}$$

But this state differs from the original state only by an overall phase factor, which we have said before does not affect any measurements. For example, if we measure an observable A, then the probability of measuring an eigenvalue a_j is given by

$$\begin{aligned} \mathcal{P}_{a_j} &= |\langle a_j|\psi(t)\rangle|^2 \\ &= |\langle a_j|e^{-iE_1 t/\hbar}|E_1\rangle|^2 \\ &= |\langle a_j|E_1\rangle|^2. \end{aligned} \tag{14}$$

This probability is time independent and is equal to the probability at the initial time. Thus, we conclude that there is no measureable time evolution for this state. Hence, the energy eigenstates are called **stationary states**. If a system begins in an energy eigenstate, then it remains in that state.

Now consider an initial state that is a superposition of two energy eigenstates:

$$|\psi(0)\rangle = c_1|E_1\rangle + c_2|E_2\rangle. \tag{15}$$

In this case, time evolution takes the initial state to the later state

$$|\psi(t)\rangle = c_1 e^{-iE_1 t/\hbar}|E_1\rangle + c_2 e^{-iE_2 t/\hbar}|E_2\rangle. \tag{16}$$

A measurement of the system energy at the time t would yield the value E_1 with a probability

$$
\begin{aligned}
\mathcal{P}_{E_1} &= |\langle E_1|\psi(t)\rangle|^2 \\
&= |\langle E_1|[c_1 e^{-iE_1 t/\hbar}|E_1\rangle + c_2 e^{-iE_2 t/\hbar}|E_2\rangle]|^2 \\
&= |c_1|^2,
\end{aligned}
\tag{17}
$$

which is independent of time. The same is true for the probability of measuring the energy E_2. Thus, the probabilities of measuring the energies are stationary, as they were in the first example.

However, now consider what happens if another observable is measured on this system in this superposition state. There are two distinct situations: (1) If the other observable A commutes with the Hamiltonian H, then A and H have common eigenstates. In this case, measuring A is equivalent to measuring H because the inner products used to calculate the probabilities use the same eigenstates. Hence, the probability of measuring any particular eigenvalue of A is time independent, as in Eq. (17). (2) If A and H do not commute, then they do not share common eigenstates. In this case, the eigenstates of A in general consist of superpositions of energy eigenstates. For example, suppose that the eigenstate of A corresponding to the eigenvalue a_1 were

$$
|a_1\rangle = \alpha_1|E_1\rangle + \alpha_2|E_2\rangle.
\tag{18}
$$

Then the probability of measuring the eigenvalue a_1 would be

$$
\begin{aligned}
\mathcal{P}_{a_1} &= |\langle a_1|\psi(t)\rangle|^2 \\
&= |[\alpha_1^*\langle E_1| + \alpha_2^*\langle E_2|][c_1 e^{-iE_1 t/\hbar}|E_1\rangle + c_2 e^{-iE_2 t/\hbar}|E_2\rangle]|^2 \\
&= |\alpha_1^* c_1 e^{-iE_1 t/\hbar} + \alpha_2^* c_2 e^{-iE_2 t/\hbar}|^2.
\end{aligned}
\tag{19}
$$

Factoring out the common phase gives

$$
\begin{aligned}
\mathcal{P}_{a_1} &= |e^{-iE_1 t/\hbar}|^2 |\alpha_1^* c_1 + \alpha_2^* c_2 e^{-i(E_2-E_1)t/\hbar}|^2 \\
&= |\alpha_1|^2|c_1|^2 + |\alpha_2|^2|c_2|^2 + 2\mathrm{Re}\left(\alpha_1 c_1^* \alpha_2^* c_2 e^{-i(E_2-E_1)t/\hbar}\right).
\end{aligned}
\tag{20}
$$

The different time-evolution phases of the two components of $|\psi(t)\rangle$ lead to a time dependence in the probability. The overall phase in Eq. (20) drops out, and only the relative phase remains in the probability calculation. Hence, the time dependence is determined by the *difference* of the energies of the two states involved in the superposition. The corresponding angular frequency of the time evolution

$$
\omega_{21} = \frac{E_2 - E_1}{\hbar}
\tag{21}
$$

is called the **Bohr frequency**.

To summarize, we list below a recipe for solving a standard time-dependent quantum mechanics problem with a time-independent Hamiltonian.

Given a Hamiltonian H and an initial state $|\psi(0)\rangle$, what is the probability that the eigenvalue a_j of the observable A is measured at time t?

1. Diagonalize H (find the eigenvalues E_n and eigenvectors $|E_n\rangle$).
2. Write $|\psi(0)\rangle$ in terms of the energy eigenstates $|E_n\rangle$.
3. Multiply each eigenstate coefficient by $e^{-iE_n t/\hbar}$ to get $|\psi(t)\rangle$.
4. Calculate the probability $\mathcal{P}_{a_j} = |\langle a_j|\psi(t)\rangle|^2$.

---

2 ■ SPIN PRECESSION

Now apply this new concept of Schrödinger time evolution to the case of a spin-1/2 system. The Hamiltonian operator represents the total energy of the system, but because only energy differences are important in time-dependent solutions (and because we can define the zero of potential energy as we wish), we need consider only energy terms that differentiate between the two possible spin states in the system. Our experience with the Stern-Gerlach apparatus tells us that the magnetic potential energy of the magnetic dipole differs for the two possible spin-component states. So to begin, we consider the potential energy of a single magnetic dipole (e.g., in a silver atom) in a uniform magnetic field as the sole term in the Hamiltonian. Recalling that the magnetic dipole is given by

$$\boldsymbol{\mu} = g\frac{q}{2m_e}\mathbf{S}, \tag{22}$$

the Hamiltonian is

$$\begin{aligned} H &= -\boldsymbol{\mu}\cdot\mathbf{B} \\ &= -g\frac{q}{2m_e}\mathbf{S}\cdot\mathbf{B} \\ &= \frac{e}{m_e}\mathbf{S}\cdot\mathbf{B}, \end{aligned} \tag{23}$$

where $q = -e$ and $g = 2$ have been used in the last line. The gyromagnetic ratio, g, is slightly different from 2, but we ignore that detail.

2.1 ■ Magnetic Field in the z-Direction

For our first example, we assume that the magnetic field is uniform and directed along the z-axis. Writing the magnetic field as

$$\mathbf{B} = B_0\hat{\mathbf{z}} \tag{24}$$

allows the Hamiltonian to be simplified to

$$\begin{aligned} H &= \frac{eB_0}{m_e}S_z \\ &= \omega_0 S_z, \end{aligned} \tag{25}$$

where we have introduced the definition

$$\omega_0 \equiv \frac{eB_0}{m_e}. \tag{26}$$

This definition of an angular frequency simplifies the notation now and will have an obvious interpretation at the end of the problem.

The Hamiltonian in Eq. (25) is proportional to the S_z operator, so H and S_z commute and therefore share common eigenstates. This is clear if we write the Hamiltonian as a matrix in the S_z representation:

$$H \doteq \frac{\hbar\omega_0}{2}\begin{pmatrix} 1 & 0 \\ 0 & -1 \end{pmatrix}. \tag{27}$$

Because H is diagonal, we have already completed step 1 of the Schrödinger time-evolution recipe. The eigenstates of H are the basis states of the representation, while the eigenvalues are the diagonal elements of the matrix in Eq. (27). The eigenvalue equations for the Hamiltonian are thus

$$H|+\rangle = \omega_0 S_z|+\rangle = \frac{\hbar\omega_0}{2}|+\rangle = E_+|+\rangle$$

$$H|-\rangle = \omega_0 S_z|-\rangle = -\frac{\hbar\omega_0}{2}|+\rangle = E_-|-\rangle,$$
(28)

with eigenvalues and eigenvectors given by

$$E_+ = \frac{\hbar\omega_0}{2} \qquad E_- = -\frac{\hbar\omega_0}{2}$$

$$|E_+\rangle = |+\rangle \qquad |E_-\rangle = |-\rangle.$$
(29)

The information regarding the energy eigenvalues and eigenvectors is commonly presented in a graphical diagram, which is shown in Fig. 1 for this case. The two energy states are separated by the energy $E_+ - E_- = \hbar\omega_0$, so the angular frequency ω_0 characterizes the energy scale of this system. The spin-up state $|+\rangle$ has a higher energy because the magnetic moment is aligned against the field in that state; the negative charge in Eq. (22) causes the spin and magnetic moment to be antiparallel.

Now we look at a few examples to illustrate the key features of the behavior of a spin-1/2 system in a uniform magnetic field. First, consider the case where the initial state is spin up along the z-axis:

$$|\psi(0)\rangle = |+\rangle.$$
(30)

This initial state is already expressed in the energy basis (step 2 of the Schrödinger recipe), so the Schrödinger equation time evolution takes this initial state to the state

$$|\psi(t)\rangle = e^{-iE_+t/\hbar}|+\rangle$$
$$= e^{-i\omega_0 t/2}|+\rangle$$
(31)

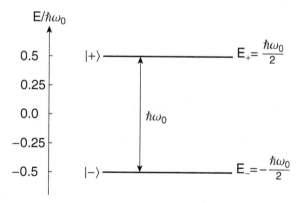

FIGURE 1   Energy level diagram of a spin-1/2 particle in a uniform magnetic field.

according to step 3 of the Schrödinger recipe. As we saw before [(Eq. (13)], because the initial state is an energy eigenstate, the time-evolved state acquires an overall phase factor, which does not represent a physical change of the state. The probability for measuring the spin to be up along the z-axis is (step 4 of the Schrödinger recipe)

$$
\begin{aligned}
\mathcal{P}_+ &= \left| \langle + | \psi(t) \rangle \right|^2 \\
&= \left| \langle + | e^{-i\omega_0 t/2} | + \rangle \right|^2 \\
&= 1.
\end{aligned}
\tag{32}
$$

As expected, this probability is not time dependent, and we therefore refer to $|+\rangle$ as a stationary state for this system. A schematic diagram of this experiment is shown in Fig. 2, where we have introduced a new element to represent the applied field. This new depiction is the same as the depictions in the SPINS software, where the number in the applied magnetic field box (42 in Fig. 2) is a measure of the magnetic field strength. In this experiment, the results shown are independent of the applied field strength, as indicated by Eq. (32), and as you can verify with the software.

Next, consider the most general initial state, which corresponds to spin up along an arbitrary direction defined by the polar angle θ and the azimuthal angle ϕ. The initial state is

$$
|\psi(0)\rangle = |+\rangle_n = \cos\frac{\theta}{2}|+\rangle + \sin\frac{\theta}{2}e^{i\phi}|-\rangle,
\tag{33}
$$

or using matrix notation:

$$
|\psi(0)\rangle \doteq \begin{pmatrix} \cos(\theta/2) \\ e^{i\phi}\sin(\theta/2) \end{pmatrix}.
\tag{34}
$$

Schrödinger time evolution introduces a time-dependent phase term for each component, giving

$$
\begin{aligned}
|\psi(t)\rangle &\doteq \begin{pmatrix} e^{-iE_+t/\hbar}\cos(\theta/2) \\ e^{-iE_-t/\hbar}e^{i\phi}\sin(\theta/2) \end{pmatrix} \\
&\doteq \begin{pmatrix} e^{-i\omega_0 t/2}\cos(\theta/2) \\ e^{i\omega_0 t/2}e^{i\phi}\sin(\theta/2) \end{pmatrix} \\
&\doteq e^{-i\omega_0 t/2}\begin{pmatrix} \cos(\theta/2) \\ e^{i(\phi+\omega_0 t)}\sin(\theta/2) \end{pmatrix}.
\end{aligned}
\tag{35}
$$

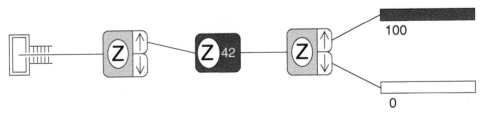

FIGURE 2 Schematic diagram of a Stern-Gerlach measurement with an applied uniform magnetic field represented by the box in the middle, with the number 42 representing the strength of the magnetic field.

Note again that an overall phase does not have a measurable effect, so the evolved state is a spin up eigenstate along a direction that has the same polar angle θ as the initial state and a new azimuthal angle $\phi + \omega_0 t$. The state appears to have simply rotated around the z-axis, the axis of the magnetic field, by the angle $\omega_0 t$. Of course, we have to limit our discussion to results of measurements, so let's first calculate the probability for measuring the spin component along the z-axis:

$$
\begin{aligned}
\mathcal{P}_+ &= |\langle + | \psi(t) \rangle|^2 \\
&= \left| (1 \quad 0) e^{-i\omega_0 t/2} \begin{pmatrix} \cos(\theta/2) \\ e^{i(\phi+\omega_0 t)} \sin(\theta/2) \end{pmatrix} \right|^2 \\
&= \left| e^{-i\omega_0 t/2} \cos(\theta/2) \right|^2 \\
&= \cos^2(\theta/2).
\end{aligned}
\tag{36}
$$

This probability is time independent because the S_z eigenstates are also energy eigenstates for this problem (i.e., H and S_z commute). The probability in Eq. (36) is consistent with the interpretation that the angle θ that the spin vector makes with the z-axis does not change.

The probability for measuring spin up along the x-axis is

$$
\begin{aligned}
\mathcal{P}_{+x} &= |_x\langle + | \psi(t) \rangle|^2 \\
&= \left| \tfrac{1}{\sqrt{2}} (1 \quad 1) e^{-i\omega_0 t/2} \begin{pmatrix} \cos(\theta/2) \\ e^{i(\phi+\omega_0 t)} \sin(\theta/2) \end{pmatrix} \right|^2 \\
&= \tfrac{1}{2} \left| \cos(\theta/2) + e^{i(\phi+\omega_0 t)} \sin(\theta/2) \right|^2 \\
&= \tfrac{1}{2} \left[\cos^2(\theta/2) + \cos(\theta/2)\sin(\theta/2) \left(e^{i(\phi+\omega_0 t)} + e^{-i(\phi+\omega_0 t)} \right) + \sin^2(\theta/2) \right] \\
&= \tfrac{1}{2} \left[1 + \sin\theta \cos(\phi + \omega_0 t) \right].
\end{aligned}
\tag{37}
$$

This probability is time dependent because the S_x eigenstates are not stationary states (i.e., H and S_x do not commute). The time dependence in Eq. (37) is consistent with the spin precessing around the z-axis.

To illustrate this **spin precession** further, it is useful to calculate the expectation values for each of the spin components. For S_z, we have

$$
\begin{aligned}
\langle S_z \rangle &= \langle \psi(t) | S_z | \psi(t) \rangle \\
&= e^{i\omega_0 t/2} \left(\cos\left(\frac{\theta}{2}\right) \quad e^{-i(\phi+\omega_0 t)} \sin\left(\frac{\theta}{2}\right) \right) \frac{\hbar}{2} \begin{pmatrix} 1 & 0 \\ 0 & -1 \end{pmatrix} e^{-i\omega_0 t/2} \begin{pmatrix} \cos(\theta/2) \\ e^{i(\phi+\omega_0 t)} \sin(\theta/2) \end{pmatrix} \\
&= \frac{\hbar}{2} \left[\cos^2(\theta/2) - \sin^2(\theta/2) \right] \\
&= \frac{\hbar}{2} \cos\theta,
\end{aligned}
\tag{38}
$$

while the other components are

$$
\begin{aligned}
\langle S_y \rangle &= \langle \psi(t) | S_y | \psi(t) \rangle \\
&= e^{i\omega_0 t/2} \left(\cos\left(\frac{\theta}{2}\right) \quad e^{-i(\phi+\omega_0 t)} \sin\left(\frac{\theta}{2}\right) \right) \frac{\hbar}{2} \begin{pmatrix} 0 & -i \\ i & 0 \end{pmatrix} e^{-i\omega_0 t/2} \begin{pmatrix} \cos(\theta/2) \\ e^{i(\phi+\omega_0 t)} \sin(\theta/2) \end{pmatrix} \quad (39) \\
&= \frac{\hbar}{2} \sin\theta \sin(\phi + \omega_0 t)
\end{aligned}
$$

and

$$
\begin{aligned}
\langle S_x \rangle &= \langle \psi(t) | S_x | \psi(t) \rangle \\
&= \frac{\hbar}{2} \sin\theta \cos(\phi + \omega_0 t).
\end{aligned}
\quad (40)
$$

The expectation value of the total spin vector $\langle \mathbf{S} \rangle$ is shown in Fig. 3, where it is seen to precess around the magnetic field direction with an angular frequency ω_0. The precession of the spin vector is known as **Larmor precession** and the frequency of precession is known as the **Larmor frequency**.

The quantum mechanical Larmor precession is analogous to the classical behavior of a magnetic moment in a uniform magnetic field. A classical magnetic moment $\boldsymbol{\mu}$ experiences a torque $\boldsymbol{\mu} \times \mathbf{B}$ when placed in a magnetic field. If the magnetic moment is associated with an angular momentum $\mathbf{L}$, then we can write

$$
\boldsymbol{\mu} = \frac{q}{2m} \mathbf{L}, \quad (41)
$$

where q and m are the charge and mass, respectively, of the system. The equation of motion for the angular momentum

$$
\frac{d\mathbf{L}}{dt} = \boldsymbol{\mu} \times \mathbf{B} \quad (42)
$$

then results in

$$
\frac{d\boldsymbol{\mu}}{dt} = \frac{q}{2m} \boldsymbol{\mu} \times \mathbf{B}. \quad (43)
$$

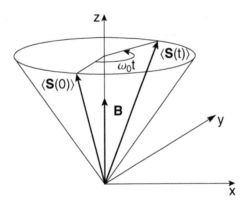

FIGURE 3   The expectation value of the spin vector precesses in a uniform magnetic field.

Because the torque $\boldsymbol{\mu} \times \mathbf{B}$ is perpendicular to the angular momentum $\mathbf{L} = 2m\boldsymbol{\mu}/q$, it causes the magnetic moment to precess about the field with the classical Larmor frequency $\omega_{cl} = qB/2m$.

In the quantum mechanical example we are considering, the charge q is negative (meaning the spin and magnetic moment are antiparallel), so the precession is counterclockwise around the field. A positive charge would result in clockwise precession. This precession of the spin vector makes it clear that the system has angular momentum, as opposed to simply having a magnetic dipole moment. The equivalence of the classical Larmor precession and the expectation value of the quantum mechanical spin vector is one example of **Ehrenfest's theorem**, which states that quantum mechanical expectation values obey classical laws.

Precession experiments like the one discussed here are of great practical value. For example, if we measure the magnetic field strength and the precession frequency, then the gyromagnetic ratio can be determined. This spin precession problem is also of considerable theoretical utility because it is mathematically equivalent to many other quantum systems that can be modeled as two-state systems. This utility is broader than you might guess at first glance, because many multistate quantum systems can be reduced to two-state systems if the experiment is designed to interact only with two of the many levels of the system.

Example 1 A spin-1/2 particle with a magnetic moment is prepared in the state $|-\rangle_x$ and is subject to a uniform applied magnetic field $\mathbf{B} = B_0\hat{\mathbf{z}}$. Find the probability of measuring spin up in the x-direction after a time t. This experiment is depicted in Fig. 4.

We solve this problem using the four steps of the Schrödinger time-evolution recipe from Section 1. The initial state is

$$|\psi(0)\rangle = |-\rangle_x. \tag{44}$$

The applied magnetic field is in the z-direction, so the Hamiltonian is $H = \omega_0 S_z$ and the energy eigenstates are $|\pm\rangle$ with energies $E_\pm = \pm\hbar\omega_0/2$ (step 1). The Larmor precession frequency is $\omega_0 = eB_0/m_e$. We must express the initial state in the energy basis (step 2):

$$|\psi(0)\rangle = |-\rangle_x = \tfrac{1}{\sqrt{2}}|+\rangle - \tfrac{1}{\sqrt{2}}|-\rangle. \tag{45}$$

The time-evolved state is obtained by multiplying each energy eigenstate coefficient by the appropriate phase factor (step 3):

$$\begin{aligned}
|\psi(t)\rangle &= \tfrac{1}{\sqrt{2}}e^{-iE_+t/\hbar}|+\rangle - \tfrac{1}{\sqrt{2}}e^{-iE_-t/\hbar}|-\rangle \\
&= \tfrac{1}{\sqrt{2}}e^{-i\omega_0 t/2}|+\rangle - \tfrac{1}{\sqrt{2}}e^{+i\omega_0 t/2}|-\rangle.
\end{aligned} \tag{46}$$

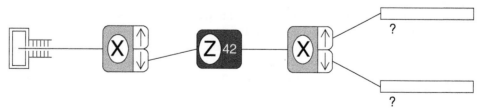

FIGURE 4 Spin precession experiment.

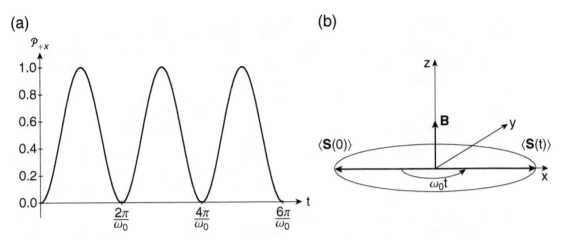

FIGURE 5 (a) Probability of a spin component measurement and (b) the corresponding precession of the expectation value of the spin.

The measurement probability is found by projecting $|\psi(t)\rangle$ onto the measured state and complex squaring (step 4):

$$
\begin{aligned}
\mathcal{P}_{+x} &= \left|{}_x\langle+|\psi(t)\rangle\right|^2 \\
&= \left|{}_x\langle+|\left(\tfrac{1}{\sqrt{2}}e^{-i\omega_0 t/2}|+\rangle - \tfrac{1}{\sqrt{2}}e^{+i\omega_0 t/2}|-\rangle\right)\right|^2 \\
&= \left|\left(\tfrac{1}{\sqrt{2}}\langle+| + \tfrac{1}{\sqrt{2}}\langle-|\right)\left(\tfrac{1}{\sqrt{2}}e^{-i\omega_0 t/2}|+\rangle - \tfrac{1}{\sqrt{2}}e^{+i\omega_0 t/2}|-\rangle\right)\right|^2 \\
&= \tfrac{1}{4}\left|e^{-i\omega_0 t/2} - e^{+i\omega_0 t/2}\right|^2 \\
&= \sin^2\left(\omega_0 t/2\right).
\end{aligned}
\tag{47}
$$

The probability that the system has spin up in the x-direction oscillates between zero and unity as time evolves, as shown in Fig. 5(a), which is consistent with the model of the spin vector precessing around the applied field, as shown in Fig. 5(b).

2.2 ■ Magnetic Field in a General Direction

For our second example, consider a more general direction for the magnetic field by adding a magnetic field component along the x-axis to the already existing field along the z-axis. The simplest approach to solving this new problem would be to redefine the coordinate system so the z-axis pointed along the direction of the new total magnetic field. Then the solution would be the same as was obtained above, with a new value for the magnitude of the magnetic field being the only change. This approach would be considered astute in many circumstances, but we will not take it because we want to get practice solving this new type of problem and because we want to address some issues that are best posed in the original coordinate system. Thus, we define a new magnetic field as

$$
\mathbf{B} = B_0\hat{\mathbf{z}} + B_1\hat{\mathbf{x}}.
\tag{48}
$$

This field is oriented in the xz-plane at an angle θ with respect to the z-axis, as shown in Fig. 6. In light of the solution above, it is useful to define Larmor frequencies associated with each of the field components:

$$\omega_0 \equiv \frac{eB_0}{m_e}, \qquad \omega_1 \equiv \frac{eB_1}{m_e}. \tag{49}$$

Using these definitions, the Hamiltonian becomes

$$\begin{aligned} H &= -\boldsymbol{\mu} \cdot \mathbf{B} \\ &= \omega_0 S_z + \omega_1 S_x, \end{aligned} \tag{50}$$

or in matrix representation

$$H \doteq \frac{\hbar}{2} \begin{pmatrix} \omega_0 & \omega_1 \\ \omega_1 & -\omega_0 \end{pmatrix}. \tag{51}$$

This Hamiltonian is *not* diagonal, so its eigenstates are not the same as the eigenstates of S_z. Rather we must use the diagonalization procedure to find the new eigenvalues and eigenvectors. The characteristic equation determining the energy eigenvalues is

$$\begin{vmatrix} \dfrac{\hbar}{2}\omega_0 - \lambda & \dfrac{\hbar}{2}\omega_1 \\[2mm] \dfrac{\hbar}{2}\omega_1 & -\dfrac{\hbar}{2}\omega_0 - \lambda \end{vmatrix} = 0 \tag{52}$$

$$-\left(\frac{\hbar}{2}\omega_0\right)^2 + \lambda^2 - \left(\frac{\hbar}{2}\omega_1\right)^2 = 0,$$

with solutions

$$\lambda = \pm\frac{\hbar}{2}\sqrt{\omega_0^2 + \omega_1^2}. \tag{53}$$

Note that the energy eigenvalues are $\pm\left(\hbar\omega_0/2\right)$ when $\omega_1 = 0$, which they must be given our previous solution. Rather than solve directly for the eigenvectors, let's make them obvious by rewriting the Hamiltonian. From Fig. 6 it is clear that the angle is determined by the equation

$$\tan\theta = \frac{B_1}{B_0} = \frac{\omega_1}{\omega_0}. \tag{54}$$

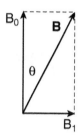

FIGURE 6 A uniform magnetic field in a general direction.

Using this, the Hamiltonian can be written as

$$H \doteq \frac{\hbar}{2}\sqrt{\omega_0^2 + \omega_1^2}\begin{pmatrix} \cos\theta & \sin\theta \\ \sin\theta & -\cos\theta \end{pmatrix}. \tag{55}$$

If we let $\hat{\mathbf{n}}$ be the unit vector in the direction of the total magnetic field, then the Hamiltonian is proportional to the spin component S_n along the direction $\hat{\mathbf{n}}$:

$$H = \sqrt{\omega_0^2 + \omega_1^2}\, S_n. \tag{56}$$

This is what we expected at the beginning: that the problem could be solved by using the field direction to define a coordinate system. Thus, the eigenvalues are as predicted and the eigenstates are the spin up and down states along the direction $\hat{\mathbf{n}}$, which are

$$|+\rangle_n = \cos\frac{\theta}{2}|+\rangle + \sin\frac{\theta}{2}|-\rangle$$
$$|-\rangle_n = \sin\frac{\theta}{2}|+\rangle - \cos\frac{\theta}{2}|-\rangle \tag{57}$$

for this case, because the azimuthal angle ϕ is zero. These are the same states you would find by directly solving for the eigenstates of the Hamiltonian. Because we have already done that for the S_n case, we do not repeat it here.

Now consider performing the following experiment: begin with the system in the spin-up state along the z-axis, and measure the spin component along the z-axis after the system has evolved in this magnetic field for some time, as depicted in Fig. 7. Let's specifically calculate the probability that the initial $|+\rangle$ is later found to have evolved to the $|-\rangle$ state. This is commonly known as a **spin flip**. According to our time-evolution prescription, we must first write the initial state in terms of the energy eigenstates of the system. In the previous examples, this was trivial because the energy eigenstates were the $|\pm\rangle$ states that we used to express all general states. But now this new problem is more involved, so we proceed more slowly. The initial state

$$|\psi(0)\rangle = |+\rangle \tag{58}$$

must be written in the $|\pm\rangle_n$ basis. Because the $|\pm\rangle_n$ basis is complete, we can use the completeness relation to decompose the initial state

$$\begin{aligned} |\psi(0)\rangle &= (|+\rangle_n{}_n\langle+| + |-\rangle_n{}_n\langle-|)|+\rangle \\ &= |+\rangle_n{}_n\langle+|+\rangle + |-\rangle_n{}_n\langle-|+\rangle \\ &= {}_n\langle+|+\rangle|+\rangle_n + {}_n\langle-|+\rangle|-\rangle_n \\ &= \cos\frac{\theta}{2}|+\rangle_n + \sin\frac{\theta}{2}|-\rangle_n. \end{aligned} \tag{59}$$

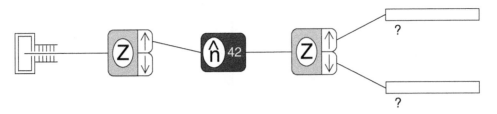

FIGURE 7 A spin precession experiment with a uniform magnetic field aligned in a general direction $\hat{\mathbf{n}}$.

Now that the initial state is expressed in the energy basis, the time-evolved state is obtained by multiplying each coefficient by a phase factor dependent on the energy of that eigenstate:

$$|\psi(t)\rangle = e^{-iE_+t/\hbar}\cos\frac{\theta}{2}|+\rangle_n + e^{-iE_-t/\hbar}\sin\frac{\theta}{2}|-\rangle_n. \tag{60}$$

We leave it in this form and substitute the energy eigenvalues

$$E_\pm = \pm\frac{\hbar}{2}\sqrt{\omega_0^2 + \omega_1^2} \tag{61}$$

at the end of the example.

The probability of a spin flip is

$$
\begin{aligned}
\mathcal{P}_{+\to-} &= |\langle-|\psi(t)\rangle|^2 \\
&= \left|\langle-|\left[e^{-iE_+t/\hbar}\cos\frac{\theta}{2}|+\rangle_n + e^{-iE_-t/\hbar}\sin\frac{\theta}{2}|-\rangle_n\right]\right|^2 \\
&= \left|e^{-iE_+t/\hbar}\cos\frac{\theta}{2}\langle-|+\rangle_n + e^{-iE_-t/\hbar}\sin\frac{\theta}{2}\langle-|-\rangle_n\right|^2 \\
&= \left|e^{-iE_+t/\hbar}\cos\frac{\theta}{2}\sin\frac{\theta}{2} + e^{-iE_-t/\hbar}\sin\frac{\theta}{2}\left(-\cos\frac{\theta}{2}\right)\right|^2 \\
&= \cos^2\frac{\theta}{2}\sin^2\frac{\theta}{2}\left|1 - e^{i(E_+-E_-)t/\hbar}\right|^2 \\
&= \sin^2\theta\,\sin^2\left(\frac{(E_+-E_-)t}{2\hbar}\right).
\end{aligned} \tag{62}
$$

The probability oscillates at the frequency determined by the difference in energies of the eigenstates. This time dependence results because the initial state was a superposition state, as we saw in Eq. (20). In terms of the Larmor frequencies used to define the Hamiltonian in Eq. (51), the probability of a spin flip is

$$\boxed{\mathcal{P}_{+\to-} = \frac{\omega_1^2}{\omega_0^2 + \omega_1^2}\sin^2\left(\frac{\sqrt{\omega_0^2 + \omega_1^2}}{2}t\right).} \tag{63}$$

Eq. (63) is often called **Rabi's formula**, and it has important applications in many problems as we shall see.

To gain insight into Rabi's formula, consider two simple cases. First, if there is no added field in the x-direction, then $\omega_1 = 0$ and $\mathcal{P}_{+\to-} = 0$ because the initial state is a stationary state. Second, if there is no field component in the z-direction, then $\omega_0 = 0$ and $\mathcal{P}_{+\to-}$ oscillates between 0 and 1 at the frequency ω_1, as shown in Fig. 8(a). The second situation corresponds to spin precession around the applied magnetic field in the x-direction, as shown in Fig. 8(b), with a complete spin flip from $|+\rangle$ to $|-\rangle$ and back again occurring at the precession frequency ω_1. In the general case where both magnetic field components are present, the probability does not reach unity and so there is no time at which the spin is certain to flip over. If the x-component of the field is small compared to the z-component, then $\omega_1 \ll \omega_0$ and $\mathcal{P}_{+\to-}$ oscillates between 0 and a value much less than 1 at a frequency approximately equal to ω_0, as shown in Fig. 9.

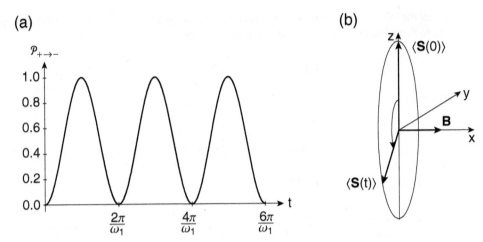

FIGURE 8 (a) Spin-flip probability for a uniform magnetic field in the *x*-direction and (b) the corresponding precession of the expectation value of the spin.

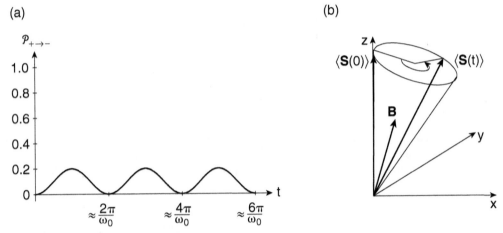

FIGURE 9 (a) Spin-flip probability for a uniform magnetic field with *x*- and *z*-components and (b) the corresponding precession of the expectation value of the spin.

Example 2 A spin-1/2 particle with a magnetic moment is prepared in the state $|-\rangle$ and is subject to a uniform applied magnetic field $\mathbf{B} = B_0 \hat{\mathbf{y}}$. Find the probability of measuring spin up in the *z*-direction after a time *t*.

The initial state is

$$|\psi(0)\rangle = |-\rangle. \tag{64}$$

The applied magnetic field is in the *y*-direction, so the Hamiltonian is $H = \omega_0 S_y$ and the energy eigenstates are $|\pm\rangle_y$ with energies $E_\pm = \pm\hbar\omega_0/2$ (step 1). The Larmor precession frequency is

$\omega_0 = eB_0/m_e$. We must express the initial state in the energy basis (step 2), which in this case is the S_y basis:

$$
\begin{aligned}
|\psi(0)\rangle = |-\rangle &= (|+\rangle_y {}_y\langle+| + |-\rangle_y {}_y\langle-|)|-\rangle \\
&= |+\rangle_y {}_y\langle+|-\rangle + |-\rangle_y {}_y\langle-|-\rangle \\
&= {}_y\langle+|-\rangle|+\rangle_y + {}_y\langle-|-\rangle|-\rangle_y \\
&= \tfrac{-i}{\sqrt{2}}|+\rangle_y + \tfrac{i}{\sqrt{2}}|-\rangle_y.
\end{aligned}
\tag{65}
$$

The time evolved state is obtained by multiplying each energy eigenstate coefficient by a phase factor (step 3):

$$
\begin{aligned}
|\psi(t)\rangle &= \tfrac{-i}{\sqrt{2}}e^{-iE_+t/\hbar}|+\rangle_y + \tfrac{i}{\sqrt{2}}e^{-iE_-t/\hbar}|-\rangle_y \\
&= \tfrac{-i}{\sqrt{2}}e^{-i\omega_0t/2}|+\rangle_y + \tfrac{i}{\sqrt{2}}e^{+i\omega_0t/2}|-\rangle_y.
\end{aligned}
\tag{66}
$$

The measurement probability is found by projecting onto the measured state and squaring (step 4):

$$
\begin{aligned}
\mathcal{P}_+ &= |\langle+|\psi(t)\rangle|^2 \\
&= \left|\langle+|\left(\tfrac{-i}{\sqrt{2}}e^{-i\omega_0t/2}|+\rangle_y + \tfrac{i}{\sqrt{2}}e^{+i\omega_0t/2}|-\rangle_y\right)\right|^2 \\
&= \left|\left(\tfrac{-i}{\sqrt{2}}e^{-i\omega_0t/2}\langle+|+\rangle_y + \tfrac{i}{\sqrt{2}}e^{+i\omega_0t/2}\langle+|-\rangle_y\right)\right|^2 \\
&= \left|\left(\tfrac{-i}{\sqrt{2}}e^{-i\omega_0t/2}\left(\tfrac{1}{\sqrt{2}}\right) + \tfrac{i}{\sqrt{2}}e^{+i\omega_0t/2}\left(\tfrac{1}{\sqrt{2}}\right)\right)\right|^2 \\
&= \tfrac{1}{4}\left|-ie^{-i\omega_0t/2} + ie^{+i\omega_0t/2}\right|^2 = \tfrac{1}{4}\left|-2\sin(\omega_0t/2)\right|^2 \\
&= \sin^2(\omega_0t/2).
\end{aligned}
\tag{67}
$$

The probability oscillates between zero and unity as time evolves, as shown in Fig. 10(a), which is consistent with the model of the spin vector precessing around the applied field, as shown in Fig. 10(b).

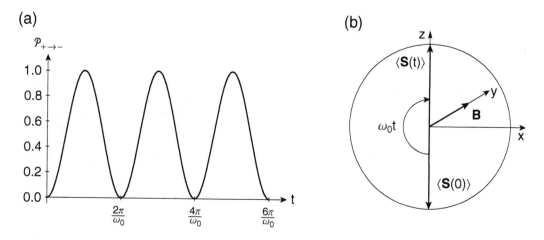

FIGURE 10 (a) Spin measurement probability and (b) the corresponding precession of the expectation value of the spin.

Schrödinger Time Evolution

Though we have derived Rabi's formula [Eq. (63)] in the context of a spin-1/2 particle in a uniform magnetic field, its applicability is much more general. If we can express the Hamiltonian of any two-state system in the matrix form of Eq. (51) with the parameters ω_0 and ω_1, then we can use Rabi's formula to find the probability that the system starts in the "spin-up" state $|+\rangle$ and is then measured to be in the "spin-down" state $|-\rangle$ after some time t. In the general case, the $|+\rangle$ and $|-\rangle$ states are whatever states of the system are used to represent the Hamiltonian operator in the form of Eq. (51). In the next section, we'll look at the example of neutrino oscillations to see how this example can be applied more generally.

3 ■ NEUTRINO OSCILLATIONS

Neutrinos have enjoyed an almost mystical history in particle physics because they are very hard to detect and yet play an important role in many fundamental processes. In 1930, the neutrino was postulated by Wolfgang Pauli as a solution to the beta decay problem. A free neutron decays to a proton and an electron with a lifetime of about 10 minutes in the most basic beta decay process. However, the decay scheme $n \rightarrow p + e^-$ violates conservation of angular momentum, and experimental data suggest that conservation of energy is also violated. That's not good. Rather than reject these two basic conservation laws, as some suggested, Pauli proposed that a third particle is involved in the decay process. Enrico Fermi named this new particle the "neutrino." Fermi developed a theory that used the neutrino to properly explain beta decay, but it was 25 more years before a neutrino was detected.

Neutrinos are uncharged, relativistic particles. In nuclear beta decay, neutrinos are produced in processes such as

$$n \rightarrow p + e^- + \bar{\nu}_e$$
$$p \rightarrow n + e^+ + \nu_e, \tag{68}$$

where the subscript labels the neutrino ν_e as an electron neutrino and the bar labels $\bar{\nu}_e$ as an antineutrino. In the standard model of particle physics, neutrinos are *massless*, like photons. Neutrinos are so elusive because they interact via the **weak force** or **weak interaction**, which is the weakest of the four fundamental forces—the strong nuclear force, electromagnetism, and gravity being the other three.

The reaction $p \rightarrow n + e^+ + \nu_e$ is part of the thermonuclear reaction chain in the sun and other stars, so we earthlings are constantly bombarded with neutrinos along with the essential photons we receive from the sun. In the 1960s and 70s, landmark experiments indicated that there are only about half as many solar neutrinos arriving on earth as we would expect, given reliable models of stellar thermonuclear reactions. This **solar neutrino problem** has recently been solved by experiments detecting neutrinos from the sun and from nuclear reactors that demonstrate that neutrinos have nonzero mass. These results are counter to the standard model and so have profound implications for particle physics and cosmology. Understanding how these experiments provide information on the neutrino mass is a powerful illustration of the applicability of Rabi's formula to other two-state systems.

In addition to the electron neutrinos in Eq. (68), there are other types of neutrinos associated with other reactions, such as

$$\pi^+ \rightarrow \mu^+ + \nu_\mu$$
$$\mu^- \rightarrow e^- + \nu_\mu + \bar{\nu}_e, \tag{69}$$

which represent the decay of a pion (π) to a muon (μ) and the decay of a muon to an electron, respectively. A muon behaves exactly like an electron but has a larger mass. Electrons, muons, and a third particle (tau) and their associated neutrinos are collectively called **leptons**. In reactions involving these particles it is convenient to define a lepton "flavor" quantum number L, with the assigned values $L_e = 1$ for the electron e^- and its associated neutrino ν_e, $L_e = -1$ for the positron e^+ and the antineutrino $\bar{\nu}_e$, $L_\mu = 1$ for the muon μ^- and its associated neutrino ν_μ, and $L_\mu = -1$ for the μ^+ and $\bar{\nu}_\mu$. With these assignments, the individual electron and muon flavor numbers are conserved in the processes shown above. However, there is no theoretical basis for this conservation, and so we allow for the possibility that these quantum numbers are only approximately conserved. This possibility then allows for reactions of the type

$$\nu_e \leftrightarrow \nu_\mu, \tag{70}$$

where an electron neutrino changes its flavor and becomes a muon neutrino, or the reverse. Such changes are called **neutrino mixing** or **neutrino oscillations**.

The labeling of neutrinos according to their association with electrons or muons arises from their behavior in the weak interaction processes described above. In other words, the quantum states $|\nu_e\rangle$ and $|\nu_\mu\rangle$ are eigenstates of the Hamiltonian describing the weak interaction. However, when neutrinos propagate in free space, the weak interaction is not relevant and the only Hamiltonian of relevance is that due to the relativistic energy of the particles, which includes their rest masses and momenta. The eigenstates of this Hamiltonian are generally referred to as the **mass eigenstates**. If the masses of the two types of neutrinos (electron and muon) are different, then, in general, the mass eigenstates do not coincide with the weak interaction eigenstates. This distinction between sets of eigenstates allows for flavor-changing processes.

To see why this is so, let the mass eigenstates be labeled $|\nu_1\rangle$ and $|\nu_2\rangle$. Either one of the two bases (mass or weak eigenstates) can be used as a complete basis upon which to expand any general state in this system. Let's assume that the relation between the bases is

$$\begin{aligned}|\nu_e\rangle &= \cos\frac{\theta}{2}|\nu_1\rangle + \sin\frac{\theta}{2}|\nu_2\rangle \\ |\nu_\mu\rangle &= \sin\frac{\theta}{2}|\nu_1\rangle - \cos\frac{\theta}{2}|\nu_2\rangle.\end{aligned} \tag{71}$$

The angle $\theta/2$ is generally referred to as the **mixing angle** (some treatments drop the factor 1/2, but we retain it to be consistent with the previous spin-1/2 discussion). If the mixing angle is small, then the relations become

$$\begin{aligned}|\nu_e\rangle &\approx |\nu_1\rangle \\ |\nu_\mu\rangle &\approx |\nu_2\rangle.\end{aligned} \tag{72}$$

Assume that an electron neutrino is created in some weak interaction process and then propagates through free space to a detector. We wish to know the probability that a muon neutrino is detected, which is the signature of neutrino flavor mixing. The initial state vector is

$$\begin{aligned}|\psi(0)\rangle &= |\nu_e\rangle \\ &= \cos\frac{\theta}{2}|\nu_1\rangle + \sin\frac{\theta}{2}|\nu_2\rangle.\end{aligned} \tag{73}$$

During the free-space propagation, the energy eigenstates of the system are the mass eigenstates because there is no weak interaction present. Thus the Schrödinger time evolution for this state is

$$|\psi(t)\rangle = \cos\frac{\theta}{2}e^{-iE_1 t/\hbar}|\nu_1\rangle + \sin\frac{\theta}{2}e^{-iE_2 t/\hbar}|\nu_2\rangle. \tag{74}$$

The energy eigenvalues are simply the relativistic energies, which are determined by the rest masses and the momenta:

$$E_i = \sqrt{(pc)^2 + (m_i c^2)^2}, \quad i = 1,2. \tag{75}$$

Schrödinger Time Evolution

Assuming that the neutrinos are highly relativistic $(mc^2 \ll pc)$, we find

$$
\begin{aligned}
E_i &= pc\left[1 + \left(\frac{m_i c^2}{pc}\right)^2\right]^{1/2} \\
&\cong pc\left[1 + \frac{1}{2}\left(\frac{m_i c^2}{pc}\right)^2\right] \\
&\cong pc + \frac{(m_i c^2)^2}{2pc}.
\end{aligned}
\tag{76}
$$

The beauty of studying two-level systems such as spin-1/2 particles and neutrino oscillations is that they are formally identical. In the spin-1/2 case, we phrased the problem in terms of finding the probability of a spin flip, whereas here we are looking for a change in the flavor of the neutrino. In both cases, the initial and final states are not energy eigenstates, but rather orthogonal states in a different basis. The problems are mathematically identical, so the probability of a transition between the orthogonal states takes the same form. The probability of a neutrino oscillation is thus given by the same equation as the spin-flip probability, Eq. (62),

$$
\begin{aligned}
\mathcal{P}_{\nu_e \to \nu_\mu} &= |\langle \nu_\mu | \psi(t) \rangle|^2 \\
&= \sin^2\theta \sin^2\left(\frac{(E_1 - E_2)t}{2\hbar}\right),
\end{aligned}
\tag{77}
$$

where the parameter θ has been defined the same in both problems and the energy difference $E_+ - E_-$ has been changed to the energy difference $E_1 - E_2$. This energy difference is

$$
\begin{aligned}
E_1 - E_2 &= \frac{(m_1 c^2)^2}{2pc} - \frac{(m_2 c^2)^2}{2pc} \\
&= \frac{c^3}{2p}(m_1^2 - m_2^2).
\end{aligned}
\tag{78}
$$

Neutrinos move at nearly the speed of light c, so we approximate the time from the creation of the electron neutrino to the detection of the muon neutrino as $t \cong L/c$, where L is the distance from the source to the detector. We also approximate the relativistic momentum as $p = E/c$. This gives a probability for neutrino flavor change of

$$
\mathcal{P}_{\nu_e \to \nu_\mu} = \sin^2\theta \sin^2\left(\frac{(m_1^2 - m_2^2)Lc^3}{4E\hbar}\right).
\tag{79}
$$

As a function of the distance L, the probability oscillates from 0 to a maximum value of $\sin^2\theta$—hence the term neutrino oscillation. By measuring the fractions of different neutrino flavors at a distance from a neutrino source (e.g., the sun or a reactor) and comparing to a model for the expected fractions, experimenters have been able to infer the masses of the different neutrinos, or at least the differences of the squares of the masses. Recent results from solar neutrino and reactor neutrino experiments indicate a squared mass difference of approximately

$$
m_1^2 - m_2^2 \cong 8 \times 10^{-5}\, eV^2/c^4.
\tag{80}
$$

These experiments also provide information on the mixing angle θ, with recent results indicating

$$
\theta \cong 69°.
\tag{81}
$$

Neutrino experiments such as these continue to provide information about the fundamental physics of the universe.

4 ■ TIME-DEPENDENT HAMILTONIANS

Up to now, we have studied the time evolution of quantum mechanical systems where the Hamiltonian is time *independent*. We solved the Schrödinger equation once for the general case and developed a recipe for the time evolution of the system that we can apply to all cases with time-independent Hamiltonians. However, if the Hamiltonian is time *dependent*, then we cannot use that simple recipe. We must know the form of the Hamiltonian time dependence in order to solve the Schrödinger equation. Fortunately, there are common forms of time dependence that we can solve in general and then apply in many cases. The most common form of time dependence is sinusoidal time dependence at one frequency. We will solve this problem in the context of a spin-1/2 particle in a magnetic field and then also apply it to atom-light interactions.

4.1 ■ Magnetic Resonance

In the spin precession example in Section 2.2, we concluded that a complete spin flip required a large magnetic field in the *x*-direction, which represents a large change or perturbation compared to the initial situation of a magnetic field in the *z*-direction. Now consider whether we can induce a complete spin flip without such a large perturbation. That is, what small magnetic field can we add to the system that will cause a $|+\rangle$ state to flip to a $|-\rangle$ state? The answer is that we must apply a time-dependent magnetic field that oscillates at a frequency close to the Larmor precession frequency ω_0 that characterizes the energy difference between the spin-up and spin-down states, as shown in Fig. 1. By making the oscillating magnetic field **resonant** with the Larmor frequency, we induce **transitions** between the energy states shown in Fig. 1. This effect is known as **magnetic resonance**. I. I. Rabi won the Nobel Prize in physics in 1944 for his work in developing the magnetic resonance technique and using it to measure the magnetic moments of nuclei. Following Rabi's work, **nuclear magnetic resonance (NMR)** became a widely used tool for studying the properties of materials. The Larmor frequency depends on the magnetic field magnitude at the location of the particular nucleus being studied. This magnetic field includes the applied external field and any internal fields created by the local environment, such that measuring the resonance frequency provides valuable information about the environment of the nucleus. In biology and chemistry, NMR has been used extensively to distinguish different types of bonds and identify structures. More recently, **magnetic resonance imaging (MRI)** has been developed for medical diagnosis.

To understand how magnetic resonance works, it is instructive to consider the classical problem first. A classical magnetic moment aligned with an angular momentum precesses around the direction of an applied magnetic field. Now imagine going to a reference frame that rotates about the field (assumed to be in the *z*-direction) with the same frequency as the precession. An observer in the rotating frame would see the magnetic moment stationary and so would conclude that there is no magnetic field in that frame. If that rotating observer were asked to flip the magnetic moment from up to down along the *z*-axis, she would answer, "Simple, just impose a small magnetic field perpendicular to the *z*-axis, which will cause the spin to precess around that direction." Because that field is the only field acting in the rotating frame, it can be as small as one likes. The magnitude simply determines the time for the spin to flip.

In this situation, the transverse applied field is stationary in the rotating frame, so it will appear to be rotating at the precessional frequency in the original frame. Thus, we could write it as

$$\mathbf{B} = B_1 \cos(\omega t)\hat{\mathbf{x}} + B_1 \sin(\omega t)\hat{\mathbf{y}}, \tag{82}$$

where we allow the frequency ω to differ from the precessional frequency ω_0 in order to solve the problem more generally. In that case, there would be some residual precession in the rotating frame, and so the rotating observer would conclude that there is some residual field in the *z*-direction. Hence, we expect that the added transverse field would not cause a complete flipping of the magnetic moment from up to down in this general case.

Let's now apply this reasoning to the quantum mechanical case. Assume a magnetic field of the form

$$\mathbf{B} = B_0\hat{\mathbf{z}} + B_1[\cos(\omega t)\hat{\mathbf{x}} + \sin(\omega t)\hat{\mathbf{y}}], \tag{83}$$

where the role of B_0 is to split the energies of the spin-up and spin-down states and the role of B_1 is to flip the spin between the the up and down states. The Hamiltonian is

$$\begin{aligned} H &= -\boldsymbol{\mu}\cdot\mathbf{B} \\ &= \omega_0 S_z + \omega_1[\cos(\omega t)S_x + \sin(\omega t)S_y], \end{aligned} \tag{84}$$

where we again define the Larmor frequencies corresponding to the two magnetic field components,

$$\omega_0 \equiv \frac{eB_0}{m_e}, \qquad \omega_1 \equiv \frac{eB_1}{m_e}. \tag{85}$$

The matrix representation of the Hamiltonian is

$$H \doteq \frac{\hbar}{2}\begin{pmatrix} \omega_0 & \omega_1 e^{-i\omega t} \\ \omega_1 e^{i\omega t} & -\omega_0 \end{pmatrix}. \tag{86}$$

This Hamiltonian is time dependent, so we can no longer use our simple recipe for Schrödinger time evolution. Rather, we must return to the Schrödinger equation and solve it with these new time-dependent terms. Because we are not using our recipe for Schrödinger time evolution, we are not bound to use the energy basis as the preferred basis. The obvious choice would be to use the basis we have used for representing the Hamiltonian as a matrix, which becomes the basis of energy states if the transverse part B_1 of the magnetic field vanishes. Using this basis, we write the state vector as

$$|\psi(t)\rangle = c_+(t)|+\rangle + c_-(t)|-\rangle \doteq \begin{pmatrix} c_+(t) \\ c_-(t) \end{pmatrix}. \tag{87}$$

Schrödinger's equation

$$i\hbar\frac{d}{dt}|\psi(t)\rangle = H(t)|\psi(t)\rangle \tag{88}$$

in matrix form is

$$i\hbar\frac{d}{dt}\begin{pmatrix} c_+(t) \\ c_-(t) \end{pmatrix} = \frac{\hbar}{2}\begin{pmatrix} \omega_0 & \omega_1 e^{-i\omega t} \\ \omega_1 e^{i\omega t} & -\omega_0 \end{pmatrix}\begin{pmatrix} c_+(t) \\ c_-(t) \end{pmatrix} \tag{89}$$

and leads to the differential equations

$$\begin{aligned} i\hbar\dot{c}_+(t) &= \frac{\hbar\omega_0}{2}c_+(t) + \frac{\hbar\omega_1}{2}e^{-i\omega t}c_-(t) \\ i\hbar\dot{c}_-(t) &= \frac{\hbar\omega_1}{2}e^{i\omega t}c_+(t) - \frac{\hbar\omega_0}{2}c_-(t), \end{aligned} \tag{90}$$

where $\dot{c}_+(t)$ denotes a time derivative. To solve these time-dependent coupled differential equations, it is useful to follow the lead of the classical discussion and consider the problem from the rotating frame. Though we don't yet have the complete tools to know how to effect this transformation, we take it on faith that after a frame transformation the state vector is

$$|\widetilde{\psi}(t)\rangle = c_+(t)e^{i\omega t/2}|+\rangle + c_-(t)e^{-i\omega t/2}|-\rangle \doteq \begin{pmatrix} c_+(t)e^{i\omega t/2} \\ c_-(t)e^{-i\omega t/2} \end{pmatrix}, \qquad (91)$$

where $|\widetilde{\psi}(t)\rangle$ is the state vector as viewed from the rotating frame. If we call the coefficients of this vector $\alpha_\pm(t)$, then we can write

$$|\widetilde{\psi}(t)\rangle = \alpha_+(t)|+\rangle + \alpha_-(t)|-\rangle \doteq \begin{pmatrix} \alpha_+(t) \\ \alpha_-(t) \end{pmatrix}, \qquad (92)$$

where the relations between the sets of coefficients are

$$\begin{aligned} c_+(t) &= e^{-i\omega t/2}\alpha_+(t) \\ c_-(t) &= e^{i\omega t/2}\alpha_-(t). \end{aligned} \qquad (93)$$

The state vector in the nonrotating frame can thus be written as

$$|\psi(t)\rangle = \alpha_+(t)e^{-i\omega t/2}|+\rangle + \alpha_-(t)e^{i\omega t/2}|-\rangle \doteq \begin{pmatrix} \alpha_+(t)e^{-i\omega t/2} \\ \alpha_-(t)e^{i\omega t/2} \end{pmatrix}. \qquad (94)$$

Another way of viewing this transformation is to say that based upon earlier solutions of similar problems [Eq. (35)], we expect the coefficients $c_\pm(t)$ to have time dependence of the form $e^{\mp i\omega t/2}$, and so we have extracted that part of the solution and now need to solve for the remaining time dependence in the coefficients $\alpha_\pm(t)$. In this view, we have simply performed a mathematical trick to make the solution easier.

If we now substitute the expressions for $c_\pm(t)$ in terms of $\alpha_\pm(t)$ into the differential equations (90), then we obtain

$$\begin{aligned} i\hbar\dot{\alpha}_+(t) &= -\frac{\hbar\Delta\omega}{2}\alpha_+(t) + \frac{\hbar\omega_1}{2}\alpha_-(t) \\ i\hbar\dot{\alpha}_-(t) &= \frac{\hbar\omega_1}{2}\alpha_+(t) + \frac{\hbar\Delta\omega}{2}\alpha_-(t), \end{aligned} \qquad (95)$$

where we have defined a new term

$$\Delta\omega \equiv \omega - \omega_0, \qquad (96)$$

which is the difference between the angular frequencies of the rotating field and the Larmor precession due to the z-component of the magnetic field. Because $\alpha_\pm(t)$ are the coefficients of the transformed state vector $|\widetilde{\psi}(t)\rangle$, these differential equations can be considered as comprising a transformed Schrödinger equation

$$i\hbar\frac{d}{dt}|\widetilde{\psi}(t)\rangle = \widetilde{H}|\widetilde{\psi}(t)\rangle, \qquad (97)$$

where the new Hamiltonian $\widetilde{H}$ has the matrix representation

$$\widetilde{H} \doteq \frac{\hbar}{2}\begin{pmatrix} -\Delta\omega & \omega_1 \\ \omega_1 & \Delta\omega \end{pmatrix}. \qquad (98)$$

Thus, we have transformed (by rotation or mathematical sleight of hand) the original problem into a new problem that has a time-independent Hamiltonian. Once we solve the new problem, we can use the transformation equations to find the solution to the original problem. However, because the new Hamiltonian $\tilde{H}$ is time independent, we already know the solution. That is, this new problem has the same form of the Hamiltonian as the spin precession problem in Section 2.2. Comparing the spin precession Hamiltonian in Eq. (51) with the transformed Hamiltonian in Eq. (98), we note that the term ω_0 is replaced by the new term $-\Delta\omega$. We are interested in finding the same probability $\mathcal{P}_{+\rightarrow-}$ that an initial $|+\rangle$ state is later found to have evolved to the $|-\rangle$ state. The rotational transformation does not alter the $|\pm\rangle$ basis states so if

$$|\psi(0)\rangle = |+\rangle, \tag{99}$$

then

$$|\tilde{\psi}(0)\rangle = |+\rangle. \tag{100}$$

The probability for a spin flip is given by

$$\mathcal{P}_{+\rightarrow-} = |\langle-|\psi(t)\rangle|^2 \tag{101}$$
$$= |c_-(t)|^2.$$

From Eq. (93) relating the coefficients, we have

$$|c_-(t)|^2 = |e^{-i\omega t/2}\alpha_-(t)|^2$$
$$= |\alpha_-(t)|^2 \tag{102}$$
$$= |\langle-|\tilde{\psi}(t)\rangle|^2,$$

which means that the probability we desire is

$$\mathcal{P}_{+\rightarrow-} = |\langle-|\tilde{\psi}(t)\rangle|^2. \tag{103}$$

We obtain this spin-flip probability using Rabi's formula in Eq. (63), with the change $\omega_0 \rightarrow -\Delta\omega$, resulting in

$$\mathcal{P}_{+\rightarrow-} = \frac{\omega_1^2}{\Delta\omega^2 + \omega_1^2}\sin^2\left(\frac{\sqrt{\Delta\omega^2 + \omega_1^2}}{2}t\right)$$
$$= \frac{\omega_1^2}{(\omega-\omega_0)^2 + \omega_1^2}\sin^2\left(\frac{\sqrt{(\omega-\omega_0)^2 + \omega_1^2}}{2}t\right). \tag{104}$$

This spin-flip probability is a generalization of Rabi's formula. Note that Eq. (104) reduces to Eq. (63) for the case $\omega = 0$, which is expected because the applied field in Eq. (83) is static and aligned the same as the static field in Eq. (48) for the case $\omega = 0$. The static magnetic field case is generally referred to as spin precession, while the rotating field case is referred to as **Rabi flopping**. Though we have used their similarities to help us derive Eq. (104), it is important to clarify their differences. In the static applied magnetic field case, the resulting spin precession is a manifestation of the natural Bohr oscillation of a quantum system that starts in a superposition of energy eigenstates. The initial superposition remains intact and there is no exchange of energy between the system and the applied field. In the rotating applied magnetic field case, the Rabi flopping represents transitions between energy eigenstates, and there is exchange of energy between the system and the applied field. The energy exchange occurs because the Hamiltonian is time dependent.

The probability of a Rabi spin flip oscillates with an angular frequency given by

$$\Omega = \sqrt{(\omega - \omega_0)^2 + \omega_1^2}, \tag{105}$$

that is typically referred to as the **generalized Rabi frequency**. The term **Rabi frequency** generally refers to the frequency ω_1, which is the value of the generalized Rabi frequency when the frequency ω of the rotating field is **on resonance** (i.e., ω is set equal to the Larmor precession frequency ω_0 of the system in the presence of the magnetic field B_0 alone). For this choice of $\omega = \omega_0$, the probability of a spin flip becomes

$$\mathcal{P}_{+\to-} = \sin^2\left(\frac{\omega_1}{2}t\right), \tag{106}$$

which implies that the spin is flipped with 100% probability at an angular frequency ω_1. For other off-resonance choices of the frequency ω, the probability of a spin flip oscillates with an amplitude smaller than one. The amplitude of the spin-flip oscillation, as a function of the frequency ω of the rotating field, is plotted in Fig. 11. This curve has the form of a **Lorentzian** curve and clearly exhibits the important **resonant** behavior of the spin-flip probability. The full width at half maximum (**FWHM**) of the resonance curve is $2\omega_1$.

For the resonance condition $\omega = \omega_0$, the probability of a spin flip as a function of time is plotted in Fig. 12. Because the frequency ω_1 is proportional to the applied field B_1, the rate of spin flipping increases with increasing rotating magnetic field strength. However, it is important to note that there is still 100% probability of a spin flip for very small fields. This is the property we were looking for at the beginning of the problem—a way to flip the spin without perturbing the system appreciably. After a time t given by $\omega_1 t = \pi$, the probability for a spin flip is 100%. We have assumed that the applied field is on continuously, but this spin flip can also be produced by a pulsed field with a magnitude and duration that satisfy $\omega_1 t = \pi$. Such a pulse is often called a π-**pulse** and is used to flip a spin, or more generally to make a transition from one energy state to another with 100% certainty. The diagram on the right of Fig. 12 illustrates the energy levels of the spin in the magnetic field and how the spin-flip oscillations are associated with transitions between the two energy levels. A transition from the upper level to the lower level takes energy from the atom and gives it to the magnetic field and is known as **emission**, while the opposite process takes energy from the field and is known as **absorption**.

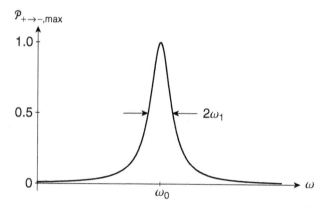

FIGURE 11 Magnetic resonance curve showing the probability of a spin flip as a function of the applied frequency.

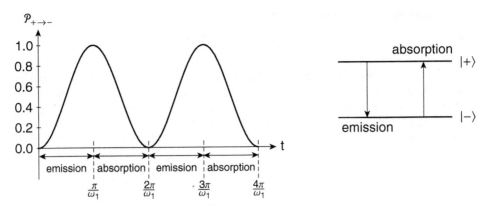

FIGURE 12 Rabi oscillations of the spin-flip probability for the resonance condition.

4.2 ■ Light-Matter Interactions

This same model of the interaction between a two-level system and an applied time-dependent field is used to explain how atoms absorb and emit light. In the magnetic resonance example above, the oscillating magnetic field interacts with the magnetic dipole and energy is exchanged between the field and the dipole. In the interaction of atoms with light, the oscillating electric field of the light wave interacts with the electric dipole of the atom, and energy exchange between the field and the atom corresponds to absorption and emission of photons. We can use the Rabi flopping formula of Eq. (104) to model the atom-light interaction as long as we express the Hamiltonian of the system in the form of Eq. (86). Though atoms have more than two energy levels, we can reduce the problem to a two-level system if the frequency ω of the applied light field is close to just one of the Bohr frequencies of the atom.

Consider two levels of an atom, as shown in Fig. 13. Following the convention used in this common problem, we label the lower state $|g\rangle$ (for ground state) and the upper state $|e\rangle$ (for excited state). The energy difference between the two levels is defined to be

$$E_e - E_g = \hbar\omega_0 \tag{107}$$

to connect to the spin notation. The applied light field (e.g., laser beam) has a frequency ω that is close to, but not necessarily equal to, the atomic Bohr frequency ω_0. Using the same notation as the spin problem [Eq. (86)], we express the Hamiltonian for this atom-light system in two parts

$$H \doteq \frac{\hbar}{2}\begin{pmatrix} \omega_0 & \omega_1 e^{-i\omega t} \\ \omega_1 e^{i\omega t} & -\omega_0 \end{pmatrix} = \frac{\hbar}{2}\begin{pmatrix} \omega_0 & 0 \\ 0 & -\omega_0 \end{pmatrix} + \frac{\hbar}{2}\begin{pmatrix} 0 & \omega_1 e^{-i\omega t} \\ \omega_1 e^{i\omega t} & 0 \end{pmatrix} \tag{108}$$

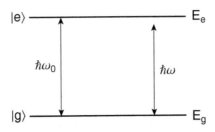

FIGURE 13 Energy level diagram of a two-level atom interacting with an applied light field of frequency ω.

and identify the first term as the atomic Hamiltonian and the second term as the interaction Hamiltonian. In this way, we see that the parameter ω_1 is really an off-diagonal matrix element of the interaction Hamiltonian that connects the two states:

$$\omega_1 = \frac{2}{\hbar}\langle e|H_{\text{int}}|g\rangle. \tag{109}$$

The Rabi formula in Eq. (104) then gives the probability for the light field to cause transitions between the two atomic energy states. Transitions between the atomic states correspond to absorption $(|g\rangle \rightarrow |e\rangle)$ and emission $(|e\rangle \rightarrow |g\rangle)$ of photons in the light field. Total energy is conserved as it is exchanged between the atom and the light field.

Studying these induced transitions is the most powerful tool we have for discovering what the energy levels of a system are and ultimately for determining the Hamiltonian of the system. This tool is known as **spectroscopy** and has played a pivotal role in relating experiments and theory in quantum mechanics. As you encounter new quantum mechanical systems, you should learn the spectroscopic aspects of these systems. For now, we can make a few general comments. If the matrix element of the interaction Hamiltonian in Eq. (109) happens to be zero, then the transition probability between the two levels is zero and we say that this is a **forbidden transition**. By studying the general properties of the matrix elements $\langle e|H_{\text{int}}|g\rangle$ for a system and an interaction, we can discover a set of basic rules governing whether transitions are allowed or forbidden. These are known as **selection rules** and are often representative of some underlying symmetry in the system.

SUMMARY

In this chapter we have learned the key aspect of quantum mechanics—how to predict the future. Schrödinger's equation

$$i\hbar\frac{d}{dt}|\psi(t)\rangle = H(t)|\psi(t)\rangle \tag{110}$$

tells us how quantum state vectors evolve with time. In the common case where the Hamiltonian is time independent, the solution to Schrödinger's equation has the same form no matter the problem. The time-evolved state includes energy-dependent phase factors for each component of the superposition that the system starts in:

$$|\psi(t)\rangle = \sum_n c_n e^{-iE_n t/\hbar}|E_n\rangle. \tag{111}$$

The general recipe for solving time-dependent problems is

Given a Hamiltonian H and an initial state $|\psi(0)\rangle$, what is the probability that the eigenvalue a_j of the observable A is measured at time t?

1. Diagonalize H (find the eigenvalues E_n and eigenvectors $|E_n\rangle$).
2. Write $|\psi(0)\rangle$ in terms of the energy eigenstates $|E_n\rangle$.
3. Multiply each eigenstate coefficient by $e^{-iE_n t/\hbar}$ to get $|\psi(t)\rangle$.
4. Calculate the probability $\mathcal{P}_{a_j} = |\langle a_j|\psi(t)\rangle|^2$.

Use this recipe to study the time evolution of quantum mechanical systems where the Hamiltonian is time independent.

RESOURCES

Activities

This activity is available at

www.physics.oregonstate.edu/qmactivities

Spins Lab 4: Students design experiments to study spin precession in a magnetic field.

Further Reading

Pedagogical articles on neutrino oscillations:

W. C. Haxton and B. R. Holstein, "Neutrino physics," *Am. J. Phys.* **68**, 15–32 (2000).

W. C. Haxton and B. R. Holstein, "Neutrino physics: An update," *Am. J. Phys.* **72**, 18–24 (2004).

E. Sassaroli, "Neutrino oscillations: A relativistic example of a two-level system," *Am. J. Phys.* **67**, 869–875 (1999).

C. Waltham, "Teaching neutrino oscillations," *Am. J. Phys.* **72**, 742–752 (2004).

The application of Rabi oscillations to atomic physics is the main focus of this book:

L. Allen and J. H. Eberly, *Optical Resonance and Two-Level Atoms*, New York: Dover Publications, Inc., 1987.

Schrödinger Time Evolution: Problem Set

1 Write out the Schrödinger equation as expressed in Eq. (5),

$$i\hbar\frac{d}{dt}\sum_n c_n(t)|E_n\rangle = H\sum_n c_n(t)|E_n\rangle, \tag{5}$$

in matrix form for the two-state system and verify the result in Eq. (8),

$$\frac{dc_k(t)}{dt} = -i\frac{E_k}{\hbar}c_k(t). \tag{8}$$

2 Show that the probability of a measurement of the energy is time independent for a general state $|\psi(t)\rangle = \sum_n c_n(t)|E_n\rangle$ that evolves due to a time-independent Hamiltonian. Show that the probability of measurements of other observables are also time independent if those observables commute with the Hamiltonian.

3 Show that the Hamiltonian in Eq. (51),

$$H \doteq \frac{\hbar}{2}\begin{pmatrix} \omega_0 & \omega_1 \\ \omega_1 & -\omega_0 \end{pmatrix}, \tag{51}$$

can be written in the simple form of Eq. (56),

$$H = \sqrt{\omega_0^2 + \omega_1^2}\, S_n, \tag{56}$$

Diagonalize the Hamiltonian in Eq. (55),

$$H \doteq \frac{\hbar}{2}\sqrt{\omega_0^2 + \omega_1^2}\begin{pmatrix} \cos\theta & \sin\theta \\ \sin\theta & -\cos\theta \end{pmatrix}, \tag{55}$$

and confirm the results in Eq. (57),

$$\begin{aligned} |+\rangle_n &= \cos\frac{\theta}{2}|+\rangle + \sin\frac{\theta}{2}|-\rangle \\ |-\rangle_n &= \sin\frac{\theta}{2}|+\rangle - \cos\frac{\theta}{2}|-\rangle. \end{aligned} \tag{57}$$

4 Consider a spin-1/2 particle with a magnetic moment placed in a uniform magnetic field aligned with the z-axis. Verify by explicit matrix calculations that the Hamiltonian commutes with the spin component operator in the z-direction but not with spin component operators in the x- and y-directions. Comment on the relevance of these results to spin precession.

5 Consider a spin-1/2 particle with a magnetic moment. At time $t = 0$, the state of the particle is $|\psi(t = 0)\rangle = |+\rangle$.

  a) If the observable S_x is measured at time $t = 0$, what are the possible results and the probabilities of those results?

  b) Instead of performing the above measurement, the system is allowed to evolve in a uniform magnetic field $\mathbf{B} = B_0\hat{\mathbf{y}}$. Calculate the state of the system (in the S_z basis) after a time t.

The companion websites for this text are http://physics.oregonstate.edu/portfolioswiki and http://physics.oregonstate.edu/qmactivities.

c) At time t, the observable S_x is measured. What is the probability that a value $\hbar/2$ will be found?

d) Draw a schematic diagram of the experiment in parts (b) and (c), similar to Fig. 2.

6 Consider a spin-1/2 particle with a magnetic moment.

    a) At time $t = 0$, the observable S_x is measured, with the result $\hbar/2$. What is the state vector $|\psi(t = 0)\rangle$ immediately after the measurement?

    b) Immediately after the measurement, a magnetic field $\mathbf{B} = B_0\hat{\mathbf{z}}$ is applied and the particle is allowed to evolve for a time T. What is the state of the system at time $t = T$?

    c) At $t = T$, the magnetic field is very rapidly changed to $\mathbf{B} = B_0\hat{\mathbf{y}}$. After another time interval T, a measurement of S_x is carried out once more. What is the probability that a value $\hbar/2$ is found?

7 A beam of identical neutral particles with spin 1/2 travels along the y-axis. The beam passes through a series of two Stern-Gerlach spin-analyzing magnets, each of which is designed to analyze the spin component along the z-axis. The first Stern-Gerlach analyzer allows only particles with spin **up** (along the z-axis) to pass through. The second Stern-Gerlach analyzer allows only particles with spin **down** (along the z-axis) to pass through. The particles travel at speed v between the two analyzers, which are separated by a region of length d in which there is a uniform magnetic field B_0 pointing in the x-direction. Determine the smallest value of d such that 25% of the particles transmitted by the first analyzer are transmitted by the second analyzer.

8 A beam of identical neutral particles with spin 1/2 is prepared in the $|+\rangle$ state. The beam enters a uniform magnetic field B_0, which is in the xz-plane and makes an angle θ with the z-axis. After a time T in the field, the beam enters a Stern-Gerlach analyzer oriented along the y-axis. What is the probability that particles will be measured to have spin up in the y-direction? Check your result by evaluating the special cases $\theta = 0$ and $\theta = \pi/2$.

9 Consider a spin-1/2 particle with a magnetic moment. At time $t = 0$, the state of the particle is $|\psi(t = 0)\rangle = |+\rangle_n$ with the direction $\hat{\mathbf{n}} = (\hat{\mathbf{x}} + \hat{\mathbf{y}})/\sqrt{2}$. The system is allowed to evolve in a uniform magnetic field $\mathbf{B} = B_0\hat{\mathbf{z}}$. What is the probability that the particle will be measured to have spin up in the y-direction after a time t?

10 Consider a spin-1/2 particle with a magnetic moment. At time $t = 0$, the state of the particle is $|\psi(t = 0)\rangle = |+\rangle$. The system is allowed to evolve in a uniform magnetic field $\mathbf{B} = B_0(\hat{\mathbf{x}} + \hat{\mathbf{z}})/\sqrt{2}$. What is the probability that the particle will be measured to have spin down in the z-direction after a time t?

11 Consider a spin-1/2 particle with a magnetic moment. At time $t = 0$, the state of the particle is $|\psi(t = 0)\rangle = |+\rangle_n$ with the direction $\hat{\mathbf{n}} = (\hat{\mathbf{x}} + \hat{\mathbf{y}})/\sqrt{2}$. The system is allowed to evolve in a uniform magnetic field $\mathbf{B} = B_0(\hat{\mathbf{x}} + \hat{\mathbf{z}})/\sqrt{2}$. What is the probability that the particle will be measured to have spin up in the y-direction after a time t?

12 Consider a two-state quantum system with a Hamiltonian

$$H \doteq \begin{pmatrix} E_1 & 0 \\ 0 & E_2 \end{pmatrix}.$$

Another physical observable A is described by the operator

$$A \doteq \begin{pmatrix} 0 & a \\ a & 0 \end{pmatrix},$$

where a is real and positive. Let the initial state of the system be $|\psi(0)\rangle = |a_1\rangle$, where $|a_1\rangle$ is the eigenstate corresponding to the larger of the two possible eigenvalues of A. What is the frequency of oscillation (i.e., the Bohr frequency) of the expectation value of A?

13 Let the matrix representation of the Hamiltonian of a three-state system be

$$H \doteq \begin{pmatrix} E_0 & 0 & A \\ 0 & E_1 & 0 \\ A & 0 & E_0 \end{pmatrix}$$

using the basis states $|1\rangle$, $|2\rangle$, and $|3\rangle$.

a) If the state of the system at time $t = 0$ is $|\psi(0)\rangle = |2\rangle$, what is the probability that the system is in state $|2\rangle$ at time t?

b) If, instead, the state of the system at time $t = 0$ is $|\psi(0)\rangle = |3\rangle$, what is the probability that the system is in state $|3\rangle$ at time t?

14 A quantum mechanical system starts out in the state

$$|\psi(0)\rangle = C(3|a_1\rangle + 4|a_2\rangle),$$

where $|a_i\rangle$ are the normalized eigenstates of the operator A corresponding to the eigenvalues a_i. In this $|a_i\rangle$ basis, the Hamiltonian of this system is represented by the matrix

$$H \doteq E_0 \begin{pmatrix} 2 & 1 \\ 1 & 2 \end{pmatrix}.$$

a) If you measure the energy of this system, what values are possible, and what are the probabilities of measuring those values?

b) Calculate the expectation value $\langle A \rangle$ of the observable A as a function of time.

15 Show that the general energy state superposition $|\psi(t)\rangle = \sum_n c_n e^{-iE_n t/\hbar}|E_n\rangle$ satisfies the Schrödinger equation, but not the energy eigenvalue equation.

16 For a spin-1/2 system undergoing Rabi oscillations, assume that the resonance condition $\omega = \omega_0$ holds.

a) Solve the differential equations for the coefficients $\alpha_\pm(t)$. Use your results to find the transformed state vector $|\tilde{\psi}(t)\rangle$ and the state vector $|\psi(t)\rangle$, assuming the most general initial state of the system.

b) Verify that a π-pulse ($\omega_1 t = \pi$) produces a complete spin flip. Calculate both the transformed state vector $|\tilde{\psi}(t)\rangle$ and the state vector $|\psi(t)\rangle$.

c) Assume that the interaction time is such that $\omega_1 t = \pi/2$. Find the effect on the system if the initial state is $|+\rangle$.

d) Discuss the differences between the original reference frame and the rotating reference frame in light of your results.

17 Consider an electron neutrino with an energy of 8 MeV. How far must this neutrino travel before it oscillates to a muon neutrino? Assume the neutrino mixing parameters given in the text. How many complete oscillations ($\nu_e \rightarrow \nu_\mu \rightarrow \nu_e$) will take place if this neutrino travels from the sun to the earth? Through the earth?

18 Many weak decay processes produce neutrinos with a spectrum of energies. Assume electron neutrinos are produced with a uniform distribution from 4 MeV to 8 MeV. By averaging the probability over the energy spectrum, calculate and plot, as a function of the travel distance L, the probability that electron neutrinos are measured at the detector. Compare the result with the probability for monoenergetic neutrinos at 8 MeV. The integral required for the averaging does not yield an elementary expression, so a computer is advisable. Assume the neutrino mixing parameters given in the text.

Quantized Energies:
Particle in a Box

Consider the spin system to illustrate the basic concepts and tools of quantum mechanics. With a firm foundation in how quantum mechanics works, you are ready to address the central question that quantum mechanics was designed to answer: How do we explain the structure of the microscopic world? All around us are nuclei, atoms, molecules, and solids with unique properties that cannot be explained with classical physics but require quantum mechanics. For example, quantum mechanics can tell us why sodium lamps are yellow, why laser diodes have a unique color, and why uranium is radioactive.

The key to understanding the structure of microscopic systems lies in the energy states that the systems are allowed to have. Each microscopic system has a unique set of energy levels that gives that system a "fingerprint" that sets it apart from other systems. With the tools of quantum mechanics, we can build a theoretical model for the system, predict that fingerprint, and compare it to the experimental measurement. Our goal in this chapter and in further study is to learn how to predict this energy fingerprint. In this chapter we will study a particularly simple model system that exhibits most of the important features that are shared by all microscopic systems.

1 ■ SPECTROSCOPY

The energy fingerprint of a system not only identifies that system uniquely, but the allowed energies determine the time evolution of the system through the Schrödinger equation. One of the primary experimental techniques for measuring the energy fingerprint of a system is spectroscopy. We see a hint of this in magnetic resonance: absorption and emission of photons causes transitions between quantized energy levels of the system only when the photon energy matches the spacing between the energy eigenstates. Historically, the spectrum of hydrogen was a key ingredient in the development of quantum mechanics, and spectroscopy continues to play an important role in characterizing new quantum systems and in verifying the rules of quantum mechanics.

In a magnetic resonance example, the two quantized energy levels arose from the two possible spin components (up or down) and their different interactions with an applied magnetic field. The more common situation that gives rise to quantized energy levels is where two or more particles interact in a way that limits their spatial motion and binds them together into a composite system. Bound systems such as nuclei, atoms, molecules, and solids are everyday examples that are characterized by distinct spectral lines associated with quantized energy states, (i.e., eigenstates of the Hamiltonian with discrete energy eigenvalues). For example, the hydrogen atom energy levels

From Chapter 5 of *Quantum Mechanics: A Paradigms Approach*, First Edition. David H. McIntyre. Copyright
© 2012 by Pearson Education, Inc. Published by Pearson Addison-Wesley. All rights reserved.

The companion websites for this text are http://physics.oregonstate.edu/portfolioswiki and http://physics.oregonstate.edu/qmactivities.

and the corresponding **optical spectrum** are shown in Fig. 1. The spectral lines appear when electrons make transitions between energy levels. Downward transitions emit photons and give rise to an **emission spectrum**, while upward transitions absorb photons and yield an **absorption spectrum**. For every pair of energy eigenvalues E_i and E_j, there is a possible spectral line with photon energy $E_i - E_j$, and photon frequency f_{ij} and wavelength λ_{ij} given by

$$f_{ij} = \frac{\omega_{ij}}{\hbar} = \frac{E_i - E_j}{h}$$

$$\lambda_{ij} = \frac{c}{f_{ij}} = \frac{hc}{E_i - E_j},$$

(1)

assuming that $E_i > E_j$. The set of spectral lines of atomic hydrogen that share a common lower level forms a series that is named after its discoverer. The first three series in hydrogen are shown in Fig. 1 and listed in Table 1. The lowest energy state ($n = 1$ for hydrogen) is called the **ground state**, and the levels above that are called **excited states**. Though the word *spectrum* often refers to the observed optical lines, the set of quantized energy states is also commonly referred to as the **energy spectrum** of the system.

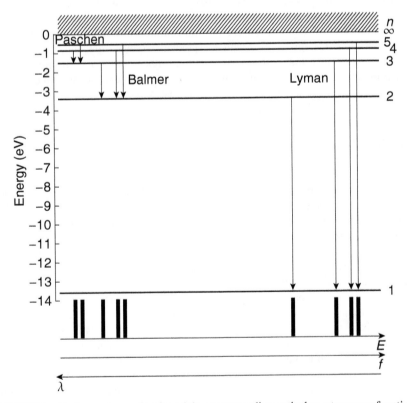

FIGURE 1 Hydrogen energy levels and the corresponding optical spectrum as a function of energy, frequency, and wavelength (the wavelength scale is not a linear scale).

Table 1 Hydrogen Transition Wavelengths

Final state	Initial state				Series
	2	3	4	5	
1	122 nm	103 nm	97 nm	95 nm	Lyman
2		656 nm	486 nm	434 nm	Balmer
3			1875 nm	1282 nm	Paschen

A spectroscopy experiment can be considered to be a measurement of the energy of a quantum state. A spectroscopic energy measurement is depicted in Fig. 2(a) in a simplified schematic that is analogous to the Stern-Gerlach spin measurement we discussed earlier. A system is prepared in an initial state $|\psi\rangle$, and we measure the probability that the state is measured to have a particular energy E_i. If we write the energy eigenstates as $|E_i\rangle$, then the probability of a particular energy measurement is

$$\mathcal{P}_{E_i} = |\langle E_i|\psi\rangle|^2. \tag{2}$$

As we do in a spins problem, we represent the collection of measurements on an ensemble of identical states as a histogram, as shown in Fig. 2(b). In a real spectroscopy experiment, the measured energies are really energy differences between levels, so it can be a bit of a puzzle to decode the energy levels from the observed spectrum. We assume that this decoding process can be done and we assume that the histogram in Fig. 2(b) faithfully represents the energy levels of the system. The energy levels E_i and the eigenstates $|E_i\rangle$ are solutions to the energy eigenvalue equation

$$\hat{H}|E_i\rangle = E_i|E_i\rangle, \tag{3}$$

so the spectroscopic measurement is how the theoretical Hamiltonian is compared with experiment. Our task in this chapter is to learn how to predict the allowed energy eigenstates of a particular system given the Hamiltonian of the system.

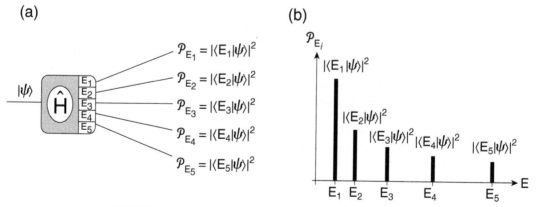

FIGURE 2 (a) Energy measurement and (b) histogram of results.

105

2 ■ ENERGY EIGENVALUE EQUATION

In classical mechanics, we often solve problems by using Newton's second law $\mathbf{F} = m\mathbf{a}$ to predict the position $\mathbf{r}(t)$ of a particle subject to some known forces. Another common method is the energy method, whereby we use conservation of energy and the relation $E = T + V$ between the total energy (E) and the kinetic (T) and potential (V) energies to predict the motion. Of course, the two methods are related because the force is related to the potential energy by

$$F_x = -\frac{dV}{dx} \tag{4}$$

in one dimension. Hence the potential energy function $V(x)$ is what determines the classical motion of a particle.

The potential energy is also the key element in quantum mechanics, because of the important role it plays in the Hamiltonian of the system in question. The Hamiltonian determines the energy states through the energy eigenvalue equation

$$\hat{H}|E_i\rangle = E_i|E_i\rangle. \tag{5}$$

Note that many other texts refer to Eq. (5) as the time-independent Schrödinger equation because it can be derived from the Schrödinger equation by separating the time and space parts; however, we refer to it always as the energy eigenvalue equation. The prescription for finding a quantum mechanical Hamiltonian operator is to find the classical form of the energy and replace the physical observables with their quantum mechanical operators. For a moving particle, the classical mechanical energy is the sum of the kinetic energy and the potential energy, which in one dimension is

$$E = \frac{p_x^2}{2m} + V(x). \tag{6}$$

We use the position x and momentum p as the primary physical observables in quantum mechanics, following the Hamiltonian approach to classical mechanics. Hence the quantum mechanical Hamiltonian operator for a particle moving in one dimension is

$$\hat{H} = \frac{\hat{p}_x^2}{2m} + V(\hat{x}). \tag{7}$$

We use carets or hats on operators on occasion to distinguish them from the same symbol used as a variable. If the distinction is clear from the context, then that notation may be dropped.

So now what? What are these new operators $\hat{x}$ and $\hat{p}$ for position and momentum? And how do we use them to solve the energy eigenvalue equation? In the spins chapters, we learned much of the machinery of quantum mechanics and would rightly expect to be able to use it in this new problem on particle motion. However, position and momentum are different enough from spin that we need to redevelop some of the mathematical machinery we have already learned.

When we discussed spin quantum states, we either used abstract kets, such as $|+\rangle$ or $|-\rangle_x$, or we used column vectors to represent the abstract kets in a particular basis of eigenstates. For example, we often used the eigenstates of the S_z operator as the preferred basis, in which case the abstract kets $|+\rangle$ and $|-\rangle_x$ are expressed as

$$|+\rangle \doteq \begin{pmatrix} 1 \\ 0 \end{pmatrix} \tag{8}$$

and

$$|-\rangle_x \doteq \frac{1}{\sqrt{2}}\begin{pmatrix}1\\-1\end{pmatrix}. \tag{9}$$

In fact, there are very few quantum mechanical problems that can be solved using abstract kets. It is generally necessary to use a representation of the kets that is convenient for solving the problem. In the problems that we wish to address now, it is most convenient to represent abstract quantum states as spatial functions, so we need to explain what that means.

The spatial functions we use to represent quantum states are called **wave functions** and are generally written using the Greek letter ψ as

$$\psi(x). \tag{10}$$

The wave function is a representation of the abstract quantum state, so we can use our representation notation to write

$$|\psi\rangle \doteq \psi(x). \tag{11}$$

We call this representation the **position representation**, which means that we are using the position eigenstates as the preferred basis (more on these eigenstates later). For clarity, we will use the Greek letter ψ when referring to generic quantum states and other Greek letters to denote specific eigenstates. For example, in the case of the energy eigenstates, we write the wave functions representing them as

$$|E_i\rangle \doteq \varphi_{E_i}(x) \tag{12}$$

to distinguish them as specific eigenstates.

Using this new wave function notation, the energy eigenvalue equation Eq. (5) becomes

$$\hat{H}\varphi_{E_i}(x) = E_i\varphi_{E_i}(x). \tag{13}$$

To solve this equation, we must know how to represent the operators in the Hamiltonian of Eq. (7) using the position representation. It turns out that in the position representation, the action of the position operator $\hat{x}$ is represented by multiplication by the position variable x, while the action of the momentum operator $\hat{p}$ is represented by application of a derivative with respect to position (see an advanced text for justification or take these as postulates). Using our representation notation, these two statements are

$$\boxed{\begin{aligned}\hat{x} &\doteq x\\\hat{p} &\doteq -i\hbar\frac{d}{dx}\end{aligned}}. \tag{14}$$

The momentum operator has a factor of $-i\hbar$ to get the dimensions correct and to ensure that the measurable results are real (not imaginary).

With these representations of the position and momentum operators, we now begin to solve the energy eigenvalue equation. Inserting Eq. (14) into the energy eigenvalue equation gives

$$\hat{H}\varphi_{E_i}(x) = E_i\varphi_{E_i}(x)$$
$$\left(\frac{\hat{p}^2}{2m} + V(\hat{x})\right)\varphi_{E_i}(x) = E_i\varphi_{E_i}(x) \tag{15}$$
$$\left(\frac{1}{2m}\left(-i\hbar\frac{d}{dx}\right)^2 + V(x)\right)\varphi_{E_i}(x) = E_i\varphi_{E_i}(x).$$

The result is that the energy eigenvalue equation becomes a differential equation

$$\left(-\frac{\hbar^2}{2m}\frac{d^2}{dx^2} + V(x)\right)\varphi_E(x) = E\varphi_E(x).$$ (16)

This differential equation is a big change from the matrix eigenvalue equations we encountered in the spin problems. This result is a common occurrence when using the wave function approach: *operator equations turn into differential equations*. Hence, when we use the wave function approach to find the allowed energy eigenstates of a system, we typically solve differential equations. We will solve this differential equation for several different potential energy functions $V(x)$ in the remainder of this book, but first we pause to examine the wave function idea more carefully.

3 ■ THE WAVE FUNCTION

To better understand the new concept of a wave function $\psi(x)$, let's see how it relates to the quantum state vector $|\psi\rangle$ we used in spins. In the spin case, we found that a useful way to represent a state vector was as a column vector of numbers, with each number being the probability amplitude for the state $|\psi\rangle$ to be measured in a particular spin eigenstate. For example, we could write the state $|\psi\rangle$ using the S_z representation as

$$|\psi\rangle \doteq \begin{pmatrix} \langle+|\psi\rangle \\ \langle-|\psi\rangle \end{pmatrix} \quad \begin{matrix} \leftarrow S_z = +\hbar/2 \\ \leftarrow S_z = -\hbar/2. \end{matrix}$$ (17)

The numbers $\langle\pm|\psi\rangle$ in the column vector are the projections of the state vector $|\psi\rangle$ onto the S_z eigenstates $|\pm\rangle$, corresponding to the two possible eigenvalues. If we measure the spin projection, as depicted in Fig. 3(a), then the amplitudes $\langle\pm|\psi\rangle$ are used to calculate the probabilities

$$\mathcal{P}_\pm = |\langle\pm|\psi\rangle|^2$$ (18)

shown in the histogram in Fig. 3(b).

If we now consider an energy measurement, such as depicted in Fig. 2(a), then the basis of energy eigenstates is the appropriate basis for representing the state vector:

$$|\psi\rangle \doteq \begin{pmatrix} \langle E_1|\psi\rangle \\ \langle E_2|\psi\rangle \\ \langle E_3|\psi\rangle \\ \vdots \end{pmatrix} \quad \begin{matrix} \leftarrow E = E_1 \\ \leftarrow E = E_2 \\ \leftarrow E = E_3. \\ \vdots \end{matrix}$$ (19)

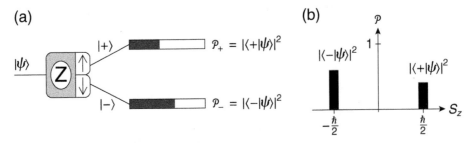

FIGURE 3 (a) Spin measurement and (b) probability histogram.

In such an energy measurement, the probabilities shown in Fig. 2(b) are calculated using the projections $\langle E_i|\psi\rangle$ of the state $|\psi\rangle$ onto the energy eigenstates $|E_i\rangle$. The probabilities of measuring the quantized energies are

$$\mathcal{P}_{E_i} = |\langle E_i|\psi\rangle|^2. \tag{20}$$

In analogy to these two examples, the wave function is a representation of a quantum state using the eigenstates of the position operator $\hat{x}$ as the basis states. If we call the position eigenstates $|x_i\rangle$, then the analog to Eqs. (17) and (19) would be

$$|\psi\rangle \doteq \begin{pmatrix} \langle x_1|\psi\rangle \\ \langle x_2|\psi\rangle \\ \langle x_3|\psi\rangle \\ \vdots \end{pmatrix} \begin{matrix} \leftarrow x_1 \\ \leftarrow x_2 \\ \leftarrow x_3, \\ \vdots \end{matrix} \tag{21}$$

where the projection $\langle x_i|\psi\rangle$ is the probability amplitude for the state $|\psi\rangle$ to be measured in the position eigenstate $|x_i\rangle$. However, experiment tells us that the physical observable x is not quantized. Rather, *all values of position x are allowed*. This is in stark contrast to the case of the spin component S_z, where only two results were possible. We say that the spectrum of eigenvalues of position is *continuous* and the spectrum of eigenvalues of spin is *discrete*. Future experiments may shed new light on this, but to date, space appears to be continuous. "Discrete vs. continuous" is an important distinction that affects how we use and interpret the quantum state vector, the probability amplitudes, and the probabilities when position is the relevant quantum mechanical observable.

For a continuous variable like position, the column vector representation of Eq. (21) is not convenient because we cannot write down the infinite number of components. Even if the number were finite but large, say 100, then we would find a column vector cumbersome. Instead, we might choose to represent the 100 discrete numbers $\langle x_i|\psi\rangle$ as points in a graph, such as shown in Fig. 4(a). However, because the position spectrum is continuous, there is an infinite continuum of the probability amplitudes $\langle x|\psi\rangle$, and the natural way to represent such a continuous set of numbers is as a continuous function, as shown in Fig. 4(b). This function is what we call the quantum mechanical wave function $\psi(x)$. The wave function is the collection of numbers that represents the quantum state vector in terms of the position eigenstates, in the same way that the column vector used to represent a general spin state is a collection of numbers that represents the quantum state vector in terms of the spin eigenstates. Whether you write the wave function as $\psi(x)$ or as $\langle x|\psi\rangle$ is ultimately a matter of taste. It is more common to

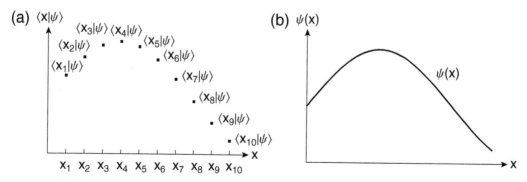

FIGURE 4   (a) Discrete basis representation and (b) continuous basis representation.

109

see the form $\psi(x)$ used as the wave function, and we will follow that convention mostly, using the Dirac notation when convenient. But it is important to remember both forms, so we repeat them here:

$$\boxed{\psi(x) = \langle x|\psi\rangle}. \tag{22}$$

In words, we say that the wave function $\psi(x)$ is the probability amplitude for the quantum state $|\psi\rangle$ to be measured in the position eigenstate $|x\rangle$.

Continuing with the analogy to the spin and energy examples above, we expect that the probability of measuring a particular value of position is obtained by taking the absolute square of the projection $\langle x|\psi\rangle$, as was done in Eqs. (18) and (20) for spin and energy representations. However, because the projection $\langle x|\psi\rangle$ is the continuous wave function $\psi(x)$, the absolute square yields a continuous probability function (actually a probability density, as we'll find in a moment), which we write as $\mathcal{P}(x)$ so as to distinguish it from the discrete case (e.g. $\mathcal{P}_{S_z=+\hbar/2}$) by making x an argument rather than a subscript. In wave function notation, this new probability function is

$$\boxed{\mathcal{P}(x) = |\psi(x)|^2}. \tag{23}$$

Thus, given a wave function $\psi(x)$, such as shown in Fig. 5(a), we use Eq. (23) to calculate the probability function $\mathcal{P}(x)$, which is shown in Fig. 5(b). The probability function in Fig. 5(b) is analogous to the histograms of discrete probabilities in Figs. 2(b) and 3(b). We must stress that measuring the probability function $\mathcal{P}(x)$ does not allow us to infer the wave function $\psi(x)$. In spin measurements, measurements of three different observables, S_x, S_y, and S_z, are required to deduce the state vector $|\psi\rangle$ because the probability amplitudes are complex numbers. The relative phases between the probability amplitudes are not accessible from measurement of a single observable.

Having a continuous function for the probability rather than a set of discrete values raises some important issues. In quantum mechanics we require that the sum of all possible probabilities be equal to unity (i.e., the state vector must be normalized). In the discrete spins case this meant that:

$$\sum_{\pm} \mathcal{P}_{\pm} = \sum_{\pm} |\langle \pm|\psi\rangle|^2 = 1. \tag{24}$$

If position were discrete instead of continuous, then the normalization condition would be:

$$\sum_{n} \mathcal{P}_{x_n} = \sum_{n} |\langle x_n|\psi\rangle|^2 = 1. \tag{25}$$

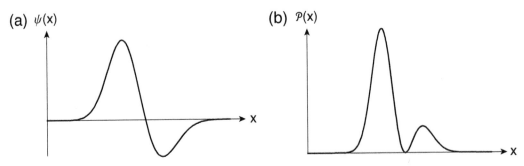

FIGURE 5　(a) Wave function and (b) corresponding probability density.

However, because the spectrum of position eigenvalues is continuous rather than discrete, the sum over discrete probabilities must be changed to an integral over the continuous probability function $\mathcal{P}(x)$, with the requisite differential term dx added. For now, we restrict the discussion to one spatial dimension. Thus the normalization condition is

$$\int_{-\infty}^{\infty} \mathcal{P}(x)\,dx = \int_{-\infty}^{\infty} |\psi(x)|^2 dx = 1. \tag{26}$$

The differential dx has dimensions of length and the total integrated probability must be dimensionless, so the probability function $\mathcal{P}(x)$ must have dimensions of inverse length. This means that $\mathcal{P}(x)$ is a **probability density** (in one dimension a probability per unit length) rather than a probability. Hence we interpret the quantity

$$\mathcal{P}(x)\,dx \tag{27}$$

as the infinitesimal probability of detecting a particle at position x within an infinitesimal region of width dx [i.e., between x and $x + dx$, as shown in Fig. 6(a)]. To calculate the probability that a particle is measured to be in a finite interval $a < x < b$, we add all the infinitesimal probabilities in that interval, which is the integral

$$\boxed{\mathcal{P}_{a<x<b} = \int_{a}^{b} |\psi(x)|^2 dx} \tag{28}$$

as depicted in Fig. 6(b). Equation (28) is an incredibly important formula. We use it, for example, to find the probability that an electron is in a certain region of an atom (extended to three dimensions, of course).

To calculate other experimental quantities, such as expectation values, we must learn how to translate bra-ket rules for discrete basis systems to wave function rules for continuous basis systems. We can learn some rules for this translation by comparing the new wave function form of the normalization condition in Eq. (26) to the bra-ket normalization condition. In Dirac notation, the requirement of probability normalization is expressed in terms of the inner product of the state vector with itself:

$$\langle \psi | \psi \rangle = 1. \tag{29}$$

Rewrite the wave function normalization condition Eq. (26) to make it look more like the bra-ket form:

$$\int_{-\infty}^{\infty} \psi^*(x)\psi(x)\,dx = 1. \tag{30}$$

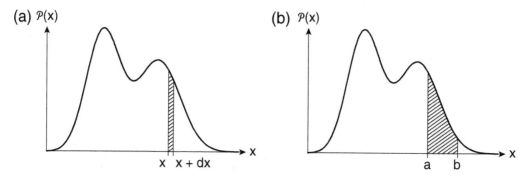

FIGURE 6 Probability for measuring a particle to be in the position range (a) x to $x + dx$, and (b) a to b.

Comparing Eq. (29) and Eq. (30), we postulate the following rules for translating bra-ket formulae to wave function formulae:

1) Replace ket with wave function	$\lvert \psi \rangle \rightarrow \psi(x)$
2) Replace bra with wave function conjugate	$\langle \psi \rvert \rightarrow \psi^*(x)$
3) Replace bracket with integral over all space	$\langle \mid \rangle \rightarrow \int_{-\infty}^{\infty} dx$
4) Replace operator with position representation	$\hat{A} \rightarrow A(x)$

where we have added a rule about operators that will become obvious in a moment.

Example 1   Normalize the wave function

$$\psi(x) = Ce^{-a\lvert x-2 \rvert}. \tag{31}$$

Use Eq. (26) for the normalization condition and integrate over all space

$$
\begin{aligned}
1 &= \int_{-\infty}^{\infty} \lvert \psi(x) \rvert^2 \, dx \\
&= \int_{-\infty}^{\infty} \left\lvert Ce^{-a\lvert x-2 \rvert} \right\rvert^2 dx \\
&= \int_{-\infty}^{\infty} \lvert C \rvert^2 \, e^{-2a\lvert x-2 \rvert} \, dx.
\end{aligned} \tag{32}
$$

Break the integral into two pieces to remove the absolute value:

$$
\begin{aligned}
1 &= \int_{-\infty}^{2} \lvert C \rvert^2 e^{2a(x-2)} \, dx + \int_{2}^{\infty} \lvert C \rvert^2 e^{-2a(x-2)} \, dx \\
&= \left[\frac{\lvert C \rvert^2}{2a} e^{2a(x-2)} \right]_{-\infty}^{2} + \left[\frac{\lvert C \rvert^2}{-2a} e^{-2a(x-2)} \right]_{2}^{\infty} \\
&= \frac{\lvert C \rvert^2}{a}.
\end{aligned} \tag{33}
$$

Once again, we have freedom to choose the overall phase, so we let C be real and positive:

$$C = \sqrt{a} \tag{34}$$

giving the normalized wave function

$$\psi(x) = \sqrt{a} \, e^{-a\lvert x-2 \rvert}. \tag{35}$$

Using the rules for translating bra-ket notation to wave function notation, a general state vector projection or probability amplitude expressed in wave function language is

$$\langle \phi \mid \psi \rangle = \int_{-\infty}^{\infty} \phi^*(x)\psi(x)\,dx. \tag{36}$$

The square of this probability amplitude is the probability that the state $\psi(x)$ is measured to be in the state $\phi(x)$

$$\boxed{\mathcal{P}_{\psi \to \varphi} = |\langle \varphi | \psi \rangle|^2 = \left| \int_{-\infty}^{\infty} \varphi^*(x) \psi_x(x) \, dx \right|^2}.$$ (37)

Technically, we should say that this is the probability that the system prepared in state $\psi(x)$ is measured to have the physical observable for which $\phi(x)$ is the eigenstate, because we measure observables, not states. But the looser language is common and does not create any ambiguity in the calculation. If we measure the energy, for example, then the probability of obtaining the result E_n is

$$\mathcal{P}_{E_n} = |\langle E_n | \psi \rangle|^2 = \left| \int_{-\infty}^{\infty} \varphi_n^*(x) \psi(x) \, dx \right|^2,$$ (38)

where $\varphi_n(x)$ is the energy eigenstate with energy E_n. Note that Eq. (28) and Eq. (37) look similar but have important differences. In Eq. (28) we integrate the probability density (wave function complex squared) over a finite range of position in order to sum the probabilities of measuring many different positions. In Eq. (37) we integrate the product of two wave functions over all space to determine their mutual overlap, *and then we complex square* that result to get the probability of measuring a single result.

To transform an expectation value to wave function language, we must consider the operator. The expectation value of an observable A is the matrix element of the operator

$$\langle \hat{A} \rangle = \langle \psi | \hat{A} | \psi \rangle.$$ (39)

If we rewrite the expectation value as

$$\langle \hat{A} \rangle = \langle \psi | \{ \hat{A} | \psi \rangle \},$$ (40)

we see that it is an inner product where one ket has been transformed by the operator $\hat{A}$. To write this in terms of wave functions, we must make sure to use the position representation form of the operator. For example, the position operator $\hat{x}$ in the position representation is simply multiplication by the scalar position x. Using the translation rules to write the expectation value of the position in wave function notation yields

$$\begin{aligned} \langle \hat{x} \rangle &= \langle \psi | \hat{x} | \psi \rangle \\ &= \int_{-\infty}^{\infty} \psi^*(x) x \psi(x) \, dx \\ &= \int_{-\infty}^{\infty} x |\psi(x)|^2 \, dx, \end{aligned}$$ (41)

where we have used the fact that scalar multiplication is commutative. For the expectation value of the momentum, we find

$$\begin{aligned} \langle \hat{p} \rangle &= \langle \psi | \hat{p} | \psi \rangle \\ &= \int_{-\infty}^{\infty} \psi^*(x) \left(-i\hbar \frac{d}{dx} \right) \psi(x) \, dx, \end{aligned}$$ (42)

which cannot be simplified more without knowing the wave function. In the next section, we will solve the energy eigenvalue equation for a specific potential energy to allow us to calculate these expectation values explicitly.

Example 2   Consider the wave function from Example 1:

$$\psi(x) = \sqrt{a}\, e^{-a|x-2|}. \tag{43}$$

Calculate the expectation value of the position and the probability that the particle is measured to be in the interval $4 < x < 6$.

The expectation value of position is given by Eq. (41)

$$
\begin{aligned}
\langle \hat{x} \rangle &= \int_{-\infty}^{\infty} x|\psi(x)|^2\,dx \\
&= \int_{-\infty}^{\infty} x\left(\sqrt{a}e^{-a|x-2|}\right)^2 dx \\
&= a\int_{-\infty}^{\infty} xe^{-2a|x-2|}\,dx \\
&= a\int_{-\infty}^{2} xe^{2a(x-2)}\,dx + a\int_{2}^{\infty} xe^{-2a(x-2)}\,dx \\
&= a\left[e^{2a(x-2)}\frac{(-1+2ax)}{4a^2}\right]_{-\infty}^{2} + a\left[e^{-2a(x-2)}\frac{(-1-2ax)}{4a^2}\right]_{2}^{\infty} \\
&= a\left[\frac{(-1+4a)}{4a^2} - 0 + 0 - \frac{(-1-4a)}{4a^2}\right] \\
&= 2.
\end{aligned}
\tag{44}
$$

This is what you expect based upon the plot of wave function shown in Fig. 7(a) and the probability density in Fig. 7(b), which are symmetric about the point $x = 2$.

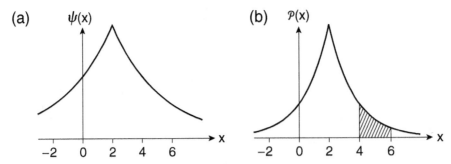

FIGURE 7   (a) Wave function and (b) corresponding probability density. The hatched region in (b) represents the probability for the particle to be measured in the region $4 < x < 6$.

To calculate the probability of finding the particle in the interval, use Eq. (28)

$$
\begin{aligned}
\mathcal{P}_{4<x<6} &= \int_4^6 \left| \sqrt{a}\, e^{-a|x-2|} \right|^2 dx \\
&= \int_4^6 a e^{-2a(x-2)}\, dx \\
&= \left[\frac{a}{-2a} e^{-2a(x-2)} \right]_4^6 \\
&= \frac{e^{-4a}}{2} \left[1 - e^{-4a} \right].
\end{aligned}
\tag{45}
$$

This probability is shown as the hatched region in Fig. 7(b). The actual value of the probability depends on the value of the parameter a.

4 ■ INFINITE SQUARE WELL

Our task now is to solve the energy eigenvalue equation, which we found to be a differential equation

$$
\left(-\frac{\hbar^2}{2m} \frac{d^2}{dx^2} + V(x) \right) \varphi_E(x) = E\varphi_E(x).
\tag{46}
$$

As you might expect, the solutions to this differential equation depend critically on the functional dependence of the potential energy $V(x)$. A generic potential energy function is depicted in Fig. 8 in a **potential energy diagram** that illustrates some important aspects of the motion of the particle. Most of the interesting systems to which we will apply Eq. (46) resemble the potential energy function depicted in Fig. 8 in that $V(x)$ has a minimum, so we refer to the potential energy function as a

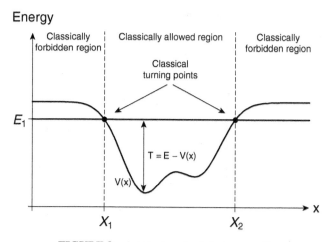

FIGURE 8   A generic potential energy well.

potential well. The particle energy is conserved, so the kinetic energy $T(x) = E - V(x)$ is illustrated in the potential energy diagram by the vertical arrow between the fixed energy E_1 and the potential energy $V(x)$. For a classical particle, the kinetic energy cannot be negative, so a classical particle with the energy E_1 chosen in Fig. 8 has its motion constrained to the region between x_1 and x_2. These extreme points of the classical motion are called **classical turning points** and the region within the turning points is called the **classically allowed region**, while the regions beyond are called **classically forbidden regions**. Particles that have their motion constrained by the potential well are said to be in **bound states**. Particles with energies above the top of the potential well do not have their motion constrained and so are in **unbound states**. Note that the extent of the classically forbidden and allowed regions depends on the specific value of the energy, E_1, for a particular bound state.

Solving Eq. (46) for various important potential energy functions is the subject of this and later chapters. In this chapter, our goal is to study a simple potential energy system and learn the mathematics required for this new wave function approach.

We begin our journey to energy quantization with the simplest example of a particle that is confined to a region of space. The classical picture is a super ball bouncing between two perfectly elastic walls. We call this system a **particle in a box**. We observe three important characteristics of this classical system: (1) the ball flies freely between the walls, (2) the ball is reflected perfectly at each bounce, and (3) the ball remains in the box no matter how large its energy. These three observations are consistent with (1) zero force on the ball when it is between the walls, (2) infinite force on the ball at the walls, and (3) infinite potential energy outside the box.

The mathematical model that is consistent with these three observations of the motion of a particle in a box is given by the potential energy function shown in Fig. 9. The potential energy is zero within the well (any constant would suffice, but we choose zero for simplicity), and it is infinite outside the well. The discontinuity at the sides of the well requires us to write the potential energy function in a piecewise fashion

$$V(x) = \begin{cases} \infty, & x < 0 \\ 0, & 0 < x < L \\ \infty, & x > L. \end{cases} \tag{47}$$

Because of the shape of the potential energy in Fig. 9, this system is also referred to as an **infinite square well**. Though this model is too simple to accurately represent any real quantum mechanical system, it does illustrate most of the important features of a particle bound to a limited region of space.

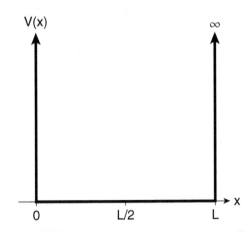

FIGURE 9 Infinite square potential energy well.

Our goal is to find the energy eigenstates and eigenvalues of the system by solving the energy eigenvalue equation using the potential energy in Eq. (47). The potential energy is piecewise, so we must solve the differential equation (46) separately inside and outside the box. Outside the box, the potential energy is infinite and the energy eigenvalue equation is

$$\left(-\frac{\hbar^2}{2m}\frac{d^2}{dx^2} + \infty \right)\varphi_E(x) = E\varphi_E(x), \qquad \textit{outside box.} \tag{48}$$

We are looking for solutions with finite energy E, so Eq. (48) is satisfied only if the energy eigenstate wave function $\varphi_E(x)$ is zero everywhere outside the box. This means that the quantum mechanical particle is excluded from the classically forbidden regions in this example. This correspondence with the classical situation holds only for the case of infinite potential energy walls on the potential well.

Inside the box, the potential energy is zero and the energy eigenvalue equation is

$$\left(-\frac{\hbar^2}{2m}\frac{d^2}{dx^2} + 0 \right)\varphi_E(x) = E\varphi_E(x), \qquad \textit{inside box.} \tag{49}$$

Thus our task reduces to solving the differential equation inside the box:

$$-\frac{\hbar^2}{2m}\frac{d^2}{dx^2}\varphi_E(x) = E\varphi_E(x). \tag{50}$$

It is worth reminding ourselves at this point what is known and what is not. The particle has a mass m and is confined to a box of size L. These quantities are known, as is $\hbar$, a fundamental constant. The unknowns that we need to find are the energy E and the wave function $\varphi_E(x)$, which is what it means to solve an eigenvalue problem (now posing as a differential equation).

It is convenient to rewrite the differential equation (50) as

$$\begin{aligned} \frac{d^2}{dx^2}\varphi_E(x) &= -\frac{2mE}{\hbar^2}\varphi_E(x) \\ &= -k^2\varphi_E(x), \end{aligned} \tag{51}$$

where we have defined a new parameter

$$k^2 = \frac{2mE}{\hbar^2}, \tag{52}$$

which is positive because the energy E is positive in this problem. The parameter k is called the **wave vector**, and its physical interpretation will be evident in Eq. (67). Equation (51) says that the energy eigenstate $\varphi_E(x)$ is a function whose second derivative is equal to that function itself times a negative constant. We can write the solution either in terms of complex exponential functions

$$\varphi_E(x) = A'e^{ikx} + B'e^{-ikx} \tag{53}$$

or in terms of sine and cosine functions

$$\varphi_E(x) = A\sin kx + B\cos kx. \tag{54}$$

Either solution includes two as yet unknown constants, as you would expect for a second-order differential equation. It turns out that bound state energy eigenstates can always be written as real functions, so we choose to work with the sine and cosine form of the general solution (if you choose the complex exponential form, you will arrive at the sine and cosine solutions at the end of the problem anyway: Problem 3). Hence the energy eigenstate wave function throughout space is

$$\varphi_E(x) = \begin{cases} 0, & x < 0 \\ A\sin kx + B\cos kx, & 0 < x < L \\ 0, & x > L. \end{cases} \tag{55}$$

We now need some more information to reach the final solution. There are three unknowns in the problem: A, B, and k [which contains the energy E through Eq. (52)], so we expect to need three pieces of information to solve for the three unknowns. We get two of these pieces of information from imposing **boundary conditions** on the wave function. To make sure that the mathematical solutions properly represent real physical systems, we require that the wave function be continuous across each boundary between different regions of space where different solutions exist. Applying this requirement on the continuity of the wave function at the sides of the box $x = 0$ and L yields two boundary condition equations:

$$\varphi_E(0): A\sin(0) + B\cos(0) = 0$$
$$\varphi_E(L): A\sin kL + B\cos kL = 0. \tag{56}$$

The boundary condition at the left side of the box yields

$$B = 0. \tag{57}$$

This tells us that the cosine part of the general solution is not allowed because the cosine solution is not zero at the edge of the box and so does not match the wave function outside the box. The exclusion of the cosine part of the solution arises because we chose to locate our box with one side at $x = 0$; if the box is located differently, then both sine and cosine solutions may be allowed. Given that the allowed wave functions must be sine functions, the boundary condition at the right side of the box yields

$$A\sin kL = 0. \tag{58}$$

This equation is satisfied if $A = 0$, but that yields a wave function that is zero everywhere, so it is uninteresting. The more interesting possibility is that

$$\sin kL = 0. \tag{59}$$

This is a transcendental equation that places limitations on the allowed values of the wave vector k. We will find other transcendental equations when we study other potentials. This transcendental equation has solutions when the sinusoid function is zero. Hence the wave vectors that satisfy this equation are

$$kL = n\pi$$
$$k_n = n\frac{\pi}{L}, \qquad n = 1, 2, 3, \dots . \tag{60}$$

Only discrete wave vectors are allowed, so this is termed the **quantization condition**. The index n is the **quantum number**, which we use to label the quantized states and energies. The value $n = 0$ is excluded because that would yield a wave function equal to zero, which is uninteresting. The negative values of n are excluded because they yield the same states as the corresponding positive n values, recalling that an overall phase $\left(-1 = e^{i\pi} \text{ in this case}\right)$ does not change the physical state. Using the definition of the wave vector in Eq. (52), we relate the quantized wave vectors to the quantized energies

$$E_n = \frac{\hbar^2 k_n^2}{2m}. \tag{61}$$

Hence, the wave vector quantization condition in Eq. (60) results directly in the energy quantization for this system:

$$\boxed{E_n = \frac{n^2 \pi^2 \hbar^2}{2mL^2}, \qquad n = 1, 2, 3, ...} \tag{62}$$

These allowed energies scale with the square of the quantum number n and produce the set of energy levels shown in Fig. 10. The ground state is the $n = 1$ level.

The allowed energy eigenstate wave functions are:

$$\varphi_n(x) = A \sin \frac{n\pi x}{L}, \qquad n = 1, 2, 3, ... \tag{63}$$

The constant A was not determined by the boundary conditions. To determine A, we need the third piece of information, which is that the wave function is normalized to unity:

$$1 = \langle E_n | E_n \rangle = \int_{-\infty}^{\infty} \varphi_n^*(x) \varphi_n(x) dx = \int_{-\infty}^{\infty} |\varphi_n(x)|^2 dx. \tag{64}$$

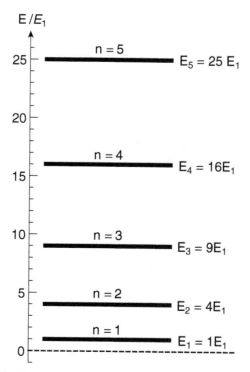

FIGURE 10   Energy spectrum of the infinite square potential energy well.

Substitute the wave function from Eq. (63) and note that the wave function is zero for $x < 0$ and $x < L$ to limit the range of integration, resulting in

$$1 = \int_0^L |A|^2 \sin^2 k_n x \, dx = |A|^2 \frac{L}{2}. \tag{65}$$

We are free to choose the normalization constant to be real and positive, because an overall phase is not measurable. Thus the normalization constant is $A = \sqrt{2/L}$ and the properly normalized energy eigenstates are

$$\boxed{\varphi_n(x) = \sqrt{\frac{2}{L}} \sin \frac{n\pi x}{L}, \qquad n = 1, 2, 3, \dots} \tag{66}$$

The first few allowed energy states are shown in Fig. 11. From these plots, it is now clear why we call $\psi(x)$ the wave function. These energy eigenstates have a "wavy" spatial dependence, much like the modes on a guitar string. For the infinite square well, the waves "fit" into the potential well such that there are an integer number of half wavelengths within the well. If we relate the wave vector k to a wavelength λ through the relation

$$k = \frac{2\pi}{\lambda}, \tag{67}$$

then we can rewrite the quantization condition in terms of the wavelength

$$\begin{aligned} k_n &= n\frac{\pi}{L} \\ \frac{2\pi}{\lambda_n} &= n\frac{\pi}{L} \\ \lambda_n &= \frac{2L}{n} \\ L &= n\frac{\lambda_n}{2}. \end{aligned} \tag{68}$$

In words, the well must contain an integer number of half wavelengths. This is the sense in which the waves must "fit" into the well. This is the same as the classical result for the allowed standing waves on a vibrating string, such as a guitar string. The distinction between the classical wave and the quantum wave is that the classical wave does not have a quantized energy. The energy of a vibrating guitar

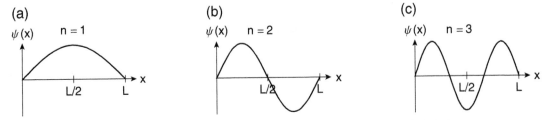

FIGURE 11 Wave functions of the first three energy eigenstates of the infinite square potential energy well.

Quantized Energies: Particle in a Box

string depends on the amplitude of oscillation, not on the wavelength or wave vector, and so it can have any energy value. The amplitude of the quantum wave function is determined by the normalization condition and is independent of the energy for the infinite square well.

The wave properties of this quantum system are a new aspect that is not evident in the classical description of a particle. In classical mechanics, waves and particles are clearly distinct, whereas in quantum mechanics a system exhibits properties that remind us of classical particles but also exhibits properties of classical waves. This is often referred to as **wave-particle duality**.

Example 3 It is useful to put some numbers into these expressions to get a sense of scale. For example, if we confine an electron $(m_e = 511 \text{ keV}/c^2)$ in a box of size 0.2 nm (about the size of an atom), the ground state $(n = 1)$ energy is

$$
\begin{aligned}
E_1 &= \frac{\pi^2 \hbar^2}{2m_e L^2} \\
&= \frac{\pi^2 (6.58 \times 10^{-16} \text{ eV s})^2}{2(0.511 \times 10^6 \text{ eV}/c^2)(0.2 \times 10^{-9} \text{ m})^2} \\
&= 9.4 \text{ eV.}
\end{aligned}
\tag{69}
$$

This is comparable to typical atomic binding energies.

The spectrum of this system will include the transition between the ground state and the first excited state. The first excited state has energy $E_2 = 2^2 E_1 = 4E_1$, so the wavelength of light for this transition is

$$
\begin{aligned}
\lambda_{21} &= \frac{hc}{E_2 - E_1} = \frac{hc}{3E_1} \\
&= \frac{1240 \text{ eV nm}}{3(9.4 \text{ eV})} = 44 \text{ nm.}
\end{aligned}
\tag{70}
$$

Note that λ_{21} is the wavelength of the *photon* emitted or absorbed in the transition, not the wavelength of the bound particle that is associated with the wave vector of the wave function, which is 0.4 nm for the ground state and 0.2 nm for the excited state, in agreement with Eq. (68).

Now that we have found the energy eigenstates, we have what we need to calculate probabilities and expectation values to compare with experiments. The square of the wave function gives us the probability density

$$
\begin{aligned}
\mathcal{P}_n(x) &= |\varphi_n(x)|^2 \\
&= \frac{2}{L} \sin^2 \frac{n\pi x}{L},
\end{aligned}
\tag{71}
$$

which is shown in Fig. 12 for the first three states. Note that the probability density is zero outside the well, so the probability of finding the particle anywhere outside the well is zero, just as in the classical case. However, in the quantum system there are positions within the well where the probability of finding the particle is zero, which does not happen in the classical case. These positions are at the nodes of the wave function and hence are characteristic of the wave nature of the particle.

(a)

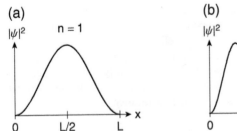

n = 1

(b)

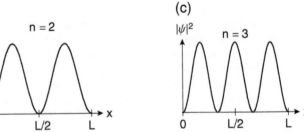

n = 2

(c)

|ψ|²

n = 3

FIGURE 12 Probability densities of the first three energy eigenstates of the infinite square potential energy well.

Example 4 Find the expectation value of the position for a particle in the ground state of an infinite square potential energy well.

The expectation value of position is given by Eq. (41)

$$
\begin{aligned}
\langle \hat{x} \rangle = \langle E_1 | \hat{x} | E_1 \rangle &= \int_{-\infty}^{\infty} \varphi_1^*(x) x \varphi_1(x) dx = \int_{-\infty}^{\infty} x \left| \varphi_1(x) \right|^2 dx \\
&= \frac{2}{L} \int_0^L x \sin^2\left(\frac{\pi x}{L}\right) dx = \frac{2}{L} \left(\frac{L}{\pi}\right)^2 \int_0^\pi y \sin^2(y) dy \\
&= \frac{2}{L} \left(\frac{L}{\pi}\right)^2 \left[\frac{y^2}{4} - \frac{y \sin 2y}{4} - \frac{\cos 2y}{8} \right]_0^\pi \\
&= \frac{2}{L} \left(\frac{L}{\pi}\right)^2 \left[\frac{\pi^2}{4} - \frac{\pi \sin(2\pi)}{4} - \frac{\cos(2\pi)}{8} + \frac{1}{8} \right] \\
&= \frac{2}{L} \left(\frac{L}{\pi}\right)^2 \left[\frac{\pi^2}{4} \right] \\
&= \frac{L}{2}.
\end{aligned}
\tag{72}
$$

This is what we would expect to get given the symmetry of the problem. There is no preference for the left or right side of the well, so the average value of a set of position measurements must be the midpoint of the well. We get the same result for any energy eigenstate of the system.

To summarize, we have solved the problem of a particle bound in an infinitely deep square potential energy well, which means we have found the energy eigenvalues and eigenstates. The well is depicted in Fig. 13(a), the spectrum of allowed energies is depicted in Fig. 13(b), and the wave functions of the energy eigenstates are depicted in Fig. 13(c). It is common practice to unify the three diagrams of Fig. 13 in a single diagram, shown in Fig. 14, that represents the quantum mechanical potential energy well problem and its solution. The well, the energies, and the wave functions are superimposed on each other, such that different aspects of the diagram have different vertical axes. The wave function for each energy eigenstate has its vertical coordinate origin located at the energy of that state.

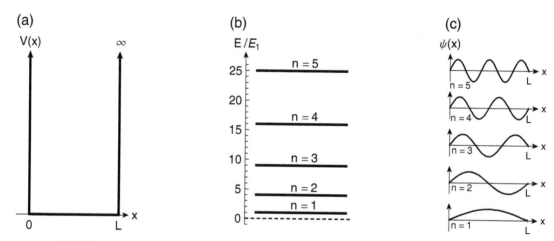

FIGURE 13 (a) Infinite square potential energy well, (b) spectrum of allowed energies, and (c) energy eigenstate wave functions.

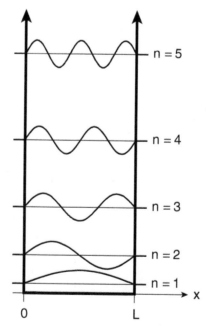

FIGURE 14 Unified schematic diagram of infinite square well problem and solution. Note that two vertical scales are implied. For the potential energy well and the energy spectrum, the vertical scale is energy with the origin at the bottom of the well. For the wave functions, the vertical scale is probability amplitude $(1/\text{length}^{1/2})$ with the $\psi = 0$ origin for each state centered on the energy of that state.

The take home message of this problem is that the imposition of boundary conditions on the wave function limits the possible states that can "fit" into the well and directly leads to the quantization of energy. This is a general result that we will return to time and again as we study other potential well landscapes.

5 ■ FINITE SQUARE WELL

Now let's make the problem a little more realistic by having the potential energy outside the well be finite instead of infinite. We still assume that the well is square, which still results in an infinite force at the walls. However, this new problem illustrates several important features of bound energy states that were not evident in the infinite well. A finite well can be used to model many real systems, such as an electron in a thin semiconductor. In Section 8, we use this model to discuss quantum well semiconductor lasers.

The finite square well potential energy is shown in Fig. 15 and is written as

$$V(x) = \begin{cases} V_0, & x < -a \\ 0, & -a < x < a \\ V_0, & x > a, \end{cases} \tag{73}$$

where we have deliberately chosen a different position origin from the infinite well case in order to give you practice and also for convenience. For now, we look for bound state solutions, that is, for energies below the potential V_0. Energies above V_0 correspond to unbound states.

With this new potential energy function, the energy eigenvalue equation is

$$\left(-\frac{\hbar^2}{2m}\frac{d^2}{dx^2} + 0\right)\varphi_E(x) = E\varphi_E(x), \qquad \textit{inside box}$$

$$\left(-\frac{\hbar^2}{2m}\frac{d^2}{dx^2} + V_0\right)\varphi_E(x) = E\varphi_E(x), \qquad \textit{outside box.} \tag{74}$$

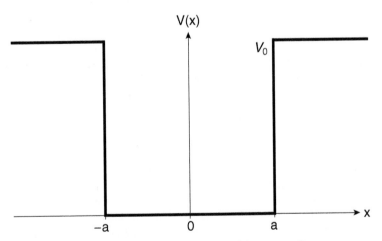

FIGURE 15 Finite square potential energy well.

In the infinite well problem, we found it useful to use the wave vector k

$$k = \sqrt{\frac{2mE}{\hbar^2}}. \tag{75}$$

In this case, it is also useful to define a similar constant outside the well

$$q = \sqrt{\frac{2m}{\hbar^2}(V_0 - E)}. \tag{76}$$

For bound states, $0 < E < V_0$, and therefore both k and q are real. We use these two constants to rewrite the energy eigenvalue equation:

$$\frac{d^2\varphi_E(x)}{dx^2} = -k^2\varphi_E(x), \qquad \textit{inside box}$$

$$\frac{d^2\varphi_E(x)}{dx^2} = q^2\varphi_E(x), \qquad \textit{outside box.} \tag{77}$$

The energy eigenvalue equation inside the box is identical to the one we solved for the infinite well potential. The differential equation outside the box is similar except the constant is positive instead of negative, giving real exponential solutions rather than complex exponentials. Thus the solution outside the box is

$$\varphi_E(x) = Ae^{qx} + Be^{-qx}. \tag{78}$$

This solution in the classically forbidden region is exponentially decaying, or growing, with a decay length, or growth length, of $1/q$.

The energy eigenstate must be constructed by connecting solutions in the three regions shown in Fig. 15 We write the general solution as

$$\varphi_E(x) = \begin{cases} Ae^{qx} + Be^{-qx}, & x < -a \\ C\sin kx + D\cos kx, & -a < x < a \\ Fe^{qx} + Ge^{-qx}, & x > a. \end{cases} \tag{79}$$

As we discussed in the infinite well problem, the solutions in the three regions must satisfy boundary conditions where the regions connect. In constructing the infinite well solutions, we used the condition that the wave function must be continuous across a boundary. We now introduce a second requirement that the slope of the wave function be continuous across a boundary. If the slope were discontinuous, that would imply an infinite kinetic energy. However, this requirement has one exception: it does not apply if the potential is infinite (Problem 24), which is why we did not use it in the infinite well problem. You can see in Fig. 14 that the infinite well solutions have a change in slope at the edges of the box where the potential energy becomes infinite. We now summarize these two boundary conditions:

---

1) $\varphi_E(x)$ is continuous

2) $\dfrac{d\varphi_E(x)}{dx}$ is continuous unless $V = \infty$.

Before we impose the boundary conditions, we make two immediate simplifications to the general solutions in Eq. (79). In the regions outside the well, the wave function must be a decaying exponential because a growing exponential term *all the way out to infinity* would not permit the wave function to be normalized. This normalization condition, which can also be termed a *boundary condition at infinity*, requires that $B = F = 0$ in Eq. (79). The second simplification comes from recognizing that the potential energy is symmetric with respect to the origin $[V(x) = V(-x)]$. This means that the energy eigenstates will either be symmetric or antisymmetric (even or odd). This symmetry is evident in the infinite well solutions shown in Fig. 14. (This can also be discussed in terms of the commutation of the Hamiltonian and the parity operator). We can thus solve for the two sets of solutions independently. If you don't impose this symmetry condition now, it will come out naturally after some algebra on the general solutions anyway (Problem 14). With these two simplifications, the even solutions reduce to

$$\varphi_{even}(x) = \begin{cases} Ae^{qx}, & x < -a \\ D\cos(kx), & -a \leq x \leq a \\ Ae^{-qx}, & x > a. \end{cases} \tag{80}$$

The odd solutions are

$$\varphi_{odd}(x) = \begin{cases} Ae^{qx}, & x < -a \\ C\sin(kx), & -a \leq x \leq a \\ -Ae^{-qx}, & x > a. \end{cases} \tag{81}$$

Let's first do the even solutions. The boundary conditions at the right side of the well $(x = a)$ give

$$\varphi_{even}(a): D\cos(ka) = Ae^{-qa}$$

$$\left. \frac{d\varphi_{even}(x)}{dx} \right|_{x=a} : -kD\sin(ka) = -qAe^{-qa}. \tag{82}$$

The boundary conditions at the left side of the well $(x = -a)$ yield the same equations, which must be true because of the symmetry. The two equations above have three unknowns: the amplitudes A and D and the energy E, which is contained in the parameters k and q. The normalization condition provides the third equation required to solve for all three unknowns. We find the energy condition rather simply by dividing the two equations, which eliminates the amplitudes and yields

$$k\tan(ka) = q. \tag{83}$$

Because both k and q are functions of the energy, this equation gives us a formula to find the allowed energies. It is independent of the constants A and D, which are found by applying the normalization condition and using Eq. (82) again. As usual with these types of problems, the eigenvalue condition is obtained first, and then the eigenfunctions are obtained later. To make the energy dependence explicit, we use Eqs. (75) and (76) to write Eq. (83) as

$$\sqrt{\frac{2m}{\hbar^2}E}\tan\left(\sqrt{\frac{2m}{\hbar^2}E}a\right) = \sqrt{\frac{2m}{\hbar^2}(V_0 - E)}. \tag{84}$$

The next step is to solve this transcendental equation for the energy E.

For the odd solutions, a similar argument leads to the transcendental equation (Problem 15)

$$-k\cot(ka) = q. \tag{85}$$

A graphical solution for the allowed energies using these two transcendental equations is most useful here. There are many ways of doing this. One way involves defining some new dimensionless parameters:

$$z = ka = \sqrt{\frac{2mEa^2}{\hbar^2}}$$

$$z_0 = \sqrt{\frac{2mV_0a^2}{\hbar^2}}$$

$$qa = \sqrt{\frac{2m(V_0 - E)a^2}{\hbar^2}},$$

(86)

where the variable z parameterizes the energy of the state and the constant z_0 characterizes the strength of the potential energy well. These definitions lead to the convenient expressions

$$(ka)^2 + (qa)^2 = z_0^2$$

$$(qa)^2 = z_0^2 - (ka)^2 = z_0^2 - z^2.$$

(87)

This allows us to write the transcendental equations in this form:

$$ka\tan(ka) = qa \quad \rightarrow \quad z\tan(z) = \sqrt{z_0^2 - z^2}$$

$$-ka\cot(ka) = qa \quad \rightarrow \quad -z\cot(z) = \sqrt{z_0^2 - z^2}.$$

(88)

In each of these new transcendental equations, the left side is a modified trig function, while the right side is a circle with radius z_0. These functions are plotted in Fig. 16 as a function of the parameter z. The intersection points of these curves determine the allowed values of z and hence the allowed energies E_n through Eq. (86). Because the constant z_0 is the radius of the circle, there are a limited number of allowed energies, and that number grows as z_0 gets larger. Wells that are deeper and wider have more allowed bound energy states.

That's it for the energies. There is no simple formula—the transcendental equations must be solved graphically or numerically for each different well. For example, the curves in Fig. 16 correspond to a well with $z_0 = 6$, which results in four intersection points and hence four bound states. The intersection points and four allowed energies are

$$z_1 = 1.34 \quad \rightarrow \quad E_1 = 1.81\frac{\hbar^2}{2ma^2}$$

$$z_2 = 2.68 \quad \rightarrow \quad E_2 = 7.18\frac{\hbar^2}{2ma^2}$$

$$z_3 = 3.99 \quad \rightarrow \quad E_3 = 15.89\frac{\hbar^2}{2ma^2}$$

$$z_4 = 5.23 \quad \rightarrow \quad E_4 = 27.31\frac{\hbar^2}{2ma^2}.$$

(89)

The energy eigenstate wave functions are characterized by the allowed values of the parameters k and q from Eq. (86). All that remains to do is normalize the wave function, which is straightforward but tedious (Problem 16). Once again, we use a unified diagram to show the potential energy well, the allowed energies, and the allowed eigenstate wave functions superimposed in Fig. 17. Note that

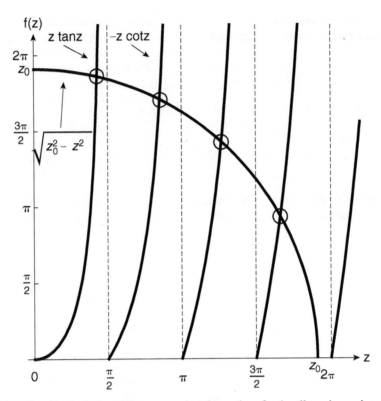

FIGURE 16   Graphical solution of the transcendental equations for the allowed energies of a finite square well $(z_0 = 6)$.

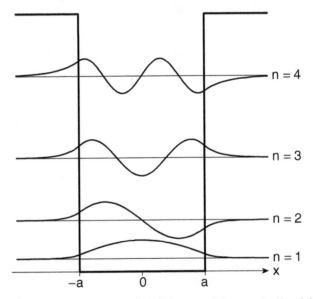

FIGURE 17   Unified schematic diagram of the finite potential energy well and the bound state solutions, showing the well, the allowed energies, and the energy eigenstate wave functions.

the finite well eigenstates share many features with the infinite well states, with one major exception—they extend into the classically forbidden region. Quantum mechanical particles have a finite probability of being found where classical particles may not exist! This is a purely quantum mechanical effect and is commonly referred to as **barrier penetration**. The ability of the particle to penetrate the potential energy barrier leads to the phenomenon of tunneling, an example of which is radioactive decay. We'll say more about these wave functions in a bit, but let's first check that our solution is consistent with the solution we derived earlier for the infinite energy well case.

The limit of an infinitely deep well corresponds to the radius z_0 in Fig. 16 going to infinity, in which case the allowed values of z become the asymptotes of the modified trig functions, shown by the dashed lines in Fig. 16. These limits are the same as for the simple trig functions and yield

$$z_n = n\frac{\pi}{2} \Rightarrow k_n a = n\frac{\pi}{2}$$
$$k_n = \frac{n\pi}{2a}, \tag{90}$$

from which we recover the infinite well energy eigenvalues:

$$E_n = \frac{n^2\pi^2\hbar^2}{2m(2a)^2}. \tag{91}$$

Note that the width of the well is $2a$ here, whereas we called the width L in the infinite well case. The infinite well eigenstate wave functions for this symmetric well position are

$$\varphi_n(x) = \sqrt{\frac{2}{2a}}\cos\frac{n\pi x}{2a}, \qquad n = 1, 3, 5, \ldots$$
$$\varphi_n(x) = \sqrt{\frac{2}{2a}}\sin\frac{n\pi x}{2a}, \qquad n = 2, 4, 6, \ldots . \tag{92}$$

There are two sets of solutions because we chose a different coordinate system to solve the problem. In the limit $z_0 \to \infty$, the decay length q becomes zero and the energy eigenstates are zero outside the well, as expected. The infinite well eigenstates are shown in Fig. 18(a) for this new choice of coordinates. Comparing the wave functions in Fig. 18(a) with those from Fig. 14, though, we see that these are the same eigenstate wave functions that we found before. In Fig. 18(b) we show the finite well states for comparison.

6 ■ COMPARE AND CONTRAST

Now that we have solved two similar problems, the infinite and finite square wells, let's discuss some of the important features of these solutions and see which features are common to both problems and others, and which are distinct.

6.1 ■ Wave Function Curvature

The first common feature is that the wave function is oscillatory ($\sin kx$ or $\cos kx$) inside the well and exponentially decaying (e^{-qx} or e^{qx}) outside the well. This aspect is explained by examining the curvature (i.e., second derivative) of the wave function. To see this, we rewrite the energy eigenvalue equation

$$\frac{d^2\varphi_E(x)}{dx^2} = -\frac{2m}{\hbar^2}[E - V(x)]\varphi_E(x), \tag{93}$$

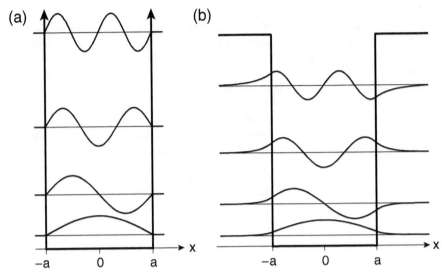

FIGURE 18 (a) Infinite and (b) finite well energy eigenstates.

which then directly relates the wave function curvature to the difference between the energy E and the potential energy $V(x)$. Thus, inside the well, in the classically allowed region, we have $E > V(x)$ and the differential equation admits only sinusoidal solutions characterized by the wave vector k or wavelength $\lambda = 2\pi/k$. Outside the well, in the classically forbidden region, we have $E < V(x)$ and the differential equation admits only real exponential solutions with a decay length of $1/q$, which is zero for the infinite square well. The growing exponential terms in these problems are excluded by the normalization requirement (i.e., the boundary condition at infinity).

These comments can be generalized as shown in Fig. 19. Equation (93) tells us that in a classically allowed region where $E > V$, the curvature has the opposite sign to the wavefunction, and in the classically forbidden region where $E < V$, the curvature has the same sign as the wavefunction. This means that in the classically allowed region the wave function is concave toward the axis, while in the classically forbidden region the wave function is convex toward the axis, as shown in Fig. 19.

We can also make some general observations regarding the length scales of the wave functions. In a general potential well, the wave vector is given by

$$k = \frac{\sqrt{2m(E - V)}}{\hbar}. \tag{94}$$

Hence, the oscillatory part of the wave function (inside the well) has a characteristic wavelength

$$\lambda = \frac{2\pi}{k} = \frac{h}{\sqrt{2m(E - V)}} \propto \frac{1}{\sqrt{T}}. \tag{95}$$

So the larger the energy difference between the eigenvalue and the potential energy (i.e., the larger the kinetic energy), the smaller the wavelength. That relationship is evident in the eigenstates shown in Fig. 18; the higher the energy, the more "wiggly" the wave function. In the forbidden region, the decay constant

$$q = \frac{\sqrt{2m(V - E)}}{\hbar} \tag{96}$$

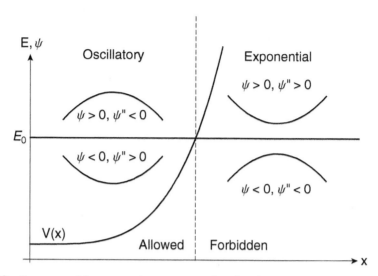

FIGURE 19   Curvature of the energy eigenstate wave functions in the allowed and forbidden regions.

decreases as the energy increases toward V, which means that the decay length becomes larger. Hence, for higher energy states the wave function penetrates further into the classically forbidden region (Problem17). This increasing penetration with increasing energy is evident in the finite well states of Fig. 17.

In comparing the finite and infinite well energies in Fig. 18, we also note that a given finite well energy eigenvalue E_n lies below the corresponding infinite well energy eigenvalue. This is consistent with the longer wavelength of the finite well eigenstate compared to the corresponding infinite well state. For the finite well eigenstate to "fit" in the well, the wavelength can be longer because part of the wave function is outside the well. The increasing penetration of the wave function into the classically forbidden region with increasing energy implies that the difference in energies between the finite and infinite wells is larger for higher energies, as is also evident in Fig. 18 (Problem19).

6.2 ■ Nodes

The ground state has a single antinode in the wave function, with each subsequent higher state acquiring an extra antinode. Thus the nth energy level has n antinodes and $(n-1)$ nodes. This is a general characteristic of the energy eigenstates of any potential energy well. In the infinite well we found an infinite number of states. In the finite well we found a finite number of states, but we looked only for bound states. We will see later that there are an infinite number of unbound states with $E > V_0$, which means that there are an infinite number of total allowed energy states. The infinite number of states is a common feature of potential energy wells. In the finite well, if the well is small enough (small V_0 and/or small a), then there might be only one bound state, but there is always at least one bound state. This is generally true for any well shape. The delta-function potential is an extreme case (Problem 25).

6.3 ■ Barrier Penetration

In the finite potential well, the wave function is nonzero in the classically forbidden region. This implies a finite probability that the quantum mechanical particle can be found where the classical particle cannot. As mentioned above, this penetration of the wave function into the potential energy barrier leads to the phenomenon of tunneling. The wave function plots in Fig. 18 indicate that the barrier penetration is more pronounced for higher energy levels and can become quite large for energies close to the top of the well. This aspect is clear quantitatively if we note that the decay constant q in the forbidden region decreases as the energy increases, which means that the decay length becomes larger, so more of the wave function is outside the well.

6.4 ■ Inversion Symmetry and Parity

In both square well problems, the allowed wave functions are either symmetric (even) or antisymmetric (odd) with respect to the center of the well. In both cases, the potential energy well, and hence the Hamiltonian, is symmetric with respect to the well center. We say that the Hamiltonian is invariant under the **parity** operation $x \rightarrow -x$. Because the Hamiltonian is invariant under the parity operation, it must commute with the parity operator, and hence the energy eigenstates are also eigenstates of the parity operator. The symmetric states satisfy $\varphi_n(x) = +\varphi_n(-x)$, have a parity eigenvalue $+1$, and are called **even parity** states. The antisymmetric states satisfy $\varphi_n(x) = -\varphi_n(-x)$, have a parity eigenvalue -1, and are called **odd parity** states. Identifying the parity of an energy eigenstate is useful because the parity of the state often indicates whether a particular matrix element involving that state is zero or not. For example, the probability of a transition between two energy eigenstates caused by incident laser light is proportional to the matrix element of the electric dipole operator ($-ex$ in one dimension) between the two states:

$$\langle \varphi_m | -ex | \varphi_n \rangle = - \int_{-\infty}^{\infty} \varphi_m(x) ex \, \varphi_m(x) d^3\mathbf{r}. \tag{97}$$

This integral is zero if the integrand has odd parity. The electric dipole operator has odd parity, so the energy eigenstates must have different parity for the transition to be allowed. If the integral is zero, then the transition is a **forbidden transition**. Many of the selection rules that determine which transitions are allowed and which are forbidden come from these types of parity arguments. More complete discussion of electric dipole transitions must wait for a discussion of time-dependent perturbation theory.

6.5 ■ Orthonormality

The energy eigenstates form an orthonormal set, as we have found for other sets of eigenstates, such as spin states. The *normalization* is not an intrinsic property of the solutions but rather something that we impose so that the total probability of finding the particle somewhere is unity. The *orthogonality* is a fundamental trait of eigenstates of Hermitian operators. The orthonormality condition is expressed in Dirac notation as

$$\langle E_n | E_m \rangle = \delta_{nm} \tag{98}$$

and in wave function language as

$$\int_{-\infty}^{\infty} \varphi_n^*(x)\varphi_m(x) dx = \delta_{nm}. \tag{99}$$

This condition is straightforward to show for the infinite well states (Problem 12) but is a little tedious for the finite well states because of the lack of a general expression for the allowed wave vectors.

6.6 ■ Completeness

The energy eigenstates form a complete basis, as we have found for other sets of basis states. Completeness is also a fundamental trait of eigenstates of Hermitian operators. Completeness means that we can use these basis functions to construct all possible solutions to the Schrödinger equation $H|\psi\rangle = i\hbar\, d|\psi\rangle/dt$ for this problem. The wave function of a general superposition state is

$$\psi(x) = \sum_n c_n \varphi_n(x). \tag{100}$$

Note that the energy eigenvalue equation $H\varphi_n(x) = E_n\varphi_n(x)$ is satisfied by each particular energy eigenstate in turn but is not satisfied by general superposition states. For the infinite well, Eq. (100) is exact, while for the finite well we must also include unbound energy states above the well in the sum over basis states. Obviously, for a well that is so small that there is only one bound state, we would expect to need more states to form a complete basis. The completeness relation is also called the closure relation and, as we saw in the spins problem, is expressed as a sum of all the projection operators

$$\sum_n |E_n\rangle\langle E_n| = \mathbf{1}, \tag{101}$$

where the right-hand side is understood to be the identity operator

7 ■ SUPERPOSITION STATES AND TIME DEPENDENCE

Solving for the energy eigenvalues and eigenstates is an important aspect of any problem, but it is not the only goal. As physicists, our aim is to predict the future of a physical system. In quantum mechanics, we do this through the Schrödinger equation

$$H|\psi\rangle = i\hbar\frac{d}{dt}|\psi\rangle \tag{102}$$

that governs the time evolution of any quantum system. Though different systems clearly have different Hamiltonians, we need not solve the Schrödinger equation for the time evolution separately for each system. For a time-independent Hamiltonian, we find the most general time-dependent solution to the Schrödinger equation is

$$|\psi(t)\rangle = \sum_n c_n e^{-iE_n t/\hbar}|E_n\rangle. \tag{103}$$

That is, the energy eigenstates form the preferred basis in which to expand a general quantum state vector, with the time evolution determined by phase factors dependent on the energy of each component state. In a general superposition, each energy eigenstate acquires a different phase. **It is critical to remember that one must use the energy basis in order to use this simple recipe for time evolution. This is why we spend much of our time finding energy eigenstates.**

To use Eq. (103) we need to know the expansion coefficients c_n for the particular state in question. The quantum state at time $t = 0$ is

$$|\psi(0)\rangle = \sum_n c_n|E_n\rangle, \tag{104}$$

so the expansion coefficients c_n are determined by the initial state of the system. The coefficients c_n are the probability amplitudes for the state $|\psi(0)\rangle$ to be in the energy eigenstates $|E_n\rangle$

$$c_n = \langle E_n|\psi(0)\rangle. \tag{105}$$

To show this again, we perform a manipulation with the closure relation in Eq. (101). The identity operator does not change the state vector, so we act on the state vector to obtain

$$
\begin{aligned}
|\psi(0)\rangle &= \mathbf{1}|\psi(0)\rangle \\
&= \left\{ \sum_n |E_n\rangle\langle E_n| \right\} |\psi(0)\rangle \\
&= \sum_n |E_n\rangle\langle E_n|\psi(0)\rangle \\
&= \sum_n \langle E_n|\psi(0)\rangle \, |E_n\rangle
\end{aligned}
\tag{106}
$$

and hence identify the coefficients c_n as given in Eq. (105).

Of course, once we know the probability amplitudes, we can calculate the probabilities for measuring the system to have one of the energy eigenvalues:

$$\mathcal{P}_{E_n} = |\langle E_n|\psi(0)\rangle|^2 = |c_n|^2. \tag{107}$$

The probabilities of energy measurements are time independent, but let's do it again here, using the time-dependent state vector in Eq. (103)

$$
\begin{aligned}
\mathcal{P}_{E_n} &= |\langle E_n|\psi(t)\rangle|^2 \\
&= \left| \langle E_n| \sum_m c_m |E_m\rangle e^{-iE_m t/\hbar} \right|^2 = \left| \sum_m c_m \langle E_n|E_m\rangle e^{-iE_m t/\hbar} \right|^2 \\
&= \left| \sum_m c_m \delta_{mn} e^{-iE_m t/\hbar} \right|^2 = \left| c_n e^{-iE_n t/\hbar} \right|^2 \\
&= |c_n|^2.
\end{aligned}
\tag{108}
$$

The Kronecker delta from the energy eigenstate orthonormality condition collapses the sum to a single term. Time independence of the energy probabilities implies that the expectation value of the energy is also time independent:

$$\langle H \rangle = \sum_n \mathcal{P}_{E_n} E_n = \sum_n |c_n|^2 E_n. \tag{109}$$

Quantized Energies: Particle in a Box

We can also show this by explicit calculation with the time-dependent states:

$$
\begin{aligned}
\langle H \rangle &= \langle \psi(t)|H|\psi(t) \rangle \\
&= \sum_m c_m^* \langle E_m| e^{iE_m t/\hbar} H \sum_n c_n |E_n\rangle e^{-iE_n t/\hbar} \\
&= \sum_{m,n} c_m^* c_n e^{iE_m t/\hbar} e^{-iE_n t/\hbar} \langle E_m|H|E_n \rangle \\
&= \sum_{m,n} c_m^* c_n e^{i(E_m - E_n)t/\hbar} E_n \langle E_m|E_n \rangle \\
&= \sum_{m,n} c_m^* c_n e^{i(E_m - E_n)t/\hbar} E_n \delta_{mn} \\
&= \sum_n c_n^* c_n E_n \\
&= \sum_n |c_n|^2 E_n.
\end{aligned}
\tag{110}
$$

Note that we had no need to use wave function notation in these calculations. Wave function calculations of Eqs. (108) and (110) would require spatial integrals that would also yield the Kronecker delta from the energy eigenstate orthonormality condition that collapses the sums. The results would clearly be the same, so the message is: if you can avoid integrals by using Dirac notation instead of wave function notation, do so.

We need to use wave function language to answer questions about the spatial distribution of the particle, so let's use the rules we developed in Section 3 to translate the Dirac notation equations to wave function notation. The time evolution of the state vector [Eq. (103)], in wave function language, is

$$
\psi(x,t) = \sum_n c_n \varphi_n(x) e^{-iE_n t/\hbar}.
\tag{111}
$$

To find the expansion coefficients c_n (i.e., the probability amplitudes), we translate Eq. (105) to wave function language:

$$
c_n = \int_{-\infty}^{\infty} \varphi_n^*(x) \psi(x,0) dx.
\tag{112}
$$

So, given the initial wave function of the system $\psi(x,0)$, the expansion coefficients are overlap integrals between each energy eigenstate and the initial wave function. These overlap integrals are analogous to the integrals used to find Fourier expansion coefficients. Let's briefly illustrate the Fourier approach for calculating the coefficients c_n. Set the time equal to zero in Eq. (111) to find the initial wave function superposition:

$$
\psi(x,0) = \sum_n c_n \varphi_n(x).
\tag{113}
$$

Quantized Energies: Particle in a Box

Project both sides of Eq. (113) onto the energy eigenstates by multiplying each side by $\varphi_m^*(x)$ and integrating over all space:

$$
\begin{aligned}
\int_{-\infty}^{\infty} \varphi_m^*(x)\psi(x,0)dx &= \int_{-\infty}^{\infty} \varphi_m^*(x)\sum_n c_n\varphi_n(x)dx \\
&= \sum_n c_n \int_{-\infty}^{\infty} \varphi_m^*(x)\varphi_n(x)dx \\
&= \sum_n c_n\delta_{nm} \\
&= c_m,
\end{aligned}
\tag{114}
$$

yielding

$$
c_m = \int_{-\infty}^{\infty} \varphi_m^*(x)\psi(x,0)dx
\tag{115}
$$

as we expected from Eq. (112). Once we have the wave function expansion coefficients in the energy basis, we can predict the future time evolution of the system. Then we can calculate any physical quantities we need to, such as probabilities and expectation values.

Example 4   Consider a particle in an infinite square well with the initial wave function

$$
\psi(x,0) = A\left[\left(\frac{x}{L}\right)^3 - \frac{11}{7}\left(\frac{x}{L}\right)^2 + \frac{4}{7}\left(\frac{x}{L}\right)\right]
\tag{116}
$$

in the interval $0 < x < L$ and zero elsewhere, as shown in Fig. 20. Find (i) the wave function at a later time, (ii) the probabilities of energy measurements, and (iii) the expectation value of the energy.
   (i)   First we must normalize the state to find the constant A:

$$
\begin{aligned}
\langle\psi|\psi\rangle = 1 &= \int_0^L |\psi(x,0)|^2 dx \\
&= |A|^2 \int_0^L \left[\left(\frac{x}{L}\right)^3 - \frac{11}{7}\left(\frac{x}{L}\right)^2 + \frac{4}{7}\left(\frac{x}{L}\right)\right]^2 dx = |A|^2\frac{L}{735}.
\end{aligned}
\tag{117}
$$

We choose the constant to be real and positive and the normalized wave function is

$$
\psi(x,0) = \sqrt{\frac{735}{L}}\left[\left(\frac{x}{L}\right)^3 - \frac{11}{7}\left(\frac{x}{L}\right)^2 + \frac{4}{7}\left(\frac{x}{L}\right)\right].
\tag{118}
$$

Now perform the overlap integral to find the expansion coefficients:

$$
\begin{aligned}
c_n = \langle E_n|\psi\rangle &= \int_{-\infty}^{\infty} \varphi_n^*(x)\psi(x,0)dx \\
&= \int_0^L \sqrt{\frac{2}{L}}\sin\left(\frac{n\pi x}{L}\right)\sqrt{\frac{735}{L}}\left[\left(\frac{x}{L}\right)^3 - \frac{11}{7}\left(\frac{x}{L}\right)^2 + \frac{4}{7}\left(\frac{x}{L}\right)\right]dx.
\end{aligned}
\tag{119}
$$

Do the integral

$$c_n = \frac{7\sqrt{30}}{L} \left\{ \left[3L \frac{(n\pi x/L)^2 - 2}{(n\pi)^4} \sin\left(\frac{n\pi x}{L}\right) - L \frac{(n\pi x/L)^3 - 6(n\pi x/L)}{(n\pi)^4} \cos\left(\frac{n\pi x}{L}\right) \right]_0^L \right.$$
$$- \frac{11}{7} \left[2L \frac{(n\pi x/L)}{(n\pi)^3} \sin\left(\frac{n\pi x}{L}\right) - L \frac{(n\pi x/L)^2 - 2}{(n\pi)^3} \cos\left(\frac{n\pi x}{L}\right) \right]_0^L \tag{120}$$
$$\left. + \frac{4}{7} \left[L \frac{1}{(n\pi)^2} \sin\left(\frac{n\pi x}{L}\right) - L \frac{(n\pi x/L)}{(n\pi)^2} \cos\left(\frac{n\pi x}{L}\right) \right]_0^L \right\}.$$

Evaluate the limits and simplify:

$$c_n = \frac{\left[22 + 20(-1)^n \right]\sqrt{30}}{(n\pi)^3}$$

$$= \begin{cases} \dfrac{2\sqrt{30}}{(n\pi)^3}, & \text{if } n \text{ is odd} \\[2ex] \dfrac{42\sqrt{30}}{(n\pi)^3}, & \text{if } n \text{ is even}. \end{cases} \tag{121}$$

The first few coefficients are

$$\begin{aligned} c_1 &= 0.3533 \\ c_2 &= 0.9274 \\ c_3 &= 0.0131 \\ c_4 &= 0.1159, \end{aligned} \tag{122}$$

so the state is composed mostly of the first excited state, which is evident from the shape of the wave function in Fig. 20.

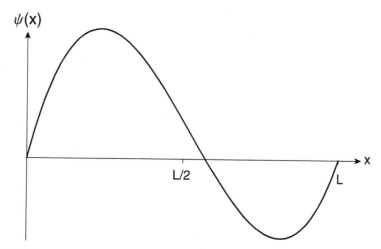

FIGURE 20 An initial state wave function [Eq. (116)] in the infinite square well.

The wave function at later times is the superposition with each energy state evolved at its prescribed frequency

$$
\psi(x,t) = \sum_{n=1}^{\infty} c_n \varphi_n(x) e^{-iE_n t} = \sum_{n=1}^{\infty} c_n \sqrt{\frac{2}{L}} \sin\frac{n\pi x}{L} e^{-in^2\pi^2\hbar t/2mL^2}
$$

$$
= \sqrt{\frac{60}{L}} \sum_{n=1}^{\infty} \frac{\left[22 + 20(-1)^n\right]}{(n\pi)^3} \sin\frac{n\pi x}{L} e^{-in^2\pi^2\hbar t/2mL^2}.
$$

(123)

(ii) The probabilities of measuring the energy eigenvalues are the squares of the expansion coefficients:

$$
\mathcal{P}_{E_n} = \left|\langle E_n | \psi(t) \rangle\right|^2 = |c_n|^2
$$

$$
= \frac{30}{(n\pi)^6}\left[22 + 20(-1)^n\right]^2
$$

$$
= \frac{120}{(n\pi)^6}\left[221 + 220(-1)^n\right].
$$

(124)

The energy probabilities are shown in the histogram in Fig. 21, reflecting the predominance of the second state.

(iii) The expectation value of the energy is

$$
\langle H \rangle = \sum_n \mathcal{P}_{E_n} E_n = \sum_n |c_n|^2 E_n
$$

$$
= \sum_{n=1}^{\infty} \frac{120}{(n\pi)^6}\left(221 + 220(-1)^n\right)\left(\frac{n^2\pi^2\hbar^2}{2mL^2}\right)
$$

$$
= \sum_{n=1,3,5\ldots}^{\infty} \frac{120}{(n\pi)^6}\left(\frac{n^2\pi^2\hbar^2}{2mL^2}\right) + \sum_{n=2,4,6\ldots}^{\infty} \frac{120(441)}{(n\pi)^6}\left(\frac{n^2\pi^2\hbar^2}{2mL^2}\right)
$$

$$
= \frac{60\hbar^2}{\pi^4 mL^2}\left[\sum_{n=1,3,5\ldots}^{\infty} \frac{1}{n^4} + 441 \sum_{n=2,4,6\ldots}^{\infty} \frac{1}{n^4}\right]
$$

$$
= \frac{60\hbar^2}{\pi^4 mL^2}\left[\frac{\pi^4}{96} + 441\frac{\pi^4}{1440}\right]
$$

$$
= 19\frac{\hbar^2}{mL^2} = \frac{38}{\pi^2}E_1 \cong 3.85E_1,
$$

(125)

which is slightly smaller than the energy ($E_2 = 4E_1$) of the first excited state, as expected from the histogram in Fig. 21.

Quantized Energies: Particle in a Box

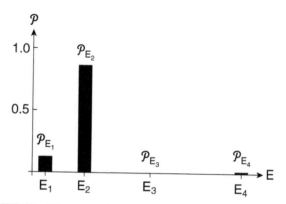

FIGURE 21 Histogram of the probabilities of energy measurements.

Notice that the energy expectation value, such as we calculated in Eq. (125), is time independent regardless of whether the system is in an energy eigenstate or a general superposition of energy eigenstates. On the other hand, the expectation values of position or momentum are time independent when the system is in an energy eigenstate, but they are time dependent for a general superposition state. Let's demonstrate this in the infinite square well where the time dependence of a general state is

$$\psi(x,t) = \sum_n c_n \sqrt{\frac{2}{L}} \sin\frac{n\pi x}{L} e^{-in^2\pi^2\hbar t/2mL^2}. \tag{126}$$

Consider a simple superposition of two states in an infinite well. If the initial state is

$$|\psi(0)\rangle = \tfrac{1}{\sqrt{2}}|E_1\rangle + \tfrac{1}{\sqrt{2}}|E_2\rangle, \tag{127}$$

then the time-evolved state is

$$|\psi(t)\rangle = \tfrac{1}{\sqrt{2}}|E_1\rangle e^{-iE_1 t/\hbar} + \tfrac{1}{\sqrt{2}}|E_2\rangle e^{-iE_2 t/\hbar}. \tag{128}$$

The wave function representation is

$$\begin{aligned}
\psi(x,t) &= \tfrac{1}{\sqrt{2}}\varphi_1(x)e^{-iE_1 t/\hbar} + \tfrac{1}{\sqrt{2}}\varphi_2(x)e^{-iE_2 t/\hbar} \\
&= \sqrt{\frac{1}{L}}\left[\sin\frac{\pi x}{L}e^{-iE_1 t/\hbar} + \sin\frac{2\pi x}{L}e^{-iE_2 t/\hbar}\right].
\end{aligned} \tag{129}$$

Now find the expectation value of the position:

$$\begin{aligned}
\langle x\rangle &= \langle\psi(t)|x|\psi(t)\rangle \\
&= \left\{\tfrac{1}{\sqrt{2}}\langle E_1|e^{iE_1 t/\hbar} + \tfrac{1}{\sqrt{2}}\langle E_2|e^{iE_2 t/\hbar}\right\} x \left\{\tfrac{1}{\sqrt{2}}|E_1\rangle e^{-iE_1 t/\hbar} + \tfrac{1}{\sqrt{2}}|E_2\rangle e^{-iE_2 t/\hbar}\right\} \\
&= \tfrac{1}{2}\left[\langle E_1|x|E_1\rangle + \langle E_2|x|E_2\rangle + \langle E_1|x|E_2\rangle e^{i(E_1-E_2)t/\hbar} + \langle E_2|x|E_1\rangle e^{-i(E_1-E_2)t/\hbar}\right].
\end{aligned} \tag{130}$$

Again notice that we are using Dirac notation to simplify the calculation. However, at this point we need to use integrals to calculate the matrix elements. Let's define them in general:

$$\langle x \rangle_n = \langle E_n | x | E_n \rangle = \int_0^L \varphi_n^*(x)\, x\, \varphi_n(x)\, dx = \int_0^L x |\varphi_n(x)|^2\, dx \tag{131}$$

$$\langle x \rangle_{nk} = \langle E_n | x | E_k \rangle = \int_0^L \varphi_n^*(x)\, x\, \varphi_k(x)\, dx.$$

We calculated the first matrix element, which is the expectation value of position in an energy eigenstate, in Example 3. We saw that the answer is the midpoint of the well $L/2$. The second integral comes from the cross term in the superposition:

$$\begin{aligned}
\langle x \rangle_{nk} &= \int_0^L \varphi_n^*(x)\, x\, \varphi_k(x)\, dx \\
&= \frac{2}{L} \int_0^L \sin\left(\frac{n\pi x}{L}\right) x \sin\left(\frac{k\pi x}{L}\right) dx \\
&= \frac{2}{L}\left(\frac{L}{\pi}\right)^2 \int_0^\pi y \sin(ny)\sin(ky)\, dy.
\end{aligned} \tag{132}$$

Simplify with a trig identity and integrate

$$\begin{aligned}
\langle x \rangle_{nk} &= \frac{2}{L}\left(\frac{L}{\pi}\right)^2 \int_0^\pi y\tfrac{1}{2}\big[\cos(n-k)y - \cos(n+k)y\big] dy \\
&= \frac{1}{L}\left(\frac{L}{\pi}\right)^2 \left[\frac{\cos(n-k)y}{(n-k)^2} + \frac{y\sin(n-k)y}{(n-k)} - \frac{\cos(n+k)y}{(n+k)^2} - \frac{y\sin(n+k)y}{(n+k)}\right]_0^\pi \\
&= \frac{1}{L}\left(\frac{L}{\pi}\right)^2 \left[\frac{\cos(n-k)\pi}{(n-k)^2} - \frac{\cos(n+k)\pi}{(n+k)^2} - \frac{1}{(n-k)^2} + \frac{1}{(n+k)^2}\right],
\end{aligned} \tag{133}$$

yielding

$$\langle x \rangle_{nk} = \frac{-4Lnk}{\pi^2(n^2 - k^2)^2}\big[1 - (-1)^{n+k}\big]. \tag{134}$$

This result is zero for states where $n + k$ is even (i.e., if the states have the same parity). The results for the two-state example are

$$\langle x \rangle_1 = \langle x \rangle_2 = \frac{L}{2} \tag{135}$$

$$\langle x \rangle_{12} = \langle x \rangle_{21} = -\frac{16L}{9\pi^2},$$

Quantized Energies: Particle in a Box

giving the final result

$$
\begin{aligned}
\langle x \rangle &= \langle \psi(t)|x|\psi(t) \rangle \\
&= \frac{1}{2}\left[\frac{L}{2} + \frac{L}{2} - \frac{16L}{9\pi^2}e^{i(E_1-E_2)t/\hbar} - \frac{16L}{9\pi^2}e^{-i(E_1-E_2)t/\hbar} \right] \\
&= \frac{L}{2}\left[1 - \frac{32}{9\pi^2}\cos\left(\frac{3\pi^2\hbar}{2mL^2}t \right) \right].
\end{aligned}
\tag{136}
$$

The position of this two-state superposition oscillates at the Bohr frequency $(E_2 - E_1)/\hbar$.
The time-dependent position is also evident in the spatial probability density:

$$
\begin{aligned}
\mathcal{P}(x,t) &= |\langle x|\psi(t)\rangle|^2 = |\psi(x,t)|^2 \\
&= \left| \sqrt{\frac{1}{L}}\left[\sin\frac{\pi x}{L}e^{-iE_1t/\hbar} + \sin\frac{2\pi x}{L}e^{-iE_2t/\hbar} \right] \right|^2 \\
&= \frac{1}{L}\left[\sin^2\frac{\pi x}{L} + \sin^2\frac{2\pi x}{L} + 2\sin\frac{\pi x}{L}\sin\frac{2\pi x}{L}\cos\frac{(E_2-E_1)t}{\hbar} \right].
\end{aligned}
\tag{137}
$$

The oscillation of the probability density is depicted in the animation frames shown in Fig. 22, where the constant τ is the oscillation period $\tau = 2\pi/\omega_{Bohr}$ (see activity on time evolution of infinite well solutions). The superposition probability distribution "sloshes back and forth" in the well at the Bohr frequency. This motion of the superposition state provides a model for how atoms and other bound systems radiate light. An electron undergoing this oscillatory motion accelerates and hence radiates electromagnetic energy. So far, our model does not account for the energy loss from this radiation,

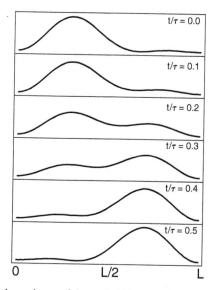

FIGURE 22   Time dependence of the probability distribution of a superposition state.

141

A calculation of the momentum expectation value (Problem 27) also yields a time-dependent result:

$$\langle p \rangle = \langle \psi(t)|p|\psi(t)\rangle$$

$$= \int_0^L \psi^*(x,t)\left(\frac{\hbar}{i}\frac{d}{dx}\right)\psi(x,t)dx \tag{138}$$

$$= \frac{8}{3}\frac{\hbar}{L}\sin\left(\frac{3\pi^2\hbar}{2mL^2}t\right).$$

If we compare Eqs. (136) and (138), we notice that the quantum mechanical position and momentum obey the classical relation $p = mv$, provided we restrict the relation to expectation values:

$$\langle p(t) \rangle = m\frac{d\langle x(t)\rangle}{dt}. \tag{139}$$

This is another example of Ehrenfest's theorem, which says that quantum mechanical expectation values obey classical laws.

8 ■ MODERN APPLICATION: QUANTUM WELLS AND DOTS

The square well potential problem has been a staple of quantum mechanics textbooks since the early days. However, for many years it was only a textbook problem because no systems in nature could be modeled accurately as a square well. The progress of semiconductor fabrication technology has changed that, as we are now able to make artificial systems of square potential energy wells. **Semiconductor quantum wells** are now routinely used to fabricate diode lasers and other semiconductor devices.

The key advance that allowed fabrication of quantum well devices was the ability to grow pure crystals of semiconductors using techniques such as molecular beam epitaxy (MBE) and metal-organic chemical vapor deposition (MOCVD). With these techniques, layers of semiconductors can be grown with atomic scale precision, yielding structures with layers thin enough (several nm or less) for quantum effects to be important.

A typical quantum well structure is shown in Fig. 23(a). Alternate layers of GaAs and AlGaAs are grown epitaxially on a GaAs substrate. GaAs and AlGaAs have similar crystal unit cell sizes that permit dislocation-free crystals to be grown. This **lattice-matched** growth is crucial to obtaining reli-

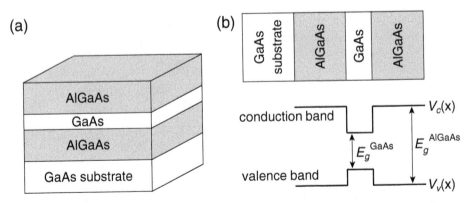

FIGURE 23 (a) Structure and (b) potential energy diagram of a GaAs quantum well.

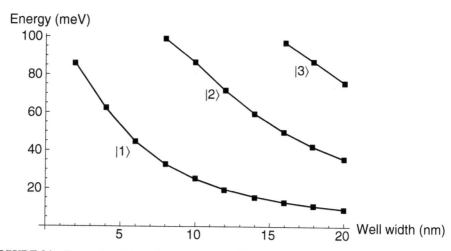

FIGURE 24 Energy levels in a GaAs quantum well as the thickness of the GaAs layer is changed.

able devices. The band gap of GaAs (1.42 eV) is smaller than the band gap of AlGaAs (2.67 eV), so the electrons in the conduction band and the holes in the valence band experience the different potentials shown in Fig. 23(b). Because the layers change on the atomic scale, this is as close to a square well as nature allows.

We can calculate the energy levels in the well using the same analysis we used for the finite square well. Figure 24 shows the energy levels and how they vary with changes in the GaAs layer thickness. Note that there are only two or three bound states in the well for the range of thickness shown.

For making practical devices with quantum wells, there are two important features. First, the energy levels can be adjusted, or "tuned," by changing the thickness of the quantum well layer, as shown in Fig. 24, or by changing the stoichiometry of the surrounding $Al_xGa_{1-x}As$ layers to adjust the band gap and hence the potential energy depth of the well. Second, the quantization of the electron energy in the confined well increases the number of electrons with specific energies (compared to the continuum of energies of unconfined electrons), which in turn increases the probability of creating photons with the corresponding wavelengths. Hence, a semiconductor diode laser made with quantum wells is more efficient than one made with bulk material, so quantum well diode lasers are now the most common type of diode lasers in use.

The quantum well structure shown in Fig. 23 confines the electron in one dimension, but the electrons are not confined in the plane of the thin well. Further confinement leads to **quantum wires** (2D confinement) and **quantum dots** (3D confinement). Quantum dots are semiconductor nanocrystals with a typical size range of 2–20 nm. The size of the dot determines the confinement size and hence the wavelength of light emitted by the dot. A simple Web search reveals beautiful pictures of quantum dots glowing in a rainbow of colors.

9 ■ ASYMMETRIC SQUARE WELL: SNEAK PEEK AT PERTURBATIONS

While the square potential wells we have studied in this chapter illustrate many of the ideas of bound state wave functions, there is one important aspect that we have not encountered. All the square well solutions have a constant wave vector and a constant wave function amplitude throughout the well, because the potential is constant throughout the well. To see how the wave vector and amplitude of

Quantized Energies: Particle in a Box

an eigenstate can vary within the well, let's make a slight modification to the infinite square well. Consider the well shown in Fig. 25, which is commonly referred to as the **asymmetric square well**. By adding a "shelf" within the well, we now have two regions of constant but different potential energy.

The potential energy for this asymmetric square well is

$$V(x) = \begin{cases} \infty, & x < 0 \\ 0, & 0 < x < L/2 \\ V_0, & L/2 < x < L \\ \infty, & x > L. \end{cases} \tag{140}$$

We know that the infinite potential outside the well demands that the energy eigenstates are zero outside the well. Inside the well, we now have different energy eigenvalue equations in the left and right halves:

$$\left(-\frac{\hbar^2}{2m}\frac{d^2}{dx^2} + 0\right)\varphi_E(x) = E\varphi_E(x), \qquad \textit{left half}$$

$$\left(-\frac{\hbar^2}{2m}\frac{d^2}{dx^2} + V_0\right)\varphi_E(x) = E\varphi_E(x), \qquad \textit{right half.} \tag{141}$$

For this discussion, let's assume that the energy E is greater than the potential V_0 so that the solutions in each half of the well are sinusoidal. We then have different wave vectors in each half, defined by

$$k_1 = \sqrt{\frac{2mE}{\hbar^2}}, \qquad \textit{left half}$$

$$k_2 = \sqrt{\frac{2m(E - V_0)}{\hbar^2}}, \qquad \textit{right half,} \tag{142}$$

which yields a smaller wave vector $(k_2 < k_1)$ and hence larger wavelength of the wave in the right half. We know that the left-half solution must be a sine function in order to match the zero wave function outside the well, so the general solution is

$$\varphi_E(x) = \begin{cases} A\sin k_1 x, & 0 < x < L/2 \\ B\sin k_2 x + C\cos k_2 x, & L/2 < x < L. \end{cases} \tag{143}$$

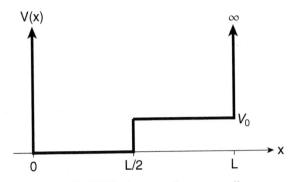

FIGURE 25   Asymmetric square well.

144

Now we apply the boundary condition on the wave function continuity at the middle and right side of the well and the boundary condition on the continuity of the first derivative of the wave function at the middle of the well (recall that the infinite potential on the right means that the derivative condition is not applicable). The three boundary conditions are

$$\varphi_E(L/2): A\sin(k_1 L/2) = B\sin(k_2 L/2) + C\cos(k_2 L/2)$$

$$\left.\frac{d\varphi_E(x)}{dx}\right|_{x=L/2}: k_1 A\cos(k_1 L/2) = k_2 B\cos(k_2 L/2) - k_2 C\sin(k_2 L/2) \tag{144}$$

$$\varphi_E(L): B\sin k_2 L + C\cos k_2 L = 0.$$

These three equations contain four unknowns: the amplitudes A, B, and C, and the energy E through the wave vectors k_1 and k_2. The normalization condition supplies the fourth equation required to solve for all unknowns. By eliminating the amplitude coefficients from the three boundary condition equations, we arrive at a transcendental equation for the energy eigenvalues (Problem 28):

$$k_1 \cos(k_1 L/2)\sin(k_2 L/2) + k_2 \cos(k_2 L/2)\sin(k_1 L/2) = 0. \tag{145}$$

This looks a bit intimidating, so how do we know it's correct? Well, we know what the solutions are for the infinite (symmetric) square well, which is the case where $V_0 = 0$; so we can check to see if our solution agrees with the infinite square well solutions. This won't tell us whether our solution is correct, but we can at least make sure that it is not obviously wrong. If $V_0 = 0$, then the two wave vectors are equal and the transcendental equation becomes:

$$k_1 \cos(k_1 L/2)\sin(k_1 L/2) + k_1 \cos(k_1 L/2)\sin(k_1 L/2) = 0$$

$$k_1 \sin\left[(k_1 L/2) + (k_1 L/2)\right] = 0 \tag{146}$$

$$k_1 \sin k_1 L = 0.$$

If we divide this result by k_1, then we have the same equation $\sin k_1 L = 0$ that we had for the infinite square well. So our intimidating result may well be correct.

In order to compare the asymmetric square well with the infinite square well, it is useful to divide each transcendental equation by the factor k_1 and plot the energy eigenvalue equations for the asymmetric square well

$$\cos(k_1 L/2)\sin(k_2 L/2) + \frac{k_2}{k_1}\cos(k_2 L/2)\sin(k_1 L/2) = 0 \tag{147}$$

and for the infinite square well:

$$\sin(k_1 L) = 0. \tag{148}$$

A plot of the two equations as a function of $k_1 L$ is shown in Fig. 26 for the case where the potential step height is 0.75 times the energy of the ground state in the infinite well case. The infinite square well eigenstates occur at the values $k_1 L = n\pi$ marked on the axis. The eigenstates for the asymmetric well are each slightly larger, with the difference decreasing as the energy increases. This is a sneak preview of perturbation theory.

Let's now use these solutions to draw the energy eigenstates. A plot of a typical energy eigenstate is shown in Fig. 27. The wavelength and the amplitude of the wave in the right half are larger, meaning that the probability to find the particle in the right half is larger than in the left half. This is consistent with our classical expectation, because a classical particle moves more slowly in the right half where its kinetic energy is lower, and so it spends more time in the right half with an increased probability to find it there.

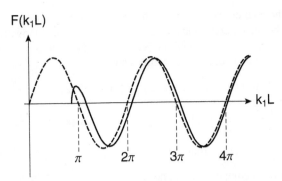

FIGURE 26 Transcendental equations for the energy eigenvalues of the asymmetric square well (solid) and the infinite square well (dashed).

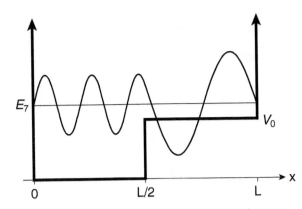

FIGURE 27 An energy eigenstate of the asymmetric square well.

10 ■ FITTING ENERGY EIGENSTATES BY EYE OR BY COMPUTER

10.1 ■ Qualitative (Eyeball) Solutions

The problems we have solved in this chapter illustrate most of the important features of bound states in potential wells. Using these common traits allows us to make qualititative estimates of energy eigenstate solutions to other potential well problems. The important features are

1(a). Oscillatory wave solution inside well

1(b). Wavelength proportional to $1/\sqrt{E - V(x)}$

2(a). Exponentially decaying solution outside well

2(b). Decay length proportional to $1/\sqrt{V(x) - E}$

3. Amplitude inside well related to wavelength

4. Match $\varphi_E(x)$ and $d\varphi_E(x)/dx$ at boundaries.

Using these rules of thumb, we can get a very good idea of the wave function before we tackle the differential equation that gives us the exact solution.

Consider the potential shown in Fig. 28. It has an infinite wall, a flat potential region, a sloped potential region, and a finite wall. Given our rules, we draw the approximate wave function. From left

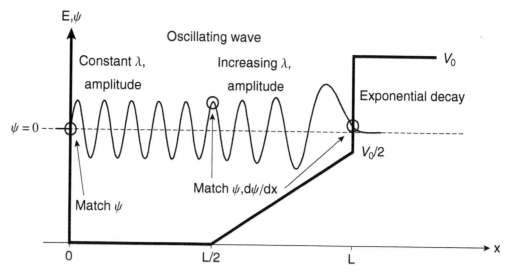

FIGURE 28 Drawing approximate energy eigenstate solutions.

to right, starting at zero at the infinite wall, the wave function oscillates with a constant wavelength and has a constant amplitude over the flat potential region; it oscillates with an increasing wavelength and has an increasing amplitude over the sloped potential region; and then it exponentially decays in the classically forbidden region. The wave function is drawn qualitatively and the main features are indicated. This wave function represents the 17th energy state because there are 17 antinodes in the wave function. Remember that the wave function oscillates about the value zero in the well and decays to zero outside the well. The figure shows the wave function $\psi(x)$ drawn superimposed on the potential well, so you have to imagine a "ψ axis" with its zero as indicated by the dashed line.

10.2 ■ Numerical Solutions

We can be more quantitative by using a computer to help us "draw" the wave functions. Rather than follow the rules listed above, we directly solve the energy eigenvalue equation by numerical integration, which is a common technique for solving differential equations and is easily accomplished in common mathematical packages like Matlab, Mathematica, and Maple, and even in a spreadsheet. The energy eigenvalue equation is

$$\frac{d^2\varphi_E(x)}{dx^2} = -\frac{2m}{\hbar^2}[E - V(x)]\varphi_E(x). \tag{149}$$

You may not yet know how to solve such a differential equation, but you do know how to solve a very similar one—Newton's second law, $F = ma$, which yields the differential equation

$$\frac{d^2x}{dt^2} = \frac{F}{m}. \tag{150}$$

In the case where the acceleration $a = F/m$ is constant, one integral of Eq. (150) gives

$$v = \frac{dx}{dt} = v_0 + at, \tag{151}$$

and a second integration gives

$$x = x_0 + v_0 t + \tfrac{1}{2} a t^2, \tag{152}$$

which are the equations of motion you learned in introductory physics. With these equations, one can predict the future if one knows the initial position x_0, the initial velocity v_0, and the acceleration a.

In the Newtonian case, the motion function $x(t)$ is determined by its curvature d^2x/dt^2, which is the acceleration a. In the quantum case, the wave function is determined by its curvature $d^2\psi/dx^2$, which depends on the energy, the potential, and the wave function itself. The potential and the wave function both depend on position, so the wave function curvature is *not* constant and the simple integrations in Eqs. (151) and (152) cannot be used. However, if the acceleration in the Newtonian example is not constant, then we can modify Eqs. (151) and (152) for use on a computer by using them to predict motion only in the very near future, say from t to $t + \Delta t$:

$$x(t + \Delta t) = x(t) + v(t)\Delta t + \tfrac{1}{2} a(t)(\Delta t)^2$$
$$v(t + \Delta t) = v(t) + a(t)\Delta t. \tag{153}$$

As long as we choose the time steps Δt small enough that the acceleration does not vary appreciably from one time step to the next, then these equations can be used to reliably update the position and velocity at each time step. These **update equations** produce estimates of the full motion by iterating from step to step.

This method works well but suffers from one failing: the update equations use "old" information about the velocity and the acceleration. We can improve this slightly by using the new acceleration in the velocity update equation:

$$x(t + \Delta t) = x(t) + v(t)\Delta t + \tfrac{1}{2} a(t)(\Delta t)^2$$
$$v(t + \Delta t) = v(t) + \tfrac{1}{2}[a(t) + a(t + \Delta t)]\Delta t. \tag{154}$$

We can't use the new acceleration in the position update equation because the acceleration typically depends on position (through the potential), so we do the position update first and then the modified velocity update. This method is known as the **velocity Verlet algorithm** and yields more reliable results than Eq. (153).

To solve the energy eigenvalue equation, we use the wave function and its spatial derivatives rather than the position and its time derivatives used in the Newtonian case. Thus, we generalize the position and velocity update equations (154) to

$$\varphi_E(x + \Delta x) = \varphi_E(x) + \left(\frac{d\varphi_E}{dx}\right)_x \Delta x + \frac{1}{2}\left(\frac{d^2\varphi_E}{dx^2}\right)_x (\Delta x)^2$$
$$\left(\frac{d\varphi_E}{dx}\right)_{x+\Delta x} = \left(\frac{d\varphi_E}{dx}\right)_x + \frac{1}{2}\left[\left(\frac{d^2\varphi_E}{dx^2}\right)_x + \left(\frac{d^2\varphi_E}{dx^2}\right)_{x+\Delta x}\right]\Delta x. \tag{155}$$

So, given the wave function (analogous to "position"), the slope of the wave function ("velocity"), and the curvature of the wave function ("acceleration") at any position x ("time"), we can predict the wave function and its slope at the next position $x + \Delta x$. At each step we calculate the wave function curvature using the energy eigenvalue equation

$$\frac{d^2\varphi_E(x)}{dx^2} = -\frac{2m}{\hbar^2}[E - V(x)]\varphi_E(x). \tag{156}$$

Quantized Energies: Particle in a Box

We don't have to impose the continuity conditions on $\varphi_E(x)$ and $d\varphi_E(x)/dx$ at boundaries; the update equations guarantee that they are met. What we do need are initial values of the wave function and the first derivative to get the update equations started. In principle, we should start at $x = -\infty$ and integrate (i.e., update) all the way to $x = +\infty$. In practice, it suffices to start a reasonable way into the left-hand forbidden region, integrate into and through the potential well, and then integrate a reasonable way into the right-hand forbidden region. The wave function in the forbidden region should be decaying toward zero as it approaches $x = \pm\infty$, which indicates how we should choose the initial values of the wave function and the first derivative. Recall, however, that the energy eigenvalue equation is linear in the wave function $\varphi_E(x)$, so we can scale the wave function by any factor and it will still solve the differential equation. This means that we can choose the initial wave function arbitrarily, but the resultant wave function will not be normalized. In principle, the initial wave function slope should be chosen to have the appropriate decay length. In practice, the method is insensitive to this choice.

Notice that the calculation of the wave function curvature from the energy eigenvalue equation (156) requires us to know the energy. But we don't know the energy—we are trying to find it! So we guess a value of the energy and then we solve for the resultant wave function and see if it "fits" into the potential well. From the problems above we have plenty of practice recognizing wave functions that fit, so it should be clear. And it is, as you will see.

As an example of how this numerical technique works, let's try it out on the finite square well and compare to the results in Eq. (89). We choose an energy and start integrating with Eq. (155). This is well suited to a spreadsheet, and the results shown in Fig. 29 are from an Excel worksheet. The trademark results of this technique are illustrated in Fig. 29(a). If the chosen energy does not match an energy eigenstate solution, then as we integrate toward $x = +\infty$ the wave function solution that should decay starts to grow exponentially, because as the integration crossed the boundary into the classically forbidden region (at $x = a$) there was a small component of the growing exponential solution contained in the numerical wave function. Only by choosing the energy exactly equal to one of the allowed energies can this "bad" component be eliminated from the integration. Because of the severity of exponential growth, combined with the discreteness of computer calculations, it is impossible to find the energy solution exactly. However, as Fig. 29 illustrates, you can find nearby energies that cause the wave function to grow either negatively [Fig. 29(a)] or positively [Fig. 29(c)]. These solutions then bracket the approximate solution [Fig. 29(b)]. The finite square well used for the calculation in Fig. 29 is the same as the well used for Fig. 16, and the resultant energy eigenvalue of this fourth energy level matches well with the result in Eq. (89). To obtain a more accurate value, one has to be more careful about the initial conditions.

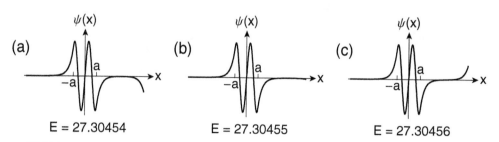

FIGURE 29 Numerical integration for solution of the finite square well eigenvalue equation.

10.3 ■ General Potential Wells

Given our approximate and numerical techniques, we can solve for the bound states in any potential well, in principle. A typical bound state solution is shown in Fig. 30. It exhibits the key features that we have mentioned above for bound state solutions:

- Oscillatory in allowed region
- Exponential decay in forbidden region
- Oscillatory wave becomes less wiggly near classical turning point as kinetic energy decreases
- Amplitude becomes larger near classical turning points

Thus, though potential energy wells may appear quite different at first glance, they all can be called "particle-in-a-box" systems, albeit with differently shaped boxes. Some common boxes are shown in Fig. 31: (a) infinite square well, (b) finite square well, (c) harmonic oscillator (mass on a spring), and (d) linear potential (bouncing ball potential).

SUMMARY

In this chapter we learned the language of the wave function, which is the representation of the quantum state vector in position space. We express this as

$$|\psi\rangle \doteq \psi(x)$$
$$\psi(x) = \langle x|\psi\rangle. \tag{157}$$

The complex square of the wave function yields the spatial probability density

$$\mathcal{P}(x) = |\psi(x)|^2. \tag{158}$$

The normalization condition is

$$1 = \langle\psi|\psi\rangle = \int_{-\infty}^{\infty} |\psi(x)|^2 \, dx = 1. \tag{159}$$

The rules for translating bra-ket formulae to wave function formulae are:

1) Replace ket with wave function $|\psi\rangle \rightarrow \psi(x)$
2) Replace bra with wave function conjugate $\langle\psi| \rightarrow \psi^*(x)$

3) Replace bracket with integral over all space $\langle\,|\,\rangle \rightarrow \int_{-\infty}^{\infty} dx$

4) Replace operator with position representation $\hat{A} \rightarrow A(x).$

The probability of measuring the position of a particle to be in a finite spatial region is

$$\mathcal{P}_{a<x<b} = \int_{a}^{b} |\psi(x)|^2 \, dx. \tag{160}$$

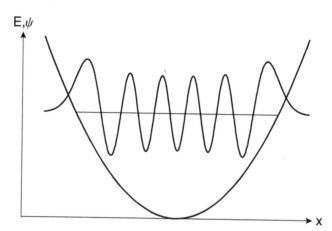

FIGURE 30 Bound state in a generic potential energy well.

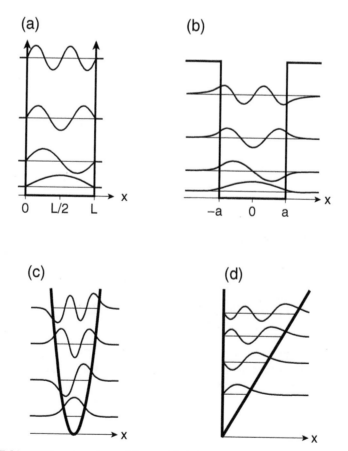

FIGURE 31 Different versions of the particle-in-a-box: (a) infinite square well, (b) finite square well, (c) harmonic oscillator (quadratic potential), and (d) linear potential.

Quantized Energies: Particle in a Box

The probability of measuring the energy to be E_n is

$$\mathcal{P}_{E_n} = \left| \langle E_n | \psi \rangle \right|^2 = \left| \int_{-\infty}^{\infty} \varphi_n^*(x) \psi(x) dx \right|^2, \tag{161}$$

where $\varphi_n(x) = \langle x | E_n \rangle$ is the wave function representation of the energy eigenstate. Position and momentum operators in the position representation are

$$\begin{aligned} \hat{x} &\doteq x \\ \hat{p} &\doteq -i\hbar \frac{d}{dx} \end{aligned} \tag{162}$$

and lead to the energy eigenvalue equation becoming a differential equation:

$$\left(-\frac{\hbar^2}{2m} \frac{d^2}{dx^2} + V(x) \right) \varphi_E(x) = E \varphi_E(x). \tag{163}$$

In solving the energy eigenvalue equation, two boundary conditions are imposed upon the wave function:

1) $\varphi_E(x)$ is continuous

2) $\dfrac{d\varphi_E(x)}{dx}$ is continuous unless $V = \infty$.

In an infinite square potential energy well, the allowed energies are

$$E_n = \frac{n^2 \pi^2 \hbar^2}{2mL^2}, \qquad n = 1, 2, 3, ..., \tag{164}$$

and the allowed energy eigenstates are

$$\varphi_n(x) = \sqrt{\frac{2}{L}} \sin \frac{n\pi x}{L}, \qquad n = 1, 2, 3, ... \tag{165}$$

The energy eigenstates obey the following properties:

Property	Dirac notation	Wave function notation
Normalization	$\langle E_n | E_n \rangle = 1$	$\int_{-\infty}^{\infty} |\varphi_n(x)|^2 dx = 1$
Orthogonality	$\langle E_n | E_m \rangle = \delta_{nm}$	$\int_{-\infty}^{\infty} \varphi_n^*(x) \varphi_m(x) dx = \delta_{nm}$
Completeness	$|\psi\rangle = \sum_n c_n |E_n\rangle$	$\psi(x) = \sum_n c_n \varphi_n(x)$

RESOURCES

Activities

The bulleted activities are available at

www.physics.oregonstate.edu/qmactivities

- **Operators and Functions:** Students investigate the differential forms of quantum mechanical operators and identify eigenfunctions and eigenvalues of quantum mechanical operators.

- **Solving the Energy Eigenvalue Equation for the Finite Well:** Students solve the energy eigenvalue equation for different regions of the finite well and make their solutions match at the boundaries.

- **Time Evolution of Infinite Well Solutions:** Students animate wave functions consisting of linear combinations of eigenstates.

Quantum Bound States: This simulation experiment from the PHET group at the University of Colorado animates wave function superpositions in bound states:

http://phet.colorado.edu/en/simulation/bound-states

Shooting Method Model: This program from the Open Source Physics group implements the shooting method to numerically solve the energy eigenvalue equation:

http://www.compadre.org/osp/items/detail.cfm?ID=6987

Further Reading

Quantum wells are discussed in these *Physics Today* articles:
  D. Chemla, "Quantum wells for photonics," *Phys. Today* **38**(5), 57–64 (1985):
  http://dx.doi.org/10.1063/1.880974
  D. Gammon, D. Steel, "Optical studies of single quantum dots," *Phys. Today* **55**(10), 36–41 (2002):
  http://dx.doi.org/10.1063/1.1522165

Further details on numerical solutions of the energy eigenvalue equation are available in these references:
  R. H. Landau, M. J. Páez and C. C. Bordeianu, *A Survey of Computational Physics: Introductory Computational Science,* Princeton, NJ: Princeton University Press, 2008.
  H. Gould, J. Tobochnik, and W. Christian, *An Introduction to Computer Simulation Methods: Applications to Physical Systems* (3rd edition), San Francisco, CA: Addison-Wesley, 2007.

Quantized Energies: Particle in a Box: Problem Set

1 Show that the operators $\hat{x}$ and $\hat{p}$ do not commute.

2 A particle in an infinite square well potential has an initial state vector
$|\psi(t=0)\rangle = A(|\varphi_1\rangle - |\varphi_2\rangle + i|\varphi_3\rangle)$ where $|\varphi_n\rangle$ are the energy eigenstates.

   a) Normalize the state vector.

   b) What are the possible outcomes of a measurement of the energy, and with what probabilities would they occur?

   c) What is the average value of the energy?

   d) Find the state vector at some later time, t.

   e) At time $t = \hbar/E_1$, what are the possible outcomes of a measurement of the energy, and with what probabilities would they occur?

3 Solve the infinite square well problem using the complex exponential form of the general solution in Eq. (53)

$$\varphi_E(x) = A'e^{ikx} + B'e^{-ikx} \tag{53}$$

as the assumed form of the wave function inside the well. Assume that the potential well boundaries are at $x = 0$ and $x = L$.

4 Solve the infinite square well problem with the well boundaries at $x = \pm a$. Comment on the differences and similarities with the solution in the text.

5 Calculate the expectation values and the uncertainties of position and momentum for the infinite square well energy eigenstates.

6 For a particle in an infinite square well, calculate the probability of finding the particle in the range $3L/4 < x < L$ for each of the first three energy eigenstates.

7 A particle in an infinite square well potential has an initial state vector
$|\psi(t=0)\rangle = (|\varphi_1\rangle - 2i|\varphi_2\rangle)/\sqrt{5}$ where the $|\varphi_n\rangle$ are the eigenfunctions of the Hamiltonian operator. Find the time evolution of the state vector.

8 A particle in an infinite square well potential has an initial wave function
$\psi(x, t=0) = Ax(L-x)$. Find the time evolution of the state vector. Find the expectation value of the position as a function of time.

9 A particle in an infinite square well has the initial wave function

$$\psi(x,0) = A\left[\left(\frac{x}{L}\right)^3 - \frac{3}{2}\left(\frac{x}{L}\right)^2 + \frac{1}{2}\left(\frac{x}{L}\right)\right]$$

in the interval $0 < x < L$ and zero elsewhere. Find (a) the wave function at a later time, (b) the probabilities of energy measurements, and (c) the expectation value of the energy.

From Chapter 5 of *Quantum Mechanics: A Paradigms Approach*, First Edition. David H. McIntyre. Copyright © 2012 by Pearson Education, Inc. Published by Pearson Addison-Wesley. All rights reserved.

The companion websites for this text are http://physics.oregonstate.edu/portfolioswiki and http://physics.oregonstate.edu/qmactivities.

10 A particle at $t = 0$ is known to be in the right half of an infinite square well with a probability density that is uniform in the right half of the well. What is the initial wave function of the particle? Calculate the expectation value of the energy. Find the probabilities that the particle is measured to have energy E_1, E_2, or E_3.

11 A particle is in the ground state of an infinite square well. The potential wall at $x = L$ suddenly moves to $x = 3L$ such that the well is now three times its original size. Find the probabilities that the particle is measured to have the ground state energy or the first excited state energy of the new well.

12 Show that the energy eigenstates of the infinite square well are orthogonal.

13 Use the closure relation in Eq. (101)

$$\sum_n |E_n\rangle\langle E_n| = 1,\qquad(101)$$

to show that the normalization condition is

$$1 = \langle\psi|\psi\rangle = \sum_n |\langle E_n|\psi\rangle|^2.$$

14 Solve the energy eigenvalue problem for the finite square well without using the symmetry assumption and show that the energy eigenstates must be either even or odd.

15 Derive the transcendental equation (85)

$$-k\cot(ka) = q.\qquad(85)$$

for the energy eigenvalues of the odd states in the finite square well.

16 Normalize the energy eigenstates of the finite square well.

17 Find the probability that a particle in the ground state of a finite square well is measured to have a position outside of the well. Derive a general relation involving only the parameters z and z_0 defined in Eqs. (86).

$$z = ka = \sqrt{\frac{2mEa^2}{\hbar^2}}$$

$$z_0 = \sqrt{\frac{2mV_0a^2}{\hbar^2}}\qquad(86)$$

$$qa = \sqrt{\frac{2m(V_0 - E)a^2}{\hbar^2}},$$

Show that the probability increases as the energy increases.

18 An electron is bound in a finite square well of depth $V_0 = 5$ eV and width $2a = 1.5$ nm. Find the allowed energies of the bound states in the well using the transcendental equations (88).

$$ka\tan(ka) = qa \quad\rightarrow\quad z\tan(z) = \sqrt{z_0^2 - z^2}$$
$$-ka\cot(ka) = qa \quad\rightarrow\quad -z\cot(z) = \sqrt{z_0^2 - z^2}.\qquad(88)$$

19 Give a qualitative, graphical argument that the difference in energy eigenvalues between the finite and infinite square wells is larger for higher energy states.

20 Find the bound energy eigenstates and eigenvalues of a "half-infinite" square well (i.e., a square well with infinite potential for $x < 0$ and finite potential with value V_0 for $x > L$).

21 Consider a quantum system with a set of energy eigenstates $|E_i\rangle$. The system is in the state

$$|\psi\rangle = \tfrac{1}{\sqrt{30}}|E_1\rangle + \tfrac{2}{\sqrt{30}}|E_2\rangle + \tfrac{3}{\sqrt{30}}|E_3\rangle + \tfrac{4}{\sqrt{30}}|E_4\rangle,$$

where the energies are given by $E_n = nE_1$. Find the probabilities for measuring the energy eigenvalues and make a histogram similar to Fig. 2(b). Find the expectation value of the energy. Find the uncertainty of the energy.

22 Consider a quantum system with a set of energy eigenstates $|E_n\rangle$ where the energies are given by $E_n = \left(n + \tfrac{1}{2}\right)\hbar\omega$ for $n = 0, 1, 2, \dots$. The system is in the state

$$|\alpha\rangle = \sum_{n=0}^{\infty} \frac{\alpha^n e^{-\alpha^2/2}}{\sqrt{n!}}|E_n\rangle,$$

where α is a positive real number. Find the probabilities for measuring the energy eigenvalues and make a histogram similar to Fig. 2(b). Find the expectation value of the energy. Find the uncertainty of the energy.

23 Consider the following wave functions

$$\psi(x) = Ae^{-x^2/3}$$

$$\psi(x) = B\frac{1}{x^2 + 2}$$

$$\psi(x) = C\,\text{sech}\left(\frac{x}{5}\right).$$

In each case, normalize the wave function, plot the wave function, and find the probability that the particle is measured to be in the range $0 < x < 1$.

24 Demonstrate the requirement that the first derivative of the wave function be continuous, unless the potential is infinite. To do this, integrate the energy eigenvalue equation from $-\varepsilon$ to $+\varepsilon$ and take the limit as $\varepsilon \to 0$ to derive a condition on the difference of the wave function derivatives between two adjacent points.

25 Find the energy eigenstates and eigenvalues of a particle confined to a delta function potential $V(x) = -\beta\delta(x)$, where β is a positive real constant. Note that you will need to follow the approach in the previous problem to properly address how the infinite potential at the origin affects the wave function derivative. How many bound energy states exist in this potential energy well?

26 Find the energy eigenstates and eigenvalues of a particle confined to a double delta function potential $V(x) = -\beta(\delta(x - a) + \delta(x + a))$, where β is a positive real constant. How many bound energy states exist in this potential energy well?

27 Calculate the expectation value of the momentum for the two-state superposition in Eq. (128)

$$|\psi(t)\rangle = \tfrac{1}{\sqrt{2}}|E_1\rangle e^{-iE_1 t/\hbar} + \tfrac{1}{\sqrt{2}}|E_2\rangle e^{-iE_2 t/\hbar}. \tag{128}$$

and verify Eq. (138).

$$\langle p \rangle = \langle \psi(t) | p | \psi(t) \rangle$$

$$= \int_0^L \psi^*(x,t) \left(\frac{\hbar}{i} \frac{d}{dx} \right) \psi(x,t) dx \tag{138}$$

$$= \frac{8}{3} \frac{\hbar}{L} \sin \left(\frac{3\pi^2 \hbar}{2mL^2} t \right).$$

28 Solve the boundary condition equations (144)

$$\varphi_E(L/2): A\sin(k_1 L/2) = B\sin(k_2 L/2) + C\cos(k_2 L/2)$$

$$\left. \frac{d\varphi_E(x)}{dx} \right|_{x=L/2} : k_1 A\cos(k_1 L/2) = k_2 B\cos(k_2 L/2) - k_2 C\sin(k_2 L/2) \tag{144}$$

$$\varphi_E(L): B\sin k_2 L + C\cos k_2 L = 0.$$

for the asymmetric square well and verify Eq. (145).

$$k_1 \cos(k_1 L/2)\sin(k_2 L/2) + k_2 \cos(k_2 L/2)\sin(k_1 L/2) = 0. \tag{145}$$

29 Find the transcendental equation that determines the energy eigenvalues in an asymmetric square well for the case $E < V_0$. Compare with Eq. (145) for the $E > V_0$ case and comment.

30 Implement the update equations (155)

$$\varphi_E(x + \Delta x) = \varphi_E(x) + \left(\frac{d\varphi_E}{dx} \right)_x \Delta x + \frac{1}{2} \left(\frac{d^2\varphi_E}{dx^2} \right)_x (\Delta x)^2$$

$$\left(\frac{d\varphi_E}{dx} \right)_{x+\Delta x} = \left(\frac{d\varphi_E}{dx} \right)_x + \frac{1}{2} \left[\left(\frac{d^2\varphi_E}{dx^2} \right)_x + \left(\frac{d^2\varphi_E}{dx^2} \right)_{x+\Delta x} \right] \Delta x. \tag{155}$$

using a spreadsheet or other computer program and find the numerical solutions for the energy eigenvalues of a finite square well with a well parameter $z_0 = 6$. Compare your results with Eq. (89).

$$z_1 = 1.34 \quad \rightarrow \quad E_1 = 1.81 \frac{\hbar^2}{2ma^2}$$

$$z_2 = 2.68 \quad \rightarrow \quad E_2 = 7.18 \frac{\hbar^2}{2ma^2} \tag{89}$$

$$z_3 = 3.99 \quad \rightarrow \quad E_3 = 15.89 \frac{\hbar^2}{2ma^2}$$

$$z_4 = 5.23 \quad \rightarrow \quad E_4 = 27.31 \frac{\hbar^2}{2ma^2}.$$

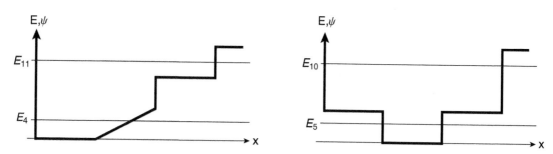

FIGURE 32   Potential wells for Problem 33.

31 Use a spreadsheet or other computer program to find the numerical solution of the ground state and first excited state energy eigenvalues and wave functions for a finite square well with parameters $V_0 = 5$ eV, $2a = 1.5$ nm, and $m = m_e$. Compare your results with the transcendental equations (88).

32 Reproduce the results for the GaAs quantum well states shown in Fig. 24 using the transcendental equations (88). The relevant GaAs parameters are $V_0 = 0.1$ eV and $m = 0.067\ m_e$.

33 For each of the potential wells shown in Fig. 32, make a qualitative sketch of the two energy eigenstate wave functions whose energies are indicated. For each energy state, identify the classically allowed and forbidden regions. Discuss the important qualitative features of each state.

34 Sketch a copy of Fig. 30 and identify the classically allowed and forbidden regions. Which energy eigenstate is drawn in Fig. 30? Make a similar plot for the next lower energy eigenstate.

Quantum Spookiness

Many aspects of quantum mechanics run counter to our physical intuition, which is formed from our experience living in the classical world. The probabilistic nature of quantum mechanics does not agree with the certainty of the classical world—we have no doubt that the sun will rise tomorrow. Moreover, the disturbance of a quantum mechanical system through the action of measurement makes us part of the system, rather than an independent observer. These issues and others make us wonder *what is really going on* in the quantum world. As quantum mechanics was being developed in the early twentieth century, many of the world's greatest physicists debated the "true meaning" of quantum mechanics. They often developed **gedanken experiments** or thought experiments to illustrate their ideas. Some of these *gedanken* experiments have now actually been performed and some are still being pursued.

In this chapter, we present a few of the *gedanken* and real experiments that demonstrate the *spookiness* of quantum mechanics. We present enough details to give a flavor of the *spookiness* and provide references for further readings on these topics at the end of the chapter.

1 ■ EINSTEIN-PODOLSKY-ROSEN PARADOX

Albert Einstein was never comfortable with quantum mechanics. He is famously quoted as saying "Gott würfelt nicht" or "God does not play dice," to express his displeasure with the probabilistic nature of quantum mechanics. But his opposition to quantum mechanics ran deeper than that. He felt that properties of physical objects have an objective reality independent of their measurement, much as Erwin felt that his socks were black or white, or long or short, independent of his pulling them out of the drawer. In quantum mechanics, we cannot say that a particle whose spin is measured to be up had that property before the measurement. It may well have been in a superposition state. Moreover, we can only know one spin component of a particle, because measurement of one component disturbs our knowledge of the other components. Because of these apparent deficiencies, Einstein believed that quantum mechanics was an *incomplete description of reality*.

In 1935, Einstein, Boris Podolsky, and Nathan Rosen published a paper presenting a *gedanken* experiment designed to expose the shortcomings of quantum mechanics. The **EPR Paradox** (Einstein-Podolsky-Rosen) tries to paint quantum mechanics into a corner and expose the "absurd" behavior of the theory. The essence of the argument is that if you believe that measurements on two widely separated particles cannot influence each other, then the quantum mechanics of an ingeniously prepared two-particle system leads you to conclude that the physical properties of each particle are really there—they are **elements of reality** in the authors' words.

Quantum Spookiness

The experimental situation is depicted in Fig. 1 (this version of the EPR experiment is due to David Bohm and has been updated by N. David Mermin). An unstable particle with spin 0 decays into two spin-1/2 particles, which by conservation of angular momentum must have opposite spin components and by conservation of linear momentum must travel in opposite directions. For example, a neutral pi meson decays into an electron and a positron: $\pi^0 \rightarrow e^- + e^+$. Observers A and B are on opposite sides of the decaying particle and each has a Stern-Gerlach apparatus to measure the spin component of the particle headed in its direction. Whenever one observer measures spin up along a given direction, then the other observer measures spin down along that same direction. The quantum state of this two-particle system is

$$|\psi\rangle = \tfrac{1}{\sqrt{2}}(|+\rangle_1 |-\rangle_2 - |-\rangle_1 |+\rangle_2), \tag{1}$$

where the subscripts label the particles and the relative minus sign ensures that this is a spin-0 state. The use of a product of kets $\left(\text{e.g., } |+\rangle_1 |-\rangle_2\right)$ is required here to describe the two-particle system (Problem 1). The kets and operators for the two particles are independent, so, for example, operators act only on their own kets

$$S_{1z}|+\rangle_1 |-\rangle_2 = (S_{1z}|+\rangle_1)|-\rangle_2 = +\frac{\hbar}{2}|+\rangle_1 |-\rangle_2, \tag{2}$$

and inner products behave as

$$(_1\langle+|_2\langle-|)(|+\rangle_1|-\rangle_2) = (_1\langle+|+\rangle_1)(_2\langle-|-\rangle_2) = 1. \tag{3}$$

As shown in Fig. 1, observer A measures the spin component of particle 1 and observer B measures the spin component of particle 2. The probability that observer A measures particle 1 to be spin up is 50% and the probability for spin down is 50%. The 50-50 split is the same for observer B. For a large ensemble of decays, each observer records a random sequence of spin up and spin down results, with a 50/50 ratio. But, because of the correlation between the spin components of the two particles, if observer A measures spin up (i.e., $S_{1z} = +\hbar/2$), then we can predict with 100% certainty that the result of observer B's measurement will be spin down ($S_{2z} = -\hbar/2$). The result is that even though each observer records a random sequence of ups and downs, the two sets of results are perfectly anticorrelated. The state $|\psi\rangle$ in Eq. (1) that produces this strange mixture of random and correlated measurement results is known as an **entangled state**. The spins of the two particles are entangled with each other and produce this perfect correlation between the measurements of observer A and observer B.

Imagine that the two observers are separated by a large distance, with observer B slightly farther from the decay source than observer A. Once observer A has made the measurement $S_{1z} = +\hbar/2$, we know that the measurement by observer B in the next instant will be spin down ($S_{2z} = -\hbar/2$). We conclude that the state $|\psi\rangle$ in Eq. (1) instantaneously collapses onto the state $|+\rangle_1 |-\rangle_2$, and the measurement by observer A has somehow determined the measurement result of observer B. Einstein referred to this as "spooky action at a distance" (*spukhafte Fernwirkungen*). The result that observer B records is still random, it is just that its randomness is perfectly anticorrelated with observer A's random result.

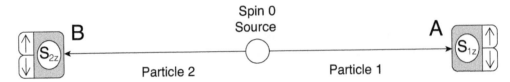

FIGURE 1   Einstein-Podolsky-Rosen *gedanken* experiment.

Hence, there is no problem with faster-than-light communication here because there is no information transmitted between the two observers.

The EPR argument contends that because we can predict a measurement result with 100% certainty (e.g., $S_{2z} = -\hbar/2$), then that result must be a "real" property of the particle—it must be an element of reality. Because the particles are widely separated, this element of reality must be independent of what observer A does, and hence, must have existed all along. The independence of the elements of reality of the two particles is called **Einstein's locality principle**, and is a fundamental assumption of the EPR argument.

The correlation of spin measurements of the two observers is independent of the choice of measurement direction, assuming the same direction for both observers. That is, if observer A measures the x-component of spin and records $S_{1x} = +\hbar/2$, then we know with 100% certainty that observer B will measure $S_{2x} = -\hbar/2$. Observer A is free to choose to measure S_{1x}, S_{1y}, or S_{1z}, so EPR argue that S_{2x}, S_{2y}, and S_{2z} must all be elements of reality for particle 2. However, quantum mechanics maintains that we can know only one spin component at a time for a single particle. EPR conclude that quantum mechanics is an incomplete description of physical reality because it does not describe all the elements of reality of the particle.

If the EPR argument is correct, then the elements of reality, which are also called **hidden variables** or **instruction sets**, are really there, but for some reason we cannot know all of them at once. Thus, one can imagine constructing a **local hidden variable theory** wherein there are different types of particles with different instruction sets that determine the results of measurements. The theory is local because the instruction sets are local to each particle so that measurements by the two observers are independent. The populations or probabilities of the different instruction sets can be properly adjusted in a local hidden variable theory to produce results consistent with quantum mechanics. Because quantum mechanics and a local hidden variable theory cannot be distinguished by experiment, the question of which is correct is then left to the realm of metaphysics. For many years, this was what many physicists believed. After all, it doesn't seem unreasonable to believe that there are things we cannot know!

However, in 1964, John Bell showed that the hidden variables that we cannot know *cannot even be there*! Bell showed that there are specific measurements that can be made to distinguish between a local hidden variable theory and quantum mechanics. The results of these quantum mechanics experiments are not compatible with any local hidden variable theory. Bell derived a very general relation, but we present a specific one here for simplicity.

Bell's argument relies on observers A and B making measurements along a set of different directions. Consider three directions $\hat{\mathbf{a}}$, $\hat{\mathbf{b}}$, $\hat{\mathbf{c}}$ in a plane as shown in Fig. 2, each 120° from any of the other two. Each observer makes measurements of the spin projection along one of these three directions, chosen randomly. Any single observer's result can be only spin up or spin down along that direction, but we record the results independent of the direction of the Stern-Gerlach analyzers, so we denote one observer's result simply as $+$ or $-$, without noting the axis of measurement. The results of the pair

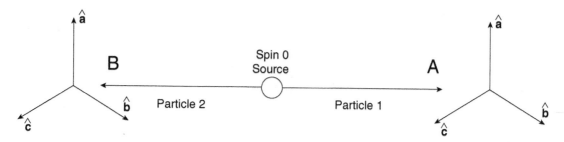

FIGURE 2 Measurement of spin components along three directions as proposed by Bell.

of measurements from one correlated pair of particles (i.e., one decay from the source) are denoted $+\,-$, for example, which means observer A recorded a $+$ and observer B recorded a $-$. There are only four possible system results: $+\,+$, $+\,-$, $-\,+$, or $-\,-$. Even more simply, we classify the results as either the *same*, $+\,+$ or $-\,-$, or *opposite*, $+\,-$ or $-\,+$.

A local hidden variable theory needs a set of instructions for each particle that specifies ahead of time what the results of measurements along the three directions $\hat{\mathbf{a}}, \hat{\mathbf{b}}, \hat{\mathbf{c}}$ will be. For example, the instruction set $(\hat{\mathbf{a}}+, \hat{\mathbf{b}}+, \hat{\mathbf{c}}+)$ means that a measurement along any one of the three directions will produce a spin up result. For the entangled state of the system given by Eq. (1), measurements by the two observers along the same direction can yield only the results $+\,-$ or $-\,+$. To reproduce this aspect of the data, a local hidden variable theory would need the eight instruction sets shown in Table 1. For example, the instruction set $(\hat{\mathbf{a}}+, \hat{\mathbf{b}}-, \hat{\mathbf{c}}+)$ for particle 1 must be paired with the set $(\hat{\mathbf{a}}-, \hat{\mathbf{b}}+, \hat{\mathbf{c}}-)$ for particle 2 in order to produce the proper correlations of the entangled state. Beyond that requirement, we allow the proponent of the local hidden variable theory freedom to adjust the populations N_i (or probabilities) of the different instruction sets as needed to make sure that the hidden variable theory agrees with the quantum mechanical results.

Now use the instruction sets (i.e., the local hidden variable theory) to calculate the probability that the results of the spin component measurements are the same $\left(\mathcal{P}_{same} = \mathcal{P}_{++} + \mathcal{P}_{--}\right)$ and the probability that the results are opposite $\left(\mathcal{P}_{opp} = \mathcal{P}_{+-} + \mathcal{P}_{-+}\right)$, considering all possible orientations of the spin measurement devices. There are nine different combinations of measurement directions for the pair of observers: $\hat{\mathbf{a}}\hat{\mathbf{a}}, \hat{\mathbf{a}}\hat{\mathbf{b}}, \hat{\mathbf{a}}\hat{\mathbf{c}}, \hat{\mathbf{b}}\hat{\mathbf{a}}, \hat{\mathbf{b}}\hat{\mathbf{b}}, \hat{\mathbf{b}}\hat{\mathbf{c}}, \hat{\mathbf{c}}\hat{\mathbf{a}}, \hat{\mathbf{c}}\hat{\mathbf{b}}, \hat{\mathbf{c}}\hat{\mathbf{c}}$. If we consider particles of type 1 (i.e., instruction set 1), then for each of these nine possibilities, the results are opposite $(+\,-)$. The results are never the same for particles of type 1. The same argument holds for type 8 particles. For type 2 particles, the instruction sets $(\hat{\mathbf{a}}+, \hat{\mathbf{b}}+, \hat{\mathbf{c}}-)$ and $(\hat{\mathbf{a}}-, \hat{\mathbf{b}}-, \hat{\mathbf{c}}+)$ yield the nine possible results $+\,-, +\,-, +\,+, +\,-, +\,-, +\,+, -\,-, -\,-, -\,+$ with four possibilities of recording the same results and five possibilities for recording opposite results. Thus, we arrive at the following probabilities for the different particle types:

$$\left. \begin{array}{l} \mathcal{P}_{opp} = 1 \\ \mathcal{P}_{same} = 0 \end{array} \right\} \text{types 1 \& 8}$$

$$\left. \begin{array}{l} \mathcal{P}_{opp} = \dfrac{5}{9} \\[2mm] \mathcal{P}_{same} = \dfrac{4}{9} \end{array} \right\} \text{types 2} \rightarrow \text{7}. \qquad (4)$$

Table 1   Instruction Sets (Hidden Variables)

Population	Particle 1	Particle 2
N_1	$(\hat{\mathbf{a}}+, \hat{\mathbf{b}}+, \hat{\mathbf{c}}+)$	$(\hat{\mathbf{a}}-, \hat{\mathbf{b}}-, \hat{\mathbf{c}}-)$
N_2	$(\hat{\mathbf{a}}+, \hat{\mathbf{b}}+, \hat{\mathbf{c}}-)$	$(\hat{\mathbf{a}}-, \hat{\mathbf{b}}-, \hat{\mathbf{c}}+)$
N_3	$(\hat{\mathbf{a}}+, \hat{\mathbf{b}}-, \hat{\mathbf{c}}+)$	$(\hat{\mathbf{a}}-, \hat{\mathbf{b}}+, \hat{\mathbf{c}}-)$
N_4	$(\hat{\mathbf{a}}+, \hat{\mathbf{b}}-, \hat{\mathbf{c}}-)$	$(\hat{\mathbf{a}}-, \hat{\mathbf{b}}+, \hat{\mathbf{c}}+)$
N_5	$(\hat{\mathbf{a}}-, \hat{\mathbf{b}}+, \hat{\mathbf{c}}+)$	$(\hat{\mathbf{a}}+, \hat{\mathbf{b}}-, \hat{\mathbf{c}}-)$
N_6	$(\hat{\mathbf{a}}-, \hat{\mathbf{b}}+, \hat{\mathbf{c}}-)$	$(\hat{\mathbf{a}}+, \hat{\mathbf{b}}-, \hat{\mathbf{c}}+)$
N_7	$(\hat{\mathbf{a}}-, \hat{\mathbf{b}}-, \hat{\mathbf{c}}+)$	$(\hat{\mathbf{a}}+, \hat{\mathbf{b}}+, \hat{\mathbf{c}}-)$
N_8	$(\hat{\mathbf{a}}-, \hat{\mathbf{b}}-, \hat{\mathbf{c}}-)$	$(\hat{\mathbf{a}}+, \hat{\mathbf{b}}+, \hat{\mathbf{c}}+)$

Quantum Spookiness

To find the probabilities of recording the same or opposite results in all the measurements, we perform a weighted average over all the possible particle types. The weight of any particular particle type, for example type 1, is simply $N_1 / \sum_i N_i$ (recall we will adjust the actual values later as needed). Thus, the averaged probabilities are:

$$\mathcal{P}_{same} = \frac{1}{\sum_i N_i} \frac{4}{9} (N_2 + N_3 + N_4 + N_5 + N_6 + N_7) \leq \frac{4}{9}$$

$$\mathcal{P}_{opp} = \frac{1}{\sum_i N_i} \left(N_1 + N_8 + \frac{5}{9} (N_2 + N_3 + N_4 + N_5 + N_6 + N_7) \right) \geq \frac{5}{9}, \tag{5}$$

where the inequalities follow because the sum of all the weights for the different particle types must be unity. In summary, we can adjust the populations all we want, but that will always produce probabilities of the same or opposite measurements that are bound by the above inequalities. That is what is meant by a **Bell inequality**.

What does quantum mechanics predict for these probabilities? For this system of two spin-1/2 particles, we can calculate the probabilities. Assume that observer A records a "+" along some direction (of the three). Define that direction as the z-axis (no law against that). Observer B measures along a direction $\hat{\mathbf{n}}$ at some angle θ with respect to the z-axis. The probability that observer A records a "+" along the z-axis and observer B records a "+" along the $\hat{\mathbf{n}}$ direction is

$$\mathcal{P}_{++} = |(_1\langle +| \, _{2\hat{\mathbf{n}}}\langle +|) |\psi\rangle|^2. \tag{6}$$

Substituting the entangled state $|\psi\rangle$ and the direction eigenstate $|+\rangle_{\hat{\mathbf{n}}}$ gives

$$\begin{aligned}
\mathcal{P}_{++} &= \left| _1\langle +| \left(\cos\frac{\theta}{2} \, _2\langle +| + e^{-i\phi}\sin\frac{\theta}{2} \, _2\langle -| \right) \frac{1}{\sqrt{2}} (|+\rangle_1 |-\rangle_2 - |-\rangle_1 |+\rangle_2) \right|^2 \\
&= \left| \frac{1}{\sqrt{2}} \left(\cos\frac{\theta}{2} \, _2\langle +| + e^{-i\phi}\sin\frac{\theta}{2} \, _2\langle -| \right) (|-\rangle_2) \right|^2 \\
&= \frac{1}{2}\sin^2\frac{\theta}{2}.
\end{aligned} \tag{7}$$

The same result is obtained for the probability that observer A records a "−" along the z-axis and observer B records a "−" along the $\hat{\mathbf{n}}$ direction. Hence, the result for the same measurements is

$$\mathcal{P}_{same} = \mathcal{P}_{++} + \mathcal{P}_{--} = \sin^2\frac{\theta}{2}. \tag{8}$$

The probability that observer B records a "−" along the direction $\hat{\mathbf{n}}$, when A records a "+" is

$$\begin{aligned}
\mathcal{P}_{+-} &= |(_1\langle +| \, _{2\hat{\mathbf{n}}}\langle -|) |\psi\rangle|^2 \\
&= \left| _1\langle +| \left(\sin\frac{\theta}{2} \, _2\langle +| - e^{-i\phi}\cos\frac{\theta}{2} \, _2\langle -| \right) \frac{1}{\sqrt{2}} (|+\rangle_1 |-\rangle_2 - |-\rangle_1 |+\rangle_2) \right|^2 \\
&= \left| \frac{1}{\sqrt{2}} \left(\sin\frac{\theta}{2} \, _2\langle +| - e^{-i\phi}\cos\frac{\theta}{2} \, _2\langle -| \right) (|-\rangle_2) \right|^2 \\
&= \frac{1}{2}\cos^2\frac{\theta}{2},
\end{aligned} \tag{9}$$

165

and the probability for opposite results is

$$\mathcal{P}_{opp} = \mathcal{P}_{+-} + \mathcal{P}_{-+} = \cos^2 \frac{\theta}{2}. \tag{10}$$

The angle θ between the measurement directions of observers A and B is $0°$ in $1/3$ of the measurements and $120°$ in $2/3$ of the measurements, so the average probabilities are

$$\mathcal{P}_{same} = \frac{1}{3} \cdot \sin^2 \frac{0°}{2} + \frac{2}{3} \cdot \sin^2 \frac{120°}{2} = \frac{1}{3} \cdot 0 + \frac{2}{3} \cdot \frac{3}{4} = \frac{1}{2}$$

$$\mathcal{P}_{opp} = \frac{1}{3} \cdot \cos^2 \frac{0°}{2} + \frac{2}{3} \cdot \cos^2 \frac{120°}{2} = \frac{1}{3} \cdot 1 + \frac{2}{3} \cdot \frac{1}{4} = \frac{1}{2}. \tag{11}$$

These predictions of quantum mechanics are inconsistent with the range of possibilities that we derived for local hidden variable theories in Eq. (5). Because these probabilities can be measured, we can do experiments to test whether local hidden variable theories are possible. The results of experiments performed on systems that produce entangled quantum states have consistently agreed with quantum mechanics and hence, exclude the possibility of local hidden variable theories. We are forced to conclude that quantum mechanics is an inherently nonlocal theory.

The EPR paradox also raises issues regarding the collapse of the quantum state and how a measurement by A can instantaneously alter the quantum state at B. However, there is no information transmitted instantaneously and so there is no violation of relativity. What observer B measures is not affected by any measurements that A makes. The two observers notice only when they get together and compare results that some of the measurements (along the same axes) are correlated.

The entangled states of the EPR paradox have truly nonclassical behavior and so appear spooky to our classically trained minds. But when you are given lemons, make lemonade. Modern quantum researchers are now using the spookiness of the entangled states to enable new technologies that take advantage of the way that quantum mechanics stores information in these correlated systems. Quantum computers, quantum communication, and quantum information processing in general are active areas of research and promise to enable a new revolution in information technology.

2 ■ SCHRÖDINGER CAT PARADOX

The Schrödinger cat paradox is a *gedanken* experiment designed by Schrödinger to illustrate some of the problems of quantum measurement, particularly in the extension of quantum mechanics to classical systems. The apparatus of Schrödinger's *gedanken* experiment consists of a radioactive nucleus, a Geiger counter, a hammer, a bottle of cyanide gas, a cat, and a box, as shown in Fig. 3. The nucleus has a 50% probability of decaying in one hour. The components are assembled such that when the nucleus decays, it triggers the Geiger counter, which causes the hammer to break the bottle and release the poisonous gas, killing the cat. Thus, after one hour there is a 50% probability that the cat is dead.

After the one hour, the nucleus is in an equal superposition of undecayed and decayed states:

$$|\psi_{nucleus}\rangle = \tfrac{1}{\sqrt{2}} (|\psi_{undecayed}\rangle + |\psi_{decayed}\rangle). \tag{12}$$

The apparatus is designed such that there is a one-to-one correspondence between the undecayed nuclear state and the live-cat state and a one-to-one correspondence between the decayed nuclear state and the dead-cat state. Though the cat is macroscopic, it is made up of microscopic particles and so should be describable by a quantum state, albeit a complicated one. Thus, we expect that the quantum state of the cat after one hour is

$$|\psi_{cat}\rangle = \tfrac{1}{\sqrt{2}} (|\psi_{alive}\rangle + |\psi_{dead}\rangle). \tag{13}$$

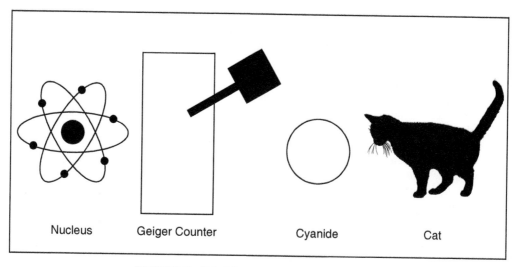

Nucleus Geiger Counter Cyanide Cat

FIGURE 3 Schrödinger cat *gedanken* experiment.

Both quantum calculations and classical reasoning would predict 50/50 probabilities of observing an alive or a dead cat when we open the box. However, quantum mechanics would lead us to believe that the cat was neither dead nor alive before we opened the box, but rather was in a superposition of states, and the quantum state collapses to the alive state $|\psi_{alive}\rangle$ or dead state $|\psi_{dead}\rangle$ only when we open the box and make the measurement by observing the cat. But our classical experiences clearly run counter to this. We would say that the cat *really* was dead or alive, we just did not know it yet. (Imagine that the cat is wearing a cyanide sensitive watch—the time will tell us when the cat was killed, if it is dead!)

Why are we so troubled by a cat in a superposition state? What is so inherently different about cats and electrons? The superposition state exhibits a clear interference effect that relies on the coherent phase relationship between the two parts of the superposition state vector for the spin-1/2 particle. No one has ever observed such an interference effect with cats, so our gut feeling that cats and electrons are different appears justified.

The main issues raised by the Schrödinger cat *gedanken* experiment are (1) Can we describe macroscopic states quantum mechanically? and (2) What causes the collapse of the wave function?

The **Copenhagen interpretation of quantum mechanics** championed by Bohr and Heisenberg maintains that there is a boundary between the classical and quantum worlds. We describe microscopic systems (the nucleus) with quantum states and macroscopic systems (the cat, or even the Geiger counter) with classical rules. The measurement apparatus causes the quantum state to collapse and to produce the single classical or meter result. The actual mechanism for the collapse of the wave function is not specified in the Copenhagen interpretation, and where to draw the line between the classical and the quantum world is not clear. Others have argued that the human consciousness is responsible for collapsing the wave function, while some have argued that there is no collapse, just bifurcation into alternate, independent universes. Many of these different points of view are untestable experimentally and thus raise more metaphysical than physical questions.

These debates about the interpretation of quantum mechanics arise when we use words, which are based on our classical experiences, to describe the quantum world. The mathematics of quantum mechanics is clear and allows us to calculate precisely. No one is disagreeing about the probability that the cat will live or die. The disagreement is all about "what it really means!" To steer us toward the clear mathematics, Richard Feynman admonished us to "Shut up and calculate!" Two physicists who disagree on the words they use to describe a quantum mechanical experiment generally agree on the mathematical description of the results.

Recent advances in experimental techniques have allowed experiments to probe the boundary between the classical and quantum worlds and address the quantum measurement issues raised by the Schrödinger cat paradox. The coupling between the microscopic nucleus and the macroscopic cat is representative of a quantum measurement whereby a classical meter (the cat) provides a clear and unambiguous measurement of the state of the quantum system (the nucleus). In this case, the two possible states of the nucleus (undecayed or decayed) are measured by the two possible positions on the meter (cat alive or cat dead). The quantum mechanical description of this complete system is the entangled state

$$|\psi_{system}\rangle = \tfrac{1}{\sqrt{2}}\left(|\psi_{undecayed}\rangle|\psi_{alive}\rangle + |\psi_{decayed}\rangle|\psi_{dead}\rangle\right). \tag{14}$$

The main issue to be addressed by experiment is whether Eq. (14) is the proper quantum mechanical description of the system. That is, is the system in a coherent quantum mechanical superposition, as described by Eq. (14), or is the system in a 50/50 statistical mixed state of the two possibilities? As discussed above, we can distinguish these two cases by looking for interference between the two states of the system.

To build a Schrödinger cat experiment, researchers use a two-state atom as the quantum system and an electromagnetic field in a cavity as the classical meter (or cat). The atom can either be in the ground $|g\rangle$ or excited $|e\rangle$ state. The cavity is engineered to be in a coherent state $|\alpha\rangle$ described by the complex number α, whose magnitude is equal to the square root of the average number of photons in the cavity. For large α, the coherent state is equivalent to a classical electromagnetic field, but for small α, the field appears more quantum mechanical. The beauty of this experiment is that the experimenters can tune the value of α between these limits to study the region between the microscopic and macroscopic descriptions of the meter (cat). In this intermediate range, the meter is a **mesoscopic system**.

Atoms travel through the cavity and disturb the electromagnetic field in the cavity. Each atom is modeled as having an index of refraction that alters the phase of the electromagnetic field. The system is engineered such that the ground and excited atomic states produce opposite phase shifts $\pm\phi$. Before the atom enters the cavity, it undergoes a π-pulse that places it in an equal superposition of ground and excited states

$$|\psi_{atom}\rangle = \tfrac{1}{\sqrt{2}}(|e\rangle + |g\rangle), \tag{15}$$

as shown in Fig. 4. Each component of this superposition produces a different phase shift in the cavity field such that after the atom passes through the cavity, the atom-cavity system is in the entangled state

$$|\psi_{atom+cavity}\rangle = \tfrac{1}{\sqrt{2}}(|e\rangle|\alpha e^{i\phi}\rangle + |g\rangle|\alpha e^{-i\phi}\rangle) \tag{16}$$

that mirrors the Schrödinger cat state in Eq. (14). The state of the cavity field is probed by sending a second atom into the cavity and looking for interference effects in the atom that are produced by the two components of the field. In this experiment, the two field states are classically distinguishable, akin to the alive and dead cat states. For small values of the phase difference 2ϕ between the two field components, the interference effect is evident. However, for large values of the phase difference 2ϕ

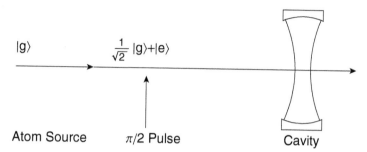

FIGURE 4 Schrödinger cat experiment with atoms in a cavity.

between the two field components, the interference effect vanishes, indicating that the superposition state in Eq. (16) has lost the fixed phase relationship between the two parts of the entangled state and can no longer produce interference effects. The system has undergone **decoherence** due to its interaction with the random aspects of the environment. The decoherence effect also increases as the number of photons in the cavity field increases, which makes the cavity field more like a classical state. Hence, the experiment demonstrates that the quantum coherence of a superposition state is rapidly lost when the state becomes complex enough to be considered classical. Further details on this recent experiment are available in the references below (Brune et al.).

RESOURCES

Further Reading

The EPR Paradox and Bell's theorem are discussed in these articles:

F. Laloe, "Do we really understand quantum mechanics? Strange correlations, paradoxes, and theorems," *Am. J. Phys.* **69**, 655–701 (2001); "Erratum: Do we really understand quantum mechanics? Strange correlations, paradoxes, and theorems," *Am. J. Phys.* **70**, 556 (2002).

N. D. Mermin, "Bringing home the atomic world: Quantum mysteries for anybody," *Am. J. Phys.* **49**, 940–943 (1981).

N. D. Mermin, "Is the moon there when nobody looks? Reality and the quantum theory," *Phys. Today* **38**(5), 38–47 (1985).

N. D. Mermin, "Quantum mysteries revisited," *Am. J. Phys.* **58**, 731–734 (1990).

N. D. Mermin, "Not quite so simply no hidden variables," *Am. J. Phys.* **60**, 25–27 (1992).

N. D. Mermin, "Quantum mysteries refined," *Am. J. Phys.* **62**, 880–887 (1994).

N. D. Mermin, "Nonlocal character of quantum theory?" *Am. J. Phys.* **66**, 920–924 (1998).

N. D. Mermin, "What is quantum mechanics trying to tell us?" *Am. J. Phys.* **66**, 753–767 (1998).

Schrödinger's cat is discussed in these references:

T. J. Axon, "Introducing Schrodinger's cat in the laboratory," *Am. J. Phys.* **57**, 317–321 (1989).

M. Brune, E. Hagley, J. Dreyer, X. MaÓtre, A. Maali, C. Wunderlich, J. M. Raimond, and S. Haroche, "Observing the progressive decoherence of the 'meter' in a quantum measurement," *Phys. Rev. Lett.* **77**, 4887–4890 (1996).

B. S. DeWitt, "Quantum mechanics and reality," *Phys. Today* **23**(9), 30–35 (1970).

A. J. Legett, "Schrodinger's cat and her laboratory cousins," *Contemp. Phys.* **25**, 583–598 (1984).

J. G. Loeser, "Three perspectives on Schrodinger's cat," *Am. J. Phys.* **52**, 1089–1093 (1984).

W. H. Zurek, "Decoherence and the transition from quantum to classical," *Phys. Today* **44**(10), 36–44 (1991).

Richard Feynman's directive to "Shut up and calculate!" is discussed in:

N. D. Mermin, "What's wrong with this pillow?" *Phys. Today* **42**(4), 9–11 (1989).

N. D. Mermin, "Could Feynman have said this?" *Phys. Today* **57**(5), 10–11 (2004).

Quantum Spookiness: Problem Set

1 Show that the quantum state vector of a two-particle system must be a product $|\psi\rangle_1|\phi\rangle_2$ of two single-particle state vectors rather than a sum $|\psi\rangle_1 + |\phi\rangle_2$. Hint: consider the action of a single-particle state operator on the two-particle state vector.

2 Consider the two-particle entangled state

$$|\psi\rangle = \tfrac{1}{\sqrt{2}}(|+\rangle_1|-\rangle_2 - |-\rangle_1|+\rangle_2).$$

    a) Show that $|\psi\rangle$ is not an eigenstate of the spin component operator S_{1z} for particle 1.
    b) Show that $|\psi\rangle$ is properly normalized.

3 Consider the two-particle entangled state

$$|\psi\rangle = \tfrac{1}{\sqrt{2}}(|+\rangle_1|-\rangle_2 - |-\rangle_1|+\rangle_2).$$

Show that the probability of observer A measuring particle 1 to have spin up is 50% for any orientation of the Stern-Gerlach detector used by observer A. To find this probability, sum over all the joint probabilities for observer A to measure spin up and observer B to measure anything.

4 Show that the state

$$|\psi_a\rangle = \tfrac{1}{\sqrt{2}}(|+\rangle_1|-\rangle_2 - |-\rangle_1|+\rangle_2)$$

is equivalent to the state

$$|\psi_b\rangle = \tfrac{1}{\sqrt{2}}(|+\rangle_{1x}|-\rangle_{2x} - |-\rangle_{1x}|+\rangle_{2x}).$$

That is, the two observers record perfect anticorrelations independent of the orientation of their detectors, as long as both are aligned along the same direction.

5 Calculate the quantum mechanical probabilities in Eqs. (7),

$$
\begin{aligned}
\mathcal{P}_{++} &= \left| {}_1\langle+|\left(\cos\frac{\theta}{2}\,{}_2\langle+| + e^{-i\phi}\sin\frac{\theta}{2}\,{}_2\langle-|\right)\tfrac{1}{\sqrt{2}}(|+\rangle_1|-\rangle_2 - |-\rangle_1|+\rangle_2)\right|^2 \\
&= \left|\tfrac{1}{\sqrt{2}}\left(\cos\frac{\theta}{2}\,{}_2\langle+| + e^{-i\phi}\sin\frac{\theta}{2}\,{}_2\langle-|\right)(|-\rangle_2)\right|^2 \\
&= \frac{1}{2}\sin^2\frac{\theta}{2},
\end{aligned}
\tag{7}
$$

From Chapter 4 of *Quantum Mechanics: A Paradigms Approach*, First Edition. David H. McIntyre. Copyright © 2012 by Pearson Education, Inc. Published by Pearson Addison-Wesley. All rights reserved.

The companion websites for this text are http://physics.oregonstate.edu/portfolioswiki and http://physics. oregonstate.edu/qmactivities.

and (9),

$$
\begin{aligned}
\mathcal{P}_{+-} &= |(_1\langle +| \; _{2\hat{n}}\langle -|)|\psi\rangle|^2 \\
&= \left| {}_1\langle +| \left(\sin\frac{\theta}{2} \; _2\langle +| \; - \; e^{-i\phi}\cos\frac{\theta}{2} \; _2\langle -| \right) \frac{1}{\sqrt{2}}(|+\rangle_1 |-\rangle_2 - |-\rangle_1 |+\rangle_2) \right|^2 \\
&= \left| \frac{1}{\sqrt{2}} \left(\sin\frac{\theta}{2} \; _2\langle +| \; - \; e^{-i\phi}\cos\frac{\theta}{2} \; _2\langle -| \right)(|-\rangle_2) \right|^2 \\
&= \frac{1}{2}\cos^2\frac{\theta}{2},
\end{aligned}
\tag{9}
$$

without assuming that observer A's Stern-Gerlach device is aligned with the z-axis. Let the direction of observer A's measurements be described by the angle θ_1 and the direction of observer B's measurements be described by the angle θ_2. Show that the averaged results in Eq. (11),

$$
\begin{aligned}
\mathcal{P}_{same} &= \frac{1}{3} \cdot \sin^2\frac{0°}{2} + \frac{2}{3} \cdot \sin^2\frac{120°}{2} = \frac{1}{3} \cdot 0 + \frac{2}{3} \cdot \frac{3}{4} = \frac{1}{2} \\
\mathcal{P}_{opp} &= \frac{1}{3} \cdot \cos^2\frac{0°}{2} + \frac{2}{3} \cdot \cos^2\frac{120°}{2} = \frac{1}{3} \cdot 1 + \frac{2}{3} \cdot \frac{1}{4} = \frac{1}{2},
\end{aligned}
\tag{11}
$$

are still obtained.

Unbound States

Consider the concept of wave functions to describe the motion of a particle in a potential well. States corresponding to particles confined within the potential well have quantized energies. We now turn our attention to unbound states, and we will find that the energies are no longer quantized. The simplest case is that of the free particle with no potential affecting the particle motion at all. The free particle states help us better understand the wave-particle duality of quantum mechanics. We then consider the case of particles that are affected by potentials but are not bound. This includes potential wells where the energy is larger than the well depth and cases where the potential has no localized minimum. Studying these unbound states is important in understanding scanning tunneling microscopy, nuclear alpha decay, and the scattering of particles.

In all cases, we are still charged with solving the energy eigenvalue equation

$$\hat{H}|E\rangle = E|E\rangle \tag{1}$$

with the Hamiltonian operator

$$\hat{H} = \frac{\hat{p}^2}{2m} + V(\hat{x}). \tag{2}$$

We work in wave function language (i.e., in the position representation), and so the energy eigenvalue equation becomes a differential equation:

$$\hat{H}\varphi_E(x) = E\varphi_E(x)$$
$$\left(-\frac{\hbar^2}{2m}\frac{d^2}{dx^2} + V(x)\right)\varphi_E(x) = E\varphi_E(x) \tag{3}$$
$$-\frac{\hbar^2}{2m}\frac{d^2}{dx^2}\varphi_E(x) + V(x)\varphi_E(x) = E\varphi_E(x).$$

1 ■ FREE PARTICLE EIGENSTATES

1.1 ■ Energy Eigenstates

For a free particle, the potential energy function $V(x)$ is zero everywhere and the energy eigenvalue differential equation is

$$\frac{d^2}{dx^2}\varphi_E(x) = -\frac{2mE}{\hbar^2}\varphi_E(x). \tag{4}$$

From Chapter 6 of *Quantum Mechanics: A Paradigms Approach*, First Edition. David H. McIntyre. Copyright © 2012 by Pearson Education, Inc. Published by Pearson Addison-Wesley. All rights reserved.

The companion websites for this text are http://physics.oregonstate.edu/portfolioswiki and http://physics.oregonstate.edu/qmactivities.

This is the same differential equation for inside the square potential energy well. It is convenient to define a wave vector

$$k^2 = \frac{2mE}{\hbar^2} \tag{5}$$

and write the differential equation as

$$\frac{d^2}{dx^2}\varphi_E(x) = -k^2\varphi_E(x). \tag{6}$$

The solutions to this differential equation are the familiar sinusoidal functions, which we can express either as the trigonometric functions $\sin kx$ and $\cos kx$ or the complex exponential functions e^{+ikx} and e^{-ikx}. Note that the energy E must be positive, so the wave vector is real for this problem. It is more convenient in this problem to use the complex exponential functions, so we write the general solution to the energy eigenvalue equation as

$$\varphi_E(x) = Ae^{+ikx} + Be^{-ikx}, \tag{7}$$

where we need to account for both possible signs of the wave vector and A and B are normalization constants.

The critical physical difference between a free particle (with $V(x) = 0$) and a bound particle is the lack of a confining potential. Because the wave function of the free particle is not required to "fit" into the potential energy well, there are no limitations on the wave functions and hence no quantization of the energy. Mathematically, there are not enough constraints on the two normalization constants A and B and the energy E (through the wave vector k). There are three unknowns in Eq. (7), but the normalization condition is the only constraining equation. The result is that the energy is a continuous variable, not quantized, in contrast to bound-state solutions. The continuous nature of the energy has important ramifications, which we will explore. But first, let's look more closely at the physics of quantum wave motion.

To understand free particle wave motion, let's look at the time evolution of the energy eigenstates of Eq. (7). The time dependence of this state is obtained by applying the recipe for Schrödinger time evolution. Because the state is already written in the energy basis, the Schrödinger time-evolution recipe says to multiply by a phase factor dependent on the energy of the state, giving

$$\begin{aligned}\psi_E(x,t) &= \varphi_E(x)e^{-iEt/\hbar} \\ &= \left(Ae^{ikx} + Be^{-ikx}\right)e^{-iEt/\hbar}.\end{aligned} \tag{8}$$

If we use the Einstein energy relation $E = \hbar\omega$, we can rewrite Eq. (8) in a suggestive way:

$$\begin{aligned}\psi_E(x,t) &= \left(Ae^{ikx} + Be^{-ikx}\right)e^{-i\omega t} \\ &= Ae^{i(kx-\omega t)} + Be^{-i(kx+\omega t)} \\ &= Ae^{ik(x-\omega t/k)} + Be^{-ik(x+\omega t/k)}.\end{aligned} \tag{9}$$

This quantum wave function has the same form we know from classical waves—a function $f(x \pm vt)$ with the argument $(x \pm vt)$. This functional form represents a wave that retains its shape as it moves, and any given point on that shape moves with a speed determined by the parameter v, which in this case yields $|v| = \omega/k$. For the sinusoidal waves of this free particle state, such points of constant phase move at the **phase velocity**. The energy eigenstate has two parts—the $e^{i(kx-\omega t)}$ part moving in the positive x-direction and the $e^{-i(kx+\omega t)}$ part moving in the negative x-direction. So now we know that whenever we see a wave function with spatial dependence $e^{\pm ikx}$, the sign of the wave vector in the exponent indicates the direction of motion. It is convenient to work with the wave vector eigenstates

$$\varphi_k(x) = Ae^{ikx} \tag{10}$$

as long as we remember that we must use both positive and negative k values to make a general energy eigenstate.

1.2 ■ Momentum Eigenstates

To learn more about the phase velocity of the wave vector eigenstates, it is useful to study the momentum of these wave functions. Let's operate on one of the states with the momentum operator, which is a differential operator in the position representation:

$$\begin{aligned}
\hat{p}\varphi_k(x) &= \left(-i\hbar\frac{d}{dx}\right)Ae^{ikx} \\
&= -i\hbar(ik)Ae^{ikx} \\
&= \hbar k\varphi_k(x).
\end{aligned} \tag{11}$$

Thus the action of the momentum operator on a wave vector eigenstate yields the same state with a constant multiplier. Well, that is an eigenvalue equation! So the wave vector eigenstates are also momentum eigenstates. The momentum eigenvalue equation is

$$\hat{p}\varphi_p(x) = p\varphi_p(x) \tag{12}$$

$(\hat{p}|p\rangle = p|p\rangle$ in bra-ket notation), so we have identified

$$p = \hbar k \tag{13}$$

as the momentum eigenvalue and

$$\varphi_p(x) = Ae^{ipx/\hbar} \tag{14}$$

as the momentum eigenstate. The momentum eigenstate wave function $\varphi_p(x)$ is a function of position and not of momentum—**x is a variable and p is the particular momentum eigenvalue**. The wave vector is related to the wavelength through $k = 2\pi/\lambda$, so we can rewrite Eq. (13) as

$$\boxed{p = \frac{h}{\lambda}}. \tag{15}$$

This equation was introduced in the early days of quantum mechanics by Louis de Broglie and provides the connection between the particle properties (momentum) and the wave properties (wavelength) of a system. The **de Broglie relation** between momentum and wavelength is at the heart of the wave-particle duality of quantum mechanics. We can turn Eq. (15) around to write an equation defining the **de Broglie wavelength** of a particle with momentum p:

$$\boxed{\lambda_{de\,Broglie} = \frac{h}{p}}. \tag{16}$$

The momentum eigenstates are also energy eigenstates for the free particle, with energy [Eq. (5)]

$$E = \frac{p^2}{2m}. \tag{17}$$

The fact that the momentum and energy operators share eigenstates is an important aspect of the free particle problem and is a consequence of the general rule that commuting operators have common eigenstates (like S_z and S^2 sharing $|\pm\rangle$ states) (Problem5). A given momentum eigenstate has a definite energy given by Eq. (17), but a given energy state does not necessarily have a definite momentum, because a general energy eigenstate is a superposition of the two momentum states $|p\rangle \doteq \varphi_p(x)$ and $|-p\rangle \doteq \varphi_{-p}(x)$ with opposite momenta, as in Eq. (7). Because a given energy state corresponds to multiple momentum states, we say that the energy state is **degenerate** with respect to momentum. In the free particle case, the energy states are two-fold degenerate. This may be your first example of degeneracy, but it will be more common when you study two- and three-dimensional systems.

The wave nature of the quantum mechanical description of the free particle is evident in Fig. 1, which shows the wave function of a momentum eigenstate. It is evident that a single wavelength characterizes the wave function, consistent with the single momentum of the eigenstate and the de Broglie relation between wavelength and momentum. The wave function is complex, so we must plot both the real and imaginary parts to completely describe the state.

Let's now return to the question of the phase velocity of the free particle eigenstates. A momentum eigenstate has time dependence

$$\psi_p(x,t) = \varphi_p(x)e^{-iE_pt/\hbar}$$

$$= Ae^{ipx/\hbar}e^{-ip^2t/2m\hbar} \tag{18}$$

$$= Ae^{ip/\hbar(x-pt/2m)}.$$

This wave is moving at a speed of $v = p/2m$, which is half the speed of a classical particle $v_{classical} = p/m$. This apparent contradiction exists because we are using the phase velocity of the wave. As we will see in Section 2, the proper way to use a wave to describe a particle leads us to the concept of "group velocity of a wave packet" as the more appropriate velocity.

A more serious problem with the momentum eigenstates becomes evident if we examine the probability density of the state. Taking the complex square of the wave function yields the probability density

$$\mathcal{P}(x) = |\varphi_p(x)|^2$$

$$= \varphi_p^*(x)\varphi_p(x)$$

$$= A^*e^{-ipx/\hbar}Ae^{ipx/\hbar} \tag{19}$$

$$= |A|^2.$$

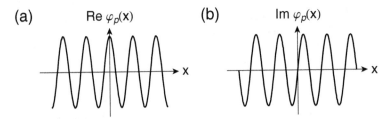

FIGURE 1 Momentum eigenstate. Both the (a) real and (b) imaginary parts of the wave function extend to $\pm\infty$. A single wavelength characterizes the momentum eigenstate.

Unbound States

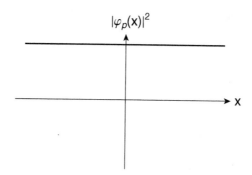

FIGURE 2   Position probability distribution for a momentum eigenstate.

As shown in Fig. 2, the probability density of a momentum eigenstate is a constant independent of position, extending to infinity. This presents us with two problems. Conceptually, we expect a particle to be localized to a small region of space, not spread out over an infinite region. Mathematically, we cannot normalize the momentum eigenstates because the integral of the probability density over all space is infinite. This is a new and quite serious problem. All previous basis states we have encountered have been normalizable. This lack of normalizability is a pathology of all continuous bases—this one being our first example. Fortunately, there is a solution to this mathematical problem that also solves our conceptual problem. By constructing *superpositions of momentum eigenstates* to make *wave packets*, we get wave functions that are normalizable and are localized to finite regions of space. Before we construct wave packets, it is useful to discuss some of the mathematical properties of the momentum eigenstates.

We expect a set of basis states to exhibit three important properties. The states should be: (1) normalized, (2) orthogonal, and (3) complete. All the discrete basis sets we have encountered have satisfied these conditions, which we express in Dirac notation as

$$\langle a_i | a_{j \neq i} \rangle = 0 \qquad \textit{orthogonality}$$
$$\langle a_i | a_i \rangle = 1 \qquad \textit{normalization}$$
$$\sum_i |a_i\rangle\langle a_i| = 1 \qquad \textit{completeness}, \tag{20}$$

assuming a set of discrete eigenstates $|a_i\rangle$. The orthogonality and normalization conditions are combined into one orthonormality equation by using the Kronecker delta:

$$\langle a_i | a_j \rangle = \delta_{ij}. \tag{21}$$

To adapt this orthonormality equation to a continuous basis, we need to use the continuous analog of the discrete Kronecker delta, which is the **Dirac delta function**. The Dirac delta function, written $\delta(x - x_0)$, is a function that is zero at every value of x, except at $x = x_0$, where it is infinite (*not* unity). This infinity means that the Dirac delta function does not strictly represent the normalization condition, but it is consistent with the infinite norm we found for the momentum eigenstates above. Thus, we expect that the "orthonormality" condition for a continuous basis set of momentum states is

$$\langle p'' | p' \rangle = \delta(p'' - p') \tag{22}$$

177

in Dirac notation. Using the rules for translating bra-ket notation to wave function notation, we express the inner product in Eq. (22) as an overlap integral

$$\int_{-\infty}^{\infty} \varphi_{p''}^*(x)\varphi_{p'}(x)dx = \delta(p'' - p'). \tag{23}$$

The momentum eigenstates defined in Eq. (14) satisfy this new form of the orthonormality equation, as long as we define the normalization constant A for the momentum eigenstates as (Problem 7)

$$A = \frac{1}{\sqrt{2\pi\hbar}}. \tag{24}$$

Although continuous basis sets, such as the momentum basis, do not strictly satisfy the normalization condition required by quantum mechanics, it is still practical to use Eqs. (22) and (23) to "normalize" a basis, and we refer to this process as **Dirac normalization**. We thus write the "normalized" momentum eigenstates as

$$\boxed{\varphi_p(x) = \frac{1}{\sqrt{2\pi\hbar}}e^{ipx/\hbar}}. \tag{25}$$

It is worth thinking about dimensions at this point. With the normalization of the momentum eigenstates in Eq. (25), we see that the dimensions of the left hand side of Eq. (23) are $[length]/[\hbar]$, which from Eq. (16) are equivalent to $1/[p]$ or inverse momentum. Thus, the Dirac delta function has dimensions of the inverse of its argument. This is another difference from the Kronecker delta that we have to live with.

The completeness of a basis implies that any function (relevant to the problem at hand) can be written as a superposition of the basis states. Completeness is difficult to prove mathematically, so we generally just assume that it is satisfied. In the discrete basis case, the completeness condition (closure relation) in Eq. (20) is a sum of the projection operators over the discrete basis set. To change to a continuous basis, we change the sum over the discrete label to an integral over the continuous label. For the momentum eigenstates, the completeness condition is

$$\int_{-\infty}^{\infty} |p\rangle\langle p|dp = \mathbf{1}, \tag{26}$$

where we understand that the right hand side is the identity operator. To demonstrate how completeness allows us to express any general state as a superposition of the basis states, insert Eq. (26) into the Dirac expression for a wave function

$$\begin{aligned}
\psi(x) &= \langle x|\psi\rangle \\
&= \langle x|\left\{\int_{-\infty}^{\infty} |p\rangle\langle p|dp\right\}|\psi\rangle \\
&= \int_{-\infty}^{\infty} \langle x|p\rangle\langle p|\psi\rangle dp.
\end{aligned} \tag{27}$$

The first term $\langle x|p\rangle$ in the integrand is the projection of the momentum eigenstate $|p\rangle$ onto the position basis, which is the wave function representation $\varphi_p(x)$ of the momentum eigenstate. The second term $\langle p|\psi\rangle$ in the integrand is the projection of the general state $|\psi\rangle$ onto the momentum basis $|p\rangle$ (i.e., the probability amplitude for the general state $|\psi\rangle$ to have momentum p). Given the rules of Dirac notation, you might expect the probability amplitude $\langle p|\psi \rangle$ to be written as $\langle p|\psi \rangle = \psi(p)$. However, there is risk of confusion here with the wave function $\psi(x)$ because $\psi(p)$ and $\psi(x)$ are not the same mathematical function with different arguments, but rather are *different mathematical functions*. To avoid this possible confusion, it is common to use a different symbol for the momentum probability amplitude, such as

$$\phi(p) = \langle p|\psi \rangle, \tag{28}$$

although such notation brings its own confusion between the different Greek symbols. The function $\phi(p)$ is known as the **momentum space wave function**. As in the position case, the probability amplitude $\phi(p) = \langle p|\psi \rangle$ is a continuous function that is the collection of numbers that represents the quantum state vector in terms of the momentum eigenstates. The wave function $\psi(x)$ and the momentum space wave function $\phi(p)$ are both representations of the state $|\psi \rangle$, but they are representing that state in different bases. Which basis we should use is up to us and is generally a matter of convenience decided by what we wish to calculate. Using this definition of the momentum space wave function, we write Eq. (27) as

$$\psi(x) = \int_{-\infty}^{\infty} \varphi_p(x)\phi(p)\,dp, \tag{29}$$

which, in words, says that a general state $|\psi \rangle \doteq \psi(x)$ can be decomposed into an integral (i.e., superposition) over all momentum eigenstates $|p \rangle \doteq \varphi_p(x)$ with a proportionality coefficient given by the probability amplitude $\phi(p) = \langle p|\psi \rangle$ for the general state to be measured in that particular momentum basis state.

If we put the explicit form of the momentum eigenstates $\varphi_p(x)$ into Eq. (29), then the superposition becomes

$$\boxed{\psi(x) = \frac{1}{\sqrt{2\pi\hbar}} \int_{-\infty}^{\infty} \phi(p)e^{ipx/\hbar}\,dp}. \tag{30}$$

This should look familiar! It is the **Fourier transform** of the function $\phi(p)$. Thus, quantum mechanical superpositions behave much like classical wave superpositions. In both cases, the Fourier transform represents a superposition of sinusoidal waves that combine to make a wave packet. We thus expect that the connection in the opposite direction (i.e., writing the momentum space wave function in terms of the position space wave function) would be an inverse Fourier transform. We can show that this is so by using our prescription for writing a probability amplitude in wave function language as an overlap integral. The momentum space wave function $\phi(p)$ is a probability amplitude $\phi(p) = \langle p|\psi \rangle$, and the rule for converting a Dirac bra-ket projection to wave function overlap integral is to convert the ket $|\psi \rangle$ to a wave function $\psi(x)$, the bra $\langle p|$ to a wave function conjugate $\varphi_p^*(x) = e^{-ipx/\hbar}/\sqrt{2\pi\hbar}$, and then integrate over all space. Thus, we get

$$\boxed{\phi(p) = \frac{1}{\sqrt{2\pi\hbar}} \int_{-\infty}^{\infty} \psi(x)e^{-ipx/\hbar}\,dx}, \tag{31}$$

which we recognize as an inverse Fourier transform. Thus, we see that the connection between the momentum space wave function $\phi(p)$ and the (position space) wave function $\psi(x)$ is the Fourier transform. As we saw in the spins case, we are free to use whichever representation of a quantum state vector that we find most convenient. The position and momentum representations are similarly equally valid representations. We focus on the position representation because it is generally the most useful.

2 ■ WAVE PACKETS

The key result from the previous section is that Fourier superpositions of momentum eigenstates are required for proper representation of free particle states. Let's first consider a discrete Fourier series example that illustrates many of the important features of wave packets, and then we'll make a real wave packet using continuous Fourier transforms.

2.1 ■ Discrete Superposition

In this example, we add just three momentum eigenstates together. We choose one "central" state with momentum p_0 to have twice the amplitude of two "side mode" states that are equally spaced at $p = p_0 \pm \delta p$ about the central state, as shown in the momentum state distribution in Fig. 3. As the dashed line hints, we are using this three-mode superposition as a model of a continuous momentum distribution characterized by a center momentum p_0 and a momentum distribution width δp that we will discuss in Section 2.2.

A graphical representation of this three-state superposition of sinusoidal waves and the resultant wave is shown in Fig. 4. The different wavelengths of the three components lead to constructive and destructive interference, as indicated in the plots. The resultant wave is localized to a region of space and hence is referred to as a **wave packet**. The wave packet shown in Fig. 4 has a characteristic wavelength determined by the central momentum, so it resembles a wave, but it also has a limited spatial extent, and so it also resembles a particle. In this case, we are using a discrete Fourier sum, so this localization is repeated periodically. For the more realistic continuum distribution, only one localized region exists and a true wave packet is realized. The coexisting particle and wave characteristics of a wave packet are the essence of the wave-particle duality of quantum mechanics.

To understand the motion of the wave packet, we must study the time evolution. The wave function at time $t = 0$ is given by the weighted superposition of the three momentum eigenstates

$$\psi(x,0) = \sum_j c_j \varphi_{p_j}(x)$$

$$\psi(x,0) = \sum_j c_j \frac{1}{\sqrt{2\pi\hbar}} e^{i p_j x/\hbar} \tag{32}$$

$$\psi(x,0) = \frac{1}{\sqrt{2\pi\hbar}} \left[\tfrac{1}{2} e^{i(p_0 - \delta p)x/\hbar} + e^{i p_0 x/\hbar} + \tfrac{1}{2} e^{i(p_0 + \delta p)x/\hbar} \right].$$

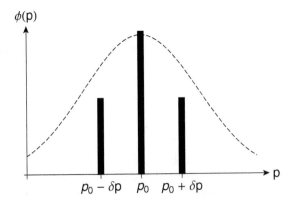

FIGURE 3 Discrete momentum distribution used to model continuous distributions and to build a discrete wave packet.

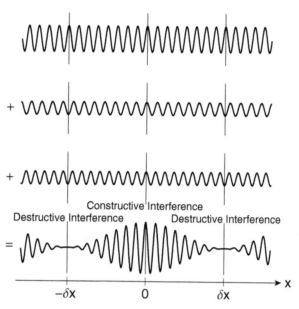

FIGURE 4   Discrete wave packet with three components.

The time-dependent wave function representing this wave packet is obtained by following the Schrödinger time-evolution recipe. Momentum eigenstates are also energy eigenstates of free particles, so the superposition is already written in the energy basis and we multiply *each* energy eigenstate by its *own* energy-dependent phase factor:

$$\psi(x,t) = \sum_j c_j \varphi_{p_j}(x) e^{-iE_j t/\hbar}. \tag{33}$$

The energy of each momentum eigenstate is given by the free particle energy

$$E_j = \frac{p_j^2}{2m}, \tag{34}$$

which for the three states yields

$$E_{p_0} = \frac{p_0^2}{2m}$$
$$E_{p_0 \pm \delta p} = \frac{(p_0 \pm \delta p)^2}{2m} = \frac{p_0^2 \pm 2p_0 \delta p + (\delta p)^2}{2m}. \tag{35}$$

We assume that the width of the momentum distribution is narrow enough that $\delta p \ll p_0$ and so we neglect the small $(\delta p)^2$ term in the energies. Hence, the time-evolved wave packet state is

$$\psi(x,t) = \frac{1}{\sqrt{2\pi\hbar}} \left[\tfrac{1}{2} e^{i(p_0 - \delta p)x/\hbar} e^{-i(p_0^2 - 2p_0 \delta p)t/2m\hbar} + e^{ip_0 x/\hbar} e^{-ip_0^2 t/2m\hbar} + \tfrac{1}{2} e^{i(p_0 + \delta p)x/\hbar} e^{-i(p_0^2 + 2p_0 \delta p)t/2m\hbar} \right]$$

$$\psi(x,t) = \frac{1}{\sqrt{2\pi\hbar}} e^{ip_0 x/\hbar} e^{-ip_0^2 t/2m\hbar} \left[\tfrac{1}{2} e^{-i\delta p x/\hbar} e^{ip_0 \delta p t/m\hbar} + 1 + \tfrac{1}{2} e^{i\delta p x/\hbar} e^{-ip_0 \delta p t/m\hbar} \right] \tag{36}$$

$$\psi(x,t) = \frac{1}{\sqrt{2\pi\hbar}} e^{ip_0 x/\hbar} e^{-ip_0^2 t/2m\hbar} \left[1 + \cos\left(\frac{\delta p}{\hbar} x - \frac{p_0 \delta p}{m\hbar} t \right) \right],$$

which yields

$$\psi(x,t) = \frac{1}{\sqrt{2\pi\hbar}} e^{ip_0(x - p_0t/2m)/\hbar} \left[1 + \cos\left(\frac{\delta p}{\hbar} \left[x - \frac{p_0}{m}t \right] \right) \right]. \qquad (37)$$

This wave packet contains the expected form $f(x \pm vt)$ of a wave, but it has two such parts with different arguments. The first part of Eq. (37) (in curly brackets) is characterized by the momentum p_0 and hence wavelength $\lambda_0 = h/p_0$ of the single harmonic wave. This part is called the **carrier wave**, and from its argument we find that it moves at the phase velocity $v_{ph} = p_0/2m$, as we discussed above. The second part of the wave packet (in square brackets) is characterized by the momentum width δp and hence a wavelength $\lambda_{env} = h/\delta p$ that is much longer than λ_0 (because $\delta p \ll p_0$). This second part is known as the **envelope** of the wave packet because it **modulates** the carrier wave, as shown in Fig. 5. Because of the different arguments of the two parts, the envelope moves at a different velocity $v_{gp} = p_0/m$ from the carrier. This velocity is called the **group velocity** because it characterizes the velocity of the group of waves together.

The different velocities are evident if the plot of the wave packet in Fig. 5 is animated (Problem 8). Several frames from such an animation are shown in Fig. 6, where you can see that the velocity of the envelope—the group velocity—is twice the velocity of the wiggles within the envelope—the phase velocity. Notice that the group velocity is equal to the classical velocity of a particle with momentum p_0. This is the sense in which this wave packet can properly represent the motion of a particle. This discrete superposition is a good starting point, but it still suffers from the pathologies of harmonic waves—it is not normalizable and it therefore cannot predict expectation values—so we must use a continuous momentum distribution to model real experiments. Moreover, the "localization" of the discrete Fourier series superposition is repeated periodically, and so cannot represent a single particle.

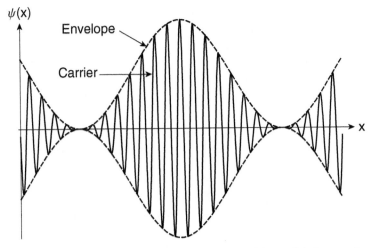

FIGURE 5 Wave packet showing the carrier wave and the modulation envelope.

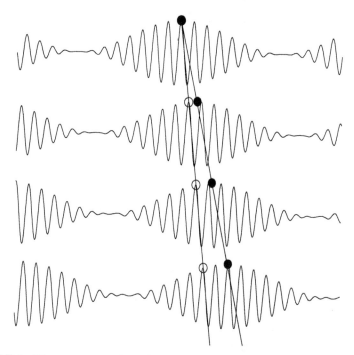

FIGURE 6 Discrete wave packet animation with time increasing from top to bottom. Open circles identify a point of constant phase, which moves at the phase velocity. Filled circles identify the peak of the envelope, which moves at the group velocity.

2.2 ■ Continuous Superposition

To go from the discrete case to the continuous case, we change the superposition sum in Eq. (32) to a superposition integral (i.e., we change the Fourier series to a Fourier integral or Fourier transform). While this may seem like a trivial extension, there are important differences. As we did in the discrete case, we perform the expansion using the momentum eigenstate basis $\varphi_p(x)$ because these states are also energy eigenstates in the free particle example, which then sets us up to use the Schrödinger time-evolution recipe. In the integral superposition, we specify the amplitudes of the momentum eigenstate as a continuous distribution $\phi(p)$ rather than specifying discrete amplitudes. Thus, we write the initial superposition state as

$$\psi(x,0) = \int_{-\infty}^{\infty} \phi(p)\varphi_p(x)dp$$

$$= \int_{-\infty}^{\infty} \phi(p)\frac{1}{\sqrt{2\pi\hbar}}e^{ipx/\hbar}\,dp, \tag{38}$$

where $\phi(p)$ is also called the momentum space wave function. The time-evolved state is found by following the recipe for Schrödinger time evolution and including the energy dependent phase factors:

$$\psi(x,t) = \int_{-\infty}^{\infty} \phi(p)\varphi_p(x)e^{-iE_pt/\hbar}\,dp. \tag{39}$$

Unbound States

Putting in the explicit momentum eigenstate wave functions and the expression for the free particle energy results in

$$\psi(x,t) = \frac{1}{\sqrt{2\pi\hbar}} \int_{-\infty}^{\infty} \phi(p) e^{ipx/\hbar} e^{-ip^2t/2m\hbar} \, dp, \tag{40}$$

which simplifies to

$$\psi(x,t) = \frac{1}{\sqrt{2\pi\hbar}} \int_{-\infty}^{\infty} \phi(p) e^{ip(x-pt/2m)/\hbar} \, dp. \tag{41}$$

This is the time-dependent generalization of the Fourier transform in Eq. (30) for the case of a free particle. The time-dependent generalization of the inverse Fourier transform in Eq. (31) is

$$\phi(p,t) = \frac{1}{\sqrt{2\pi\hbar}} \int_{-\infty}^{\infty} \psi(x,t) e^{-ipx/\hbar} \, dx. \tag{42}$$

To evaluate the Fourier integral in Eq. (41) and determine the wave function for any particular case, we need to know the particular momentum distribution $\phi(p)$, which may be specified as an initial condition, or can be determined from the initial wave function $\psi(x,0)$ via the Fourier transform in Eq. (31) that relates the spatial and momentum space wave functions.

As an example, consider the case of a Gaussian momentum distribution. This is a very common example because Gaussian functions are easy to integrate—you get another Gaussian in the Fourier space. In addition, the Gaussian distribution is a very good representation of many real experimental situations. The Gaussian function is one of the standard classical probability distributions and is commonly written as

$$f(z) = \frac{e^{-(z-\mu)^2/2\sigma^2}}{\sigma\sqrt{2\pi}}, \tag{43}$$

where μ is the mean value or average of the distribution and σ is the standard deviation of the distribution. Relating these definitions to the quantum mechanical quantities, the mean value is the expectation value $\langle z \rangle$ and the standard deviation is the uncertainty Δz. The probability distribution in Eq. (43) is normalized to unity:

$$\int_{-\infty}^{\infty} f(z) dz = 1. \tag{44}$$

Notice that the function $f(z)$ is not squared in the normalization integral in Eq. (44), contrary to the normalization of quantum mechanical wave functions to which you have become accustomed. In quantum mechanics, we have to square the wave function to get the probability density, which is then normalized, analogous to Eq. (44). So, technically speaking, the phrase "normalize the quantum mechanical wave function" is not correct, because we actually normalize the probability distribution, not the wave function. But that phrase is ingrained into all practicing physicists, so we are stuck with it.

Just as we did in the discrete case, let's assume that the momentum distribution is peaked at p_0 and has a width characterized by a parameter β. The Gaussian momentum space wave function is

$$\phi(p) = \left(\frac{1}{2\pi\beta^2}\right)^{1/4} e^{-(p-p_0)^2/4\beta^2}, \tag{45}$$

where the scale factor ensures proper normalization. This momentum space wave function is shown in Fig. 7, with the previous discrete case for comparison. The momentum probability distribution (per unit momentum) is the absolute square of the momentum space wave function:

$$\mathcal{P}(p) = |\phi(p)|^2 = \frac{e^{-(p-p_0)^2/2\beta^2}}{\beta\sqrt{2\pi}}. \tag{46}$$

Comparison of this quantum mechanical momentum probability distribution with the standard Gaussian probability function in Eq. (43) allows us to determine the momentum expectation value $\langle p \rangle$ and momentum uncertainty Δp by inspection as

$$\langle p \rangle = p_0$$
$$\Delta p = \beta. \tag{47}$$

The time-evolved spatial wave function for this Gaussian wave packet is obtained by substituting Eq. (45) into the Fourier transform in Eq. (41):

$$\psi(x,t) = \frac{1}{\sqrt{2\pi\hbar}}\int_{-\infty}^{\infty}\left(\frac{1}{2\pi\beta^2}\right)^{1/4} e^{-(p-p_0)^2/4\beta^2}\, e^{ipx/\hbar}\, e^{-ip^2t/2m\hbar}\, dp. \tag{48}$$

This integral can be performed using the standard Gaussian integral: (Problem 9). The result is

$$\psi(x,t) = \frac{\sqrt{2\beta}}{\sqrt{\hbar\gamma\sqrt{2\pi}}}\, e^{ip_0(x-p_0t/2m)/\hbar}\, e^{-(x-p_0t/m)^2\beta^2/\hbar^2\gamma}, \tag{49}$$

where the new parameters are

$$\gamma = 1 + \frac{it}{\tau}$$
$$\tau = \frac{m\hbar}{2\beta^2}. \tag{50}$$

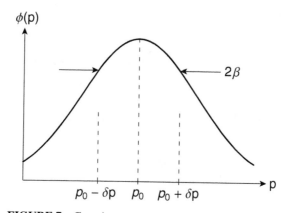

FIGURE 7 Gaussian momentum space wave function.

If we define

$$\alpha = \frac{\hbar}{2\beta}, \tag{51}$$

then we can express the wave function as

$$\psi(x,t) = \left(\frac{1}{2\pi\alpha^2}\right)^{1/4} \frac{1}{\sqrt{\gamma}} e^{ip_0(x-p_0t/2m)/\hbar} e^{-(x-p_0t/m)^2/4\alpha^2\gamma}, \tag{52}$$

where α is useful later as a measure of the width in position space.

Just as in Eq. (37) for the discrete momentum distribution, this wave packet has a carrier wave part (in curly brackets) that is characterized by p_0 and propagates at the phase velocity $p_0/2m$, and an envelope part (in square brackets) that is characterized by the momentum width β (through the α parameter) and propagates at the group velocity p_0/m. As we expected, the envelope is a Gaussian function. To isolate the envelope propagation, calculate the spatial probability density by taking the square modulus of the wave function:

$$\mathcal{P}(x,t) = |\psi(x,t)|^2 = \frac{1}{\sqrt{2\pi}\alpha\Gamma} e^{-(x-p_0t/m)^2/2\alpha^2\Gamma^2}, \tag{53}$$

where we have defined a new parameter

$$\Gamma = \sqrt{|\gamma|^2} = \sqrt{1 + \frac{t^2}{\tau^2}}. \tag{54}$$

The only velocity that appears in the probability density is the group velocity p_0/m, which agrees with our classical expectation that the particle propagates at this velocity. This Gaussian wave packet is shown in Fig. 8(a) and the probability density is shown in Fig. 8(b). This wave packet is truly localized; the probability density decays to zero away from the central peak in Fig. 8(b) with none of the secondary peaks that were evident in the discrete superposition in Fig. 4. The continuum of momentum states used in this superposition ensures that the destructive interference of the constituent waves away from the central peak is effective in truly localizing the wave/particle. This localization through interference means that this wave packet superposition is normalizable even though the individual waves used are not themselves normalizable.

The experimental parameters that one would like to measure in order to fully characterize a wave packet are the position and momentum. The expectation value of the position is, formally,

$$\langle x \rangle = \int_{-\infty}^{\infty} x\mathcal{P}(x,t)\,dx = \int_{-\infty}^{\infty} x|\psi(x,t)|^2\,dx, \tag{55}$$

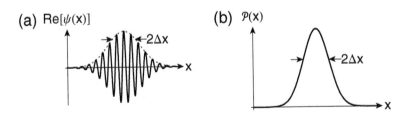

FIGURE 8 Gaussian wave packet (a) wave function and (b) probability density.

but it can also be obtained by inspection of the Gaussian probability density [compare Eq. (53) with Eq. (43)]:

$$\langle x \rangle = \frac{p_0}{m} t. \tag{56}$$

This result again shows that the wave packet moves with the group velocity p_0/m.

The expectation value of the momentum can be calculated either with a spatial integral

$$\langle p \rangle = \int_{-\infty}^{\infty} \psi^*(x,t)\, \hat{p}\, \psi(x,t)\, dx \tag{57}$$

or a momentum integral

$$\langle p \rangle = \int_{-\infty}^{\infty} p\, \mathcal{P}(p,t)\, dp = \int_{-\infty}^{\infty} p\, |\phi(p,t)|^2\, dp. \tag{58}$$

Either way, we get the result found by inspection previously in Eq. (47):

$$\langle p \rangle = p_0. \tag{59}$$

The uncertainties of position and momentum are (again by inspection)

$$\Delta x = \alpha \Gamma = \frac{\hbar}{2\beta} \sqrt{1 + \left(\frac{2\beta^2 t}{m\hbar} \right)^2} \tag{60}$$

$$\Delta p = \beta.$$

The wave packet momentum width remains constant, which is consistent with the conservation of momentum. The position width grows in time because the different momentum components used to construct the wave packet all move with different phase velocities. The spatial spreading of the quantum mechanical wave packet agrees with our classical ideas about waves. It could be considered analogous to a short laser pulse propagating through glass with dispersion in the index of refraction such that different colors in the pulse travel at different speeds. However, the wave packet spreading is *not* what we expect for a classical particle, and we have uncovered one of the counterintuitive realities of the quantum world—quantum particles do not stay intact.

As we did for the discrete wave packet, we visualize the motion of the continuous Gaussian wave packet with frames of an animation in Fig. 9. Again, we note that the carrier wave moves at the phase velocity, which in this case is half of the group velocity of the envelope motion. From previous study of optics or waves, you may recall that the formal definitions of the phase and group velocities that work for any wave packet are

$$v_{phase} = \frac{\omega}{k}$$

$$v_{group} = \left. \frac{d\omega}{dk} \right|_{k_0}, \tag{61}$$

where the derivative in the group velocity is evaluated at the peak of the distribution of wave vector states comprising the group. Applying these wave relations to the quantum mechanical free particle, we find that the phase velocity of the wave is

$$v_{phase} = \frac{\omega}{k} = \frac{\hbar \omega}{\hbar k} = \frac{E}{p} = \frac{p^2/2m}{p} = \frac{p}{2m} = \frac{v_{classical}}{2}, \tag{62}$$

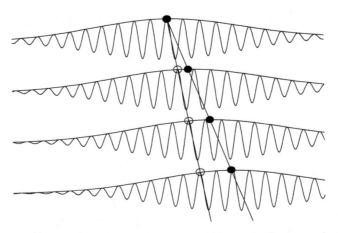

FIGURE 9 Gaussian wave packet animation with time increasing from top to bottom. Open circles identify a point of constant phase, which moves at the phase velocity. Filled circles identify the peak of the envelope, which moves at the group velocity.

which is half the classical particle velocity. The group velocity is

$$v_{group} = \left.\frac{d\omega}{dk}\right|_{k_0} = \left.\frac{d(\hbar\omega)}{d(\hbar k)}\right|_{k_0} = \left.\frac{dE}{dp}\right|_{p_0} = \left.\frac{d(p^2/2m)}{dp}\right|_{p_0} = \frac{p_0}{m} = v_{classical}, \quad (63)$$

which is equal to the classical particle velocity. Both results agree with the results we obtained by inspection of the Gaussian wave packet for a free particle.

3 ■ UNCERTAINTY PRINCIPLE

The Fourier connection between position space and momentum space is also important for understanding the Heisenberg uncertainty principle as it applies to position and momentum. Spin projection measurements along different axes are incompatible, meaning that we cannot simultaneously measure both observables. In general, two observables cannot be measured simultaneously if they do not commute. We express this incompatibility in terms of the product of the measurement uncertainties of the two observables

$$\Delta A \Delta B \geq \tfrac{1}{2}|\langle[A,B]\rangle|, \quad (64)$$

where the uncertainty is defined as the standard deviation

$$\Delta A = \sqrt{\langle(A - \langle A\rangle)^2\rangle} = \sqrt{\langle A^2\rangle - \langle A\rangle^2}. \quad (65)$$

We can now ask whether position and momentum measurements are compatible. Because we know how to represent the position and momentum operators, we can calculate their commutator to answer this question. The answer is that position and momentum do *not* commute (Problem 6). Their commutator is

$$[\hat{x}, \hat{p}] = i\hbar. \quad (66)$$

Thus, the Heisenberg uncertainty principle as applied to position and momentum is

$$\Delta x \Delta p \geq \frac{\hbar}{2}. \tag{67}$$

This condition limits the product of the uncertainties of position and momentum to a minimum value. The Heisenberg uncertainty principle represents a tradeoff between our knowledge of position and our knowledge of momentum. The Fourier connection between position and momentum helps us to understand this limitation.

Consider the Fourier wave packet constructed from discrete momentum components. The uncertainty in momentum Δp is approximately the spacing δp of the side modes from the central mode, as shown in the momentum distribution of Fig. 3. We estimate the uncertainty in position Δx as the separation δx of the two destructive interference minima from the central maximum of the corresponding spatial wave function in Fig. 4. The minima are located where the phases of the side mode waves are π out of phase with the central sinusoid. These phases are determined by the arguments of the $e^{ip_j x/\hbar}$ terms in Eq. (32). If we assume that the wave packet maximum, where the three waves are in phase, is at $x = 0$, then the destructive interference minimum on the right is at $x = \delta x$, as indicated in Fig. 4. To calculate δx, set the phase difference between the upper side mode $(p = p_0 + \delta p)$ and the central mode $(p = p_0)$ equal to π and solve:

$$\frac{(p_0 + \delta p)\delta x}{\hbar} - \frac{p_0 \delta x}{\hbar} = \pi$$
$$\frac{\delta p \delta x}{\hbar} = \pi. \tag{68}$$

The uncertainty product for this discrete wave packet is approximately

$$\Delta x \Delta p \approx \pi \hbar. \tag{69}$$

Hence, there is an inverse relationship between the width Δx of the position distribution and the width Δp of the momentum distribution. A wave packet that is well localized in space (small Δx) requires a broad distribution Δp of momentum states, while a broad spatial distribution requires a narrow momentum distribution. While this wave packet of discrete momentum components (i.e., a Fourier series) does not strictly obey Eq. (69) because the "localization" is repeated out to infinity, the inverse relation between the position and momentum widths is a hallmark of Fourier transforms of continuous distributions.

We learned in the last section that a Gaussian momentum distribution leads to a Gaussian position distribution because the Fourier transform of a Gaussian function is itself a Gaussian function. In Fig. 10 we plot these Fourier transform pairs for a range of widths; the inverse relation between the position and momentum spaces is graphically evident. Using the position and momentum uncertainties in Eq. (60), we calculate the uncertainty product of a Gaussian wave packet:

$$\Delta x \Delta p = \frac{\hbar}{2} \sqrt{1 + \left(\frac{2\beta^2 t}{m\hbar}\right)^2}. \tag{70}$$

At time $t = 0$ the Gaussian wave packet obeys the equality of the Heisenberg uncertainty relation $\Delta x \Delta p = \hbar/2$. For this reason, a Gaussian wave function $(\text{at } t = 0)$ is a **minimum uncertainty state**. As the wave packet evolves in time, it broadens in position space and the uncertainty product increases (Problem 12).

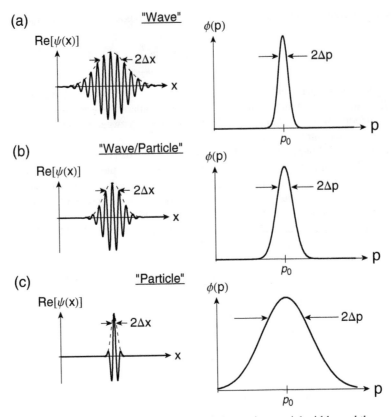

FIGURE 10 Gaussian wave packets with decreasing spatial widths and the corresponding momentum space wave functions obtained by Fourier transform.

The wave packet in Fig. 10(a) extends spatially over many wavelengths, so the "wave" nature of the packet is evident. In contrast, the wave packet in Fig. 10(c) extends only over one wavelength and so is more representative of a well-localized "particle." If we take this wave-particle duality to its logical extremes, we get the states shown in Fig. 11. A pure "wave" has an infinite spatial extent, which corresponds to an infinitesimal momentum width, as shown in Fig. 11(a). The pure wave state is the momentum eigenstate wave function $|p_0\rangle \doteq \varphi_{p_0}(x) = e^{ip_0x/\hbar}/\sqrt{2\pi\hbar}$, and the corresponding momentum space wave function must be a Dirac delta function because there is only one momentum value. This is consistent with the Fourier connection between position and momentum because the Fourier transform of a pure sinusoid is a delta function:

$$
\begin{aligned}
\phi_{p_0}(p) &= \frac{1}{\sqrt{2\pi\hbar}} \int_{-\infty}^{\infty} \varphi_{p_0}(x) e^{-ipx/\hbar}\, dx \\
&= \frac{1}{\sqrt{2\pi\hbar}} \int_{-\infty}^{\infty} \frac{1}{\sqrt{2\pi\hbar}} e^{ip_0x/\hbar}\, e^{-ipx/\hbar}\, dx \\
&= \frac{1}{2\pi\hbar} \int_{-\infty}^{\infty} e^{i(p_0-p)x/\hbar}\, dx \\
&= \delta(p - p_0).
\end{aligned}
\tag{71}
$$

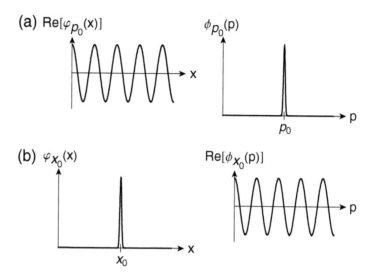

FIGURE 11 (a) Momentum eigenstate wave function and its corresponding delta-function momentum distribution, and (b) position eigenstate wave function and its corresponding infinite extent momentum distribution.

A pure "particle" state has an infinitesimally narrow spatial extent, which corresponds to an infinite momentum width, as shown in Fig. 11(b). This state represents a particle that is measured to be at a unique position, x_0 for example. A state with a unique value of the position observable is a position eigenstate $|x_0\rangle$. In analogy with the momentum space representation of the momentum eigenstate above, the position representation (i.e., spatial wave function) of a position eigenstate is the Dirac delta function

$$|x_0\rangle \doteq \varphi_{x_0}(x) = \delta(x - x_0). \tag{72}$$

This state satisfies the position eigenvalue equation

$$\begin{aligned}
\hat{x}|x_0\rangle &= x_0|x_0\rangle \\
\hat{x}\,\delta(x - x_0) &= x_0\,\delta(x - x_0).
\end{aligned} \tag{73}$$

So we have finally found the wave function for the position eigenstate we introduced in the last chapter. The infinite extent of the momentum space representation of this state is now clear, because the Fourier transform of a delta function is a pure sinusoid:

$$\begin{aligned}
\phi_{x_0}(p) &= \frac{1}{\sqrt{2\pi\hbar}} \int_{-\infty}^{\infty} \varphi_{x_0}(x) e^{-ipx/\hbar}\, dx \\
&= \frac{1}{\sqrt{2\pi\hbar}} \int_{-\infty}^{\infty} \delta(x - x_0) e^{-ipx/\hbar}\, dx \\
&= \frac{1}{\sqrt{2\pi\hbar}}\, e^{-ipx_0/\hbar}.
\end{aligned} \tag{74}$$

The position eigenstates have the same pathologies as the momentum eigenstates—they cannot be normalized and so they cannot truly represent physical states.

In summary, the eigenstates of position and momentum in the two representations

	Position space	Momentum space
Position eigenstate	$\lvert x_0\rangle \doteq \delta(x - x_0)$	$\lvert x_0\rangle \doteq \dfrac{1}{\sqrt{2\pi\hbar}} e^{-i p_0 x/\hbar}$
Momentum eigenstate	$\lvert p_0\rangle \doteq \dfrac{1}{\sqrt{2\pi\hbar}} e^{i p_0 x/\hbar}$	$\lvert p_0\rangle \doteq \delta(p - p_0)$

(75)

demonstrate an appealing parallel between position and momentum. This parallel is also evident in the position and momentum operators. In the position representation, the position operator is simple multiplication, while the momentum operator is a derivative with respect to position. Similar to the correspondence of the wave functions in Eq. (75), it turns out that in the momentum representation, the momentum operator is simple multiplication, while the position operator is a derivative with respect to momentum:

Position space	Momentum space
$\hat{x} \doteq x$	$\hat{x} \doteq i\hbar \dfrac{d}{dp}$
$\hat{p} \doteq -i\hbar \dfrac{d}{dx}$	$\hat{p} \doteq p$

(76)

The incompatibility of position and momentum measurements inherent in the Heisenberg uncertainty principle is in stark contrast to the classical notion that position and momentum are independent quantities that can each be measured with precision limited only by experimental technique. In quantum mechanics, position and momentum are **complementary** rather than independent quantities. The result is that we cannot know the trajectory of a particle in quantum mechanics. We can make predictions of the probability that the particle is in a region of space, but we cannot know the trajectory as we do in classical physics.

3.1 ■ Energy Estimation

We can also use the uncertainty principle to estimate the minimum energy of a particle. If we know that a particle is localized to a finite region Δx of space, then the uncertainty principle tells us that the momentum distribution required to produce that localization must satisfy

$$\Delta p \geq \frac{\hbar}{2\Delta x}.$$

(77)

If the momentum distribution has this minimum width, then we can use this width as a rough estimate of the minimum momentum

$$p_{min} \simeq \frac{\hbar}{2\Delta x}.$$

(78)

Ignoring the potential energy for the moment, we can then estimate the minimum energy of the particle

$$E_{min} = \frac{p_{min}^2}{2m}$$

$$E_{min} \simeq \frac{\hbar^2}{8m(\Delta x)^2}.$$

(79)

This approach is a common "back-of-the-envelope" calculation used to get a rough estimate of bound-state energies.

Consider a particle bound in a square well potential. The potential energy well by its nature confines the particle to a spatial region Δx approximately the size L of the box. We then use the uncertainty principle to find the corresponding uncertainty in the particle momentum:

$$\Delta p \Delta x \geq \frac{\hbar}{2}$$

$$\Delta p \geq \frac{\hbar}{2\Delta x} \tag{80}$$

$$\Delta p \geq \frac{\hbar}{2L}.$$

If the particle momentum is uncertain to this degree, then the value of the particle momentum must be at least this big, and possibly much larger:

$$p_{min} = \frac{\hbar}{2L}. \tag{81}$$

Now use this estimate of the minimum momentum to estimate the minimum energy that the bound particle can have:

$$E_{min} = \frac{p_{min}^2}{2m}$$

$$= \frac{\hbar^2}{8mL^2}. \tag{82}$$

Compare this with the ground-state energy in the infinite well:

$$E_{\infty,n=1} = \frac{\pi^2 \hbar^2}{2mL^2} \cong 5\frac{\hbar^2}{mL^2}. \tag{83}$$

While not a great match, the energy estimate from the Heisenberg uncertainty principle does predict the correct dependence of the energy on the well size. As the well gets smaller the energy levels go up, which is a general feature of bound energy states. The proportionality depends on the well width and is $1/L^2$ for the square well.

The actual ground-state energy in the infinite square well [Eq. (83)] is about 40 times larger than the uncertainty principle estimate in Eq. (82). There are two reasons for this poor agreement. (1) We overestimated the position spread of the particle; a particle confined to a well of size L has a position uncertainty less than L (Problem 20). (2) The minimum energy estimate comes from assuming that the uncertainty product is a minimum $\Delta x \Delta p = \hbar/2$, which is true only for Gaussian wave functions. Both of these factors lead to an underestimate of the minimum momentum, which leads to an even bigger underestimate of the energy because it depends on the square of the momentum. This method of estimating energies with the Heisenberg uncertainty principle must be taken with a grain of salt, as this example shows.

4 ■ UNBOUND STATES AND SCATTERING

We have discussed bound states in potential wells and free particle states in flat potentials. To complete our introduction to the quantum mechanics of particle motion, we now discuss unbound states in potential energy wells. Unbound states have an energy that is greater than the potential energy at infinity, in contrast to bound states, which have an energy that is less than the potential energy at infinity, as illustrated in Fig. 12. Bound states must "fit" into the potential well, which leads to energy quantization, while unbound states "lie" above the well with sinusoidal wave functions that extend to infinity, "and beyond!" Unbound states are similar to free particle states in that there are not enough constraints to fully determine the wave function, with the result that there is *no energy quantization for unbound states*. However, the unbound states are not simply free particle states with a well-defined momentum. Unbound states are affected by the potential energy profile, which causes the states to "scatter." We often use the term **scattering states** in this context.

To begin our study of unbound states, we return to the finite square well potential. For the study of scattering states, it is more convenient to choose the zero of potential energy to be the energy at infinity, rather than the energy at the bottom of the well as we did for bound states. Hence, we define the potential energy shown in Fig. 13 as

$$V(x) = \begin{cases} 0, & x < -a \\ -V_0, & -a < x < a \\ 0, & x > a. \end{cases} \tag{84}$$

With this choice of potential energy origin, bound states have $E < 0$ and scattering states have $E > 0$. It turns out that we are also able to use the solutions to this problem to study an inverted well (a **barrier**) by changing the sign of V_0.

We follow the same approach we have used in all previous wave function problems—we first solve the energy eigenvalue equation. As in the previous well problems, we get separate equations in the different regions:

$$\left(-\frac{\hbar^2}{2m}\frac{d^2}{dx^2} - V_0\right)\varphi_E(x) = E\varphi_E(x), \qquad |x| < a$$

$$\left(-\frac{\hbar^2}{2m}\frac{d^2}{dx^2} + 0\right)\varphi_E(x) = E\varphi_E(x), \qquad |x| > a. \tag{85}$$

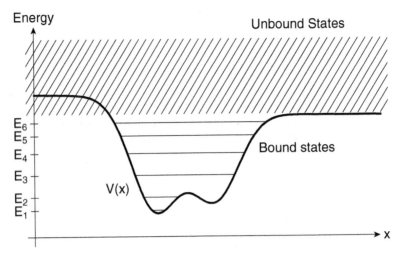

FIGURE 12 Bound $(E < E(\infty))$ and unbound $(E > E(\infty))$ states in a generic potential energy well.

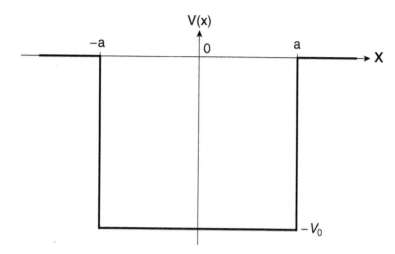

FIGURE 13   Finite square potential energy well.

Scattering states have $E > 0$ and so we expect sinusoidal solutions in both regions. Hence, it is useful to define two wave vectors

$$k_1 = \sqrt{\frac{2mE}{\hbar^2}}$$

$$k_2 = \sqrt{\frac{2m(E + V_0)}{\hbar^2}}.$$

(86)

These two parameters are used to rewrite the energy eigenvalue equations as

$$\frac{d^2\varphi_E(x)}{dx^2} = -k_2^2\varphi_E(x), \qquad |x| < a$$

$$\frac{d^2\varphi_E(x)}{dx^2} = -k_1^2\varphi_E(x), \qquad |x| > a.$$

(87)

The solutions to these differential equations are sinusoids or complex exponentials. Which form we choose to start with is a matter of convenience; the solution dictates the final form. It turns out that bound-state wave functions are real and unbound state wave functions are complex, so the complex exponentials are more convenient here. We write the general solutions as

$$\varphi_E(x) = \begin{cases} Ae^{ik_1x} + Be^{-ik_1x}, & x < -a \\ Ce^{ik_2x} + De^{-ik_2x}, & -a < x < a \\ Fe^{ik_1x} + Ge^{-ik_1x}, & x > a. \end{cases}$$

(88)

In principle, we should now proceed as we did in the bound-state problems earlier. That is, we should impose the boundary conditions and solve for the allowed energies and wave function amplitudes. However, that road quickly becomes a heavy slog. So it is instructive to focus on specific physical problems of interest and consider what we can actually measure.

First, observe that there are seven unknowns (coefficients A, B, C, D, F, G, and energy E) in this problem. To solve for all seven unknowns, we need seven equations, or seven pieces of information. When we impose the boundary conditions of wave function amplitude and derivative continuity at the two sides of the well, we get four pieces of information. For bound-state systems, the remaining three pieces of information come from the normalization condition, resulting in energy quantization. We saw this explicitly in the discussion of numerical solutions of energy eigenvalue equations; only by choosing the energy perfectly could we achieve a wave function that decayed to zero as it approached infinity. Unbound or scattering states need not decay to zero at infinity, so we cannot and do not need to impose the normalization condition. However, the absence of the normalization condition implies that the energy is not quantized and any energy is allowed for a scattering state. So our first conclusion is that *scattering states have a continuous energy spectrum*; therefore, we treat the energy E as an initial condition rather than as an unknown.

In a typical scattering experiment, we shoot particles at each other and ask how their motion is affected by their interactions. We usually consider one particle as fixed—the target—and the other as moving—the projectile. The potential energy well represents the interaction between them. The wave function we solve for then represents the motion of the projectile. In an experiment, projectile particles originate from a source, which we assume is at negative infinity. In the general solution then, the $Ae^{ik_1 x}$ term represents the incoming projectile particles, as illustrated in Fig. 14. These incoming projectile particles can interact with the well (target) in two possible ways: they might reflect and head back to the left, which would be the $Be^{-ik_1 x}$ term, or they might continue to the right, which would be the $Fe^{ik_1 x}$ term after passing the well region. In this scenario, there are no particles on the right side of the barrier that are moving to the left—the $Ge^{-ik_1 x}$ term. That term could come about only if there were a source of particles at positive infinity headed back toward the origin, or if another potential energy change occurred to the right of the well that could reflect the original particles back to the left. Hence, the typical scattering experiment is consistent with setting $G = 0$. Using this viewpoint and treating the energy E as an initial condition rather than as an unknown, we have now reduced the number of unknowns in the problem from seven to five.

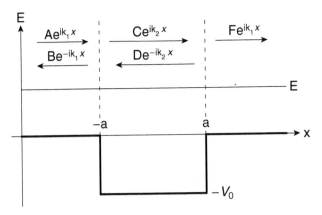

FIGURE 14 Waves incident upon, reflected from, and transmitted through a square potential energy well.

Unbound States

Unfortunately, we still have one more unknown than we can solve for because we have only four equations or pieces of information from the boundary conditions. We get that one extra piece of information by using a new way to normalize the wave function. The coefficient A represents the amplitude of the incoming wave, B the amplitude of the reflected wave, and F the amplitude of the transmitted wave, all of which are things we can measure. But we only expect our theory to predict the amplitudes of the reflected and transmitted waves. The amplitude of the incident wave is something we control in the experiment. Moreover, we expect that more incoming wave amplitude (input particle flux) will lead to more reflected and transmitted wave amplitude (output particle flux), so we really want to predict the ratios B/A and F/A of the reflected and transmitted waves, respectively, to the incoming wave. In this sense, we are normalizing our solutions to the amplitude of the incoming wave. In practice, we divide the boundary condition equations by A, which effectively gives us four equations with four unknowns. C and D represent the amplitudes of the wave function inside the potential well and are typically not amenable to measurement, so we try to eliminate those in favor of the measurables.

In light of this new way of approaching the problem, the general solution is

$$\varphi_E(x) = \begin{cases} Ae^{ik_1x} + Be^{-ik_1x}, & x < -a \\ Ce^{ik_2x} + De^{-ik_2x}, & -a < x < a \\ Fe^{ik_1x}, & x > a. \end{cases} \tag{89}$$

Now apply the boundary conditions of wave function amplitude and derivative continuity at the two sides of the well:

$$\varphi_E(-a): \quad Ae^{-ik_1a} + Be^{ik_1a} = Ce^{-ik_2a} + De^{ik_2a}$$

$$\left.\frac{d\varphi_E(x)}{dx}\right|_{x=-a}: \quad ik_1Ae^{-ik_1a} - ik_1Be^{ik_1a} = ik_2Ce^{-ik_2a} - ik_2De^{ik_2a}$$

$$\varphi_E(a): \quad Ce^{ik_2a} + De^{-ik_2a} = Fe^{ik_1a} \tag{90}$$

$$\left.\frac{d\varphi_E(x)}{dx}\right|_{x=a}: \quad ik_2Ce^{ik_2a} - ik_2De^{-ik_2a} = ik_1Fe^{ik_1a}.$$

Solve the last two equations for C and D in terms of F and then substitute into the first two equations to eliminate C and D, which are not so interesting. Then solve the first two equations for the ratios B/A and F/A (Problem 24):

$$\frac{F}{A} = \frac{e^{-2ik_1a}}{\cos(2k_2a) - i\frac{k_1^2 + k_2^2}{2k_1k_2}\sin(2k_2a)}$$

$$\frac{B}{A} = i\frac{F}{A}\frac{k_2^2 - k_1^2}{2k_1k_2}\sin(2k_2a). \tag{91}$$

The ratio F/A is the ratio of the amplitude of the transmitted wave to the amplitude of the incoming wave. The absolute square of this ratio gives the relative probability T that an incident particle is transmitted through the potential well, which we call the **transmission coefficient**. The transmission coefficient for a finite square well is

$$T = \frac{|F|^2}{|A|^2} = \frac{1}{1 + \frac{(k_1^2 - k_2^2)^2}{4k_1^2k_2^2}\sin^2(2k_2a)}. \tag{92}$$

Expressed in terms of the energy E and the potential well depth V_0, the transmission coefficient is

$$T = \frac{1}{1 + \dfrac{V_0^2}{4E(E + V_0)} \sin^2\left(\dfrac{2a}{\hbar}\sqrt{2m(E + V_0)}\right)}.$$ (93)

This is the probability that a particle with an incoming energy E is transmitted through the potential region.

The **reflection coefficient** R is the probability that an incident particle is reflected from the potential well and is given by the absolute square of the ratio B/A of the amplitude of the reflected wave to the amplitude of the incoming wave:

$$R = \frac{|B|^2}{|A|^2} = \frac{1}{1 + \dfrac{4k_1^2 k_2^2}{\left(k_1^2 - k_2^2\right)^2 \sin^2(2k_2 a)}}.$$ (94)

In this finite square well problem, there is no absorption of particles by the well, so the reflection and transmission coefficients add up to unity:

$$T + R = 1$$ (95)

and the reflection coefficient is simply $R = 1 - T$. In contrast to quantum mechanical particles, classical particles do not reflect from potential wells. They merely speed up and then slow down as they traverse the well. The reflection of quantum mechanical particles is thus further evidence of the wave nature of particle motion. It is analogous to classical wave motion through different media. For example, a light wave incident on a slab of glass is also partially reflected and partially transmitted.

The transmission and reflection coefficients for a finite square well are plotted in Fig. 15 as a function of the incident energy E. For large energy, the transmission goes to unity, which is to be expected because the potential well becomes insignificant. The transmission is also unity for particular energies, commonly called resonances. These resonances occur whenever the sine term in the transmission coefficient is zero, which occurs if

$$2k_2 a = n\pi.$$ (96)

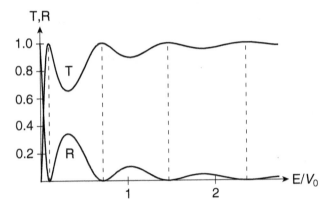

FIGURE 15 Reflection and transmission coefficients for scattering from a finite square well. The vertical lines indicate resonances where the transmission is unity.

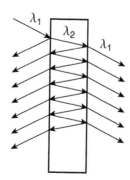

FIGURE 16 Optics interference analogy.

The reason for these resonances is evident if we rewrite this expression in terms of the wavelength $\lambda_2 = 2\pi/k_2$ inside the potential well:

$$2\left(\frac{2\pi}{\lambda_2}\right)a = n\pi$$
$$2a = n\frac{\lambda_2}{2}. \tag{97}$$

When the width of the potential well ($2a$) contains an integer number of half wavelengths, the transmission is unity and the reflection is zero. This effect is well known in physical optics, where light undergoes multiple reflections from the front and back surfaces of a glass slab, as shown in Fig. 16. Forward-going waves all interfere constructively and backward-going waves all interfere destructively when the thickness of the glass slab contains an integer number of half wavelengths. In the optics case, the changes in transmission and reflectivity that come from changing the wavelength (or the slab thickness) are known as interference fringes. One of the most common manifestations of this effect is the appearance of colored bands in a thin film of oil on water, as in the street after a rainstorm. In the optics case, the transmission and reflection are found by explicitly adding up all the interfering waves shown in Fig. 16. In the quantum case, we solved the energy eigenvalue equation and imposed the boundary conditions to achieve the same result. In both cases, the waves look like those shown in Fig. 17.

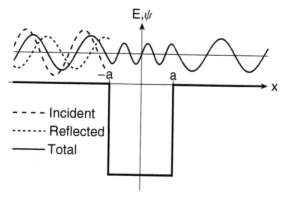

FIGURE 17 Waves incident upon, reflected from, and transmitted through a finite square well. Note that there are two vertical axes, energy and wave function, with different zeroes.

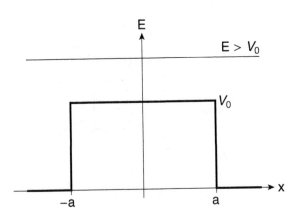

FIGURE 18   A finite square barrier with the incident particle energy above the barrier height.

If we write the resonance condition in terms of the energy, we get

$$\left(\frac{2a}{\hbar}\right)^2 2m(E + V_0) = n^2\pi^2$$

$$E = -V_0 + \frac{n^2\pi^2\hbar^2}{2m(2a)^2}.$$

(98)

Thus, the energies of the transmission resonances (with respect to the bottom of the well) correspond to the bound-state eigenenergies of the infinite well. A similar effect is seen in atomic physics, where it is called the Ramsauer-Townsend effect.

We can use these same solutions to solve the problem of a barrier potential, as shown in Fig. 18, as long as the energy is above the barrier height. We simply change the well depth from V_0 to $-V_0$ in all the formulae above. The results are the same; there are still resonances at the same energy levels. The only difference is that now the wavelength in the potential region is longer rather than shorter than the wavelength outside. This corresponds to the classical optics case where light from glass is incident on a slab of air.

5 ■ TUNNELING THROUGH BARRIERS

If the energy of the particle is below the barrier height, then the barrier region is classically forbidden and a classical particle reflects perfectly from the barrier. In the quantum mechanical treatment there is a possibility that the particle can penetrate the barrier and come out on the other side! This is because the quantum mechanical wave function penetrates into the classically forbidden region. This phenomenon is called **quantum mechanical tunneling**, and it is responsible for radioactive decay and the current in high frequency semiconductor diodes, for example. Quantum tunneling has an optical analogue where a light wave penetrates into air while being totally internally reflected from inside a glass prism. This penetrating wave is called an **evanescent wave**.

A square potential energy barrier is shown in Fig. 19. The potential energy is described as

$$V(x) = \begin{cases} 0, & x < -a \\ V_0, & -a < x < a \\ 0, & x > a. \end{cases} \tag{99}$$

If the energy E of the incident particle beam is less than the well height V_0, then the region $-a < x < a$ is classically forbidden. As in the previous well problems, there are separate eigenvalue equations in the different regions:

$$\left(-\frac{\hbar^2}{2m}\frac{d^2}{dx^2} + V_0\right)\varphi_E(x) = E\varphi_E(x), \qquad |x| < a$$

$$\left(-\frac{\hbar^2}{2m}\frac{d^2}{dx^2} + 0\right)\varphi_E(x) = E\varphi_E(x), \qquad |x| > a. \tag{100}$$

The energy E is less than the potential barrier height V_0, so the interior solutions must be real exponentials and the exterior solutions must be complex exponentials. It is useful to define a wave vector k outside the well and a decay constant q inside the well:

$$k = \sqrt{\frac{2mE}{\hbar^2}}$$

$$q = \sqrt{\frac{2m(V_0 - E)}{\hbar^2}}. \tag{101}$$

Use these two constants to rewrite the energy eigenvalue equations as

$$\frac{d^2\varphi_E(x)}{dx^2} = q^2\varphi_E(x), \qquad |x| < a$$

$$\frac{d^2\varphi_E(x)}{dx^2} = -k^2\varphi_E(x), \qquad |x| > a. \tag{102}$$

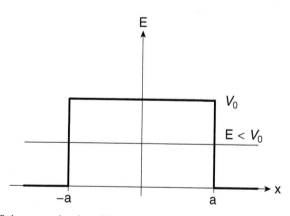

FIGURE 19 A finite square barrier with the incident particle energy below the barrier height.

Unbound States

The general solutions to these equations are

$$
\varphi_E(x) = \begin{cases} Ae^{ikx} + Be^{-ikx}, & x < -a \\ Ce^{qx} + De^{-qx}, & -a < x < a \\ Fe^{ikx}, & x > a, \end{cases}
$$

(103)

where we have again assumed that there are particles incident from the left, but not from the right. It is important that the wave function in the classically forbidden region contains *both* the exponentially decreasing *and* the exponentially growing terms. The growing term cannot vanish as it does in the case where the classically forbidden region extends to infinity. The boundary condition equations for continuity of the wave function and of the derivative of the wave function are

$$
\varphi(-a): \quad Ae^{-ika} + Be^{ika} = Ce^{-qa} + De^{qa}
$$

$$
\left. \frac{d\varphi(x)}{dx} \right|_{x=-a} : \quad ikAe^{-ika} - ikBe^{ika} = qCe^{-qa} - qDe^{qa}
$$

(104)

$$
\varphi(a): \quad Ce^{qa} + De^{-qa} = Fe^{ika}
$$

$$
\left. \frac{d\varphi(x)}{dx} \right|_{x=a} : \quad qCe^{qa} - qDe^{-qa} = ikFe^{ika}.
$$

As before, we solve for the ratios of the amplitudes to get the transmission probability:

$$
T = \frac{|F|^2}{|A|^2} = \frac{1}{1 + \dfrac{(k^2 + q^2)^2}{4k^2q^2} \sinh^2(2qa)}
$$

$$
= \frac{1}{1 + \dfrac{V_0^2}{4E(V_0 - E)} \sinh^2\left(\dfrac{2a}{\hbar}\sqrt{2m(V_0 - E)}\right)}.
$$

(105)

This transmission probability for quantum mechanical tunneling quantifies the probability for a particle incident upon the barrier to penetrate the barrier and come out the other side. Remember that the classical result would be zero—a classical particle only reflects from such a barrier.

The reflection coefficient for the incident beam is

$$
R = \frac{|B|^2}{|A|^2} = 1 - T = \frac{1}{1 + \dfrac{4k^2q^2}{(k^2 + q^2)^2 \sinh^2(2qa)}}
$$

$$
= \frac{1}{1 + \dfrac{4E(V_0 - E)}{V_0^2 \sinh^2\left(\dfrac{2a}{\hbar}\sqrt{2m(V_0 - E)}\right)}}.
$$

(106)

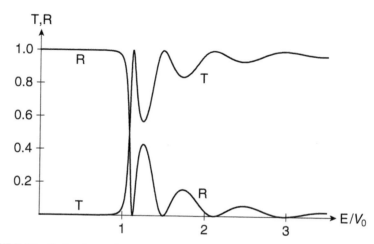

FIGURE 20   Reflection and transmission coefficients for scattering from a square barrier.

The reflection and transmission coefficients are plotted in Fig. 20 for the tunneling situation $(E/V_0 < 1)$, along with the coefficients for the "over the barrier" situation $(E/V_0 > 1)$, using Eqs. (93) and (94) with V_0 replaced by $-V_0$. In the tunneling case, the transmission is nearly zero except near the top of the barrier, where the tunneling probability increases exponentially. As the energy of the incident particle exceeds the barrier height, the transmission becomes large and exhibits the same resonances seen in the finite well problem. For large energy, the transmission goes to unity, which is to be expected because the potential barrier becomes insignificant.

The wave function of a particle that tunnels through a barrier is shown in Fig. 21. On the left side of the potential barrier are the incident and transmitted oscillatory waves. On the right side is the transmitted oscillatory wave. Inside the barrier there is an exponentially damped wave function (the evanescent wave of optics). The growing exponential term is part of the interior wave function [see Eq. (103)], but the decaying term dominates (Problem 32).

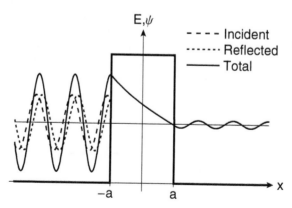

FIGURE 21   Wave function (real part) of a particle tunneling through a square barrier. Note that there are two vertical axes, energy and wave function, with different zeroes.

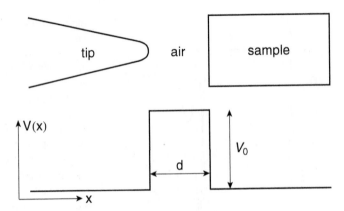

FIGURE 22 Schematic diagram of the scanning tunneling microscope, and the representation in terms of a potential energy diagram.

A beautiful example of quantum mechanical tunneling is the scanning tunneling microscope, which was invented by Gerd Binnig and Heinrich Rohrer in 1981 and earned them the Nobel Prize in physics in 1986. This imaging device employs a small sharp conducting tip that is brought up close to a sample, as shown in Fig. 22. The air (or vacuum) region between the tip and sample is a potential energy barrier because the electrons inside the two materials have lower potential energy than they would in the free space between them due to the work functions of the materials. The probability that an electron can tunnel from the tip to the sample (or vice versa) is given by Eq. (105) and can be approximated as (Problem 33)

$$T \propto e^{-2qd}, \tag{107}$$

where d is the separation of the tip and sample. In the microscope, a small bias voltage is applied between the tip and sample to create a preferential direction for current flow. The tip and sample do not "touch" so the current is due only to tunneling and is proportional to the tunneling probability:

$$I = I_0 e^{-2qd}. \tag{108}$$

The exponential dependence makes the current extremely sensitive to the tip-sample separation, which is typically in the nanometer range to produce measurable currents. As the tip is moved laterally above and parallel to the sample surface, the current provides a measure of the surface topology. A scanning tunneling microscope produces images with typical lateral resolution of 0.1 nm and depth resolution of 0.01 nm, sufficient to image individual atoms on the surface. A Web image search of "scanning tunneling microscope" reveals many beautiful pictures of natural and man-made atomic scale objects.

6 ■ ATOM INTERFEROMETRY

Many of the examples we have discussed have clearly demonstrated the inherent wave nature of particle motion in quantum mechanics. So can some of the classical light experiments like diffraction and interference be translated to electrons, or even to bigger particles like atoms and molecules? Yes! Electron diffraction experiments have been used for a long time and have played an important role in studying the atomic level structure of solid state crystals and DNA molecules. In recent years, the advent of laser cooling and trapping of atoms has made it possible to perform interference experiments with atoms and molecules. This new field of **atom interferometry** is leading to new ways to measure a variety of phenomena with unprecedented precision and to probe the mysteries of quantum measurement theory.

Let's discuss how an atom interferometer works by starting with the canonical double-slit interference experiment, as depicted in Fig. 23. You may have already seen this experiment when you studied optics, where it is commonly referred to as Young's double-slit experiment. The beauty is that the experiment can be performed with light or with particles such as electrons, neutrons, or atoms. Moreover, we can use it to discuss the wave-particle duality of quantum mechanics.

Let's first explain how the double-slit experiment works with light and then extend that to other particles. A source of light illuminates two narrow slits and the light passing through the slits lands on a distant screen. Each slit by itself produces on the screen a diffraction pattern whose spatial extent depends inversely on the width of the slit. We assume that the slits are narrow enough that these two diffraction patterns overlap substantially. If both slits are open, the overlapping diffraction patterns exhibit an additional interference pattern on the screen, within the overall single-slit diffraction pattern, as shown in Fig. 23. These interference fringes are comfortably explained by using our notions about waves. The important wave idea is that the measured pattern of light cannot be explained by adding intensities, but rather we must add amplitudes and then square the result to find the total intensity. The total field at the screen is thus the sum of the fields from each of the two slits:

$$E(x) = E_1(x) + E_2(x)$$
$$= E_0 e^{ikr_1} + E_0 e^{ikr_2},$$
(109)

where the distances r_1 and r_2 depend on the transverse position x of the observation point, the wave vector $k = 2\pi/\lambda$, and λ is the wavelength of light. The intensity at the screen is proportional to the complex square of the electric field

$$I(x) \propto |E(x)|^2$$
$$\propto |E_0 e^{ikr_1} + E_0 e^{ikr_2}|^2$$
$$= I_0 |e^{ikr_1} + e^{ikr_2}|^2.$$
(110)

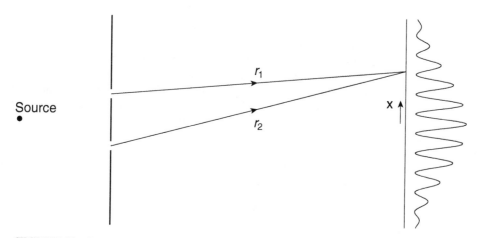

FIGURE 23 Double-slit interference experiment and resulting interference intensity pattern on the screen.

The interference comes from the cross term in the complex square in Eq. (110):

$$I(x) = 2I_0(1 + \cos k(r_2 - r_1))$$
$$= 2I_0\left(1 + \cos 2\pi \frac{(r_2 - r_1)}{\lambda}\right). \tag{111}$$

As you move the observation point up and down on the screen, the path length difference $r_2 - r_1$ varies, resulting in the sinusoidal intensity pattern characteristic of two interfering waves. The maxima in the interference pattern occur when the path length difference $r_2 - r_1$ is an integer multiple of the wavelength λ.

This same wave-optics analysis applies to the wave function analysis of a quantum mechanics particle, using the de Broglie wavelength to characterize the wave nature of the particle. A beam of particles directed toward the double slits of Young's experiment results in interference fringes at the distant screen. The wave function at the screen resulting from equal contributions from the two slits is analogous to the electric field of the light above

$$\psi = A\left(e^{ipr_1/\hbar} + e^{ipr_2/\hbar}\right). \tag{112}$$

The probability density for detecting a particle on the screen is

$$\mathcal{P}(x) = |\psi(x)|^2 = |A|^2 \left|e^{ipr_1/\hbar} + e^{ipr_2/\hbar}\right|^2$$
$$= 2|A|^2\left(1 + \cos\frac{p}{\hbar}(r_2 - r_1)\right), \tag{113}$$

which we rewrite in terms of the de Broglie wavelength using $p = h/\lambda_{dB}$:

$$\mathcal{P}(x) = 2|A|^2\left(1 + \cos 2\pi \frac{(r_2 - r_1)}{\lambda_{dB}}\right). \tag{114}$$

This has the same form as Eq. (111) and gives rise to the same interference pattern.

Young performed the original double-slit experiment with sunlight in 1801. Soon after de Broglie's hypothesis in 1923 that matter can be described as a wave, diffraction experiments were performed with particles such as electrons, atoms, molecules, and neutrons to demonstrate matter waves. Since then, Young's double-slit interference experiment has been performed with electrons (1961), neutrons (1988), helium atoms (1991), and even with C_{60} buckyballs (1999). How about baseballs? Could we see interference fringes from something so large? Probably not. A macroscopic object interacts strongly with the environment and its wave function suffers decoherence, which washes out the interference fringes.

The double-slit experiment is entirely consistent with the wave picture of light or matter, and so would not appear to include any particle-like behavior. However, if we can control the source well enough to turn down the incident intensity so low that only one particle per second leaves the source, then we can observe particle behavior with our own eyes. In the case of the light beam, the particles of light are **photons**. Given that the screen is sensitive enough, the low intensity source produces individual blips on the screen corresponding to the arrivals of the individual particles. At first, these blips appear at seemingly random places on the screen, as shown in Fig. 24(a). However, as more blips are recorded [Figs. 24(b) and (c)] we begin to see that the density of blips coincides with the interference pattern [Fig. 24(d)] from the wave model, as described by Eq. (114). The individual blips are consistent with our notion of a particle and its spatial localization, but they are inconsistent with our notion of a wave because they do not individually exhibit the interference pattern predicted above. On the other hand, the interference pattern that builds up after many particles is consistent with our wave interference model, but is inconsistent with our idea that particles travel in straight lines such that each particle from the source should go through one slit and arrive at the corresponding upper or lower spot on the screen.

Thus, we appear to arrive at a paradox. Some aspects of the experiment are consistent with a particle model, while others are consistent with a wave model. The quantum mechanical resolution is to say that we use the *wave* model to predict the probabilities of detecting individual *particles*. This is consistent with the interpretation we used in the spins sections where the quantum state vector was used to predict the probability that a spin projection was measured to be up or down. So what we called the light intensity in the classical wave description is now transformed into a probability of detecting photons at particular places on the screen. Any given photon arrival occurs randomly on the screen and the pattern builds up only after many arrivals. This is what we mean by wave-particle duality. (More complete discussions of this example can be found in Feynman and Cohen-Tannoudji et al.)

If you are not a little confused at this point, try this: What if you could measure which slit the particle went through? That is, which path did the particle take to arrive at the screen? Well, if you knew which slit the particle went though, then the wave description wouldn't be right, because it requires that the wave goes through *both* slits in order to define the path length difference in Eqs. (111) and (114). If the wave picture isn't right, then the interference pattern shouldn't be present. As it turns out, the interference pattern does indeed disappear if you know which slit the particle went through.

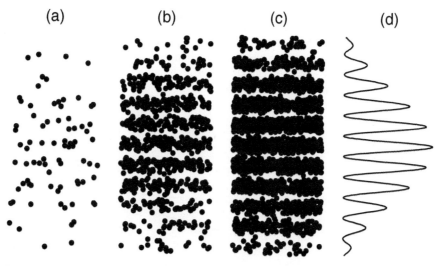

FIGURE 24   A computer simulation of the arrival of particles at the detection screen in a double-slit experiment, showing (a) random early arrivals, (b) and (c) the buildup of an interference pattern, and (d) a plot of the predicted interference intensity distribution.

The answer to this conundrum lies at the heart of quantum mechanical measurement theory. As hard as you might try, you cannot measure, and therefore cannot know, which slit the "particle" goes through without disturbing it just a little bit. The simplest way to measure which slit the particle goes through is to watch, but you need some light to watch. If you see the particle, then at least one photon must have scattered from the particle toward your eye, and the change in momentum of that photon in the scattering process will (through conservation of momentum) impart an equal and opposite change to the particle's momentum. This change is enough to alter the phase of the particle's wave function and destroy the interference fringes. In the early days of quantum mechanics, such "which path" experiments were merely "thought" experiments or **gedanken** experiments because they were too hard to perform. However, in recent years careful experiments have demonstrated these effects beyond doubt.

One of the important features of an atom interferometer is its ability to measure extremely small changes in potential energy. This ability arises from the dependence of the de Broglie wavelength of the particle on the potential energy. If the potential energy varies, then the kinetic energy and hence the momentum varies because the energy is conserved. The de Broglie wavelength depends on the particle momentum, so a varying potential gives rises to a varying wavelength

$$\lambda_{dB} = \frac{h}{p}$$

$$= \frac{h}{\sqrt{2m(E - V)}}.$$

(115)

A measurement of the potential energy with an atom interferometer proceeds as shown in Fig. 25. Different regions of potential energy are placed behind slit 1 and behind slit 2. A difference in the two potential energies produces a phase shift between the two wave functions that interfere at the distant screen. Hence, a measurement of the fringe shift in the interference pattern is a measurement of the potential energy difference. The different regions might, for example, have different electric fields, which produce different energies in atomic states. Or, if the atom interferometer is oriented vertically (or at an angle) instead of horizontally, then the two paths experience different gravitational potential energies. Recent experiments have been precise enough to test features of Einstein's general theory of relativity. Atom interferometers can also measure rotation and acceleration, similar to fiber optic gyroscopes that are commonly used for navigation.

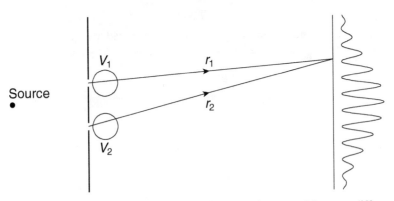

FIGURE 25   Double-slit atom interferometer for measuring potential energy differences.

SUMMARY

In this chapter, we learned about the unbound states of quantum particles. The momentum eigenstate wave functions are

$$|p\rangle \doteq \varphi_p(x) = \frac{1}{\sqrt{2\pi\hbar}} e^{ipx/\hbar}. \tag{116}$$

For a free particle $[V(x) = 0]$, the momentum eigenstates are also energy eigenstates with energy

$$E = \frac{p^2}{2m}. \tag{117}$$

A free particle has a characteristic wavelength given by the de Broglie relation

$$\lambda_{de\ Broglie} = \frac{h}{p}. \tag{118}$$

A more realistic representation of particle motion is obtained by superposing momentum eigenstates in a wave packet. The amplitude of each momentum component is $\phi(p)$ and the resultant superposition is

$$\psi(x) = \frac{1}{\sqrt{2\pi\hbar}} \int_{-\infty}^{\infty} \phi(p) e^{ipx/\hbar}\, dp, \tag{119}$$

which has the form of a Fourier transform. The momentum amplitudes are related to the position space wave function through the inverse Fourier transform

$$\phi(p) = \frac{1}{\sqrt{2\pi\hbar}} \int_{-\infty}^{\infty} \psi(x) e^{-ipx/\hbar}\, dx. \tag{120}$$

The Heisenberg uncertainty relation between position and momentum is

$$\Delta x \Delta p \geq \frac{\hbar}{2} \tag{121}$$

and tells us that tight spatial localization requires a broad range of momenta, and a particle with a well-defined momentum is spread over a large spatial region. The Gaussian wave packet is the only wave packet that satisfies the equality of the uncertainty relation and so is referred to as a minimum uncertainty state.

If a potential energy is present, the unbound states are scattering states. A particle incident on a potential well is partially transmitted and partially reflected, except at certain resonance energies where there is no reflection. A particle with energy below the height of a potential barrier can tunnel through the barrier, a phenomenon that is not observed classically.

RESOURCES

Activities

The bulleted activity is available at

www.physics.oregonstate.edu/qmactivities

- **Time Evolution of a Gaussian Wave Packet:** Students predict and study the time evolution of a Gaussian wave packet.

Quantum Tunneling and Wave Packets: This simulation experiment from the PHET group at the University of Colorado animates wave functions tunneling through barriers:

http://phet.colorado.edu/en/simulation/quantum-tunneling

Further Reading

Interference experiments with particles are discussed in these articles:

A. Tonomura, J. Endo, T. Matsuda, T. Kawasaki, and H. Ezawa, "Demonstration of single-electron buildup of an interference pattern," *Am. J. Phys.* **57**, 117–120 (1989).

O. Nairz, M. Arndt, and A. Zeilinger, "Quantum interference experiments with large molecules," *Am. J. Phys.* **71**, 319–325 (2003).

D. E. Pritchard, A. D. Cronin, S. Gupta, D. A. Kokorowski, "Atom optics: Old ideas, current technology, and new results," *Ann. Phys.* (Leipzig) **10**, 35–54 (2001).

The Nobel Prize for scanning tunneling microscopy is described here:

nobelprize.org/nobel_prizes/physics/laureates/1986/

Unbound States: Problem Set

1 Calculate the de Broglie wavelengths of the following items:

    a) an electron with a kinetic energy of 3 eV

    b) a proton with a kinetic energy of 7 MeV

    c) a buckyball (C_{60}) with a speed of 200 m/s

    d) an oxygen molecule at room temperature

    e) a raindrop

    f) yourself walking to class

In which of the above cases might you expect quantum mechanics to play an important role and why?

2 The wave function for a particle in one dimension is

    (i)
$$\psi(x) = Ae^{-x^2/a^2}.$$

    a) Normalize the wave function.

    b) Calculate the expectation value $\langle x \rangle$ of the position.

    c) Calculate the uncertainty Δx of the position.

    d) Calculate the probability that the particle is found in the region $0 < x < a$.

    e) Plot the wave function and the probability density and indicate the results to (b), (c), and (d) on the plot.

    f) Calculate the expectation value $\langle p \rangle$ of the momentum.

    g) Calculate the uncertainty Δp of the momentum.

    h) Does this state satisfy the uncertainty principle?

Repeat for other wave functions:

    (ii)
$$\psi(x) = Axe^{-x^2/a^2}$$

    (iii)
$$\psi(x) = A\frac{1}{x^2 + a^2}$$

3 A beam of particles is prepared in a momentum eigenstate $|p_0\rangle$. The beam is directed to a shutter that is open for a finite time τ.

    a) Find the wave function of the system immediately after passing through the shutter.

    b) Find the momentum probability distribution of the beam after the shutter.

4 Calculate the momentum space wave function for a particle in an energy eigenstate of the infinite square well. Plot the momentum probability densities for the $n = 1, 2$, and 10 energy eigenstates. Discuss your results.

5 Show that the momentum and Hamiltonian operators commute for a free particle. Do this two ways, using both the differential form (position representation) of the operators and the abstract form.

6 Calculate the commutator of the position and momentum operators. Do this two ways, using both the position representation of the operators and the momentum representation.

From Chapter 6 of *Quantum Mechanics: A Paradigms Approach*, First Edition. David H. McIntyre. Copyright © 2012 by Pearson Education, Inc. Published by Pearson Addison-Wesley. All rights reserved.

The companion websites for this text are http://physics.oregonstate.edu/portfolioswiki and http://physics.oregonstate.edu/qmactivities.

7 Show that the momentum eigenstates $\varphi_p(x) = Ae^{ipx/\hbar}$ satisfy the Dirac orthogonality condition in Eq. (23),

$$\int_{-\infty}^{\infty} \varphi_{p''}^*(x)\varphi_{p'}(x)dx = \delta(p'' - p'),\tag{23}$$

and that the normalization constant is $A = 1/\sqrt{2\pi\hbar}$. Use the Dirac orthogonality condition to normalize the wave vector eigenstates $\varphi_k(x) = Ae^{ikx}$ and explain why the result differs from that for the momentum eigenstates.

8 Use your favorite computational plotting tool to create and plot a wave packet comprising three sinusoidal waves. Vary the separation δp of the side modes from the central mode and notice the effect upon the spatial extent δx of the "localized" wave packet. Quantify the relationship between the momentum spread δp and the position spread δx. Animate your plots and distinguish the motion of the wave packet envelope and the motion of the sinusoidal waves inside the envelope.

9 Perform the Gaussian integral in Eq. (48),

$$\psi(x,t) = \frac{1}{\sqrt{2\pi\hbar}}\int_{-\infty}^{\infty}\left(\frac{1}{2\pi\beta^2}\right)^{1/4} e^{-(p-p_0)^2/4\beta^2}\, e^{ipx/\hbar}\, e^{-ip^2t/2m\hbar}\, dp,\tag{48}$$

and verify the result in Eq. (49),

$$\psi(x,t) = \frac{\sqrt{2\beta}}{\sqrt{\hbar\gamma\sqrt{2\pi}}} e^{ip_0(x-p_0t/2m)/\hbar} e^{-(x-p_0t/m)^2\beta^2/\hbar^2\gamma}.\tag{49}$$

10 Calculate the expectation values of position and momentum for a Gaussian wave packet by direct integration and verify Eqs. (56),

$$\langle x \rangle = \frac{p_0}{m}t,\tag{56}$$

and (59),

$$\langle p \rangle = p_0.\tag{59}$$

11 Use your favorite computational plotting tool to create and plot a Gaussian wave packet. Vary the width β of the momentum distribution and notice the effect upon the spatial extent Δx of the wave packet. Quantify the relationship between the momentum spread and the position spread. Animate your plots and distinguish the motion of the wave packet envelope and the motion of the sinusoidal waves inside the envelope.

12 Show that a propagating Gaussian wave packet broadens in position space but not in momentum space. Plot the position-momentum uncertainty product as a function of time and show that the Gaussian wave packet is a minimum uncertainty state. Discuss your results.

13 Discuss each step in the calculation of the phase and group velocities in Eqs. (62) and (63),

$$v_{phase} = \frac{\omega}{k} = \frac{\hbar\omega}{\hbar k} = \frac{E}{p} = \frac{p^2/2m}{p} = \frac{p}{2m} = \frac{v_{classical}}{2},\tag{62}$$

$$v_{group} = \frac{d\omega}{dk}\bigg|_{k_0} = \frac{d(\hbar\omega)}{d(\hbar k)}\bigg|_{k_0} = \frac{dE}{dp}\bigg|_{p_0} = \frac{d(p^2/2m)}{dp}\bigg|_{p_0} = \frac{p_0}{m} = v_{classical}.\tag{63}$$

14 Consider a particle whose wave function is $\psi(x) = A\sin(p_0 x/\hbar)$. Is this wave function an eigenstate of momentum? Find the expectation value $\langle p \rangle$ of the momentum and the momentum probability distribution. Calculate the uncertainty Δp of the momentum. What are the possible results of a measurement of the momentum?

15 Use the uncertainty principle to estimate the ground state energy of a particle of mass m confined to a box with a size of a. Calculate the energy in electron volts for an electron confined in a box with $a = 0.1$ nm, which is roughly the size of an atom.

16 Use the uncertainty principle to estimate the ground-state energy of a particle of mass m bound in the harmonic oscillator potential $V(x) = \frac{1}{2}kx^2$.

17 Use the uncertainty principle to estimate the ground-state energy of a particle of mass m bound in the potential $V(x) = a|x|$.

18 Use the uncertainty principle to estimate the ground-state energy of a particle of mass m bound in the potential $V(x) = bx^4$.

19 Use the uncertainty principle to estimate the ground-state energy of the hydrogen atom.

20 Calculate the position uncertainty for a particle bound to an infinite square well of width L if (a) the particle is in the ground state, and (b) if the probability density is uniform across the well.

21 A beam of particles is described by the wave function

$$\psi(x) = Ae^{ip_0/\hbar x}e^{-x^2/4\alpha^2}.$$

a) Calculate the expectation value $\langle p \rangle$ of the momentum by working in the position representation.

b) Calculate the expectation value $\langle p \rangle$ of the momentum by working in the momentum representation.

22 A beam of particles is described by the wave function

$$\psi(x) = \begin{cases} Ae^{ip_0 x/\hbar}(b-|x|), & |x| < b \\ 0, & |x| > b. \end{cases}$$

a) Normalize the wave function.

b) Plot the wave function.

c) Calculate and plot the momentum probability distribution.

23 Some radioactive nuclei emit electrons (beta radiation), so you might speculate that electrons can exist within a nucleus. Use the uncertainty principle to estimate the minimum kinetic energy (beware of relativity) of an electron confined within a nucleus of size 2 fm. Compare that with the Coulomb potential energy of the electron and comment on the possibility of electron confinement within the nucleus.

24 Solve the boundary condition equations (90),

$$\varphi_E(-a): \quad Ae^{-ik_1 a} + Be^{ik_1 a} = Ce^{-ik_2 a} + De^{ik_2 a}$$

$$\left.\frac{d\varphi_E(x)}{dx}\right|_{x=-a}: \quad ik_1 Ae^{-ik_1 a} - ik_1 Be^{ik_1 a} = ik_2 Ce^{-ik_2 a} - ik_2 De^{ik_2 a}$$

$$\varphi_E(a): \quad Ce^{ik_2 a} + De^{-ik_2 a} = Fe^{ik_1 a} \qquad (90)$$

$$\left.\frac{d\varphi_E(x)}{dx}\right|_{x=a}: \quad ik_2 Ce^{ik_2 a} - ik_2 De^{-ik_2 a} = ik_1 Fe^{ik_1 a},$$

to find the amplitudes for transmission and reflection in Eq. (91),

$$\frac{F}{A} = \frac{e^{-2ik_1 a}}{\cos(2k_2 a) - i\frac{k_1^2 + k_2^2}{2k_1 k_2}\sin(2k_2 a)}$$

$$\frac{B}{A} = i\frac{F}{A}\frac{k_2^2 - k_1^2}{2k_1 k_2}\sin(2k_2 a).$$

(91)

25 Electrons incident upon a finite square well of depth 12 eV are transmitted with unit probability when their kinetic energy is 20 eV. What is the minimum width of the well? Assuming this minimum width, for what other kinetic energies are the electrons also transmitted completely? Does this well have any bound states?

26 A finite square well of depth 8 eV has 5 bound states. Electrons incident upon the well are transmitted with unit probability when their kinetic energy is 11 eV. What is the width of the well? For what other kinetic energies are the electrons also transmitted completely?

27 A finite square well has depth 5 eV and width 0.5 nm. What are the bound-state energies of this well? Find the kinetic energies of electrons incident upon the well that are transmitted with unit probability.

28 A finite square barrier has height 5 eV and width 1 nm. Find the kinetic energies of electrons incident upon the well that are transmitted with unit probability.

29 Consider a potential energy step as shown in Fig. 26 with a beam of particles incident from the left.

   a) Calculate the reflection coefficient for the case where the energy of the incident particles is less than the height of the potential energy step.

   b) Calculate the reflection coefficient for the case where the energy of the incident particles is greater than the height of the step.

   c) Plot your results as a function of the incident energy and comment.

30 Show that a double step potential can be designed such that particles of particular energies are transmitted with unit probability. The optical analogue is an antireflection coating.

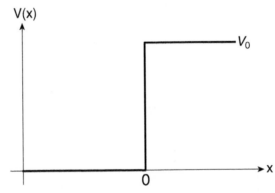

FIGURE 26 Step potential.

31 Calculate the probability of transmission of an electron with kinetic energy 5 eV through a barrier of height 10 eV and width 1 nm.

32 Consider a particle incident upon a potential energy barrier with a barrier height larger than the kinetic energy. Show that the growing exponential wave inside the barrier is always less than or equal to the decaying exponential term.

33 Show that the tunneling probability through a barrier of width d is proportional to e^{-2qd} for $qd \gg 1$.

34 If the tunneling current in a scanning tunneling microscope is 1 nA at 1 nm tip-surface separation, how much current will flow at tip-surface separations of 0.8 nm, 1.2 nm, or 2 nm? Assume that the work functions of the metals are 5 eV and that the bias voltage is minimal.

Angular Momentum

From Chapter 7 of *Quantum Mechanics: A Paradigms Approach*, First Edition. David H. McIntyre. Copyright © 2012 by Pearson Education, Inc. Published by Pearson Addison-Wesley. All rights reserved.

The companion websites for this text are http://physics.oregonstate.edu/portfolioswiki and http://physics.oregonstate.edu/qmactivities.

Angular Momentum

Consider the fundamentals of solving quantum mechanical problems with the wave function approach. Recall particles bound in idealized square potential energy wells and free particles. We are now ready to attack the most important problem in the history of quantum mechanics—the hydrogen atom. The ability to solve this problem and compare it with precision experiments has played a central role in making quantum mechanics the best proven theory in physics.

The hydrogen atom is the bound state of a positively charged proton and a negatively charged electron that are attracted to each other by the Coulomb force. Classically, we expect the electron ($m_e = 9.11 \times 10^{-31}$ kg) to orbit around the more massive proton ($m_p = 1.67 \times 10^{-27}$ kg), in the same manner that the earth orbits around the sun, as depicted in Fig. 1(a). However, the uncertainty principle dictates that we cannot know the position of the electron well enough for Fig. 1(a) to be a valid representation, but rather, the electron is represented by a probability cloud as in Fig. 1(b).

As always in quantum mechanics, we begin by identifying the Hamiltonian of the system of interest because of its role in determining the dynamics of the system through the Schrödinger equation

$$i\hbar \frac{d}{dt}|\psi\rangle = H|\psi\rangle. \tag{1}$$

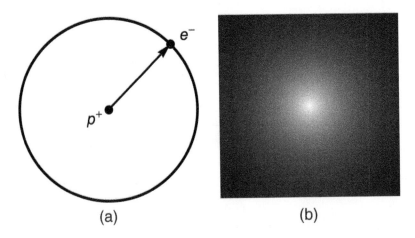

FIGURE 1   (a) A classical atom and (b) a quantum atom.

Once we know the Hamiltonian, we find the energy eigenstates by solving the energy eigenvalue equation

$$H|E\rangle = E|E\rangle. \tag{2}$$

The energy eigenstates form the preferred basis for expanding any initial state and applying the Schrödinger time evolution recipe, so solving the energy eigenvalue equation is the primary task required to solve most quantum mechanical problems.

The hydrogen atom system presents us with two major complications: two particles and three dimensions. The goal of this chapter is to simplify both these aspects of the problem. Analogous to the approach taken in classical mechanics, we reduce the two-body problem to a fictitious one-body problem and we separate the three spatial degrees of freedom in a way that each spherical coordinate can be treated independently. A flowchart depicting these two simplifications is shown in Fig. 2. In this chapter, we perform all the steps of Fig. 2 except the radial coordinate part. In particular, we focus on the two angular degrees of freedom because they relate to the angular momentum, which is a conserved quantity. In the next chapter, we solve the radial aspect of the problem for a $1/r$ Coulomb potential energy, which leads to the quantized energy levels of the hydrogen atom. The journey through the next two chapters requires some mathematics that may appear daunting; we provide the roadmaps in Figs. 2 and 6 so you *can* see the forest for the trees.

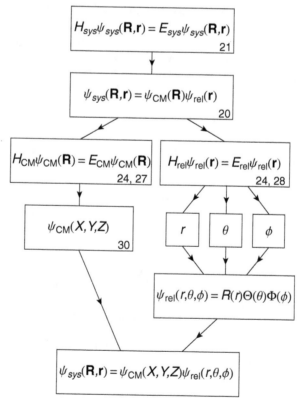

FIGURE 2 Flowchart for solving the hydrogen atom energy eigenvalue problem by reducing the two-body problem to a one-body problem and by separation of the spherical coordinate variables. The numbers in the corners of the boxes refer to the relevant equation numbers in the chapter.

For a three-dimensional system of two particles, the Hamiltonian is the sum of the kinetic energies of the two individual particles and the potential energy that describes the interaction between them:

$$H_{sys} = \frac{\mathbf{p}_1^2}{2m_1} + \frac{\mathbf{p}_2^2}{2m_2} + V(\mathbf{r}_1, \mathbf{r}_2). \tag{3}$$

Particle 1 has mass m_1, position $\mathbf{r}_1$, and momentum $\mathbf{p}_1$; particle 2 has mass m_2, position $\mathbf{r}_2$, and momentum $\mathbf{p}_2$, and the interaction of the two particles is characterized by the potential energy $V(\mathbf{r}_1, \mathbf{r}_2)$. We assume that the potential energy depends only on the magnitude of the separation of the two particles

$$V(\mathbf{r}_1, \mathbf{r}_2) = V(|\mathbf{r}_1 - \mathbf{r}_2|), \tag{4}$$

which we refer to as a **central potential**. In this chapter, we do not need to know the actual form of the central potential. In fact, the quantum mechanical angular wave functions we find in this chapter are valid for *any* central potential, which is a very powerful result.

1 ■ SEPARATING CENTER-OF-MASS AND RELATIVE MOTION

In classical mechanics, we simplify the motion of a system of particles by separating the motion of the composite system into the motion *of the center of mass* and the motion *about the center of mass*. We take this same approach to simplify the quantum mechanical description of the hydrogen atom. We will work this through in some detail because the procedure of separating the motion is very common and needs to be understood, but, in fact, we will not pursue the motion *of* the center of mass beyond this section. In the next section, we'll begin the discussion of the motion *about* the center of mass, which is where many treatments of the hydrogen atom start.

As illustrated in Fig. 3, we define the center-of-mass coordinate position vector for this two-body system as

$$\mathbf{R} = \frac{m_1 \mathbf{r}_1 + m_2 \mathbf{r}_2}{m_1 + m_2} \tag{5}$$

and the relative position vector as

$$\mathbf{r} = \mathbf{r}_2 - \mathbf{r}_1. \tag{6}$$

In classical mechanics, we typically use velocities, which are obtained by differentiation of position with respect to time. In quantum mechanics, we use momentum as the preferred quantity, so the appropriate quantities to separate the two-body motion are the momentum of the center of mass

$$\mathbf{P} = \mathbf{p}_1 + \mathbf{p}_2 \tag{7}$$

and the relative momentum

$$\mathbf{p}_{rel} = \frac{m_1 \mathbf{p}_2 - m_2 \mathbf{p}_1}{m_1 + m_2}. \tag{8}$$

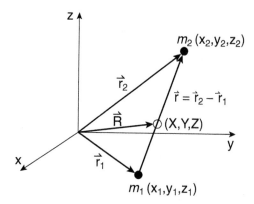

FIGURE 3   The center-of-mass and relative coordinates for a two-body system.

The relative momentum takes the simpler form that looks like a relative velocity

$$\frac{\mathbf{p}_{rel}}{\mu} = \frac{\mathbf{p}_2}{m_2} - \frac{\mathbf{p}_1}{m_1} \tag{9}$$

if we define the **reduced mass** μ:

$$\frac{1}{\mu} = \frac{1}{m_1} + \frac{1}{m_2}$$
$$\mu = \frac{m_1 m_2}{m_1 + m_2}. \tag{10}$$

With the definitions in Eqs. (7) and (8), the two-body Hamiltonian in Eq. (3) becomes (Problem 1)

$$H_{sys} = \frac{\mathbf{P}^2}{2M} + \frac{\mathbf{p}_{rel}^2}{2\mu} + V(r), \tag{11}$$

where the relative particle separation r is the magnitude $|\mathbf{r}_2 - \mathbf{r}_1|$. This procedure has separated the system Hamiltonian into two independent parts:

$$H_{sys} = H_{CM} + H_{rel}, \tag{12}$$

with a center-of-mass term

$$H_{CM} = \frac{\mathbf{P}^2}{2M} \tag{13}$$

representing the motion of a particle of mass $M = m_1 + m_2$ located at position $\mathbf{R}$ with momentum $\mathbf{P} = \mathbf{p}_1 + \mathbf{p}_2$, and a relative term

$$H_{rel} = \frac{\mathbf{p}_{rel}^2}{2\mu} + V(r) \tag{14}$$

representing the motion of a single fictitious particle of mass μ located at position $\mathbf{r} = \mathbf{r}_2 - \mathbf{r}_1$ with momentum $\mathbf{p}_{rel}$ subject to a potential energy $V(r)$ created by a force-center that is fixed at the origin. Notice that the center-of-mass Hamiltonian H_{CM} does *not* depend on the relative motion variables $\mathbf{p}_{rel}$ and $\mathbf{r}$, and the relative Hamiltonian H_{rel} does *not* depend on the center-of-mass motion variables $\mathbf{P}$ and $\mathbf{R}$; this is what we mean by "separable." In contrast, Eq. (3) presents the same Hamiltonian in terms of $\mathbf{p}_1$ and $\mathbf{r}_1$ and $\mathbf{p}_2$ and $\mathbf{r}_2$, but the potential energy V contains both $\mathbf{r}_1$ and $\mathbf{r}_2$, so H is not separable in those coordinates. Notice also that the center-of-mass position vector $\mathbf{R}$ does not appear in the Hamiltonian at all, which, classically, is a reflection of the fact that the momentum of the center of mass is conserved because there are no external forces. For the hydrogen atom system, the reduced mass is $\mu = 0.9995 m_e$ and the center of mass is located very near the proton.

The separation of the Hamiltonian into center-of-mass motion and relative motion can also be done using the explicit position representation of the momentum operators as differentials. In the position representation, the one-dimensional momentum operator is

$$p \doteq -i\hbar \frac{d}{dx}.$$

(15)

In three dimensions, the momentum operator is cast in terms of the gradient operator ∇:

$$\mathbf{p} \doteq -i\hbar \left(\frac{\partial}{\partial x}\hat{\mathbf{i}} + \frac{\partial}{\partial y}\hat{\mathbf{j}} + \frac{\partial}{\partial z}\hat{\mathbf{k}} \right) = -i\hbar \nabla.$$

(16)

For a two-particle system, the momentum operators for the two particles are

$$\mathbf{p}_1 \doteq -i\hbar \left(\frac{\partial}{\partial x_1}\hat{\mathbf{i}} + \frac{\partial}{\partial y_1}\hat{\mathbf{j}} + \frac{\partial}{\partial z_1}\hat{\mathbf{k}} \right) = -i\hbar \nabla_1$$

$$\mathbf{p}_2 \doteq -i\hbar \left(\frac{\partial}{\partial x_2}\hat{\mathbf{i}} + \frac{\partial}{\partial y_2}\hat{\mathbf{j}} + \frac{\partial}{\partial z_2}\hat{\mathbf{k}} \right) = -i\hbar \nabla_2.$$

(17)

Substituting these position representations into the Hamiltonian in Eq. (3) leads to the same separation as in Eq. (11), where the center-of-mass momentum operator has the position representation (Problem 1)

$$\mathbf{P} \doteq -i\hbar \left(\frac{\partial}{\partial X}\hat{\mathbf{i}} + \frac{\partial}{\partial Y}\hat{\mathbf{j}} + \frac{\partial}{\partial Z}\hat{\mathbf{k}} \right) = -i\hbar \nabla_R.$$

(18)

X, Y, and Z are the Cartesian coordinates of the center-of-mass vector $\mathbf{R}$, and ∇_R is the gradient operator corresponding to the center-of-mass coordinates. The relative momentum operator has the position representation

$$\mathbf{p}_{rel} \doteq -i\hbar \left(\frac{\partial}{\partial x}\hat{\mathbf{i}} + \frac{\partial}{\partial y}\hat{\mathbf{j}} + \frac{\partial}{\partial z}\hat{\mathbf{k}} \right) = -i\hbar \nabla_r,$$

(19)

where x, y, and z are the Cartesian coordinates of the relative position vector $\mathbf{r} = \mathbf{r}_2 - \mathbf{r}_1$ and ∇_r is the gradient operator corresponding to the relative coordinates.

With the Hamiltonian separated into center-of-mass motion and relative motion, we expect that the quantum state vector can also be separated. This is not always the case, as we see with entanglement, but it is a valid assumption for the hydrogen atom problem we want to solve because the potential energy is a function only of the relative coordinate $\mathbf{r}$. Hence, we write the wave function for the system as

$$\psi_{sys}(\mathbf{R}, \mathbf{r}) = \psi_{CM}(\mathbf{R}) \, \psi_{rel}(\mathbf{r}).$$

(20)

The energy eigenvalue equation for the system is

$$H_{sys}\psi_{sys}(\mathbf{R},\mathbf{r}) = E_{sys}\,\psi_{sys}(\mathbf{R},\mathbf{r}),\qquad(21)$$

and substituting the separated Hamiltonian [Eq. (12)] and separated wave function [Eq. (20)] gives

$$(H_{CM} + H_{rel})\psi_{CM}(\mathbf{R})\,\psi_{rel}(\mathbf{r}) = E_{sys}\,\psi_{CM}(\mathbf{R})\,\psi_{rel}(\mathbf{r}).\qquad(22)$$

The separate center-of-mass and relative Hamiltonians act only on their respective wave functions because the gradients ∇_R and ∇_r are independent, so Eq. (22) becomes

$$\psi_{rel}(\mathbf{r})H_{CM}\psi_{CM}(\mathbf{R}) + \psi_{CM}(\mathbf{R})H_{rel}\psi_{rel}(\mathbf{r}) = E_{sys}\,\psi_{CM}(\mathbf{R})\,\psi_{rel}(\mathbf{r}).\qquad(23)$$

We assert that the separate center-of-mass and relative Hamiltonians satisfy their own energy eigenvalue equations (Problem 2)

$$H_{CM}\psi_{CM}(\mathbf{R}) = E_{CM}\psi_{CM}(\mathbf{R})$$
$$H_{rel}\psi_{rel}(\mathbf{r}) = E_{rel}\psi_{rel}(\mathbf{r})\qquad(24)$$

and arrive at the energy eigenvalue equation for the system

$$H_{sys}\psi_{CM}(\mathbf{R})\,\psi_{rel}(\mathbf{r}) = (E_{CM} + E_{rel})\psi_{CM}(\mathbf{R})\,\psi_{rel}(\mathbf{r}),\qquad(25)$$

which demonstrates that the system energy is the additive energy of the two parts

$$E_{sys} = E_{CM} + E_{rel}.\qquad(26)$$

Using the separate Hamiltonians in Eqs. (13) and (14), the separated energy eigenvalue equations are

$$\frac{\mathbf{P}^2}{2M}\psi_{CM}(\mathbf{R}) = E_{CM}\psi_{CM}(\mathbf{R})\qquad(27)$$

and

$$\left(\frac{\mathbf{p}_{rel}^2}{2\mu} + V(\mathbf{r})\right)\psi_{rel}(\mathbf{r}) = E_{rel}\psi_{rel}(\mathbf{r}).\qquad(28)$$

The center-of-mass energy eigenvalue equation (27) is the free particle eigenvalue equation, while the relative motion energy eigenvalue equation (28) contains the interaction potential and so has the interesting physics of the hydrogen atom. Using the position representation of the momentum operator in Eq. (18), the center-of-mass energy eigenvalue equation is

$$-\frac{\hbar^2}{2M}\left(\frac{\partial^2}{\partial X^2} + \frac{\partial^2}{\partial Y^2} + \frac{\partial^2}{\partial Z^2}\right)\psi_{CM}(X,Y,Z) = E_{CM}\psi_{CM}(X,Y,Z).\qquad(29)$$

The solution to Eq. (29) is the three-dimensional extension of free-particle eigenstates

$$\psi_{CM}(X,Y,Z) = \frac{1}{(2\pi\hbar)^{3/2}}\,e^{i(P_X X + P_Y Y + P_Z Z)/\hbar}\qquad(30)$$

with energy eigenvalues

$$E_{CM} = \frac{1}{2M}\left(P_X^2 + P_Y^2 + P_Z^2\right).\qquad(31)$$

For measurements of observables associated with the relative motion, the center-of-mass wave function contributes only an overall phase to the system wave function and so has no effect on calculating probabilities of relative motion quantities. We can therefore leave the center-of-mass motion and concentrate only on the relative motion dictated by the energy eigenvalue equation (28). That is the problem we want to solve for the hydrogen atom. Remember that the angular momentum discusssion that will follow in this chapter is valid for any central potential.

2 ■ ENERGY EIGENVALUE EQUATION IN SPHERICAL COORDINATES

The relative motion Hamiltonian that governs the hydrogen atom is

$$H = \frac{\mathbf{p}^2}{2\mu} + V(r),\tag{32}$$

where we drop the "relative" subscripts because we are now focusing exclusively on the relative motion and ignoring the center-of-mass motion. Using the position representation of the momentum operator from Eq. (19), the Hamiltonian is represented by

$$H \doteq -\frac{\hbar^2}{2\mu}\nabla^2 + V(r)\tag{33}$$

and the energy eigenvalue equation is the differential equation

$$\left(-\frac{\hbar^2}{2\mu}\nabla^2 + V(r)\right)\psi(\mathbf{r}) = E\psi(\mathbf{r}).\tag{34}$$

Because the potential energy in Eq. (34) depends on the parameter r only, this problem is clearly asking for the use of spherical coordinates centered at the origin of the central potential. The system of spherical coordinates is shown in Fig. 4(a) and the relations between the spherical coordinates r, θ, ϕ and the Cartesian coordinates x, y, z are

$$\begin{aligned} x &= r\sin\theta\,\cos\phi \\ y &= r\sin\theta\,\sin\phi \\ z &= r\cos\theta. \end{aligned}\tag{35}$$

The differential volume element $dV = dx\,dy\,dz$ expressed in spherical coordinates is

$$dV = r^2\sin\theta\,d\theta\,d\phi\,dr.\tag{36}$$

This volume element is shown in Fig. 4(b), leading one to consider the grouping

$$dV = (r\,d\theta)(r\sin\theta\,d\phi)(dr).\tag{37}$$

However, for calculating the normalization of wave functions, we will group the terms as

$$dV = (\sin\theta\,d\theta)(d\phi)(r^2 dr)\tag{38}$$

and normalize each coordinate piece of the wave function separately. It is also convenient to express the volume element as

$$dV = r^2 dr \, d\Omega, \tag{39}$$

where

$$d\Omega = \sin\theta \, d\theta \, d\phi \tag{40}$$

is the differential solid angle element.

In spherical coordinates, the gradient operator is

$$\nabla = \hat{\mathbf{r}} \frac{\partial}{\partial r} + \hat{\theta} \frac{1}{r} \frac{\partial}{\partial \theta} + \hat{\phi} \frac{1}{r\sin\theta} \frac{\partial}{\partial \phi} \tag{41}$$

and the Laplacian operator $\nabla^2 = \nabla \cdot \nabla$ is

$$\nabla^2 = \frac{1}{r^2} \frac{\partial}{\partial r} \left(r^2 \frac{\partial}{\partial r} \right) + \frac{1}{r^2 \sin\theta} \frac{\partial}{\partial \theta} \left(\sin\theta \frac{\partial}{\partial \theta} \right) + \frac{1}{r^2 \sin^2\theta} \frac{\partial^2}{\partial \phi^2}. \tag{42}$$

Using this spherical coordinate representation, the energy eigenvalue equation (34) becomes the differential equation

$$-\frac{\hbar^2}{2\mu} \left[\frac{1}{r^2} \frac{\partial}{\partial r} \left(r^2 \frac{\partial}{\partial r} \right) + \frac{1}{r^2 \sin\theta} \frac{\partial}{\partial \theta} \left(\sin\theta \frac{\partial}{\partial \theta} \right) + \frac{1}{r^2 \sin^2\theta} \frac{\partial^2}{\partial \phi^2} \right] \psi(r,\theta,\phi)$$
$$+ V(r)\psi(r,\theta,\phi) = E\psi(r,\theta,\phi) . \tag{43}$$

This looks formidable, so it is worth remembering that this is just the position representation of the energy eigenvalue equation

$$H|E\rangle = E|E\rangle. \tag{44}$$

Solving Eq. (43) for the energy E and the eigenstates $|E\rangle \doteq \psi(r,\theta,\phi)$ is our primary task, but first let's discuss the important role that angular momentum plays in this equation.

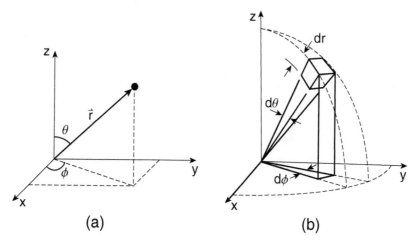

FIGURE 4   (a) Spherical coordinates and (b) the differential volume element.

3 ■ ANGULAR MOMENTUM

3.1 ■ Classical Angular Momentum

The classical angular momentum is defined as

$$\mathbf{L} = \mathbf{r} \times \mathbf{p}. \tag{45}$$

In the case of central forces, the torque $\mathbf{r} \times \mathbf{F}$ is zero and angular momentum is a conserved quantity:

$$\tau = \frac{d\mathbf{L}}{dt} = 0 \quad \Rightarrow \quad \mathbf{L} = constant. \tag{46}$$

A central force $\mathbf{F}(r)$ depends only on the distance of the reduced mass from the center of force (i.e., the separation of the two particles) and not on the angular orientation of the system. Therefore, the system is spherically symmetric; it is invariant (unchanged) under rotations. Noether's theorem states that whenever the laws of physics are invariant under a particular motion or other operation, there will be a corresponding conserved quantity. In this case, the conservation of angular momentum is related to the invariance of the physical system under rotations.

3.2 ■ Quantum Mechanical Angular Momentum

In quantum mechanics, the Cartesian components of the angular momentum operator $\mathbf{L} = \mathbf{r} \times \mathbf{p}$ in the position representation are

$$L_x = yp_z - zp_y \doteq -i\hbar \left(y\frac{\partial}{\partial z} - z\frac{\partial}{\partial y} \right)$$

$$L_y = zp_x - xp_z \doteq -i\hbar \left(z\frac{\partial}{\partial x} - x\frac{\partial}{\partial z} \right) \tag{47}$$

$$L_z = xp_y - yp_x \doteq -i\hbar \left(x\frac{\partial}{\partial y} - y\frac{\partial}{\partial x} \right).$$

Position and momentum operators for a given axis do not commute ($[x, p_x] = i\hbar$, etc.), whereas position and momentum operators for different axes do commute ($[x, p_y] = 0$, etc.). We can use these commutators to calculate the commutators of the components of the angular momentum operator. For example,

$$[L_x, L_y] = [yp_z - zp_y, zp_x - xp_z]$$
$$= yp_z zp_x - yp_z xp_z - zp_y zp_x + zp_y xp_z - zp_x yp_z + zp_x zp_y + xp_z yp_z - xp_z zp_y. \tag{48}$$

Now use the commutation relations to move commuting operators through each other (e.g., $yp_z zp_x = yp_x p_z z$) and cancel terms:

$$[L_x, L_y] = yp_x p_z z - xyp_z p_z - zzp_x p_y + xp_y zp_z - yp_x zp_z + zzp_x p_y + xyp_z p_z - xp_y p_z z$$
$$= yp_x p_z z + xp_y zp_z - yp_x zp_z - xp_y p_z z. \tag{49}$$

Finally, collect terms and use the commutator relation $[z, p_z] = i\hbar$:

$$[L_x, L_y] = xp_y(zp_z - p_z z) - yp_x(zp_z - p_z z)$$
$$= xp_y[z, p_z] - yp_x[z, p_z]$$
$$= i\hbar(xp_y - yp_x) \tag{50}$$
$$= i\hbar L_z.$$

Cyclic permutations of this identity give the three commutation relations

$$\boxed{\begin{aligned} [L_x, L_y] &= i\hbar L_z \\ [L_y, L_z] &= i\hbar L_x \\ [L_z, L_x] &= i\hbar L_y \end{aligned}} \tag{51}$$

These are exactly the same commutation relations that spin angular momentum obeys! So *orbital* and *spin* angular momentum appear to have something in common, as you might expect. Indeed, this is why the physical property of spin angular momentum was given this name.

When we studied spin, we found it useful to consider the $\mathbf{S}^2 = \mathbf{S} \cdot \mathbf{S}$ operator. The corresponding operator for orbital angular momentum is

$$\mathbf{L}^2 = \mathbf{L} \cdot \mathbf{L} = L_x^2 + L_y^2 + L_z^2. \tag{52}$$

In the spin case, the operator $\mathbf{S}^2$ commutes with all three component operators. Let's try the same with orbital angular momentum. For example,

$$\begin{aligned} [\mathbf{L}^2, L_x] &= [L_x^2 + L_y^2 + L_z^2, L_x] \\ &= [L_x^2, L_x] + [L_y^2, L_x] + [L_z^2, L_x] \\ &= L_y^2 L_x - L_x L_y^2 + L_z^2 L_x - L_x L_z^2. \end{aligned} \tag{53}$$

Add zero to this equation, but choose the terms that sum to zero cleverly so they help:

$$\begin{aligned} [\mathbf{L}^2, L_x] &= L_y L_y L_x \underbrace{- L_y L_x L_y + L_y L_x L_y}_{=0} - L_x L_y L_y + L_z L_z L_x \underbrace{- L_z L_x L_z + L_z L_x L_z}_{=0} - L_x L_z L_z \\ &= L_y[L_y, L_x] + [L_y, L_x]L_y + L_z[L_z, L_x] + [L_z, L_x]L_z \\ &= -i\hbar L_y L_z - i\hbar L_z L_y + i\hbar L_z L_y + i\hbar L_y L_z \\ &= 0. \end{aligned} \tag{54}$$

The other two components also commute with $\mathbf{L}^2$ (Problem 4):

$$\boxed{\begin{aligned} [\mathbf{L}^2, L_x] &= 0 \\ [\mathbf{L}^2, L_y] &= 0 \\ [\mathbf{L}^2, L_z] &= 0 \end{aligned}} \tag{55}$$

So *orbital* and *spin* angular momentum obey all the same commutation relations.

The eigenvalues and the eigenstates of spin angular momentum can be derived solely from the commutation relations of the operators. The spin eigenvalue equations are

$$\begin{aligned} \mathbf{S}^2 |s m_s\rangle &= s(s+1)\hbar^2 |s m_s\rangle \\ S_z |s m_s\rangle &= m_s \hbar |s m_s\rangle. \end{aligned} \tag{56}$$

The states $|s m_s\rangle$ are simultaneously eigenstates of $\mathbf{S}^2$ and S_z, which is possible because the two operators commute with each other. Because orbital angular momentum obeys the same commutation relations as spin, the eigenvalue equations for $\mathbf{L}^2$ and L_z have the same form:

$$\boxed{\begin{aligned} \mathbf{L}^2 |\ell m_\ell\rangle &= \ell(\ell+1)\hbar^2 |\ell m_\ell\rangle \\ L_z |\ell m_\ell\rangle &= m_\ell \hbar |\ell m_\ell\rangle \end{aligned}} \tag{57}$$

and the states $|\ell m_\ell\rangle$ are simultaneously eigenstates of $\mathbf{L}^2$ and L_z. Hence, you can draw on all the work you've done on spins to help understand orbital angular momentum. The quantum number ℓ is the **orbital angular momentum quantum number** and gives a measure of the "size" of the angular momentum vector in that the magnitude is $\sqrt{\ell(\ell + 1)}\hbar$. The quantum number m_ℓ is the **orbital magnetic quantum number** and indicates that the magnitude of the z-component of the angular momentum is $m_\ell \hbar$.

There is one crucial difference between spin angular momentum and orbital angular momentum. In the spin case, the allowed quantized values of the spin angular momentum quantum number s are the integers and half integers:

$$s = 0, \tfrac{1}{2}, 1, \tfrac{3}{2}, 2, \tfrac{5}{2}, 3, \tfrac{7}{2}, 4, \dots . \tag{58}$$

Recall spin-1/2 and spin-1 systems. In the case of orbital angular momentum, the quantum number ℓ is allowed to take on *only* integer values

$$\boxed{\ell = 0, 1, 2, 3, 4, \dots} . \tag{59}$$

Other than this important distinction, spin and orbital angular momentum behave the same in quantum mechanical calculations of probabilities, expectation values, etc. The spin magnetic quantum number m_s spans the range from $-s \rightarrow +s$ in integer steps. The orbital magnetic quantum number m_ℓ is similarly restricted to the $2\ell + 1$ values

$$\boxed{m_\ell = -\ell, -\ell + 1, \dots, -1, 0, 1, \dots, \ell - 1, \ell} . \tag{60}$$

In the spin-1/2 system, we represent the spin operators as matrices:

$$\mathbf{S}^2 \doteq \frac{3}{4}\hbar^2 \begin{pmatrix} 1 & 0 \\ 0 & 1 \end{pmatrix} \qquad S_z \doteq \frac{\hbar}{2} \begin{pmatrix} 1 & 0 \\ 0 & -1 \end{pmatrix}$$

$$S_x \doteq \frac{\hbar}{2} \begin{pmatrix} 0 & 1 \\ 1 & 0 \end{pmatrix} \qquad S_y \doteq \frac{\hbar}{2} \begin{pmatrix} 0 & -i \\ i & 0 \end{pmatrix}, \tag{61}$$

where the basis states of the representation are the eigenstates of $\mathbf{S}^2$ and S_z as defined in Eq. (56). For orbital angular momentum, we also represent the operators as matrices, with the exception that only integer values of ℓ are allowed. For example, the matrix representations of the orbital angular momentum operators for $\ell = 1$ are

$$\mathbf{L}^2 \doteq 2\hbar^2 \begin{pmatrix} 1 & 0 & 0 \\ 0 & 1 & 0 \\ 0 & 0 & 1 \end{pmatrix} \qquad L_z \doteq \hbar \begin{pmatrix} 1 & 0 & 0 \\ 0 & 0 & 0 \\ 0 & 0 & -1 \end{pmatrix}$$

$$L_x \doteq \frac{\hbar}{\sqrt{2}} \begin{pmatrix} 0 & 1 & 0 \\ 1 & 0 & 1 \\ 0 & 1 & 0 \end{pmatrix} \qquad L_y \doteq \frac{\hbar}{\sqrt{2}} \begin{pmatrix} 0 & -i & 0 \\ i & 0 & -i \\ 0 & i & 0 \end{pmatrix}, \tag{62}$$

where the basis states of the representation are the eigenstates of $\mathbf{L}^2$ and L_z as defined in Eq. (57). These matrices are exactly the same as spin-1 matrices.

Example 1   A particle with orbital angular momentum $\ell = 1$ is in the state

$$|\psi\rangle = \sqrt{\tfrac{1}{3}}|11\rangle + \sqrt{\tfrac{2}{3}}|10\rangle. \tag{63}$$

Find the probability that a measurement of L_z yields the value $\hbar$ for this state and calculate the expectation value of L_z.

The eigenstate of L_z with eigenvalue $L_z = +\hbar$ (and eigenvalue $\mathbf{L}^2 = 2\hbar^2$) is $|\ell = 1, m_\ell = 1\rangle = |11\rangle$, so the probability of measuring $L_z = +\hbar$ is

$$\begin{aligned}
\mathcal{P}_\hbar &= |\langle 11|\psi\rangle|^2 \\
&= \left|\langle 11|\left(\sqrt{\tfrac{1}{3}}|11\rangle + \sqrt{\tfrac{2}{3}}|10\rangle\right)\right|^2 \\
&= \left|\sqrt{\tfrac{1}{3}}\langle 11|11\rangle + \sqrt{\tfrac{2}{3}}\langle 11|10\rangle\right|^2.
\end{aligned} \tag{64}$$

The states $|\ell m_\ell\rangle$ form an orthonormal basis, so $\langle 11|11\rangle = 1$ and $\langle 11|10\rangle = 0$, and the probability is

$$\begin{aligned}
\mathcal{P}_\hbar &= \left|\sqrt{\tfrac{1}{3}}\right|^2 \\
&= \tfrac{1}{3}.
\end{aligned} \tag{65}$$

The expectation value of L_z is

$$\langle L_z\rangle = \langle\psi|L_z|\psi\rangle. \tag{66}$$

Let's calculate this with matrices. Using the matrix (column) representation of $|\psi\rangle$:

$$|\psi\rangle \doteq \frac{1}{\sqrt{3}}\begin{pmatrix} 1 \\ \sqrt{2} \\ 0 \end{pmatrix}, \tag{67}$$

we get

$$\begin{aligned}
\langle L_z\rangle &= \frac{1}{\sqrt{3}}\begin{pmatrix} 1 & \sqrt{2} & 0 \end{pmatrix}\hbar\begin{pmatrix} 1 & 0 & 0 \\ 0 & 0 & 0 \\ 0 & 0 & -1 \end{pmatrix}\frac{1}{\sqrt{3}}\begin{pmatrix} 1 \\ \sqrt{2} \\ 0 \end{pmatrix} \\
&= \frac{\hbar}{3}\begin{pmatrix} 1 & \sqrt{2} & 0 \end{pmatrix}\begin{pmatrix} 1 \\ 0 \\ 0 \end{pmatrix} \\
&= \frac{\hbar}{3}.
\end{aligned} \tag{68}$$

These calculations are no different than if this were a spin-1 problem.

So it looks like we can solve orbital angular momentum problems using our spin knowledge, and you may well ask: Is that all there is to it? *Yes and no!* If you can solve a problem like Example 1 using the bra-ket or matrix notation then do that. But there are problems where we need to do more.

You have probably never discussed a position representation of spin operators or eigenstates, because it is not possible to describe spin angular momentum using wave function language. In contrast, it is possible to represent orbital angular momentum operators and eigenstates in the position representation. We have already presented the position representation of the orbital angular momentum operators L_x, L_y, and L_z in Eq. (47), and the end result of this chapter is a position representation of the angular momentum eigenstates $|\ell m_\ell\rangle$. In solving for the allowed spatial wave functions, we will prove that the orbital angular momentum is quantized according to Eqs. (59) and (60).

Armed with wave functions detailing the spatial dependence of orbital angular momentum, we will then be able to visualize the angular probability distribution of the electron around the proton in the hydrogen atom. We will be able to understand why two hydrogen atoms form a molecule and why the carbon bonds in a diamond lattice are oriented in such a way to make diamond so unique. For example, Fig. 5 shows the angular orientation of the four tetrahedral bonds that one carbon atom makes within the diamond lattice.

To see the importance of orbital angular momentum in solving the hydrogen atom energy eigenvalue equation, we change the angular momentum operators in Eq. (47) to spherical coordinates. Using the relations in Eq. (35), one can show that the angular momentum operator L_z has the spherical coordinate representation (Problem 8)

$$L_z \doteq -i\hbar \frac{\partial}{\partial \phi} \tag{69}$$

and depends on ϕ alone. Likewise, we convert L_x and L_y to spherical coordinates (Problem 8) and obtain the operator $\mathbf{L}^2 = \mathbf{L}\cdot\mathbf{L} = L_x^2 + L_y^2 + L_z^2$:

$$\mathbf{L}^2 \doteq -\hbar^2 \left[\frac{1}{\sin\theta} \frac{\partial}{\partial \theta} \left(\sin\theta \frac{\partial}{\partial \theta} \right) + \frac{1}{\sin^2\theta} \frac{\partial^2}{\partial \phi^2} \right], \tag{70}$$

which depends on θ and ϕ, and not on r. We now have the expressions for the two operators $\mathbf{L}^2$ and L_z that we need to express the angular momentum eigenvalue equations (57) in the spherical coordinate representation, which we do later in this chapter.

Now compare the $\mathbf{L}^2$ operator in Eq. (70) with the energy eigenvalue equation (43). You notice that the $\mathbf{L}^2$ operator is part of the differential operator in the energy eigenvalue equation. Hence, we can rewrite the energy eigenvalue equation $H|\psi\rangle = E|\psi\rangle$ with the $\mathbf{L}^2$ operator

$$-\frac{\hbar^2}{2\mu}\left[\frac{1}{r^2}\frac{\partial}{\partial r}\left(r^2 \frac{\partial}{\partial r}\right) - \frac{1}{\hbar^2 r^2}\mathbf{L}^2 \right]\psi(r,\theta,\phi) + V(r)\psi(r,\theta,\phi) = E\psi(r,\theta,\phi). \tag{71}$$

All of the angular part of the Hamiltonian is contained in the $\mathbf{L}^2$ angular momentum operator. In this form, it is clear that the central force Hamiltonian commutes with the orbital angular momentum operators $\mathbf{L}^2$ and L_z (Problem 9)

$$\left[H, \mathbf{L}^2 \right] = 0$$
$$\left[H, L_z \right] = 0, \tag{72}$$

which implies that we can find simultaneous eigenstates of all three operators.

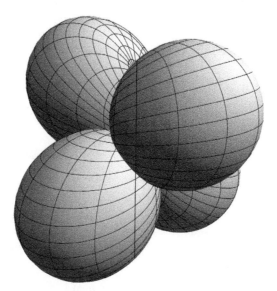

FIGURE 5 Angular dependence of the four sp^3 hybrid orbitals in a diamond lattice.

4 ■ SEPARATION OF VARIABLES: SPHERICAL COORDINATES

We have already simplified the two-body nature of the hydrogen atom problem to an effective one-body problem by separating the relative motion (interesting) from the center-of-mass motion (not so interesting). We now proceed to simplify the three-dimensional aspect of the problem by separating the three spherical coordinate dimensions from each other. To do this, we apply the standard technique of separation of variables to the energy eigenvalue differential equation (71). The flowchart in Fig. 6 shows how the separation and recombination process will progress over the remainder of this chapter.

In the first instance, we apply the six steps of the separation of variables procedure to isolate the radial r dependence and the angular θ, ϕ dependence into two separate equations.

Step 1: Write the partial differential equation in the appropriate coordinate system. We have done this already in Eq. (71)

$$-\frac{\hbar^2}{2\mu}\left[\frac{1}{r^2}\frac{\partial}{\partial r}\left(r^2\frac{\partial}{\partial r}\right) - \frac{1}{\hbar^2 r^2}\mathbf{L}^2\right]\psi(r,\theta,\phi) + V(r)\psi(r,\theta,\phi) = E\psi(r,\theta,\phi). \quad (73)$$

Step 2: *Assume* that the solution $\psi(r, \theta, \phi)$ can be written as the product of functions, at least one of which depends on only one variable, in this case r. The other function(s) must not depend at all on this variable, that is, assume

$$\psi(r,\theta,\phi) = R(r)Y(\theta,\phi). \quad (74)$$

Plug this assumed solution into the partial differential equation (73) from Step 1. Because of the special form of ψ, the partial derivatives each act on only one of the functions in ψ. Any partial derivatives that act only on a function of a single variable may be rewritten as total derivatives, yielding

$$-\frac{\hbar^2}{2\mu}\left[Y\frac{1}{r^2}\frac{d}{dr}\left(r^2\frac{dR}{dr}\right)-\frac{1}{\hbar^2 r^2}R(\mathbf{L}^2 Y)\right]+V(r)RY=ERY. \tag{75}$$

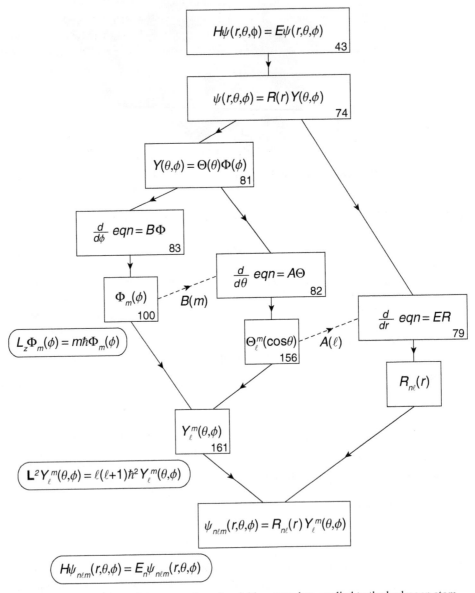

FIGURE 6 Flowchart of the separation of variables procedure applied to the hydrogen atom. The numbers in the corners of the boxes refer to the relevant equation numbers in the chapter.

Note that the orbital angular momentum operator $\mathbf{L}^2$ acts only on angular spatial functions [Eq. (70)].

Step 3: Divide both sides of the equation by $\psi = RY$:

$$-\frac{\hbar^2}{2\mu}\left[\frac{1}{R}\frac{1}{r^2}\frac{d}{dr}\left(r^2\frac{dR}{dr}\right) - \frac{1}{Y}\frac{1}{\hbar^2 r^2}(\mathbf{L}^2 Y)\right] + V(r) = E. \tag{76}$$

Step 4: Isolate *all* of the dependence on one coordinate on one side of the equation. To isolate the r dependence, we multiply Eq. (76) by r^2 to clear the r dependence from the denominator of the angular term (involving angular derivatives in $\mathbf{L}^2$ and angular functions in Y). Further rearranging Eq. (76) to get all of the r dependence on the left-hand side, we obtain:

$$\underbrace{\frac{1}{R(r)}\frac{d}{dr}\left(r^2\frac{dR(r)}{dr}\right) - \frac{2\mu}{\hbar^2}(E - V(r))r^2}_{\text{function of } r \text{ only}} = \underbrace{\frac{1}{\hbar^2}\frac{1}{Y(\theta,\phi)}\mathbf{L}^2 Y(\theta,\phi).}_{\text{function of } \theta,\phi \text{ only}} \tag{77}$$

The left-hand side of Eq. (77) is a function of r only, while the right-hand side is a function of θ,ϕ only.

Step 5: Now imagine changing the isolated variable r by a small amount. In principle, the left-hand side of Eq. (77) could change, but nothing on the right-hand side would. Therefore, if the equation is to be true for all values of r, the particular combination of r dependences on the left-hand side must result in no overall dependence on r—*the left-hand side must be a constant*. We thus define a **separation constant**, which we call A in this case:

$$\frac{1}{R(r)}\frac{d}{dr}\left(r^2\frac{dR(r)}{dr}\right) - \frac{2\mu}{\hbar^2}(E - V(r))r^2 = \frac{1}{\hbar^2}\frac{1}{Y(\theta,\phi)}\mathbf{L}^2 Y(\theta,\phi) \equiv A. \tag{78}$$

Step 6: Write each equation in standard form by multiplying each equation by its unknown function to clear it from the denominator. Rearranging Eq. (78) slightly, we obtain the radial and angular equations in the more standard forms:

$$\left[-\frac{\hbar^2}{2\mu r^2}\frac{d}{dr}\left(r^2\frac{d}{dr}\right) + V(r) + A\frac{\hbar^2}{2\mu r^2}\right]R(r) = ER(r) \tag{79}$$

$$\mathbf{L}^2 Y(\theta,\phi) = A\hbar^2 Y(\theta,\phi). \tag{80}$$

Notice that the only place that the central potential $V(r)$ enters the set of differential equations is in the radial equation (79), which is not yet in the form of an eigenvalue equation because it contains *two* unknown constants, E and A. Equation (80) is an eigenvalue equation for the orbital angular momentum operator $\mathbf{L}^2$ with eigenvalue $A\hbar^2$. It has the same form as Eq. (57), so we fully expect that the separation constant $A = \ell(\ell + 1)$, which we will prove shortly. The angular momentum eigenvalue equation is independent of the central potential $V(r)$, so once we have solved for the orbital angular momentum eigenstates, we will have solved that aspect of the problem for *all central potentials*. Only the radial equation need be solved again for different potentials.

The separation of variables procedure can be applied again to separate the θ dependence from the ϕ dependence in the angular equation (80). If we let

$$Y(\theta,\phi) = \Theta(\theta)\Phi(\phi), \tag{81}$$

then the separated equations are (Problem 10)

$$\left[\frac{1}{\sin\theta}\frac{d}{d\theta}\left(\sin\theta\frac{d}{d\theta}\right) - B\frac{1}{\sin^2\theta}\right]\Theta(\theta) = -A\,\Theta(\theta) \tag{82}$$

$$\frac{d^2\Phi(\phi)}{d\phi^2} = -B\,\Phi(\phi), \tag{83}$$

where we have defined the new separation constant as B. Equation (83) is an eigenvalue equation for the operator $d^2/d\phi^2$ with eigenvalue $-B$. Equation (82) is not yet in the form of an eigenvalue equation because it contains two unknown constants A and B.

We started with a partial differential equation in three variables and we ended up with three ordinary differential equations by introducing *two* separation constants A and B. You should always get one fewer separation constant than the number of variables you started with; each separation constant should appear in two equations of the final set.

So in turn we have identified a radial differential equation for $R(r)$, a polar angle differential equation for $\Theta(\theta)$, and an azimuthal differential equation for $\Phi(\phi)$. But note that the radial equation contains the polar separation constant A and the polar equation contains the azimuthal separation constant B. So we must solve the azimuthal equation first, then the polar equation, and finally the radial equation. The azimuthal solution to Eq. (83) determines the constant B, which then goes into Eq. (82) to determine the polar angle solution and the constant A. The combined azimuthal and polar solutions also satisfy the eigenvalue equation (80) for the orbital angular momentum operator L^2. Finally, the constant A goes into the radial equation (79) and the energy eigenvalues are determined.

Rather than simply solving these mathematical equations, we will place each of these three eigenvalue equations in some physical context by identifying situations that isolate the different equations from the original energy eigenvalue equation $H|E\rangle = E|E\rangle$. In this chapter, we focus on the two angular equations, which are independent of the central potential energy $V(r)$.

5 ■ MOTION OF A PARTICLE ON A RING

To isolate the azimuthal eigenvalue problem in Eq. (83), we consider a system with no radial or polar angle dependence. This system comprises a particle of mass μ confined to move on a ring of constant radius r_0, as shown in Fig. 7. We assume that the ring lies in the x, y plane, so that in spherical coordinates $\theta = \pi/2$. Thus, the motion takes place at constant r and constant θ, with the azimuthal angle ϕ as the sole degree of freedom. The wave function ψ is independent of r and θ, so derivatives with respect to those variables are zero. Hence, the energy eigenvalue equation [Eq. (43)] reduces to

$$\frac{-\hbar^2}{2\mu}\frac{1}{r_0^2}\frac{\partial^2}{\partial\phi^2}\psi + V(r_0)\psi = E_{ring}\psi, \tag{84}$$

which is the position representation of

$$H_{ring}|E_{ring}\rangle = E_{ring}|E_{ring}\rangle. \tag{85}$$

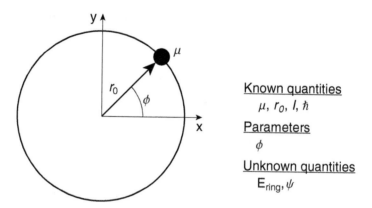

Known quantities

$\mu, r_0, I, \hbar$

Parameters

ϕ

Unknown quantities

E_{ring}, ψ

FIGURE 7 Particle confined to move on a ring.

Following our notation in the previous section, we call the wave function $\Phi(\phi)$ and we change the partial derivative in Eq. (84) to a total derivative because there is only one variable. For this simplified ring problem, the potential energy is a constant $V(r_0)$, which we choose to be zero, but we have to remember that we cannot make this choice when we are working on the full hydrogen atom problem. We also identify $\mu r_0^2 = I$ as the moment of inertia of a classical particle of mass μ traveling in a ring about the origin. With these choices, the energy eigenvalue equation becomes

$$-\frac{\hbar^2}{2I}\frac{d^2}{d\phi^2}\Phi(\phi) = E_{ring}\Phi(\phi). \tag{86}$$

This is the same eigenvalue equation we found in Eq. (83) for the azimuthal function $\Phi(\phi)$ as long as we identify the separation constant B as

$$B = \frac{2I}{\hbar^2}E_{ring} \tag{87}$$

in this problem of a particle on a ring. Thus, this idealized particle-on-a-ring example has the same differential equation, and hence the same wave function solutions, as the separated azimuthal equation in the three-dimensional hydrogen atom problem.

If we compare the azimuthal differential equation (86) with the orbital angular momentum operator in Eq. (69), we note that the energy eigenvalue equation can be expressed as

$$\frac{L_z^2}{2I}\Phi(\phi) = E_{ring}\Phi(\phi), \tag{88}$$

which again emphasizes the importance of angular momentum. This energy eigenvalue equation is what you would expect for a classical particle rotating in a circular path in the x, y plane with kinetic energy $T = I\omega^2/2 = L_z^2/2I$ and resultant Hamiltonian

$$H_{ring} = T = \frac{L_z^2}{2I}, \tag{89}$$

assuming zero potential energy. We noted earlier that eigenstates of L_z obey an eigenvalue equation

$$L_z|m\rangle = m\hbar|m\rangle, \tag{90}$$

where we suppress the ℓ quantum number (for the moment) because it is not applicable to this idealized one-dimensional particle-on-a-ring problem. The $|m\rangle$ states are also eigenstates of L_z^2:

$$L_z^2|m\rangle = m^2\hbar^2|m\rangle \tag{91}$$

and hence of the Hamiltonian of the particle on a ring:

$$H_{ring}|m\rangle = E_{ring}|m\rangle$$
$$\frac{L_z^2}{2I}|m\rangle = m^2\frac{\hbar^2}{2I}|m\rangle. \tag{92}$$

So it looks like we already know the answer; that the energy eigenvalues are $E = m^2\hbar^2/2I$ and the separation constant is $B = m^2$. However, we know the properties of the $|m\rangle$ states in the abstract only; we do not know their spatial representation. That comes from solving the differential equation (86), which is the position representation of the abstract equation (92). Let's solve it and confirm our expectations about the energy eigenvalues.

5.1 ■ Azimuthal Solution

The azimuthal differential equation written in terms of the separation constant is

$$\frac{d^2\Phi(\phi)}{d\phi^2} = -B\Phi(\phi). \tag{93}$$

The solutions to this differential equation are the complex exponentials

$$\Phi(\phi) = Ne^{\pm i\sqrt{B}\phi}, \tag{94}$$

where N is the normalization constant. Mathematically B could have any value, but the physics imposes some constraints.

There is no "boundary" on the ring, so we cannot impose boundary conditions like we do for potential energy well problems. However, there is one very important property of the wave function that we can invoke: it must be single-valued. The variable ϕ is the azimuthal angle around the ring, so that $\phi + 2\pi$ is physically the same point as ϕ. If we go once around the ring and return to our starting point, the value of the wave function must remain the same. Therefore, the solutions must satisfy the periodicity condition $\Phi(\phi + 2\pi) = \Phi(\phi)$. In order for the eigenstate wave function $\Phi(\phi)$ to be periodic, the value of $\sqrt{B}$ must be real (complex $\sqrt{B}$ would result in real exponential solutions). Furthermore, the solutions must have the correct period, which requires that $\sqrt{B}$ be an integer:

$$m = 0, \pm1, \pm2, ... \tag{95}$$

So we see that there are many solutions, each corresponding to a different integer (which can be zero, positive, or negative). We write the solutions as

$$\Phi_m(\phi) = Ne^{im\phi}. \tag{96}$$

The quantum number m is the orbital magnetic quantum number we introduced in Section 3. We don't use a subscript on m here because there is no need to distinguish it from spin for now.

If we operate on the eigenstate wave function $\Phi_m(\phi)$ with the derivative form of the L_z operator, we obtain

$$\begin{aligned}
L_z\Phi_m(\phi) &= -i\hbar\frac{\partial}{\partial\phi}(Ne^{im\phi}) \\
&= -i\hbar(im)(Ne^{im\phi}) \\
&= m\hbar(Ne^{im\phi}) \\
&= m\hbar\Phi_m(\phi).
\end{aligned} \tag{97}$$

As expected, we have found that the energy eigenstates for the particle on a ring are the states $|m\rangle$ that satisfy the L_z eigenvalue equation (90).

As usual, we find the normalization constant N in Eq. (94) by requiring that the probability of finding the particle somewhere on the ring is unity:

$$1 = \int_0^{2\pi} \Phi_m^*(\phi)\Phi_m(\phi)d\phi = \int_0^{2\pi} N^*e^{-im\phi}Ne^{im\phi}\,d\phi = 2\pi|N|^2. \tag{98}$$

We are free to choose the constant to be real and positive:

$$N = \frac{1}{\sqrt{2\pi}}. \tag{99}$$

We have thus found the position representation $\Phi_m(\phi) = \langle\phi|m\rangle$ of the $|m\rangle$ states:

$$\boxed{|m\rangle \doteq \Phi_m(\phi) = \frac{1}{\sqrt{2\pi}}e^{im\phi}.} \tag{100}$$

The eigenfunctions of the ring form an orthonormal set (Problem 11):

$$\int_0^{2\pi} \Phi_k^*(\phi)\Phi_m(\phi)d\phi = \delta_{km}. \tag{101}$$

To reiterate, these functions are eigenstates of the ring Hamiltonian

$$\boxed{\begin{aligned} H_{ring}|m\rangle &= E_{ring}|m\rangle \\ H_{ring}\Phi_m(\phi) &= E_{ring}\Phi_m(\phi) \end{aligned}} \tag{102}$$

as well as eigenstates of the z-component of orbital angular momentum

$$\boxed{\begin{aligned} L_z|m\rangle &= m\hbar|m\rangle \\ L_z\Phi_m(\phi) &= m\hbar\Phi_m(\phi). \end{aligned}} \tag{103}$$

The allowed values of the separation constant B are $B = m^2$, so the possible energy eigenvalues using Eq. (87) are

$$E_{|m|} = m^2 \frac{\hbar^2}{2I}, \tag{104}$$

which is exactly what we expected from Eq. (92). The spectrum of allowed energies is shown in Fig. 8. The eigenstates corresponding to $+|m|$ and $-|m|$ states have the same energy, so there are two energy states at every allowed energy except for the one corresponding to $m = 0$. Thus the particle-on-a-ring system exhibits degeneracy, which we encounter in the free-particle system. For the particle-on-a-ring system, all states are two-fold degenerate except for $m = 0$, which is nondegenerate. The $\pm m$ degeneracy of the energy eigenstates corresponds to the angular momentum states with $L_z = +m\hbar$ and $L_z = -m\hbar$. That is, the two degenerate energy states represent states with opposite components of the angular momentum along the z-axis. The energy is the same regardless of the direction of rotation, which is analogous to the free particle in one dimension where the energy is independent of the direction of travel.

The particle on a ring is a one-dimensional system even though it exists in a two-dimensional space. This is because there is only one degree of freedom ϕ, similar to the particle-in-a-box system, where the single degree of freedom is x. The solutions to both problems have the same oscillatory form. As in the particle-in-a-box problem, the energy eigenvalues of the particle-on-a-ring system are discrete because of a boundary condition. The difference is that the boundary condition appropriate to the ring problem is periodicity because ϕ is a physical angle, rather than $\psi(x) = 0$ at the boundaries, which is appropriate to an infinite potential.

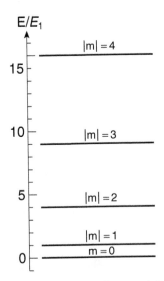

FIGURE 8 Energy spectrum for a particle on a ring.

5.2 ■ Quantum Measurements on a Particle Confined to a Ring

Many of the aspects of quantum measurement applied to this system are similar to spin and particle-in-a-box examples. However, the degeneracy of energy levels presents a new aspect. Because the states $|m\rangle$ and $|-m\rangle$ have the same energy, the probability of measuring the energy $E_{|m|}$ is the sum

$$\mathcal{P}_{E_{|m|}} = |\langle m|\psi\rangle|^2 + |\langle -m|\psi\rangle|^2, \tag{105}$$

except for the $m = 0$ state. On the other hand, the state $|m\rangle$ uniquely specifies the orbital angular momentum component along the z-direction, so the probability of measuring the angular momentum component is

$$\mathcal{P}_{L_z = m\hbar} = |\langle m|\psi\rangle|^2. \tag{106}$$

Example 2 A particle on a ring is in the superposition state

$$|\psi\rangle = \tfrac{1}{\sqrt{7}}(|0\rangle + 2|1\rangle + |-1\rangle + |2\rangle). \tag{107}$$

If we measure the energy, what is the probability of measuring the value $E_1 = \hbar^2/2I$ and what is the state of the system after measuring that value?

The probability of measuring the value $E_1 = \hbar^2/2I$ is obtained using Eq. (105):

$$
\begin{aligned}
\mathcal{P}_{E_1} &= |\langle 1|\psi\rangle|^2 + |\langle -1|\psi\rangle|^2 \\
&= \left|\langle 1|\tfrac{1}{\sqrt{7}}(|0\rangle + 2|1\rangle + |-1\rangle + |2\rangle)\right|^2 + \left|\langle -1|\tfrac{1}{\sqrt{7}}(|0\rangle + 2|1\rangle + |-1\rangle + |2\rangle)\right|^2 \\
&= \left|\tfrac{2}{\sqrt{7}}\right|^2 + \left|\tfrac{1}{\sqrt{7}}\right|^2 \\
&= \tfrac{5}{7}.
\end{aligned}
\tag{108}
$$

After the measurement, the new state vector is the normalized projection of the input state onto the kets corresponding to the result of the measurement (postulate 5):

$$|\psi_{after\,E_{|m|}}\rangle = \frac{|m\rangle\langle m| + |-m\rangle\langle -m|}{\sqrt{\mathcal{P}_{E_{|m|}}}}|\psi\rangle, \tag{109}$$

which in this case is

$$
\begin{aligned}
|\psi_{after\,E_1}\rangle &= \frac{|1\rangle\langle 1| + |-1\rangle\langle -1|}{\sqrt{\mathcal{P}_{E_1}}}\tfrac{1}{\sqrt{7}}(|0\rangle + 2|1\rangle + |-1\rangle + |2\rangle) \\
&= \tfrac{1}{\sqrt{5}}(2|1\rangle + |-1\rangle).
\end{aligned}
\tag{110}
$$

Using Stern-Gerlach analyzers, measurements of the angular momentum component L_z could be made after the energy measurement, and would yield the results shown in Fig. 9 (Problem 12).

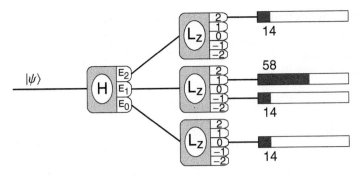

FIGURE 9   Energy measurement and orbital angular momentum component measurements.

5.3 ■ Superposition States

The eigenstate wave functions for the particle on a ring are complex, so we must plot both the real and imaginary components for a proper graphical representation of the wave function. Plots of three $\Phi_m(\phi)$ eigenstates are shown in Fig. 10. The probability density of an eigenstate is

$$\mathcal{P}_m(\phi) = \left|\Phi_m(\phi)\right|^2. \tag{111}$$

Substituting in the eigenstate wave function from Eq. (100), we obtain

$$\mathcal{P}_m(\phi) = \left|\frac{1}{\sqrt{2\pi}} e^{im\phi}\right|^2 = \frac{1}{2\pi}, \tag{112}$$

which is a constant independent of the quantum number m. So there is no measurable spatial dependence of the $|m\rangle$ eigenstates.

However, there is spatial dependence in the probability density for superposition states. For example, consider a state of the system with an initial wave function comprising two eigenstates:

$$\psi(\phi,0) = c_1\Phi_{m_1}(\phi) + c_2 e^{i\theta}\Phi_{m_2}(\phi). \tag{113}$$

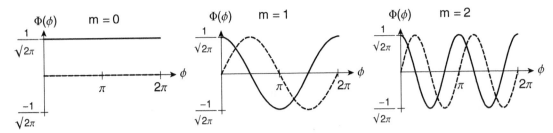

FIGURE 10   Eigenstate wave functions for a particle on a ring. The real part of the wave function is the solid line and the imaginary part is the dashed line.

We assume that this function is already properly normalized $\left(\text{so that } c_1^2 + c_2^2 = 1\right)$, and we assume that the constants c_1 and c_2 are real. An *overall phase* has no physical meaning (cannot be measured), so we can always choose one coefficient to be real. *Relative phases* play a crucial role in measurement, so we have made the relative phase explicit by separating the phase $e^{i\theta}$ from the coefficient of the second term. Using the Schrödinger time-evolution recipe, the initial state in Eq. (113) becomes

$$
\begin{aligned}
\psi(\phi, t) &= c_1 \Phi_{m_1}(\phi) e^{-iE_{|m_1|}t/\hbar} + c_2 e^{i\theta} \Phi_{m_2}(\phi) e^{-iE_{|m_2|}t/\hbar} \\
&= c_1 \frac{1}{\sqrt{2\pi}} e^{im_1\phi} e^{-iE_{|m_1|}t/\hbar} + c_2 e^{i\theta} \frac{1}{\sqrt{2\pi}} e^{im_2\phi} e^{-iE_{|m_2|}t/\hbar}.
\end{aligned}
\tag{114}
$$

For this state, the probability density for measuring the position of the particle on the ring is

$$
\begin{aligned}
\mathcal{P}(\phi, t) &= |\psi(\phi, t)|^2 = \psi^*(\phi, t)\psi(\phi, t) \\
&= \frac{1}{2\pi} \left(c_1 e^{-im_1\phi} e^{+iE_{|m_1|}t/\hbar} + c_2 e^{-i\theta} e^{-im_2\phi} e^{+iE_{|m_2|}t/\hbar} \right) \left(c_1 e^{im_1\phi} e^{-iE_{|m_1|}t/\hbar} + c_2 e^{i\theta} e^{im_2\phi} e^{-iE_{|m_2|}t/\hbar} \right) \\
&= \frac{1}{2\pi} \left[c_1^2 + c_2^2 + c_1 c_2 \left(e^{-im_1\phi} e^{+iE_{|m_1|}t/\hbar} e^{i\theta} e^{im_2\phi} e^{-iE_{|m_2|}t/\hbar} + e^{im_1\phi} e^{-iE_{|m_1|}t/\hbar} e^{-i\theta} e^{-im_2\phi} e^{+iE_{|m_2|}t/\hbar} \right) \right] \\
&= \frac{1}{2\pi} \left[1 + 2 c_1 c_2 \cos\left\{ (m_1 - m_2)\phi - \theta - \left(E_{|m_1|} - E_{|m_2|} \right) t/\hbar \right\} \right].
\end{aligned}
\tag{115}
$$

This probability density exhibits spatial dependence and time dependence in the form of a wave moving around the ring. There are four measurable properties of this probability density wave: the spatial frequency, the temporal frequency, the amplitude, and the phase of the wave. These four quantities are determined by the factors $(m_1 - m_2)$, $\left(E_{|m_1|} - E_{|m_2|} \right)$, $c_1 c_2$, and θ, respectively, in Eq. (115). Using the measured values for these four quantities, the direction of the wave, and the normalization condition $c_1^2 + c_2^2 = 1$ allows us to determine the five constants c_1, c_2, m_1, m_2, and θ that specify the wave function superposition in Eq. (113) (Problem 17).

Example 3   Calculate and plot the probability density for the initial superposition state

$$
\psi(\phi, 0) = \sqrt{\tfrac{1}{3}} \Phi_3(\phi) + i\sqrt{\tfrac{2}{3}} \Phi_{-1}(\phi).
\tag{116}
$$

The time-evolved wave function is

$$
\psi(\phi, t) = \frac{1}{\sqrt{2\pi}} \sqrt{\tfrac{1}{3}} e^{i3\phi} e^{-i9\hbar t/2I} + i \frac{1}{\sqrt{2\pi}} \sqrt{\tfrac{2}{3}} e^{-i\phi} e^{-i\hbar t/2I}
\tag{117}
$$

and the probability density is

$$
\begin{aligned}
\mathcal{P}(\phi, t) &= \frac{1}{2\pi} \left[1 + \tfrac{2\sqrt{2}}{3} \cos\left(4\phi - \frac{\pi}{2} - \frac{8\hbar}{2I} t \right) \right] \\
&= \frac{1}{2\pi} \left[1 + \tfrac{2\sqrt{2}}{3} \sin\left(4\phi - \frac{4\hbar}{I} t \right) \right].
\end{aligned}
\tag{118}
$$

The probability density varies around the ring and at $t = 0$ is a maximum where $\sin 4\phi = +1$, or $\phi = \pi/8, 5\pi/8, 9\pi/8$, and $13\pi/8$. The spatial dependence of the probability density is plotted in Fig. 11 in three different graphical representations. The traditional plot in Fig. 11(a) is similar to the particle-in-a-box plots and conveys the idea of a varying density, but the single dimension fails to make it clear that the left and right ends are connected on the ring and must have the same density. The plot in Fig. 11(b) makes the connection between $\phi = 0$ and $\phi = 2\pi$ clear by plotting the probability density using grayscale (color) as a parameter along the ring. The plot in Fig. 11(c) combines the ideas of the previous two plots by using both the vertical scale and grayscale to represent the probability density. Because the probability density varies with time, each of the plots in Fig. 11 moves (toward increasing ϕ in this example) when they are animated. (See the activity on a particle confined to a ring.)

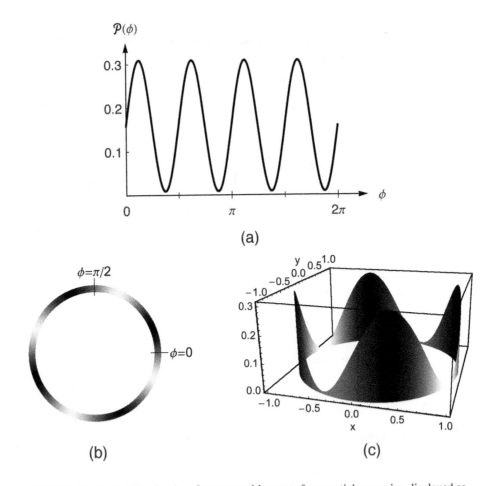

(a)

(b)

(c)

FIGURE 11 Probability density of a superposition state for a particle on a ring displayed as (a) a linear plot, (b) grayscale around the ring, and (c) height and grayscale around the ring.

We have now completed our investigation of the particle on a ring. We have identified the Hamiltonian, found the energy spectrum, found the position representation of the eigenstates, and studied the probability distributions, including the time dependence. These eigenstates are the same ones we use as the azimuthal part of the three-dimensional wave function to solve the hydrogen atom problem.

6 ■ MOTION ON A SPHERE

We have now solved for the azimuthal part of the hydrogen atom wave function, so we turn our attention to the polar angle part of the wave function. This is best done in the context of a system that involves both angular variables θ and ϕ, so that we find the solutions $\Theta(\theta)$ to Eq. (82) and then combine them with the azimuthal states $\Phi_m(\phi)$ to form the solutions $Y(\theta, \phi)$ to the angular momentum eigenvalue equation (80). The system we choose to discuss angular wave functions is that of a particle of mass μ confined to the surface of a sphere of radius r_0, as shown in Fig. 12, which is a natural extension of the ring problem. The results of this analysis yield predictions that can be successfully compared with experiments on molecules and nuclei that rotate more than they vibrate. For this reason, the problem of a mass confined to a sphere is often called the **rigid rotor problem**. Furthermore, the solutions $Y(\theta, \phi)$ that we find, called **spherical harmonics**, occur whenever one solves a partial differential equation that involves spherical symmetry.

For a particle confined to a sphere, the wave function ψ is independent of r, so derivatives with respect to r are zero and the energy eigenvalue equation (43) reduces to

$$-\frac{\hbar^2}{2\mu r_0^2}\left[\frac{1}{\sin\theta}\frac{\partial}{\partial\theta}\left(\sin\theta\frac{\partial}{\partial\theta}\right) + \frac{1}{\sin^2\theta}\frac{\partial^2}{\partial\phi^2}\right]\psi + V(r_0)\psi = E_{sphere}\psi, \qquad (119)$$

which is the position representation of

$$H_{sphere}|E_{sphere}\rangle = E_{sphere}|E_{sphere}\rangle. \qquad (120)$$

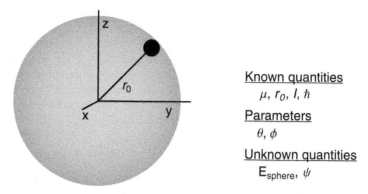

Known quantities
μ, r_0, l, $\hbar$

Parameters
θ, ϕ

Unknown quantities
E_{sphere}, ψ

FIGURE 12 Particle confined to move on the surface of a sphere.

Following our previous notation, we call the wave function $Y(\theta, \phi) = \Theta(\theta)\Phi(\phi)$. For this simplified sphere problem, we choose the potential energy $V(r_0)$ to be zero, as in the ring problem. We identify $\mu r_0^2 = I$ as the moment of inertia of a classical particle of mass μ moving on a sphere. With these changes, the energy eigenvalue equation is

$$-\frac{\hbar^2}{2I}\left[\frac{1}{\sin\theta}\frac{\partial}{\partial\theta}\left(\sin\theta\frac{\partial}{\partial\theta}\right) + \frac{1}{\sin^2\theta}\frac{\partial^2}{\partial\phi^2}\right]Y(\theta,\phi) = E_{sphere}Y(\theta,\phi). \tag{121}$$

Using Eq. (70), we identify the angular differential operator as the position representation of the angular momentum operator $\mathbf{L}^2$ and write the energy eigenvalue equation in operator form:

$$\frac{\mathbf{L}^2}{2I}Y(\theta,\phi) = E_{sphere}Y(\theta,\phi). \tag{122}$$

This eigenvalue equation appears similar to the ring problem but is actually very different, because now the particle can move anywhere on the sphere and so the angular momentum is no longer confined to the z-direction. Equation (122) is the same eigenvalue equation we obtained in Eq. (80) through separation of variables for the angular function $Y(\theta,\phi) = \Theta(\theta)\Phi(\phi)$, as long as we identify the separation constant A as

$$A = \frac{2I}{\hbar^2}E_{sphere}. \tag{123}$$

As noted above, we expect that the separation constant A is equal to $\ell(\ell + 1)$ because the $\mathbf{L}^2$ operator obeys the eigenvalue equation (57). Now that we know that this sphere problem is equivalent to the angular momentum eigenvalue equation, we proceed to solve for the polar angle function $\Theta(\theta)$ that we identified in the differential equation (82). We have already solved for the azimuthal angle wave function $\Phi_m(\phi)$, so at the end we combine $\Theta(\theta)$ and $\Phi_m(\phi)$ to yield the eigenstates $Y(\theta,\phi) = \Theta(\theta)\Phi_m(\phi)$ for the particle on the sphere. In due course, we'll find that the $\Theta(\theta)$ eigenstates have their own quantum numbers, and so we'll label the polar angle states as $\Theta_\ell^m(\theta)$ and the spherical harmonics as $Y_\ell^m(\theta,\phi)$ (the m label is a superscipt, *not* an exponent).

6.1 ■ Series Solution of Legendre's Equation

The polar angle equation (82) is our first encounter with a differential equation that requires a sophisticated solution method. The next two sections detail the series solution method and arrive at the Legendre and associated Legendre functions that solve the polar angle equation. If you are already experienced with this method and are knowledgeable about the Legendre functions, you may safely skip these two sections.

The solutions $\Phi_m(\phi)$ to the ϕ equation (83) that we found in the ring problem told us the possible values of the separation constant $B = m^2$, where m is any integer. We now substitute these known values into the polar angle differential equation (82). The θ equation becomes an eigenvalue equation for the unknown function $\Theta(\theta)$ and the separation constant A:

$$\left[\frac{1}{\sin\theta}\frac{d}{d\theta}\left(\sin\theta\frac{d}{d\theta}\right) - \frac{m^2}{\sin^2\theta}\right]\Theta(\theta) = -A\Theta(\theta). \tag{124}$$

To solve this differential equation, we start with a change of independent variable $z = \cos\theta$, where z is the rectangular coordinate for the particle, assuming a unit sphere. We also introduce a new function

$$P(z) = \Theta(\theta). \tag{125}$$

This step is not mathematically necessary but resolves the difference between the required normalization properties of quantum mechanial wave functions [$\Theta(\theta)$] and the standard normalization used for the solutions [$P(z)$] to Eq. (124). As θ ranges from 0 to π, z ranges from 1 to -1. Using the chain rule for derivatives and $\sin\theta = \sqrt{1 - z^2}$, the differential term becomes

$$\frac{d}{d\theta} = \frac{dz}{d\theta}\frac{d}{dz} = -\sin\theta\frac{d}{dz} = -\sqrt{1 - z^2}\frac{d}{dz}. \tag{126}$$

Notice, particularly, the last equality: we are trying to change variables from θ to z, so it is important to make sure we change *all* the θ's to z's. Multiplying by $\sin\theta$, we obtain:

$$\sin\theta\frac{d}{d\theta} = -\left(1 - z^2\right)\frac{d}{dz}. \tag{127}$$

Be careful finding the second derivative; it involves a product rule:

$$\frac{1}{\sin\theta}\frac{d}{d\theta}\left(\sin\theta\frac{d}{d\theta}\right) = \frac{d}{dz}\left(\left(1 - z^2\right)\frac{d}{dz}\right)$$
$$= \left(1 - z^2\right)\frac{d^2}{dz^2} - 2z\frac{d}{dz}. \tag{128}$$

Inserting Eq. (128) into Eq. (124), we obtain a standard form of the **associated Legendre equation**:

$$\left(\left(1 - z^2\right)\frac{d^2}{dz^2} - 2z\frac{d}{dz} + A - \frac{m^2}{\left(1 - z^2\right)}\right)P(z) = 0. \tag{129}$$

Once we solve this equation for the eigenfunctions $P(z)$, we substitute $z = \cos\theta$ everywhere to find the quantum mechanical eigenfunctions $\Theta(\theta)$ of the original equation (124).

It is easiest to begin the solution of Eq. (129) with the $m = 0$ case, which corresponds to the simplest possible ϕ dependence: $\Phi_0(\phi) = 1/\sqrt{2\pi}$. Setting $m = 0$ in equation (129) gives us the special case known as **Legendre's equation**:

$$\left(\left(1 - z^2\right)\frac{d^2}{dz^2} - 2z\frac{d}{dz} + A\right)P(z) = 0. \tag{130}$$

By dividing this equation by $\left(1 - z^2\right)$, we express it as

$$\left(\frac{d^2}{dz^2} - \frac{2z}{\left(1 - z^2\right)}\frac{d}{dz} + \frac{A}{\left(1 - z^2\right)}\right)P(z) = 0, \tag{131}$$

which emphasizes the mathematical singularities at $z = \pm 1$.

We use the series method to find a solution of Legendre's equation; that is, we assume that the solution can be written as a series

$$P(z) = \sum_{n=0}^{\infty}a_nz^n \tag{132}$$

Angular Momentum

and solve for the coefficients a_n. The differentials

$$\frac{dP}{dz} = \sum_{n=0}^{\infty} a_n n z^{n-1} \tag{133}$$

$$\frac{d^2P}{dz^2} = \sum_{n=0}^{\infty} a_n n(n-1) z^{n-2} \tag{134}$$

substituted into Eq. (130) yield

$$0 = \sum_{n=0}^{\infty} a_n n(n-1) z^{n-2} - z^2 \sum_{n=0}^{\infty} a_n n(n-1) z^{n-2} - 2z \sum_{n=0}^{\infty} a_n n z^{n-1} + A \sum_{n=0}^{\infty} a_n z^n$$
$$= \sum_{n=0}^{\infty} a_n n(n-1) z^{n-2} - \sum_{n=0}^{\infty} a_n n(n-1) z^n - 2 \sum_{n=0}^{\infty} a_n n z^n + A \sum_{n=0}^{\infty} a_n z^n. \tag{135}$$

To combine the sums, we must collect terms of the same powers. To do this, we note that the first two terms of the first sum are zero:

$$a_0(0)(-1) z^{-2} + a_1(1)(0) z^{-1} = 0 + 0, \tag{136}$$

so we shift the dummy variable $n \to n+2$ in the first sum, giving

$$\sum_{n=0}^{\infty} a_n n(n-1) z^{n-2} = \sum_{n=-2}^{\infty} a_{n+2}(n+2)(n+1) z^n$$
$$= \sum_{n=0}^{\infty} a_{n+2}(n+2)(n+1) z^n. \tag{137}$$

Now all the sums in Eq. (135) have the same power and we group the sums together to yield

$$\sum_{n=0}^{\infty} [a_{n+2}(n+2)(n+1) - a_n n(n-1) - 2a_n n + Aa_n] z^n = 0. \tag{138}$$

Now comes the *magic* part. Because Eq. (138) is true *for all values of z*, the coefficient of z^n for each term in the sum must separately be zero:

$$a_{n+2}(n+2)(n+1) - a_n n(n-1) - 2a_n n + Aa_n = 0. \tag{139}$$

Therefore, we can solve Eq. (139) for the **recurrence relation**, giving the later coefficient a_{n+2} in terms of the earlier coefficient a_n:

$$a_{n+2} = \frac{n(n+1) - A}{(n+2)(n+1)} a_n. \tag{140}$$

Plugging successive even values of n into the recurrence relation Eq. (140) allows us to find a_2, a_4, etc. in terms of the arbitrary constant a_0, and successive odd values of n allow us to find a_3, a_5, etc. in terms of the arbitrary constant a_1. Thus, for the second-order differential equation (130), we obtain two solutions as expected. The coefficient a_0 becomes the normalization constant for a solution with only even powers of z, and a_1 becomes the normalization constant for a solution with only odd powers of z. For example, some even coefficients are

$$a_2 = -\frac{A}{2}a_0$$

$$a_4 = \frac{6 - A}{12}a_2 = -\left(\frac{6 - A}{12}\right)\left(\frac{A}{2}\right)a_0 \tag{141}$$

and some odd coefficients are

$$a_3 = \frac{2 - A}{6}a_1$$

$$a_5 = \frac{12 - A}{20}a_3 = \left(\frac{12 - A}{20}\right)\left(\frac{2 - A}{6}\right)a_1 \tag{142}$$

so that

$$P(z) = a_0\left[z^0 - \left(\frac{A}{2}\right)z^2 + \ldots\right] + a_1\left[z^1 + \left(\frac{2 - A}{6}\right)z^3 + \ldots\right]. \tag{143}$$

We seek solutions that are normalizable, so we must address the convergence of the series solution. Note that for large n, the recurrence relation gives

$$\frac{a_{n+2}}{a_n} \cong 1, \tag{144}$$

which implies that the series solution we have assumed does not converge at the end points where $z = \pm 1$. This is to be expected because the coefficients of Eq. (131) are singular at $z = \pm 1$, which correspond to the north and south poles $\theta = 0, \pi$. But there is nothing special about the physics at these points, only the choice of coordinates is special here. This is an important example of a problem where the choice of coordinates for a partial differential equation ends up imposing boundary conditions on the ordinary differential equation which comes from it. To ensure convergence, we thus require that the series not be infinite, but rather that it terminate at some finite power $n_{\max}$. Inspection of the recurrence relation in Eq. (140) tells us that the series terminates if we choose

$$A = n_{max}(n_{max} + 1), \tag{145}$$

where n_{max} is a non-negative integer. When we started this problem, we expected the separation constant to be $A = \ell(\ell + 1)$ and we have found just that, as long as we identify the termination index n_{max} with the orbital angular momentum quantum number ℓ. We have now succeeded in finding the quantization condition for orbital angular momentum, and it is just as we expected from our work with spin angular momentum. But we came to it from a very different perspective, which is one of the beautiful aspects of physics. We have now found that the orbital angular momentum quantum number ℓ must be a non-negative integer:

$$\boxed{\ell = 0, 1, 2, 3, 4, \ldots}. \tag{146}$$

The solutions to Eq. (130) for these special values of A are polynomials of degree ℓ, denoted $P_\ell(z)$, and are called **Legendre polynomials**.

The Legendre polynomials can also be calculated using Rodrigues' formula:

$$P_\ell(z) = \frac{1}{2^\ell \ell!}\frac{d^\ell}{dz^\ell}(z^2 - 1)^\ell. \tag{147}$$

Table 1   Legendre Polynomials

$$P_0(z) = 1$$
$$P_1(z) = z$$
$$P_2(z) = \tfrac{1}{2}(3z^2 - 1)$$
$$P_3(z) = \tfrac{1}{2}(5z^3 - 3z)$$
$$P_4(z) = \tfrac{1}{8}(35z^4 - 30z^2 + 3)$$
$$P_5(z) = \tfrac{1}{8}(63z^5 - 70z^3 + 15z)$$

The first few Legendre polynomials are shown in Table 1 and are plotted in Fig. 13. There are several useful patterns to the Legendre polynomials:

- The overall coefficient for each solution is conventionally chosen so that $P_\ell(1) = 1$. As discussed in the next section, this is an inconvenient convention that we are stuck with.

- $P_\ell(z)$ is a polynomial of degree ℓ.

- Each $P_\ell(z)$ contains only odd or only even powers of z, depending on whether ℓ is even or odd. Therefore, each $P_\ell(z)$ is either an even or an odd function.

- Because the differential operator in Eq. (130) is Hermitian, we are guaranteed that the Legendre polynomials are orthogonal for different values of ℓ (just as with Fourier series), that is,

$$\int_{-1}^{1} P_k^*(z) P_\ell(z)\,dz = \frac{2}{2\ell + 1}\,\delta_{k\ell}. \tag{148}$$

Note that the Legendre polynomials are not normalized to unity, rather the "squared norm" of P_ℓ is $2/(2\ell + 1)$.

Notice that when we substitute the separation constant $A = \ell(\ell + 1)$ back into the original differential equation (130)

$$\left(1 - z^2\right)\frac{d^2 P}{dz^2} - 2z\frac{dP}{dz} + \ell(\ell + 1)P = 0, \tag{149}$$

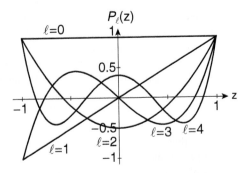

FIGURE 13   Legendre polynomials.

the result is a different equation for different values of ℓ. For a given value of ℓ, you should expect two solutions of Eq. (149), but we have only given one. The "other" solution for each value of ℓ is not regular (i.e., it blows up) at $z = \pm 1$. In cases where the separation constant A does not have the special value $\ell(\ell + 1)$ for non-negative integer values of ℓ, it turns out that *both* solutions blow up. We discard these irregular solutions as unphysical for the problem we are solving.

6.2 ■ Associated Legendre Functions

We now return to Eq. (129) to consider the cases with $m \neq 0$. We need a slightly more sophisticated version of the series technique from the $m = 0$ case, and we do not detail this here. We again find solutions that are regular at $z = \pm 1$ whenever we choose $A = \ell(\ell + 1)$ for $\ell \in \{0, 1, 2, 3, ...\}$. With these values for A, we obtain the standard form of the associated Legendre equation, namely

$$\left(\left(1 - z^2\right)\frac{d^2}{dz^2} - 2z\frac{d}{dz} + \ell(\ell + 1) - \frac{m^2}{\left(1 - z^2\right)} \right) P(z) = 0. \tag{150}$$

Solutions of this equation that are regular at $z = \pm 1$ are called **associated Legendre functions**, and are calculated from the Legendre functions by differentiation:

$$P_\ell^m(z) = P_\ell^{-m}(z) = \left(1 - z^2\right)^{m/2}\frac{d^m}{dz^m}P_\ell(z)$$

$$= \frac{1}{2^\ell \ell!}\left(1 - z^2\right)^{m/2}\frac{d^{m+\ell}}{dz^{m+\ell}}\left(z^2 - 1\right)^\ell, \tag{151}$$

where $m \geq 0$. In Eq. (151), the integer m is a superscript label—*not* an exponent—on the associated Legendre function $P_\ell^m(z)$, but m is an exponent on the right hand side of the equation. The associated Legendre equation (150) is independent of the sign of the integer m, so

$$P_\ell^{-m}(z) = P_\ell^m(z). \tag{152}$$

The Legendre function $P_\ell(z)$ is a polynomial of order ℓ, so the mth derivative in Eq. (151), and hence the associated Legendre function $P_\ell^m(z)$, vanishes if $m > \ell$. In the ring problem, we learned that m must be an integer, but there was no limit on the possible values of those integers. Now we have discovered an additional constraint on the magnetic quantum number for the sphere problem

$$\boxed{m = -\ell, -\ell + 1, ..., -1, 0, 1, ..., \ell - 1, \ell}. \tag{153}$$

Again, this is consistent with our expectations from the spin problem.

It is more useful for us to express the Legendre polynomials and the associated Legendre functions in terms of the polar angle θ rather than the variable z, so we substitute $z = \cos\theta$ into the functions. The Legendre polynomial $P_\ell(\cos\theta)$ is a polynomial in $\cos\theta$, while the associated Legendre function $P_\ell^m(\cos\theta)$ is a polynomial in $\cos\theta$ times a factor of $\sin^m\theta$ because of the additional term

$$\left(1 - z^2\right)^{m/2} = \left(\sin^2\theta\right)^{m/2} = \sin^m\theta \tag{154}$$

in Eq. (151). Some of the associated Legendre functions are shown in Table 2 and are plotted in Fig. 14. The plots in Fig. 14 are polar plots where the "radius" r at each angle θ is the absolute value of the function $P_\ell^m(\cos\theta)$, as illustrated further in Fig. 15. The associated Legendre functions are defined over the interval $0 \leq \theta \leq \pi$, but the convention is to plot the functions reflected in the z-axis in anticipation of their application to the full three-dimensional hydrogen atom.

Some useful properties of the associated Legendre functions are:

- $P_\ell^m(z) = 0$ if $|m| > \ell$
- $P_\ell^{-m}(z) = P_\ell^m(z)$
- $P_\ell^m(\pm 1) = 0$ for $m \neq 0 \left(cf.\ \text{factor of } (1 - z^2)^{m/2}\right)$
- $P_\ell^m(-z) = (-1)^{\ell - m} P_\ell^m(z)$ (behavior under parity)
- $\displaystyle \int_{-1}^1 P_\ell^m(z) P_q^m(z)\, dz = \frac{2}{(2\ell + 1)} \frac{(\ell + m)!}{(\ell - m)!} \delta_{\ell q}.$

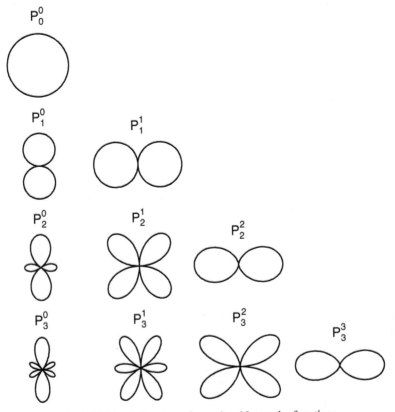

FIGURE 14 Polar plots of associated Legendre functions.

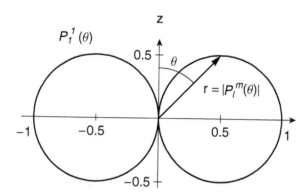

FIGURE 15 Polar plot of an associated Legendre function.

The last property shows that for each given value of m, the associated Legendre functions form an orthogonal basis on the interval $-1 \leq z \leq 1$. Any function on this interval can be expanded in terms of any one of these bases. The associated Legendre functions are not normalized to unity, but by multiplying by the appropriate factor we construct the eigenstates $\Theta_\ell^m(\theta)$ that solve the eigenvalue equation (124) and are normalized to unity over the interval $0 \leq \theta \leq \pi$:

$$\int_0^\pi \Theta_\ell^m(\theta)\Theta_q^m(\theta)\sin\theta \, d\theta = \delta_{\ell q}. \tag{155}$$

These eigenstates are

$$\Theta_\ell^m(\theta) = (-1)^m \frac{(2\ell + 1)}{2} \frac{(\ell - m)!}{(\ell + m)!} P_\ell^m(\cos\theta), \quad m \geq 0, \tag{156}$$

with the negative m states defined by

$$\Theta_\ell^{-m}(\theta) = (-1)^m \Theta_\ell^m(\theta), \quad m \geq 0. \tag{157}$$

Table 2   Associated Legendre Functions

$P_0^0 = 1$	
$P_1^0 = \cos\theta$	$P_3^0 = \frac{1}{2}(5\cos^3\theta - 3\cos\theta)$
$P_1^1 = \sin\theta$	$P_3^1 = \frac{3}{2}\sin\theta(5\cos^2\theta - 1)$
$P_2^0 = \frac{1}{2}(3\cos^2\theta - 1)$	$P_3^2 = 15\sin^2\theta \cos\theta$
$P_2^1 = 3\sin\theta \cos\theta$	$P_3^3 = 15\sin^3\theta$
$P_2^2 = 3\sin^2\theta$	

6.3 ■ Energy Eigenvalues of a Rigid Rotor

We now know the separation constant A in Eq. (124), which determines the energy of the particle bound to the sphere through Eq. (123). Substituting $A = \ell(\ell + 1)$ into Eq. (123) gives the allowed energy eigenvalues

$$E_\ell = \frac{\hbar^2}{2I}\ell(\ell + 1). \tag{158}$$

The energy is independent of the magnetic quantum number m, so each energy level is degenerate, with $(2\ell + 1)$ possible m states for a given ℓ. The free particle and the particle on a ring both exhibited degeneracy because the kinetic energy was independent of the direction of the motion. Similarly, the rotational kinetic energy of the particle on a sphere is independent of the orientation of the angular momentum. The spectrum of energy levels is shown in Fig. 16. The selection rule for transitions between these levels is $\Delta\ell = \pm 1$, yielding the emission lines in Fig. 16. The transition energies are

$$\begin{aligned}
\Delta E &= E_{\ell+1} - E_\ell \\
&= \frac{\hbar^2}{2I}(\ell + 1)(\ell + 2) - \frac{\hbar^2}{2I}\ell(\ell + 1) \\
&= \frac{\hbar^2}{2I}2(\ell + 1) \\
&= \frac{\hbar^2}{2I}\{2, 4, 6, 8, 10, ...\}.
\end{aligned} \tag{159}$$

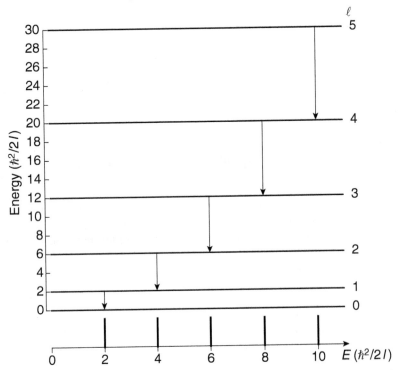

FIGURE 16 Energy spectrum and transitions of a rigid rotor.

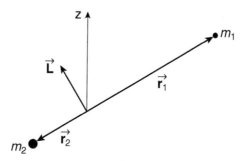

FIGURE 17 A diatomic molecule is the simplest example of a rigid rotor. The two-atom system rotates around an axis perpendicular to the symmetry axis of the molecule.

A physical example of this particle-on-a-sphere model is the rigid rotor. The simplest rigid rotor is a diatomic molecule, as illustrated in Fig. 17. The two atoms with a separation r_0 have a moment of inertia about the center of mass of $I = \mu r_0^2$, just as we have assumed in our particle-on-a-sphere model. Molecular spectroscopists call the energy $\hbar^2/2I$ the **rotational constant** of the molecule.

For example, consider the diatomic molecule hydrogen chloride HCl. The equilibrium bond length is $r_0 = 0.127$ nm, which gives a rotational constant

$$\left.\frac{\hbar^2}{2I}\right|_{HCl} = 1.32 \text{ meV} = 10.7 \text{ cm}^{-1}. \tag{160}$$

The experimentally measured value is 10.4 cm^{-1}. That seems close, but is in fact a clue that something is missing from the model. It turns out that the coupling of the vibrational motion to the rotational motion changes the energy levels of a real molecule. Refining simple models leads to better understanding; our job here is to gain basic understanding.

6.4 ■ Spherical Harmonics

We have in hand the eigenfunctions of the two angular equations, so we can construct the energy eigenstates of the particle on the sphere. The normalized solutions of the ϕ equation (83) that satisfy periodic boundary conditions are the $\Phi_m(\phi)$ states in Eq. (100) with the restriction that the magnetic quantum number m be an integer. The normalized solutions of the θ equation (82) that are regular at the poles are the $\Theta_\ell^m(\theta)$ states in Eq. (156) with the restriction that $\ell = 0, 1, 2, \ldots$ and $m = -\ell, \ldots, \ell$ in integer steps. The product $\Theta_\ell^m(\theta)\Phi_m(\phi)$ of the two solutions yields the function $Y_\ell^m(\theta,\phi)$ that we assumed when we applied the separation of variables procedure to the angular equation (80). These angular functions are the spherical harmonics

$$Y_\ell^m(\theta,\phi) = (-1)^{(m+|m|)/2}\sqrt{\frac{(2\ell+1)}{4\pi}\frac{(\ell-|m|)!}{(\ell+|m|)!}}\, P_\ell^m(\cos\theta)e^{im\phi}, \tag{161}$$

the first few of which are listed in Table 3. The somewhat peculiar choice of sign is conventional and gives the useful result

$$Y_\ell^{-m}(\theta,\phi) = (-1)^m Y_\ell^{m*}(\theta,\phi). \tag{162}$$

Angular Momentum

Table 3 Spherical Harmonics

ℓ	m	$Y_\ell^m(\theta,\phi)$
0	0	$Y_0^0 = \sqrt{\frac{1}{4\pi}}$
1	0	$Y_1^0 = \sqrt{\frac{3}{4\pi}}\cos\theta$
	± 1	$Y_1^{\pm1} = \mp\sqrt{\frac{3}{8\pi}}\sin\theta e^{\pm i\phi}$
2	0	$Y_2^0 = \sqrt{\frac{5}{16\pi}}(3\cos^2\theta - 1)$
	± 1	$Y_2^{\pm1} = \mp\sqrt{\frac{15}{8\pi}}\sin\theta\cos\theta e^{\pm i\phi}$
	± 2	$Y_2^{\pm2} = \sqrt{\frac{15}{32\pi}}\sin^2\theta e^{\pm i2\phi}$
3	0	$Y_3^0 = \sqrt{\frac{7}{16\pi}}(5\cos^3\theta - 3\cos\theta)$
	± 1	$Y_3^{\pm1} = \mp\sqrt{\frac{21}{64\pi}}\sin\theta(5\cos^2\theta - 1)e^{\pm i\phi}$
	± 2	$Y_3^{\pm2} = \sqrt{\frac{105}{32\pi}}\sin^2\theta\cos\theta e^{\pm i2\phi}$
	± 3	$Y_3^{\pm3} = \sqrt{\frac{35}{64\pi}}\sin^3\theta e^{\pm i3\phi}$

Let's now discuss the important properties of the spherical harmonics.

- *Orthonormality*

The spherical harmonics are orthonormal on the unit sphere

$$\langle \ell_1 m_1 | \ell_2 m_2 \rangle = \int_0^{2\pi}\int_0^{\pi} Y_{\ell_1}^{m_1*}(\theta,\phi)\, Y_{\ell_2}^{m_2}(\theta,\phi)\sin\theta\, d\theta\, d\phi = \delta_{\ell_1\ell_2}\delta_{m_1m_2}, \quad (163)$$

which means that two wave functions must have the same angular momentum ($\ell_1 = \ell_2$) and the same z-component ($m_1 = m_2$) or else the overlap integral is zero. The ℓ orthogonality comes from the associated Legendre θ functions and the m orthogonality comes from the complex exponential ϕ functions. The orthonormality condition is also written compactly as an integral over the full solid angle

$$\int Y_{\ell_1}^{m_1*}(\theta,\phi)Y_{\ell_2}^{m_2}(\theta,\phi)d\Omega = \delta_{\ell_1\ell_2}\delta_{m_1m_2} \quad (164)$$

for those common occasions when there is no need to consider separate angular integrals.

- *Completeness*

The spherical harmonics are complete in the sense that any sufficiently smooth function $\psi(\theta,\phi)$ on the unit sphere can be expanded in a *Laplace series* as

$$\psi(\theta,\phi) = \sum_{\ell=0}^{\infty}\sum_{m=-\ell}^{\ell} c_{\ell m} Y_\ell^m(\theta,\phi). \quad (165)$$

The $c_{\ell m}$ expansion coefficients are found by projecting the superposition wave function onto the $|\ell m\rangle$ eigenstates:

$$c_{\ell m} = \langle \ell m | \psi \rangle = \int_0^{2\pi}\int_0^{\pi} Y_\ell^{m*}(\theta,\phi)\psi(\theta,\phi)\sin\theta\, d\theta\, d\phi. \quad (166)$$

- *Parity*

  The behavior of the spherical harmonics under the parity operation $\mathbf{r} \to -\mathbf{r}$ is determined by the angular momentum quantum number ℓ. Spherical harmonics with even ℓ have even parity and those with odd ℓ have odd parity:

$$Y_\ell^m(\pi - \theta, \phi + \pi) = (-1)^\ell Y_\ell^m(\theta, \phi). \tag{167}$$

To summarize, we have found that the spherical harmonics $Y_\ell^m(\theta, \phi)$ are eigenstates of the Hamiltonian for the particle on a sphere [Eq. (121)]. Because the Hamiltonian for this problem is proportional to the $\mathbf{L}^2$ orbital angular momentum operator [Eq. (122)], the spherical harmonics are also eigenstates of $\mathbf{L}^2$ [Eq. (80)]. The spherical harmonics contain the $\Phi_m(\phi)$ eigenstates, so they are also eigenstates of the L_z operator (Problem 24). These three eigenvalue equations are

$$\boxed{\begin{aligned} H_{sphere} Y_\ell^m(\theta, \phi) &= \frac{\hbar^2}{2I}\ell(\ell + 1) Y_\ell^m(\theta, \phi) \\ \mathbf{L}^2 Y_\ell^m(\theta, \phi) &= \ell(\ell + 1)\hbar^2 Y_\ell^m(\theta, \phi) \\ L_z Y_\ell^m(\theta, \phi) &= m\hbar Y_\ell^m(\theta, \phi) \end{aligned}} \tag{168}$$

These three operators share eigenstates because they commute with each other (Problem 9).

For a particle on a sphere, the measurement probabilities are complicated by the degeneracy, just as we saw in the particle on a ring [Eq. (105)]. For a state $|\psi\rangle$, the probability of measuring the energy E_ℓ is a sum over all the degenerate states:

$$\mathcal{P}_{E_\ell} = \sum_{m=-\ell}^{\ell} |\langle \ell m|\psi\rangle|^2. \tag{169}$$

The probability of measuring the $\mathbf{L}^2$ angular momentum observable to be $\ell(\ell + 1)\hbar^2$ is also given by Eq. (169) because the energy eigenstates and the $\mathbf{L}^2$ eigenstates exhibit the same degeneracy. The probability of measuring the L_z angular momentum observable to be $m\hbar$ is the sum over all the ℓ states for which that value of m is allowed:

$$\mathcal{P}_{L_z=m\hbar} = \sum_{\ell=m}^{\infty} |\langle \ell m|\psi\rangle|^2. \tag{170}$$

Let's practice using the spherical harmonics.

Example 4   A particle on a sphere is in the state

$$\psi(\theta, \phi) = \sqrt{\tfrac{15}{16\pi}} \sin 2\theta \cos \phi. \tag{171}$$

What are the probabilities of energy (H) and angular momentum $\left(\mathbf{L}^2 \text{ and } L_z\right)$ measurements?

This wave function looks almost like a spherical harmonic eigenstate, so we try to do this problem by inspection. Using trigonometric identities, rewrite the wave function as

$$\begin{aligned} \psi(\theta, \phi) &= \sqrt{\tfrac{15}{16\pi}}\,(2\sin\theta\cos\theta)\left(\frac{e^{i\phi} + e^{-i\phi}}{2}\right) \\ &= \sqrt{\tfrac{15}{16\pi}}\,\sin\theta\cos\theta\, e^{i\phi} + \sqrt{\tfrac{15}{16\pi}}\,\sin\theta\,\cos\theta e^{-i\phi} \\ &= -\tfrac{1}{\sqrt{2}}\left(-\sqrt{\tfrac{15}{8\pi}}\,\sin\theta\cos\theta e^{i\phi}\right) + \tfrac{1}{\sqrt{2}}\left(\sqrt{\tfrac{15}{8\pi}}\,\sin\theta\cos\theta e^{-i\phi}\right), \end{aligned} \tag{172}$$

which we recognize from Table 3 of spherical harmonics as the superposition

$$\psi(\theta,\phi) = -\tfrac{1}{\sqrt{2}}Y_1^1(\theta,\phi) + \tfrac{1}{\sqrt{2}}Y_1^{-1}(\theta,\phi).\tag{173}$$

In Dirac notation, this state is

$$|\psi\rangle = -\tfrac{1}{\sqrt{2}}|11\rangle + \tfrac{1}{\sqrt{2}}|1,-1\rangle.\tag{174}$$

So, without doing any integrals, we obtain the expansion coefficients

$$c_{\ell m} = \langle \ell m|\psi\rangle = -\tfrac{1}{\sqrt{2}}\delta_{\ell 1}\delta_{m1} + \tfrac{1}{\sqrt{2}}\delta_{\ell 1}\delta_{m,-1}\tag{175}$$

and the energy measurement probabilities

$$\begin{aligned}\mathcal{P}_{E_\ell} &= \sum_{m=-\ell}^{\ell}|\langle \ell m|\psi\rangle|^2\\ &= \left(-\tfrac{1}{\sqrt{2}}\delta_{\ell 1}\right)^2 + \left(\tfrac{1}{\sqrt{2}}\delta_{\ell 1}\right)^2\\ &= \delta_{\ell 1}.\end{aligned}\tag{176}$$

The probability of measuring the energy to be $E_1 = \hbar^2/I$ is 100%, as is the probability for measuring $\mathbf{L}^2 = 2\hbar^2$.

The probability of measuring $L_z = \hbar$ is

$$\begin{aligned}\mathcal{P}_{L_z=\hbar} &= \sum_{\ell=m}^{\infty}|\langle \ell 1|\psi\rangle|^2\\ &= \left(-\tfrac{1}{\sqrt{2}}\right)^2\\ &= \tfrac{1}{2}.\end{aligned}\tag{177}$$

Similarly $\mathcal{P}_{L_z=-\hbar} = 1/2$.

Solution by inspection is nice when it works, but sometimes we must bite the bullet and integrate, as we'll see in the example in the next section.

6.5 ■ Visualization of Spherical Harmonics

Visualization of spherical harmonics is a challenge because of the two-dimensional structure of the wave functions and the fact that they are represented by complex numbers. To overcome the complex problem, it is common to plot the complex square, which is the probability density, or to plot the absolute value. In either case, the azimuthal dependence vanishes as we saw with the ring problem earlier. A two-dimensional polar plot, like we used for the Legendre polynomials, is therefore sufficient to display the polar angle dependence, as shown in Fig. 18(a). To convey the uniform azimuthal dependence, one should visualize the polar plot as rotated around the vertical z-axis, as displayed in the three-dimensional polar plot in Fig. 18(b). In this plot, the "radius" at each angle θ,ϕ is the complex square of the spherical harmonic function. In the ring case, we also displayed the probability density as a grayscale on the ring itself, which suggests plotting the spherical harmonic probability density as grayscale (or color) on the sphere, as shown in Fig. 18(c). The grayscale sphere can then also be projected onto a flat surface, as mapmakers do, yielding the two-dimensional representations in Figs. 18(d) and (e). Note that these plots do not yet give the three-dimensional electron probability density because the spherical harmonics are not functions of the radius r. You still have to learn about radial wave function.

The three-dimensional polar plots for the first four sets of spherical harmonics are shown in Fig. 19. The standard convention is to label the spherical harmonics, or orbitals, with a letter corresponding to the value of the orbital angular momentum quantum number ℓ:

$$\ell = 0 \quad 1 \quad 2 \quad 3 \quad 4 \quad 5 \quad 6 \quad 7 \ldots$$
$$\text{letter} = s \quad p \quad d \quad f \quad g \quad h \quad i \quad k \ldots .$$

(178)

The plots in Fig. 19 show angular momentum eigenstate wave functions. In many cases, such as the carbon atom in Fig. 5, the actual orbitals are superpositions, or **hybrids**, of the angular momentum eigenstates.

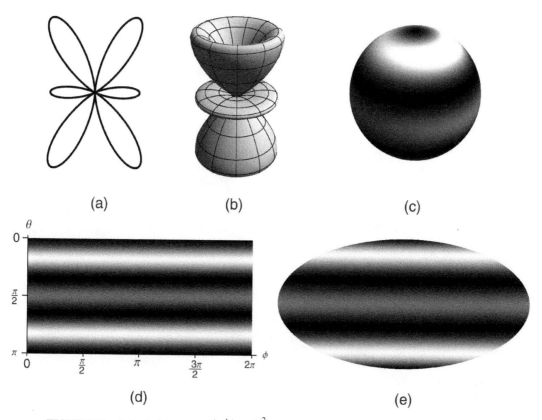

(a)   (b)   (c)

(d)   (e)

FIGURE 18 Spherical harmonic $\left| Y_3^1(\theta, \phi) \right|^2$ displayed as (a) a two-dimensional polar plot, (b) a three-dimensional polar plot, (c) grayscale on a sphere, (d) grayscale on a flat rectangular projection, and (e) grayscale on a flat Mollweide projection.

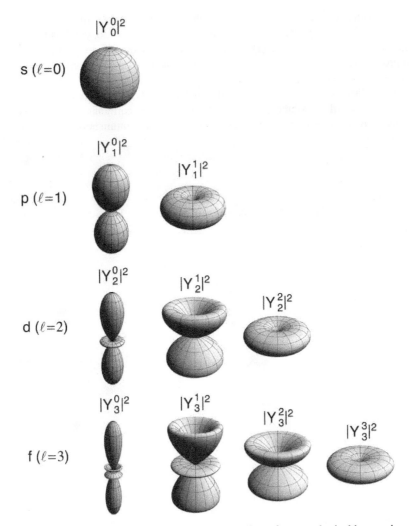

FIGURE 19 Three-dimensional polar plots of some spherical harmonics.

Example 5 Given the angular wave function for a particle on a sphere

$$\psi(\theta, \phi) = \sqrt{\tfrac{60060}{139301\pi}}\left(\frac{1}{4} + \cos^3 2\theta + \sin^2 \phi\right), \tag{179}$$

generate the histogram of possible energy measurements.

To find the probabilities of energy measurements

$$\mathcal{P}_{E_\ell} = \sum_{m=-\ell}^{\ell} |\langle \ell m | \psi \rangle|^2, \tag{180}$$

we must find the overlap integrals

$$c_{\ell m} = \langle \ell m | \psi \rangle = \int_0^{2\pi} \int_0^{\pi} Y_\ell^{m*}(\theta,\phi)\psi(\theta,\phi)\sin\theta\, d\theta\, d\phi. \tag{181}$$

This wave function looks like it could be a finite sum of spherical harmonics, but the wild normalization constant is a clue that an infinite sum is required. You could try to calculate the $c_{\ell m}$ coefficients by hand, but this problem is a good chance to explore the power of mathematical packages such as Mathematica, Maple, or Matlab. Mathematica, for example, has the spherical harmonics built into its system and the overlap integral requires one command line

```
Table[Integrate[Conjugate[SphericalHarmonicY[l,m,θ,ϕ]]
ψ[θ,ϕ]Sin[θ],{θ,0,π},{ϕ,0,2π}],{l,0,7},{m,-l,l}],     (182)
```

which generates a table of the $c_{\ell m}$ coefficients for $\ell = 0 \to 7$ and $m = -\ell \to \ell$, assuming $\psi(\theta,\phi)$ has been defined previously. A subset of the results is presented in Table 4. The last column of the table is the probability of measuring the energy E_ℓ. From the explicit square roots in the results, it is evident that Mathematica does the integral analytically, not numerically. The results also indicate the symmetries of the wave function. Only $m = -2, 0, 2$ states contribute nonzero terms to the expansion because of the symmetry of the azimuthal dependence of the wave function:

$$\begin{aligned} \sin^2\phi &= \left[\left(e^{i\phi} - e^{-i\phi}\right)/2i\right]^2 \\ &= \tfrac{1}{4}\left(e^{i2\phi} + e^{-i2\phi} - 2\right). \end{aligned} \tag{183}$$

For $m = 0$, the coefficients beyond $\ell = 6$ are zero because the polar angle term $\cos^3 2\theta$ has no $\cos^\ell\theta$ or $\sin^\ell\theta$ terms beyond $\ell = 6$. The $m = \pm 2$ coefficients extend to $\ell = \infty$.

Table 4 Coefficients of Spherical Harmonic Expansion

$c_{\ell m}$	$m = -3$	-2	-1	0	1	2	3	$\sum_{m=-\ell}^{\ell} \lvert c_{\ell m}\rvert^2$
$\ell =$ 0				$69\sqrt{\frac{429}{4875535}}$				$\frac{2042469}{4875535}$
1			0	0	0			0
2		$-5\sqrt{\frac{1001}{278602}}$	0	$80\sqrt{\frac{143}{2925321}}$	0	$5\sqrt{\frac{1001}{278602}}$		$\frac{1440725}{2925321}$
3	0	0	0	0	0	0	0	0
4	0	$\sqrt{\frac{3003}{278602}}$	0	$-128\sqrt{\frac{39}{53630885}}$	0	$\sqrt{\frac{3003}{278602}}$	0	$\frac{1795131}{5360885}$
5	0	0	0	0	0	0	0	0
6	0	$-\frac{13}{2}\sqrt{\frac{11}{139301}}$	0	$512\sqrt{\frac{5}{32178531}}$	0	$\frac{13}{2}\sqrt{\frac{11}{139301}}$	0	$\frac{3050869}{64357062}$
7	0	0	0	0	0	0	0	0

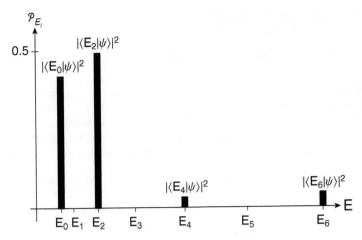

FIGURE 20 Histogram of energy measurements.

A partial histogram of energy measurement probabilities is shown in Fig. 20. The energy probabilities for the states up to $\ell = 6$ shown in Table 4 and Fig. 20 sum to 0.9923, so we expect that the finite spherical harmonic expansion

$$\psi_{finite}(\theta, \phi) = \sum_{\ell=0}^{6} \sum_{m=-\ell}^{\ell} c_{\ell m} Y_{\ell}^{m}(\theta, \phi) \qquad (184)$$

should be a good approximation to the actual wave function. The original wave function and the finite spherical harmonic expansion are shown in Fig. 21. The match between the two is good, except at the endpoints $\theta = 0, \pi$, which is a phenomenon similar to that seen in Fourier series expansions. Note that this wave function exhibits azimuthal dependence because it is a superposition of different m states.

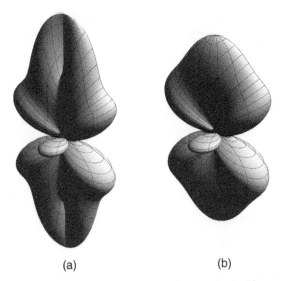

(a)   (b)

FIGURE 21 (a) Original wave function and (b) 6-term spherical harmonic expansion.

SUMMARY

In this chapter, we introduced the idea of orbital angular momentum and illustrated its importance in solving the three-dimensional differential equation that is the energy eigenvalue equation for the hydrogen atom. By separating variables in the eigenvalue equation $H|E\rangle = E|E\rangle$, we isolated the differential equations for the angular variables θ and ϕ from the differential equation for the radial variable r. Only the radial differential equation includes the potential energy, so the solutions to the angular equations are valid for all central potentials. The ϕ equation yielded the azimuthal wave functions

$$\Phi_m(\phi) = \frac{1}{\sqrt{2\pi}} e^{im\phi} \tag{185}$$

and the θ equation yielded the polar wave functions

$$\Theta_\ell^m(\theta) = \sqrt{\frac{(2\ell + 1)}{2} \frac{(\ell - |m|)!}{(\ell + |m|)!}} P_\ell^m(\cos\theta). \tag{186}$$

The products of these two are the total angular wave functions, which are the spherical harmonics

$$|\ell m\rangle \doteq Y_\ell^m(\theta,\phi) = (-1)^{(m+|m|)/2} \sqrt{\frac{(2\ell + 1)}{4\pi} \frac{(\ell - |m|)!}{(\ell + |m|)!}} P_\ell^m(\cos\theta) e^{im\phi}. \tag{187}$$

The spherical harmonics are eigenstates of the angular momentum operators $\mathbf{L}^2$ and L_z. In Dirac notation, the eigenvalue equations are

$$\mathbf{L}^2|\ell m\rangle = \ell(\ell + 1)\hbar^2|\ell m\rangle$$
$$L_z|\ell m\rangle = m\hbar|\ell m\rangle. \tag{188}$$

In wave function notation, the eigenvalue equations are

$$\mathbf{L}^2 Y_\ell^m(\theta,\phi) = \ell(\ell + 1)\hbar^2 Y_\ell^m(\theta,\phi)$$
$$L_z Y_\ell^m(\theta,\phi) = m\hbar Y_\ell^m(\theta,\phi). \tag{189}$$

The limitations on the quantum numbers m and ℓ arise from requiring the wave function to be periodic in ϕ and finite at $\theta = 0, \pi$, respectively. The quantum numbers m and ℓ must be integers with the limitations

$$m = -\ell, -\ell + 1, \dots 0, \dots, \ell - 1, \ell$$
$$\ell = 0, 1, 2, 3, \dots \infty. \tag{190}$$

RESOURCES

Activities

These activities are available at

www.physics.oregonstate.edu/qmactivities

Eigenstates of a Particle Confined to a Ring: Students investigate eigenstates of a quantum particle confined to a ring.

Guessing the Legendre Polynomial Expansion of a Function: Students try to fit a given function with a linear combination of Legendre polynomials using the guess and check method.

Finding Legendre Coefficients: Students use Maple to find the first few coefficients of a Legendre series to approximate a function.

Particle Confined to a Ring: Students visualize linear combinations of eigenstates and study animations of time evolution of the probability density.

Particle Confined to a Sphere: Students visualize the spherical harmonics.

Linear Combinations of Spherical Harmonics: Students visualize states that are made up of linear combinations of spherical harmonics.

Angular Momentum: Problem Set

1 Show that the two-body Hamiltonian in Eq. (3)

$$H_{sys} = \frac{\mathbf{p}_1^2}{2m_1} + \frac{\mathbf{p}_2^2}{2m_2} + V(\mathbf{r}_1, \mathbf{r}_2). \tag{3}$$

can be separated into center-of-mass and relative Hamiltonians, as in Eq. (11).

$$H_{sys} = \frac{\mathbf{P}^2}{2M} + \frac{\mathbf{p}_{rel}^2}{2\mu} + V(r), \tag{11}$$

Do this in two ways: (a) with momentum operators in the abstract, and (b) momentum operators in the position representation.

2 Use the separation of variables procedure to separate the two-body energy eigenvalue equation into the center-of-mass and relative energy eigenvalue equations in Eq. (24).

$$H_{CM}\psi_{CM}(\mathbf{R}) = E_{CM}\psi_{CM}(\mathbf{R})$$
$$H_{rel}\psi_{rel}(\mathbf{r}) = E_{rel}\psi_{rel}(\mathbf{r}) \tag{24}$$

3 Use the separation of variables procedure to separate equation Eq. (29)

$$-\frac{\hbar^2}{2M}\left(\frac{\partial^2}{\partial X^2} + \frac{\partial^2}{\partial Y^2} + \frac{\partial^2}{\partial Z^2}\right)\psi_{CM}(X,Y,Z) = E_{CM}\psi_{CM}(X,Y,Z). \tag{29}$$

into three ordinary differential equations for each Cartesian coordinate.

4 Verify the angular momentum commutation relations in Eqs. (51)

$$\boxed{\begin{aligned} [L_x, L_y] &= i\hbar L_z \\ [L_y, L_z] &= i\hbar L_x \\ [L_z, L_x] &= i\hbar L_y \end{aligned}} \tag{51}$$

and (55).

$$\boxed{\begin{aligned} [\mathbf{L}^2, L_x] &= 0 \\ [\mathbf{L}^2, L_y] &= 0 \\ [\mathbf{L}^2, L_z] &= 0 \end{aligned}} \tag{55}$$

5 An angular momentum system with $\ell = 1$ is prepared in the state

$$|\psi\rangle = \tfrac{2}{\sqrt{29}}|11\rangle + i\tfrac{3}{\sqrt{29}}|10\rangle - \tfrac{4}{\sqrt{29}}|1,-1\rangle.$$

a) What are the possible results of a measurement of the angular momentum component L_z, and with what probabilities would they occur?

From Chapter 7 of *Quantum Mechanics: A Paradigms Approach*, First Edition. David H. McIntyre. Copyright © 2012 by Pearson Education, Inc. Published by Pearson Addison-Wesley. All rights reserved.

The companion websites for this text are http://physics.oregonstate.edu/portfolioswiki and http://physics.oregonstate.edu/qmactivities.

b) What are the possible results of a measurement of the angular momentum component L_x, and with what probabilities would they occur?

c) Plot histograms of the predicted measurement results from parts (a) and (b).

6 An angular momentum system with $\ell = 1$ is prepared in the state

$$|\psi\rangle = \tfrac{1}{\sqrt{14}}|11\rangle - \tfrac{3}{\sqrt{14}}|10\rangle + i\tfrac{2}{\sqrt{14}}|1,-1\rangle.$$

a) What are the possible results of a measurement of the angular momentum component L_z, and with what probabilities would they occur?

b) Suppose that the L_z measurement on the system yields the result $L_z = -\hbar$. Subsequent to that result, a second measurement is performed to measure the angular momentum component L_x. What are the possible results of that measurement, and with what probabilities would they occur?

c) Draw a schematic diagram depicting the successive measurements in parts (a) and (b).

7 An angular momentum system is prepared in the state

$$|\psi\rangle = \tfrac{1}{\sqrt{10}}|11\rangle - \tfrac{2}{\sqrt{10}}|10\rangle + i\tfrac{2}{\sqrt{10}}|22\rangle + i\tfrac{1}{\sqrt{10}}|20\rangle.$$

a) What are the possible results of a measurement of the angular momentum observable $\mathbf{L}^2$, and with what probabilities would they occur?

b) What are the possible results of a measurement of the angular momentum component L_z, and with what probabilities would they occur?

c) Plot histograms of the predicted measurement results from parts (a) and (b).

8 Using Eqs. (35)

$$x = r\sin\theta\,\cos\phi$$
$$y = r\sin\theta\,\sin\phi \tag{35}$$
$$z = r\cos\theta.$$

and (47),

$$L_x = yp_z - zp_y \doteq -i\hbar\left(y\frac{\partial}{\partial z} - z\frac{\partial}{\partial y}\right)$$

$$L_y = zp_x - xp_z \doteq -i\hbar\left(z\frac{\partial}{\partial x} - x\frac{\partial}{\partial z}\right) \tag{47}$$

$$L_z = xp_y - yp_x \doteq -i\hbar\left(x\frac{\partial}{\partial y} - y\frac{\partial}{\partial x}\right).$$

show that the orbital angular momentum operators L_x, L_y, and L_z are represented in spherical coordinates as

$$L_x \doteq i\hbar\left(\sin\phi\frac{\partial}{\partial\theta} + \cos\phi\cot\theta\frac{\partial}{\partial\phi}\right)$$

$$L_y \doteq i\hbar\left(-\cos\phi\frac{\partial}{\partial\theta} + \sin\phi\cot\theta\frac{\partial}{\partial\phi}\right)$$

$$L_z \doteq -i\hbar\frac{\partial}{\partial\phi}$$

and verify that the operator $\mathbf{L}^2 = \mathbf{L}\cdot\mathbf{L} = L_x^2 + L_y^2 + L_z^2$ is represented in spherical coordinates as in Eq. (70).

$$\mathbf{L}^2 \doteq -\hbar^2 \left[\frac{1}{\sin\theta} \frac{\partial}{\partial\theta} \left(\sin\theta \frac{\partial}{\partial\theta} \right) + \frac{1}{\sin^2\theta} \frac{\partial^2}{\partial\phi^2} \right], \tag{70}$$

9 Verify that the angular momentum operators $\mathbf{L}^2$ and L_z commute with the central force Hamiltonian.

10 Use the separation of variables procedure on the angular equation (80)

$$\mathbf{L}^2 Y(\theta,\phi) = A\,\hbar^2\,Y(\theta,\phi). \tag{80}$$

to obtain Eq. (82)

$$\left[\frac{1}{\sin\theta} \frac{d}{d\theta} \left(\sin\theta \frac{d}{d\theta} \right) - B\frac{1}{\sin^2\theta} \right] \Theta(\theta) = -A\,\Theta(\theta) \tag{82}$$

and Eq. (83)

$$\frac{d^2\Phi(\phi)}{d\phi^2} = -B\,\Phi(\phi), \tag{83}$$

for the polar and azimuthal angles.

11 Show by direct integration that the azimuthal eigenstates $\Phi_m(\phi)$ are orthonormal.

12 Consider the particle-on-a-ring state in Example 2. What are the possible values of a measurement of the observable L_z? Calculate the measurement probabilities and show that they agree with the results indicated in Fig. 9.

13 Consider the normalized state $|\psi\rangle$ for a quantum mechanical particle of mass μ constrained to move on a circle of radius r_0, given by:

$$|\psi\rangle = \tfrac{\sqrt{3}}{2}|3\rangle + \tfrac{i}{2}|-2\rangle.$$

a) What is the probability that a measurement of L_z will yield $2\hbar$? $3\hbar$?

b) What is the probability that a measurement of the energy yields $E = 2\hbar^2/I$?

c) What is the expectation value of L_z in this state?

d) What is the expectation value of the energy in this state?

14 A particle on a ring is in the normalized state

$$|\psi\rangle = \tfrac{1}{\sqrt{15}}\big(|0\rangle + i|1\rangle - 2i|2\rangle + 3|-2\rangle\big).$$

a) What are the possible results of an energy measurement and what are the corresponding probabilities? Calculate the expectation value of the energy.

b) What are the possible results of an L_z measurement and what are the corresponding probabilities? Calculate the expectation value of L_z.

15 Consider the normalized state $|\psi\rangle$ for a quantum mechanical particle of mass μ constrained to move on a circle of radius r_0, given by

$$|\psi\rangle \doteq \frac{N}{2 + \cos(3\phi)},$$

where N is the normalization constant.

a) Find the normalization constant N.

b) Plot the wave function.

c) What is the expectation value of L_z in this state?

16 A particle on a ring is prepared in the initial state

$$|\psi\rangle = \sqrt{\tfrac{1}{5}}|2\rangle - i\sqrt{\tfrac{4}{5}}|-1\rangle.$$

Find the probability density as a function of time.

17 The time-dependent probability density for a particle on a ring is measured to be

$$\mathcal{P}(\phi, t) = \frac{1}{2\pi}\left[1 - \tfrac{2\sqrt{2}\sqrt{3}}{13}\sin\left(3\phi + \frac{3\hbar}{2I}t\right)\right].$$

Determine the initial state of the particle.

18 Calculate the moment of inertia of a diatomic molecule, as depicted in Fig. 17. Express the moment two ways: (1) in terms of the individual masses m_1 and m_2 and the coordinates r_1 and r_2, and (2) in terms of the reduced mass μ and the atom-atom separation r_0.

19 Calculate the rotational constant for the hydrogen iodide (HI) molecule.

20 In each of the following sums, shift the dummy index $n \rightarrow n + 2$. Don't forget to shift the limits of the sum as well. Then write out all of the terms in the sum (if the sum has a finite number of terms) or the first five terms in the sum (if the sum has an infinite number of terms) and convince yourself that the two different expressions for each sum are the same:

a) $\displaystyle\sum_{n=0}^{3} n$

b) $\displaystyle\sum_{n=1}^{5} e^{in\phi}$

c) $\displaystyle\sum_{n=0}^{\infty} a_n n(n-1) z^{n-2}$

21 Use Rodrigues' formula, by hand, to generate the first five Legendre polynomials. Show by direct integration that $P_2(\cos\theta)$ is orthogonal to $P_4(\cos\theta)$, and that $P_2(\cos\theta)$ is normalized according to Eq. (148).

$$\int_{-1}^{1} P_k^*(z) P_\ell(z)\, dz = \frac{2}{2\ell + 1}\delta_{k\ell}. \tag{148}$$

22 Generate the associated Legendre functions $P_2^1(z)$ and $P_3^3(z)$ by hand. Express each function both as a function of the argument z and as a function of θ.

Angular Momentum: Problems Set

23 Use the definitions in Eqs. (151)

$$P_\ell^m(z) = P_\ell^{-m}(z) = \left(1 - z^2\right)^{m/2} \frac{d^m}{dz^m} P_\ell(z)$$

$$= \frac{1}{2^\ell \ell!} \left(1 - z^2\right)^{m/2} \frac{d^{m+\ell}}{dz^{m+\ell}} \left(z^2 - 1\right)^\ell, \tag{151}$$

and (161)

$$Y_\ell^m(\theta, \phi) = (-1)^{(m+|m|)/2} \sqrt{\frac{(2\ell + 1)}{4\pi} \frac{(\ell - |m|)!}{(\ell + |m|)!}} \; P_\ell^m(\cos\theta) e^{im\phi}, \tag{161}$$

to generate the spherical harmonics $Y_1^0(\theta, \phi)$ and $Y_2^{-2}(\theta, \phi)$. Ensure that they are normalized and orthogonal by direct integration.

24 Verify that the spherical harmonics are eigenstates of the orbital angular momentum component operator L_z by direct application of the position representation of L_z. What are the eigenvalues?

25 Verify that the spherical harmonics are eigenstates of the orbital angular momentum operator $\mathbf{L}^2$. What are the eigenvalues?

26 Consider the new operators L_+ and L_- defined by $L_\pm = L_x \pm iL_y$. Use the results of Problem 8 to show that the position representations of these operators in spherical coordinates are

$$L_\pm = \hbar e^{\pm i\phi} \left(\pm \frac{\partial}{\partial \theta} + i\cot\theta \frac{\partial}{\partial \phi}\right).$$

Act with these new operators on all the $\ell = 1$ spherical harmonic wave functions and summarize your results in Dirac notation. Based on your results, postulate the names of these new operators.

27 Express the $\ell = 1$ spherical harmonics in Cartesian coordinates. Combine the $m = \pm 1$ functions in two possible ways to make real functions that closely resemble the $m = 0$ function.

28 Use your favorite tool (e.g., Maple, Mathematica, Matlab, pencil) to generate the Legendre polynomial expansion of the function $f(z) = \sin(\pi z)$. How many terms do you need to include in a partial sum to get a "good" approximation to $f(z)$ for $-1 < z < 1$? What do you mean by a "good" approximation? How about the interval $-2 < z < 2$? How good is your approximation then? Discuss your answers. Answer the same set of questions for the function $g(z) = \sin(3\pi z)$.

29 Consider the normalized state of a particle on a sphere given by:

$$|\psi\rangle = \tfrac{1}{\sqrt{2}}|1, -1\rangle + \tfrac{1}{\sqrt{3}}|10\rangle + \tfrac{i}{\sqrt{6}}|00\rangle.$$

a) What is the probability that a measurement of L_z will yield $2\hbar$? $-\hbar$? $0\hbar$?
b) What is the expectation value of L_z in this state?
c) What is the expectation value of $\mathbf{L}^2$ in this state?
d) What is the expectation value of the energy in this state?
e) What is the expectation value of L_y in this state?

30 A particle confined to the surface of a sphere is in the state

$$\psi(\theta,\phi) = \begin{cases} N\left(\dfrac{\pi^2}{4} - \theta^2\right), & 0 < \theta < \dfrac{\pi}{2} \\[2mm] 0, & \dfrac{\pi}{2} < \theta < \pi, \end{cases}$$

where the normalization constant is

$$N = \frac{1}{\sqrt{\dfrac{\pi^5}{8} + 2\pi^3 - 24\pi^2 + 48\pi}}.$$

a) Find the coefficients for the $|\ell m\rangle = |00\rangle$, $|1,-1\rangle$, $|10\rangle$, and $|11\rangle$ terms in a spherical harmonics expansion of $\psi(\theta,\phi)$.

b) What is the probability that a measurement of the square of the total angular momentum will yield $2\hbar^2$? $0\hbar^2$?

c) What is the probability that the particle can be found in the region $0 < \theta < \pi/6$ and $0 < \phi < \pi/6$? Repeat the question for the region $5\pi/6 < \theta < \pi$ and $0 < \phi < \pi/6$. Plot your approximation from part (a) above on and check to see if your answers seem reasonable. (The activity on linear combinations of spherical harmonics has a Maple worksheet *ylmcombo.mws* for plotting.)

Hydrogen Atom

From Chapter 8 of *Quantum Mechanics: A Paradigms Approach*, First Edition. David H. McIntyre. Copyright © 2012 by Pearson Education, Inc. Published by Pearson Addison-Wesley. All rights reserved.

The companion websites for this text are http://physics.oregonstate.edu/portfolioswiki and http://physics.oregonstate.edu/qmactivities.

Hydrogen Atom

Angular wave functions are independent of the particular form of the central potential that binds the system. The radial part of the wave function, however, depends critically on the central potential you choose. The radial part of the problem determines the allowed energies of the system and hence the spectroscopic fingerprint of the system that we observe in experiments. In this chapter, we solve for the quantized energies and the radial wave functions of the bound states of the hydrogen atom, which is the simplest atomic system, comprising one electron bound to one proton in the nucleus. The electron and proton are bound together by the Coulomb potential, which underlies the bonding in all atoms, molecules, liquids, and solids.

1 ■ THE RADIAL EIGENVALUE EQUATION

Recall separating the three-dimensional energy eigenvalue equation into differential equations for each of the spherical coordinates r, θ, and ϕ. We solve the ϕ eigenvalue equation and find the azimuthal eigenstates $\Phi_m(\phi)$ and eigenvalues m, which determine the separation constant $B = m^2$. We then use the separation constant B to make the θ differential equation into an eigenvalue equation and solve for the polar eigenstates $\Theta_\ell^m(\theta)$ and the eigenvalues $\ell(\ell + 1)$, which determine the separation constant $A = \ell(\ell + 1)$. We now use the separation constant A to make the radial differential equation into an eigenvalue equation for the energy E:

$$\left[-\frac{\hbar^2}{2\mu r^2} \frac{d}{dr}\left(r^2 \frac{d}{dr} \right) + V(r) + \ell(\ell + 1)\frac{\hbar^2}{2\mu r^2} \right] R(r) = ER(r). \tag{1}$$

Solving this differential equation will give us the radial eigenstates $R(r)$ and the allowed energies E. We then combine the three separated eigenstates into the three-dimensional eigenstate $\psi(r,\theta,\phi) = R(r)Y_\ell^m(\theta,\phi)$, where the spherical harmonics $Y_\ell^m(\theta,\phi) = \Theta_\ell^m(\theta)\Phi_m(\phi)$ are the products of the azimuthal and polar eigenstates.

Before we begin the solution, notice that the radial eigenvalue equation (1) resembles a one-dimensional eigenvalue equation with an **effective potential energy** V_{eff}:

$$V_{eff}(r) = V(r) + \frac{\hbar^2\ell(\ell + 1)}{2\mu r^2}. \tag{2}$$

The term $\hbar^2\ell(\ell + 1)/2\mu r^2$ in the effective potential energy is called the **centrifugal barrier**. It behaves like a repulsive potential, and it increases with ℓ in exact analogy with classical mechanics. In this viewpoint, the effective potential energy that determines the radial motion of the electron is different for each state with a different angular momentum quantum number ℓ, as shown in Fig. 1.

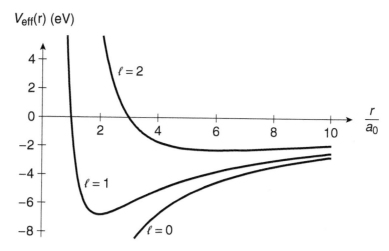

FIGURE 1   The effective potential for different values of the angular momentum quantum number ℓ.

For the hydrogen atom, the Coulomb potential energy is responsible for attracting the electron to the proton. This Coulomb potential energy is

$$V(r) = -\frac{Ze^2}{4\pi\varepsilon_0 r}, \tag{3}$$

where we assume that the nucleus has a charge $+Ze$ so that our solution applies to the general case of a **hydrogenic atom**: H, He$^+$, Li^{++}, etc. With this choice of $V(r)$, the radial differential equation is

$$\frac{d^2R}{dr^2} + \frac{2}{r}\frac{dR}{dr} + \frac{2\mu}{\hbar^2}\left[E + \frac{Ze^2}{4\pi\varepsilon_0 r} - \frac{\hbar^2\ell(\ell+1)}{2\mu r^2}\right]R = 0. \tag{4}$$

The potential energy at $r = \infty$ is $V(\infty) = 0$, so bound states have energy $E < 0$ while unbound states have energy $E > 0$.

It is convenient at this point to rewrite the radial differential equation in terms of dimensionless energy and position parameters. The angular differential equations are treated similarly because the separation constants A and B are dimensionless. We define a characteristic length scale of the hydrogenic atom as a, such that the dimensionless radius is

$$\rho = \frac{r}{a}. \tag{5}$$

Without knowing what this scale is yet, we write the differential equation for $R(\rho)$ as

$$\frac{1}{a^2}\frac{d^2R}{d\rho^2} + \frac{1}{a^2}\frac{2}{\rho}\frac{dR}{d\rho} + \frac{2\mu}{\hbar^2}\left[E + \frac{Ze^2}{4\pi\varepsilon_0 a\rho} - \frac{\hbar^2\ell(\ell+1)}{2\mu a^2\rho^2}\right]R = 0. \tag{6}$$

Multiplying Eq. (6) by a^2, we obtain

$$\frac{d^2R}{d\rho^2} + \frac{2}{\rho}\frac{dR}{d\rho} + \left[\frac{2\mu a^2}{\hbar^2}E + \left(\frac{\mu Ze^2}{4\pi\varepsilon_0\hbar^2}\right)\frac{2a}{\rho} - \frac{\ell(\ell+1)}{\rho^2}\right]R = 0. \tag{7}$$

The terms inside the square brackets of Eq. (7) are now dimensionless, so we identify the hydrogen characteristic length scale as

$$a = \frac{4\pi\varepsilon_0 \hbar^2}{\mu Z e^2} \qquad (8)$$

and the characteristic energy scale as $\hbar^2/2\mu a^2$. We define a dimensionless energy parameter as

$$-\gamma^2 = \frac{E}{\left(\dfrac{\hbar^2}{2\mu a^2}\right)}, \qquad (9)$$

where we assume that $E < 0$ because we are seeking bound-state solutions. Using $\hbar^2/2\mu a^2$ as the energy scale is reasonable in light of the ground state energy being $E_1 = \pi^2 \hbar^2/2ma^2$ for a particle in a box of size a. With the dimensionless length and energy parameters, the radial differential equation becomes

$$\frac{d^2 R}{d\rho^2} + \frac{2}{\rho}\frac{dR}{d\rho} + \left[-\gamma^2 + \frac{2}{\rho} - \frac{\ell(\ell+1)}{\rho^2}\right]R = 0. \qquad (10)$$

In this dimensionless form, the eigenvalue we are seeking is γ^2 and the eigenfunction is $R(\rho)$.

2 ■ SOLVING THE RADIAL EQUATION

2.1 ■ Asymptotic Solutions to the Radial Equation

To solve the radial eigenvalue equation (10), it is instructive to first get some clues about the form of the solution by looking at the limiting behavior of the solutions for large and small ρ (i.e., large and small r). For large ρ, the terms in Eq. (10) involving ρ^{-1} and ρ^{-2} can be neglected, so Eq. (10) becomes approximately

$$\frac{d^2 R}{d\rho^2} - \gamma^2 R = 0. \qquad (11)$$

This equation has the familiar exponential solutions $R(\rho) = e^{\pm\gamma\rho}$, where the $\pm$ symbol is required because Eq. (11) involves the second derivative of $R(\rho)$. We eliminate one of these signs by noting that the solution $e^{+\gamma\rho}$ blows up as ρ goes to infinity. We want solutions for the wave functions to yield reasonably behaved probability densities (that is, they must be finite everywhere), and we must therefore discard any solution that leads to an infinite probability. Our solution for the radial wave function in this limit then becomes:

$$R(\rho) \sim e^{-\gamma\rho} \quad (large\ \rho). \qquad (12)$$

Now let's look at the behavior of the solutions when ρ is small. Now the ρ^{-2} term dominates and we neglect the other terms in the square brackets in Eq. (10). In this case, we obtain the approximate equation

$$\frac{d^2 R}{d\rho^2} + \frac{2}{\rho}\frac{dR}{d\rho} - \frac{\ell(\ell+1)}{\rho^2}R = 0. \qquad (13)$$

We see by inspection that a solution of the form $R(\rho) = \rho^q$ satisfies Eq. (13). For this choice of $R(\rho)$, each term in Eq. (13) is proportional to ρ^{q-2}, and the three terms sum to zero for all values of ρ when

$$q(q-1)\rho^{q-2} + \frac{2}{\rho}q\rho^{q-1} - \frac{\ell(\ell+1)}{\rho^2}\rho^q = 0, \tag{14}$$

which leads to

$$q(q+1) - \ell(\ell+1) = 0. \tag{15}$$

This quadratic equation for q yields two solutions: $q = \ell$ and $q = -\ell - 1$. For small ρ, the solution $\rho^{-\ell-1}$ blows up, so we discard this solution. We then have the limiting form

$$R(\rho) \sim \rho^\ell \qquad (small\ \rho). \tag{16}$$

Combining Eqs. (12) and (16), we expect the radial solution to look something like $R(\rho) \sim \rho^\ell e^{-\gamma\rho}$. We have not violated the proper behavior at the limits by combining these two solutions; $R(\rho)$ remains well-behaved for $\rho = 0$ and $\rho \to \infty$. What else do we need to complete the solution? We need to know the radial dependence at intermediate ρ, so let's try an additional function $H(\rho)$ that is well-behaved by remaining finite at $\rho = 0$ (or blowing up more slowly than ρ^{-l}) and as $\rho \to \infty$ (or blowing up more slowly than $e^{\gamma\rho}$). We therefore seek solutions to the radial equation of the form

$$R(\rho) = \rho^\ell e^{-\gamma\rho} H(\rho), \tag{17}$$

and our next goal is to determine the function $H(\rho)$.

2.2 ■ Series Solution to the Radial Equation

We substitute the trial function $R(\rho) = \rho^\ell e^{-\gamma\rho} H(\rho)$ into the radial differential equation (10) in order to find the differential equation for the new function $H(\rho)$. Immediately, we find that we need the first two derivatives of $R(\rho)$:

$$\frac{dR}{d\rho} = \rho^{\ell-1}e^{-\gamma\rho}\left[\ell H(\rho) - \gamma\rho H(\rho) + \rho H'(\rho)\right], \tag{18}$$

where $H'(\rho) = dH/d\rho$, and

$$\frac{d^2R}{d\rho^2} = \rho^{\ell-1}e^{-\gamma\rho}\left[(2 - 2\gamma - 2\gamma\ell)H(\rho) + (2 + 2\ell - 2\gamma\rho)H'(\rho) + \rho H''(\rho)\right]. \tag{19}$$

Now we substitute Eqs. (18) and (19) into Eq. (10) and collect terms to obtain the differential equation for $H(\rho)$:

$$\rho\frac{d^2H}{d\rho^2} + 2(\ell + 1 - \gamma\rho)\frac{dH}{d\rho} + 2(1 - \gamma - \gamma\ell)H(\rho) = 0. \tag{20}$$

Just as we do with the θ differential equation, we use a power series expansion to solve the radial equation (20). We assume that $H(\rho)$ has the form

$$H(\rho) = \sum_{j=0}^{\infty} c_j\rho^j, \tag{21}$$

and now our job is to find the c_j coefficients. The derivatives of $H(\rho)$ in this series form that we need are

$$\frac{dH}{d\rho} = \sum_{j=0}^{\infty} jc_j\rho^{j-1} = \sum_{j=0}^{\infty}(j+1)c_{j+1}\rho^j$$

$$\frac{d^2H}{d\rho^2} = \sum_{j=0}^{\infty} j(j+1)c_{j+1}\rho^{j-1},$$
(22)

where we have shifted indices in the first equation, as we do in the angular solutions. Substituting Eq. (22) into Eq. (20), we obtain

$$\sum_{j=0}^{\infty} j(j+1)c_{j+1}\rho^j + 2(\ell+1)\sum_{j=0}^{\infty}(j+1)c_{j+1}\rho^j$$

$$-2\gamma\sum_{j=0}^{\infty} jc_j\rho^j + 2(1-\gamma-\gamma\ell)\sum_{j=0}^{\infty} c_j\rho^j = 0.$$
(23)

In order for all terms of the series in Eq. (23) to sum to zero for any and all values of ρ, the coefficient of each power of ρ must be zero, just as for the Legendre equation solution. The coefficient of the general term ρ^j is

$$j(j+1)c_{j+1} + 2(\ell+1)(j+1)c_{j+1} - 2\gamma jc_j + 2(1-\gamma-\gamma\ell)c_j = 0,$$
(24)

which leads to the recurrence relation

$$c_{j+1} = \frac{2\gamma(1+j+\ell)-2}{(j+1)(j+2\ell+2)}c_j.$$
(25)

The recurrence relation shows us that the starting coefficient c_0 determines all of the remaining expansion coefficients in the function $H(\rho)$. The normalization requirement determines c_0, as you have probably already realized, and we'll return to this point in Section 4.

In our study of the polar angle wave functions $\Theta(\theta)$, we found that we had to force the series to terminate to prevent the wave function from becoming infinite. So far, we have assumed that the series expansion of $H(\rho)$ includes an infinite number of terms $(j \to \infty)$. We have forced the asymptotic forms of $R(\rho)$ to remain finite, so let's see how the new part of the solution, $H(\rho)$, behaves for large values of j and how that affects the radial function $R(\rho) = \rho^\ell e^{-\gamma\rho}H(\rho)$.

For large j, the recurrence relation in Eq. (25) is

$$c_{j+1} \cong \frac{2\gamma j}{j^2}c_j = \frac{2\gamma}{j}c_j.$$
(26)

This is exactly the same recurrence relation we find for the exponential function! The series expansion of the exponential function

$$e^{\alpha x} = \sum_{n=0}^{\infty} \frac{\alpha^n}{n!}x^n = 1 + \frac{\alpha}{1!}x + \frac{\alpha^2}{2!}x^2 + \frac{\alpha^3}{3!}x^3 + \dots$$
(27)

has a recurrence relation $c_{j+1} = (\alpha/(j+1))c_j \cong (\alpha/j)c_j$ for large j. Hence, the large j limit in Eq. (26) implies that for large ρ,

$$H(\rho) \cong e^{2\gamma\rho},$$
(28)

which leads to an asymptotic radial function

$$R(\rho) \cong \rho^\ell e^{-\gamma\rho} e^{2\gamma\rho} = \rho^\ell e^{\gamma\rho}. \tag{29}$$

This asymptotic behavior has the same exponential pathology that we rejected in arriving at Eq. (12), so we must reject it once again. We do that by forcing the series expansion of $H(\rho)$ to terminate at a finite value of j, just as we did for the Legendre polynomials.

Hence, the requirement that the wave function be normalizable leads us to define a value j_{max} such that the numerator of the recurrence relation, Eq. (25), goes to zero and terminates the series:

$$2\gamma(1 + j_{max} + \ell) - 2 = 0. \tag{30}$$

Because j and ℓ are integers, $(1 + j_{max} + \ell)$ is also an integer, which we denote as n:

$$n = j_{max} + \ell + 1. \tag{31}$$

This new integer is the **principal quantum number** of the hydrogen atom. The definition of the principal quantum number in Eq. (31) leads us to three important conclusions.

- The integers j and ℓ both start at 0 (make sure you know why), so the principal quantum number n starts at 1 and continues to infinity because ℓ can go to infinity:

$$\boxed{n = 1, 2, 3, \dots \infty}. \tag{32}$$

- The dimensionless energy parameter γ has discrete values! We learn this by substituting the new quantum number n into Eq. (30) and solving:

$$\gamma = \frac{1}{n}. \tag{33}$$

Furthermore, the energy itself takes on only discrete values, and we find those values by substituting Eq. (33) into the definition of γ in Eq. (9). We also need the length scale in Eq. (8) and arrive at

$$-\frac{1}{n^2} = \frac{E}{\left(\frac{\hbar^2}{2\mu a^2}\right)} = \frac{E}{\left(\frac{\hbar^2}{2\mu}\right)} \left(\frac{4\pi\varepsilon_0\hbar^2}{\mu Z e^2}\right)^2. \tag{34}$$

So the requirement that the radial wave function be well behaved has led us to the quantization condition on the allowed energies of the hydrogen atom. Solving Eq. (34) for the allowed energy yields

$$\boxed{E_n = -\frac{1}{2n^2}\left(\frac{Ze^2}{4\pi\varepsilon_0}\right)^2 \frac{\mu}{\hbar^2}, \qquad n = 1, 2, 3, \dots}, \tag{35}$$

which relates the hydrogen energy to the newly defined principal quantum number n. We'll say more about the energy spectrum in the next section.

- The angular momentum quantum number ℓ is limited to a *finite* set of values for every n. We learn this by solving Eq. (31) for ℓ:

$$\ell = n - j_{max} - 1. \tag{36}$$

The polar angle eigenstate solution tells us that the angular momentum quantum number ℓ has a range from 0 to infinity. The lower limit of 0 is consistent with Eq. (36), in which case $n = j_{max} + 1$. However, the upper limit of infinity is consistent with Eq. (36) only for the special case of $n = \infty$. For finite values of n, ℓ cannot exceed $n - j_{max} - 1$, which is largest for the case of $j_{max} = 0$, implying that $\ell_{max} = n - 1$. Thus, the radial eigenvalue solution places a new limit on the allowed values of the angular momentum quantum number ℓ that came from the polar eigenvalue equation:

$$\boxed{\ell = 0, 1, 2, \ldots \quad n - 1}. \tag{37}$$

We now know all the quantum numbers for the hydrogen atom, so let's take a moment to summarize our journey. We solved the ϕ eigenvalue equation and found that the magnetic quantum number m was any integer from negative infinity to positive infinity. We then solved the θ eigenvalue equation and found that the angular momentum quantum number ℓ was an integer from 0 to infinity, but that the absolute value of the magnetic quantum number m could be no larger than ℓ. Finally, we have now solved the r eigenvalue equation and found that the principal quantum number n is an integer from 1 to infinity, but the angular momentum quantum number ℓ can be no larger than $n - 1$. In summary, the hydrogen atom quantum numbers are

$$\boxed{\begin{aligned} &n = 1, 2, 3, \ldots \infty \\ &\ell = 0, 1, 2, \ldots, n - 1 \\ &m = -\ell, -\ell + 1, \ldots 0, \ldots, \ell - 1, \ell \end{aligned}}. \tag{38}$$

3 ■ HYDROGEN ENERGIES AND SPECTRUM

The solution to the radial eigenvalue equation has now given us the quantized energy eigenvalues of the hydrogenic atom:

$$\boxed{E_n = -\frac{1}{2n^2}\left(\frac{Ze^2}{4\pi\varepsilon_0}\right)^2 \frac{\mu}{\hbar^2}, \qquad n = 1, 2, 3, \ldots}. \tag{39}$$

The principal quantum number n ranges from 1 to infinity and is sometimes referred to as the **shell number**. The quantized energies are less than zero because the zero of potential energy is taken to be where the electron and nucleus are separated to infinity—also called the **ionization limit**. Note that E depends only on n and not on ℓ, even though the radial wave function $R_{n\ell}(r)$ depends on both n and ℓ through the j_{max} in Eq. (31).

It is common to express the hydrogen energy in different forms that are more instructive than the jumble of constants in Eq. (39). To simplify our discussion, we focus on the hydrogen atom itself and set $Z = 1$. We also follow the convention of using the electron mass m_e rather than the reduced mass μ at this stage, and then using the correct reduced mass in later calculations. With these simplifications and a few rearrangements of constants, the hydrogen energy levels are

$$E_n = -\frac{1}{2n^2} m_e c^2 \left(\frac{e^2}{4\pi\varepsilon_0 \hbar c}\right)^2. \tag{40}$$

This form is useful because it contains the electron rest mass energy $E_{rest} = m_e c^2$ and a collection of fundamental constants, which must be dimensionless. The dimensionless constant inside the parentheses is the **fine structure constant**

$$\alpha = \frac{e^2}{4\pi\varepsilon_0 \hbar c},$$

(41)

so named because of its role in the fine structure of the hydrogen spectra. More important, the fine structure constant is a measure of the fundamental strength of the electromagnetic interaction, and is also called the **electromagnetic coupling constant**. In terms of the fine structure constant, the hydrogen energy levels take on the simple form

$$\boxed{E_n = -\frac{1}{n^2}\frac{1}{2}\alpha^2 m_e c^2}.$$

(42)

The fine structure constant has the approximate value

$$\boxed{\alpha = \frac{1}{137}}.$$

(43)

The electron rest mass energy has the approximate value

$$\boxed{m_e c^2 = 511 \text{ keV}}.$$

(44)

At this level of precision, the hydrogen energy levels are

$$\boxed{E_n = -\frac{1}{n^2} 13.6 \text{ eV}}.$$

(45)

You should commit the three numerical values in Eqs. (43), (44), and (45) to memory.

Another common and convenient form of the hydrogen energy level formula is obtained by using the length scale we defined in Eq. (8). In the case of hydrogen, the nuclear charge is $Z = 1$, and using the electron mass rather than the reduced mass, we define the quantity

$$\boxed{a_0 = \frac{4\pi\varepsilon_0 \hbar^2}{m_e e^2}}$$

(46)

as the **Bohr radius**, with the approximate value

$$\boxed{a_0 = 0.0529 \text{ nm} = 0.529 \text{ Å}}.$$

(47)

In terms of the Bohr radius, the hydrogen energy levels are

$$\boxed{E_n = -\frac{1}{2n^2}\left(\frac{1}{4\pi\varepsilon_0}\frac{e^2}{a_0}\right)},$$

(48)

which emphasizes the Coulomb binding of the atom.

The spectrum of hydrogen energy states is shown in Fig. 2. There are several noteworthy features of the hydrogen energies:

- There are an infinite number of bound states in the hydrogen atom because the Coulomb potential energy falls off slowly for $r \to \infty$. In contrast, a three-dimensional finite square well has a finite number of bound states, similar to the one-dimensional case.

- The hydrogen energy levels are degenerate with respect to the ℓ and m quantum numbers because the energy depends on n only. For each energy level E_n, there are n possible ℓ states ranging from $\ell = 0$ to $\ell = n - 1$ in unit steps. For each of those ℓ states, there are $2\ell + 1$ possible m states ranging from $m = -\ell$ to $m = +\ell$ in unit steps. The total number of states at each energy level E_n is the sum of these possibilities:

$$\sum_{\ell=0}^{n-1} (2\ell + 1) = 2 \sum_{\ell=0}^{n-1} \ell + \sum_{\ell=0}^{n-1} 1 = 2\frac{n(n-1)}{2} + n = n^2. \tag{49}$$

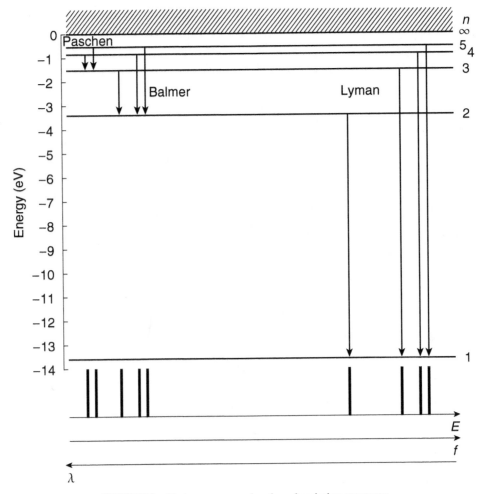

FIGURE 2 Hydrogen energy levels and emission spectrum.

Hydrogen Atom

When we include the two spin possibilities of the electron—spin up and spin down along the
z-axis—then there are $2n^2$ possible states per energy level. The m degeneracy is a result of the
spherical symmetry of the hydrogen atom and is removed if we break this symmetry, for example by applying an electric or magnetic field in a given direction. The ℓ degeneracy is a result
of a special symmetry of the $1/r$ Coulomb potential and is removed when we account for non-
Coulomb interactions in the atom.

- The results we have obtained for the hydrogen energy levels are the same as those obtained
with the semi-classical Bohr model. That is a bit surprising because the Bohr model used
some incorrect physics. Because of this equality of results, the energy levels we have derived
here are often still referred to as the **Bohr energies**.

- The Bohr energies require corrections due to relativity and internal magnetic fields
that change the energies at the level of about 1 part in 10^4, and considering that today's
spectroscopic techniques permit a precision of 1 part in 10^{14}, 1 part in 10^4 is huge! This
means that hydrogen is a wonderful playground to test refinements of the simplest
models.

Hydrogen atoms absorb or emit light when electrons make transitions between energy levels.
When an electron transitions from a higher-lying to a lower-lying level, a photon is emitted. Some of
these emission lines are shown in Fig. 2. Transitions to the $n = 1$ ground state comprise the **Lyman
series**, with the lowest energy transition $(n = 2 \rightarrow 1)$ referred to as the **Lyman-α** line or L_α, the next
one L_β, etc. Transitions from higher levels down to the $n = 2$ level comprise the **Balmer series** and
transitions down to the $n = 3$ level comprise the **Paschen series**. Transitions to higher-lying levels
require the absorption of light.

Whether the photon is emitted or absorbed, its energy matches the energy difference between the
two atomic states involved:

$$E_{photon} = \Delta E_{fi} = |E_f - E_i| = \frac{1}{2}m_e c^2 \left(\frac{e^2}{4\pi\varepsilon_0 \hbar c}\right)^2 \left|\frac{1}{n_i^2} - \frac{1}{n_f^2}\right|. \tag{50}$$

The energy of the photon is related to its wavelength via

$$E_{photon} = \hbar\omega = hf = \frac{hc}{\lambda}, \tag{51}$$

so the wavelength of the photon obeys the relation

$$\frac{1}{\lambda} = R_\infty \left|\frac{1}{n_i^2} - \frac{1}{n_f^2}\right|, \tag{52}$$

where we define the **Rydberg constant** as

$$R_\infty = \frac{m_e}{4\pi\hbar^3 c}\left(\frac{e^2}{4\pi\varepsilon_0}\right)^2. \tag{53}$$

The Rydberg constant was discovered empirically in the nineteenth century through experimental
measurements of the spectrum of hydrogen. The subscript ∞ refers to our use of the electron mass
in Eq. (53) as opposed to the reduced mass, which must be done to get accurate results. If we use the
reduced mass for hydrogen in Eq. (53), then the result is referred to as R_H. R_H and R_∞ differ by 5 parts
in 10^4 (huge!), so in precision measurement it's important to be clear which is being used. Today the
Rydberg constant is the second most precisely measured fundamental constant (the g-factor of the
electron being the most precise). The latest measured value is

$$R_\infty = 109\,737.315\,685\,27(73)\ \text{cm}^{-1}. \tag{54}$$

It is also common to use the term Rydberg (without the word "constant") in reference to the energy instead of the inverse wavelength. For example, one often writes the hydrogen energies in the form

$$E_n = -\frac{1}{n^2} Ryd, \tag{55}$$

where one Rydberg (Ryd) is equal to 13.6 eV.

Not all transitions between states are allowed in the hydrogen atom. The probability of a transition is proportional to the matrix element of the light interaction between the two states: $\langle \psi_{n_f \ell_f m_f} | V_{int} | \psi_{n_i \ell_i m_i} \rangle$. The general properties of these matrix elements determine the selection rules that tell us which transitions are allowed and which are forbidden. For the electromagnetic interaction that characterizes the emission and absorption of light, the selection rules for transitions in the hydrogen atoms are

$$\begin{aligned} \Delta\ell = \ell_f - \ell_i &= \pm 1 \\ \Delta m = m_f - m_i &= 0, \pm 1 \end{aligned}. \tag{56}$$

These selection rules are primarily due to the conservation of angular momentum. The photon has spin angular momentum 1, so when an atom absorbs or emits light, the atom must change its angular momentum by one unit. Some of the allowed transitions in hydrogen are shown in Fig. 3 where the different angular momentum states s, p, d, etc. are identified in order to emphasize the $\Delta\ell = \pm 1$ transitions.

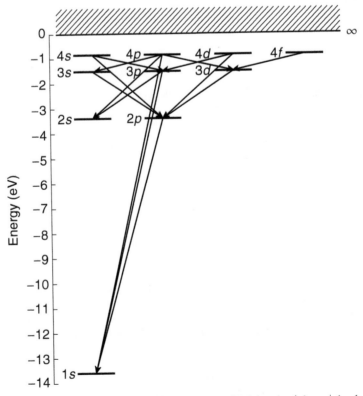

FIGURE 3   Transitions between states in hydrogen, emphasizing the $\Delta\ell = \pm 1$ selection rule.

4 ■ THE RADIAL WAVE FUNCTIONS

Let's now return to the radial wave function solution $R(\rho) = \rho^\ell e^{-\gamma\rho} H(\rho)$ [Eq. (17)]. We have determined that $\gamma = 1/n$, established that n and ℓ are restricted integers, and found the recurrence relation for the coefficients in the series $H(\rho)$. The next thing to do is to put the dimensions back into the problem. In terms of the Bohr radius a_0, the length scale parameter a is

$$a = \frac{4\pi\varepsilon_0\hbar^2}{m_e Z e^2} = \frac{a_0}{Z}, \tag{57}$$

and we have continued the convention of using the electron mass m_e rather than the reduced mass μ. The dimensionless radial position ρ is then

$$\rho = \frac{r}{a} = \frac{Zr}{a_0}. \tag{58}$$

The radial wave function with the dimensions back in place is

$$R_{n\ell}(r) = \left(\frac{Zr}{a_0}\right)^\ell e^{-Zr/na_0} H\left(\frac{Zr}{a_0}\right). \tag{59}$$

We label the radial wave functions as $R_{n\ell}$ using the two quantum numbers n and ℓ that affect the radial dependence. Now we're ready to use our knowledge of the allowed quantum numbers and the recurrence relation to find the polynomial $H(Zr/a_0)$ for each state. The polynomial terminates at the value

$$j_{max} = n - \ell - 1. \tag{60}$$

Let's look at solutions for a few particular values of n and ℓ, and then we'll discuss the general results for the radial wave function.

The ground state of hydrogen has the principal quantum number $n = 1$ and the angular momentum quantum number $\ell = 0$, so Eq. (60) tells us that the polynomial terminates at $j_{max} = 0$. That's the simplest polynomial possible! Hence, we have $H(Zr/a_0) = c_0$ and the radial wave function is

$$R_{10}(r) = c_0 e^{-Zr/a_0}. \tag{61}$$

The constant c_0 is determined from the normalization requirement (Problem 1).

The first excited state of hydrogen has $n = 2$ and two possible values for ℓ: $\ell = 0$ and $\ell = 1$. For the $2s$ state $(\ell = 0)$, Eq. (60) tells us that the polynomial terminates at $j_{max} = 1$. The polynomial is therefore $H(Zr/a_0) = c_0 + c_1(Zr/a_0)$. The coefficients c_0 and c_1 are related by the recurrence relation Eq. (25):

$$c_1 = -\frac{1}{2}c_0 \tag{62}$$

so that $H(Zr/a_0) = c_0(1 - Zr/2a_0)$. The radial wave function is therefore

$$R_{20}(r) = c_0 e^{-Zr/2a_0} \left(1 - Zr/2a_0\right). \tag{63}$$

Again, the constant c_0 is determined from the normalization requirement, and it must be emphasized that the coefficients for different sets of quantum numbers n and ℓ are not related to each other.

For the $2p$ state $(\ell = 1)$, the polynomial terminates at $j_{max} = 0$, so $H(Zr/a_0) = c_0$. The radial wave function is therefore

$$R_{21}(r) = c_0 r e^{-Zr/2a_0}. \tag{64}$$

Table 1   Radial Wave Functions of Hydrogenic Atoms

$$R_{10}(r) = 2\left(\frac{Z}{a_0}\right)^{3/2} e^{-Zr/a_0}$$

$$R_{20}(r) = 2\left(\frac{Z}{2a_0}\right)^{3/2} \left[1 - \frac{Zr}{2a_0}\right] e^{-Zr/2a_0}$$

$$R_{21}(r) = \frac{1}{\sqrt{3}}\left(\frac{Z}{2a_0}\right)^{3/2} \frac{Zr}{a_0} e^{-Zr/2a_0}$$

$$R_{30}(r) = 2\left(\frac{Z}{3a_0}\right)^{3/2} \left[1 - \frac{2Zr}{3a_0} + \frac{2}{27}\left(\frac{Zr}{a_0}\right)^2\right] e^{-Zr/3a_0}$$

$$R_{31}(r) = \frac{4\sqrt{2}}{9}\left(\frac{Z}{3a_0}\right)^{3/2} \frac{Zr}{a_0}\left(1 - \frac{Zr}{6a_0}\right) e^{-Zr/3a_0}$$

$$R_{32}(r) = \frac{2\sqrt{2}}{27\sqrt{5}}\left(\frac{Z}{3a_0}\right)^{3/2} \left(\frac{Zr}{a_0}\right)^2 e^{-Zr/3a_0}$$

Continuing this procedure results in the complete set of radial wave functions, some of which are shown in Table 1 and illustrated graphically in Fig. 4.

It turns out that the radial wave functions can also be written in terms of a common set of functions known as the **associated Laguerre polynomials** $L_q^p(x)$, which are defined as

$$L_q^p(x) = \frac{d^p}{dx^p}L_q(x). \tag{65}$$

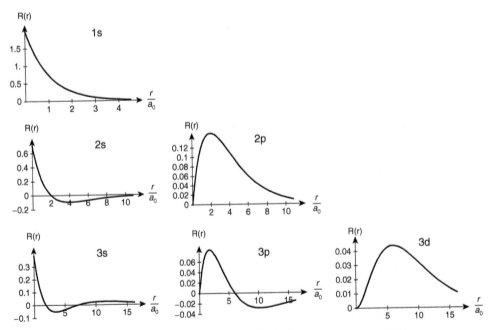

FIGURE 4   Radial wave functions for hydrogen energy eigenstates.

The ordinary **Laguerre polynomials** $L_q(x)$ are defined as

$$L_q(x) = e^x \frac{d^q}{dx^q}(x^q e^{-x}).$$ (66)

The Laguerre polynomials $L_q(x)$ are of degree q, so the associated Laguerre polynomials $L_q^p(x)$ are of degree $q - p$. Using these defintions, the radial wave functions are

$$R_{n\ell}(r) = -\left\{ \left(\frac{2Z}{na_0}\right)^3 \frac{(n - \ell - 1)!}{2n[(n + \ell)!]^3} \right\}^{1/2} e^{-Zr/na_0} \left(\frac{2Zr}{na_0}\right)^\ell L_{n+\ell}^{2\ell+1}(2Zr/na_0).$$ (67)

The associated Laguerre polynomial $L_{n+\ell}^{2\ell+1}(2Zr/na_0)$ is a polynomial of degree $(n + \ell) - (2\ell + 1) = n - \ell - 1$, as expected from the value of j_{max} given by Eq. (60). Be aware that there are differing definitions of the Laguerre polynomials, so the expression for the radial wave function may look different in other texts.

Recall, we normalize each of the angular wave functions separately, and we do the same here with the radial function. This isn't mathematically or physically necessary; it's just a convenient way to do it. The radial normalization condition is

$$\int_0^\infty r^2 \, dr \left[R_{n\ell}(r)\right]^2 = 1.$$ (68)

The normalization condition in Eq. (68) is what we need to find the c_0 coefficients in Eqs. (61), (63), and (64) and was used to normalize the radial wave functions in Eq. (67).

5 ■ THE FULL HYDROGEN WAVE FUNCTIONS

Finally, we're finished! We've solved each of the separated differential equations, we've found the three quantum numbers n, ℓ, and m for the hydrogen atom, and we've found the allowed energies. We're now ready to recombine the three separated parts of the wave function to form the full three-dimensional energy eigenstate wave functions of the hydrogen atom

$$|n\ell m\rangle \doteq \psi_{n\ell m}(r,\theta,\phi) = R_{n\ell}(r)Y_\ell^m(\theta,\phi).$$ (69)

The full eigenstates for the first few energy levels of a hydrogenic atom are given in Table 2; the radial part comes from Eq. (67). These states are also eigenstates of the angular momentum operators $\mathbf{L}^2$ and L_z. They can be eigenstates of H, $\mathbf{L}^2$, and L_z simultaneously because these three operators commute with each other. The three eigenvalue equations are:

$$H\psi_{n\ell m}(r,\theta,\phi) = -\frac{13.6\,\text{eV}}{n^2}\psi_{n\ell m}(r,\theta,\phi)$$
$$\mathbf{L}^2\psi_{n\ell m}(r,\theta,\phi) = \ell(\ell + 1)\hbar^2\psi_{n\ell m}(r,\theta,\phi)$$
$$L_z\psi_{n\ell m}(r,\theta,\phi) = m\hbar\psi_{n\ell m}(r,\theta,\phi).$$ (70)

Table 2 Energy Eigenstate Wave Functions of Hydrogenic Atoms

$$\psi_{100}(r,\theta,\phi) = \frac{1}{\sqrt{\pi}}\left(\frac{Z}{a_0}\right)^{3/2} e^{-Zr/a_0}$$

$$\psi_{200}(r,\theta,\phi) = \frac{1}{\sqrt{\pi}}\left(\frac{Z}{2a_0}\right)^{3/2}\left[1-\frac{Zr}{2a_0}\right] e^{-Zr/2a_0}$$

$$\psi_{210}(r,\theta,\phi) = \frac{1}{2\sqrt{\pi}}\left(\frac{Z}{2a_0}\right)^{3/2}\frac{Zr}{a_0} e^{-Zr/2a_0}\cos\theta$$

$$\psi_{21,\pm1}(r,\theta,\phi) = \mp\frac{1}{2\sqrt{2\pi}}\left(\frac{Z}{2a_0}\right)^{3/2}\frac{Zr}{a_0} e^{-Zr/2a_0}\sin\theta e^{\pm i\phi}$$

$$\psi_{300}(r,\theta,\phi) = \frac{1}{\sqrt{\pi}}\left(\frac{Z}{3a_0}\right)^{3/2}\left[1-\frac{2Zr}{3a_0}+\frac{2}{27}\left(\frac{Zr}{a_0}\right)^2\right] e^{-Zr/3a_0}$$

$$\psi_{310}(r,\theta,\phi) = \frac{2\sqrt{2}}{3\sqrt{3\pi}}\left(\frac{Z}{3a_0}\right)^{3/2}\frac{Zr}{a_0}\left(1-\frac{Zr}{6a_0}\right) e^{-Zr/3a_0}\cos\theta$$

$$\psi_{31,\pm1}(r,\theta,\phi) = \mp\frac{2}{3\sqrt{3\pi}}\left(\frac{Z}{3a_0}\right)^{3/2}\frac{Zr}{a_0}\left(1-\frac{Zr}{6a_0}\right) e^{-Zr/3a_0}\sin\theta e^{\pm i\phi}$$

$$\psi_{320}(r,\theta,\phi) = \frac{1}{27\sqrt{2\pi}}\left(\frac{Z}{3a_0}\right)^{3/2}\left(\frac{Zr}{a_0}\right)^2 e^{-Zr/3a_0}(3\cos^2\theta-1)$$

$$\psi_{32,\pm1}(r,\theta,\phi) = \mp\frac{\sqrt{3}}{27\sqrt{\pi}}\left(\frac{Z}{3a_0}\right)^{3/2}\left(\frac{Zr}{a_0}\right)^2 e^{-Zr/3a_0}\sin\theta\cos\theta e^{\pm i\phi}$$

$$\psi_{32,\pm2}(r,\theta,\phi) = \frac{\sqrt{3}}{54\sqrt{\pi}}\left(\frac{Z}{3a_0}\right)^{3/2}\left(\frac{Zr}{a_0}\right)^2 e^{-Zr/3a_0}\sin^2\theta e^{\pm i2\phi}$$

The normalization condition for the full wave function is the three-dimensional integral

$$1 = \langle n\ell m|n\ell m\rangle = \int |\psi_{n\ell m}(r,\theta,\phi)|^2 dV$$

$$= \int_0^\infty\int_0^{2\pi}\int_0^\pi |R_{n\ell}(r)|^2 |Y_\ell^m(\theta,\phi)|^2 r^2\sin\theta\, d\theta\, d\phi\, dr. \tag{71}$$

It is instructive to rewrite Eq. (71) to emphasize our choice to normalize the radial and angular parts of the wave function independently:

$$1 = \langle n\ell m|n\ell m\rangle = \underbrace{\left\{\int_0^\infty r^2|R_{n\ell}(r)|^2 dr\right\}}_{=1}\underbrace{\left\{\int_0^{2\pi}\int_0^\pi |Y_\ell^m(\theta,\phi)|^2\sin\theta\, d\theta\, d\phi\right\}}_{=1}. \tag{72}$$

We could break this down further into θ and ϕ pieces, but that step is not generally necessary. Note again that the r^2 part of the differential volume element goes with the radial integral.

The probability density is the absolute square of the wave function, so for an energy eigenstate

$$
\begin{aligned}
\mathcal{P}(r,\theta,\phi) &= |\psi_{n\ell m}(r,\theta,\phi)|^2 \\
&= |R_{n\ell}(r)Y_\ell^m(\theta,\phi)|^2.
\end{aligned}
\tag{73}
$$

Multiplying the probability density by the infinitesimal volume element $dV = r^2\,dr\sin\theta\,d\theta\,d\phi$ gives the probability of measuring the electron to be within that volume element:

$$
\begin{aligned}
\mathcal{P}(r,\theta,\phi)dV &= |\psi_{n\ell m}(r,\theta,\phi)|^2\,r^2\,dr\sin\theta\,d\theta\,d\phi \\
&= |R_{n\ell}(r)Y_\ell^m(\theta,\phi)|^2\,r^2 dr\sin\theta\,d\theta\,d\phi.
\end{aligned}
\tag{74}
$$

To calculate the probability of finding the electron within some finite volume, we integrate Eq. (74) over that region.

Because the probability density is three dimensional, it is difficult to represent graphically on a flat piece of paper. We needed three dimensions to properly visualize the two-dimensional spherical harmonic probability densities, so we would need four dimensions to visualize the three-dimensional atomic probability density. A variety of different visualization schemes are possible, many aided by the power of modern computers.

Let's start with the ground state of the hydrogen atom. The wave function is

$$
\psi_{100}(r,\theta,\phi) = \frac{1}{\sqrt{\pi a_0^3}}e^{-r/a_0}
\tag{75}
$$

and the probability density is

$$
\mathcal{P}_{100}(r,\theta,\phi) = |\psi_{100}(r,\theta,\phi)|^2 = \frac{1}{\pi a_0^3}e^{-2r/a_0}.
\tag{76}
$$

The dimensions of the probability density are $1/length^3$ as you would expect for a three-dimensional density. For the hydrogen ground state, the probability density is independent of the angles θ and ϕ, which means that the electron cloud around the nucleus is spherically symmetric. The three-dimensional electron probability distribution of the $1s$ state is illustrated in Fig. 5. In Fig. 5(a) the three axes represent physical space and the value of the probability density is represented by a grayscale (white is high, black is low). Just three parallel planes are shown, allowing us to "peek" at the distribution. In Fig. 5(b), the grayscale density plot in the x-z plane ($y = 0$) is shown. On a computer, you can animate the motion of the slicing planes in Fig. 5(a) to visualize the full electron cloud, and you can also use color while you're at it (see the activity on hydrogen probability densities). Figure 6(a) represents the $1s$ probability density in the x-z plane using height above the plane as the indicator of probability density, and Fig. 6(b) shows the probability density in a one-dimensional plot as a function of r, the distance from the nucleus. All of these representations demonstrate that the probability density for measuring the electron position in the $1s$ state is largest at the origin.

Grayscale density plots in the x-z plane for the eigenstates in the first three energy levels of the hydrogen atom are shown in Fig. 7. The density plots for negative values of m are indistinguishable from those for positive m, so they are not included. In the grayscale plots in Fig. 7, we plot the absolute value of the wave function, which is the square root of the probability density, to provide a better visual representation of the electron distribution. The spatial scales are different for each value of n. Each plot has a range of $-3n^2a_0$ to $+3n^2a_0$.

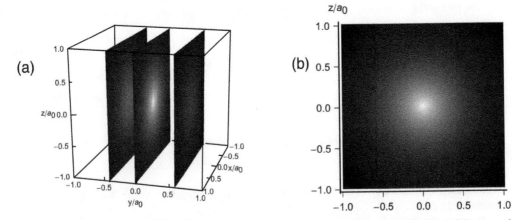

FIGURE 5 (a) Two-dimensional slices of the three-dimensional electron distribution of the ground state of hydrogen. In each slice, the probability density is represented by grayscale (black = 0, white = maximum). (b) The particular two-dimensional probability density slice at $y = 0$.

Here are some important features of the radial wave functions and the probability densities.

- All the radial functions have an r^ℓ dependence, so the wave function vanishes at the origin except for the s states $(\ell = 0)$. This is caused by the centrifugal barrier that "repels" the electron from the nucleus for $\ell \geq 1$, as we saw in the effective potential in Fig. 1. For s states, the probability density at the origin is

$$\mathcal{P}_{ns}(0,\theta,\phi) = \left|\psi_{n00}(0,\theta,\phi)\right|^2 = \left|R_{n0}(0)Y_0^0(\theta,\phi)\right|^2 = \frac{1}{4\pi}\left|R_{n0}(0)\right|^2$$

$$= \frac{1}{\pi}\left(\frac{Z}{na_0}\right)^3. \tag{77}$$

This nonzero probability density is important because it means that the electron has some finite probability of being inside the nucleus, which affects the real energy levels when we consider the nucleus not to be a point particle.

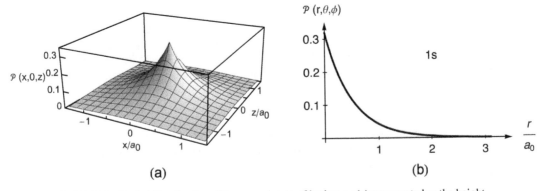

FIGURE 6 Probability density of the ground state of hydrogen (a) represented as the height above the x-z plane and (b) plotted as a function of radius.

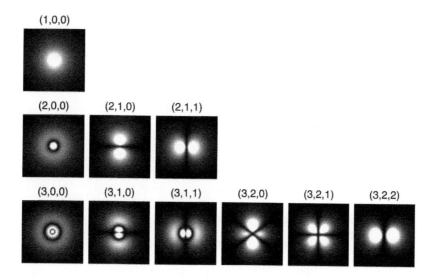

FIGURE 7 Grayscale density plots in the *x-z* plane of the absolute value of the wave function for hydrogen energy eigenstates $|n\ell m\rangle$ denoted by the labels above each plot. The spatial range of each plot is $-3n^2 a_0$ to $+3n^2 a_0$.

- Each radial wave function $R_{n\ell}(r)$ has $n - \ell - 1$ nodes and $n - \ell$ antinodes. The particle-in-a-box energy eigenstates also have more nodes as the energy increases. The hydrogen radial functions for a given n have fewer nodes for higher ℓ states, but the angular wave functions compensate for that by having more nodes.

- The full wave function has parity $(-1)^\ell$ (recall that the parity operation is $\mathbf{r} \to -\mathbf{r}$). The parity of the wave function derives from the parity of the spherical harmonics. The parity is important later in calculating matrix elements.

- The probability densities are independent of the azimuthal angle ϕ, which you have probably already seen from the nature of the spherical harmonics.

The probability plots we have shown are informative, but ultimately we need to calculate probabilities or expectation values to compare with experiments. These are often done with computers, but you need to know what to tell the computer to do. Let's work an example that is analytically tractable.

Example 1 Find the probability that the electron in the ground state of hydrogen is measured to be within one Bohr radius of the nucleus and calculate the expectation value of the radial position r.

The probability is the integral of the probability density over a sphere of radius a_0, so we limit the r integral to $r < a_0$ and integrate over the full range of θ and ϕ:

$$\mathcal{P}_{r<a_0} = \int_{sphere\ r<a_0} \mathcal{P}(r,\theta,\phi)\,dV$$

$$= \int_0^{a_0} \int_0^{2\pi} \int_0^{\pi} \mathcal{P}(r,\theta,\phi)\, r^2 \sin\theta\, d\theta\, d\phi\, dr \tag{78}$$

$$= \int_0^{a_0} \int_0^{2\pi} \int_0^{\pi} \left| R_{n\ell}(r) Y_\ell^m(\theta,\phi) \right|^2 r^2 \sin\theta\, d\theta\, d\phi\, dr.$$

We separate the radial and angular integrals

$$\mathcal{P}_{r<a_0} = \left\{ \int_0^{a_0} r^2 |R_{n\ell}(r)|^2 \, dr \right\} \left\{ \int_0^{2\pi} \int_0^{\pi} |Y_\ell^m(\theta,\phi)|^2 \sin\theta \, d\theta \, d\phi \right\}. \tag{79}$$

The angular integral is unity because the spherical harmonics are normalized (See! The separate normalization is useful!), leaving

$$\mathcal{P}_{r<a_0} = \int_0^{a_0} r^2 |R_{n\ell}(r)|^2 \, dr. \tag{80}$$

Now we put in the radial ground state wave function to get

$$\mathcal{P}_{r<a_0} = \int_0^{a_0} r^2 \frac{4Z^3}{a_0^3} e^{-2Zr/a_0} \, dr. \tag{81}$$

Substituting $x = 2Zr/a_0$ and integrating gives

$$\mathcal{P}_{r<a_0} = \frac{1}{2} \int_0^{2Z} x^2 e^{-x} \, dx = \frac{1}{2} (-x^2 - 2x - 2) e^{-x} \Big|_0^{2Z} = \frac{1}{2} \left[(-4Z^2 - 4Z - 2) e^{-2Z} + 2 \right]. \tag{82}$$

For the hydrogen case, $Z = 1$, and the probability is

$$\mathcal{P}_{r<a_0} = \left[1 - (2 + 2 + 1) e^{-2} \right] = 1 - 5e^{-2} \tag{83}$$
$$= 0.323.$$

In a set of radial position measurements, 32% of the results will be within one Bohr radius of the nucleus.

The expectation value of the radius is

$$\langle r \rangle = \langle n\ell m | r | n\ell m \rangle = \langle 100 | r | 100 \rangle$$
$$= \int r |\psi_{n\ell m}(r,\theta,\phi)|^2 \, dV \tag{84}$$
$$= \int_0^\infty \int_0^{2\pi} \int_0^\pi r |R_{n\ell}(r) Y_\ell^m(\theta,\phi)|^2 r^2 \sin\theta \, d\theta \, d\phi \, dr.$$

Again, we separate the radial and angular integrals

$$\langle r \rangle = \left\{ \int_0^\infty r^3 |R_{n\ell}(r)|^2 \, dr \right\} \left\{ \int_0^{2\pi} \int_0^\pi |Y_\ell^m(\theta,\phi)|^2 \sin\theta \, d\theta \, d\phi \right\}. \tag{85}$$

The angular integral is unity and we get

$$\langle r \rangle = \int_0^\infty r^3 |R_{n\ell}(r)|^2 \, dr. \tag{86}$$

Substituting in the radial ground state wave function, we get

$$\langle r \rangle = \int_0^\infty r^3 \frac{4Z^3}{a_0^3} e^{-2Zr/a_0} \, dr. \tag{87}$$

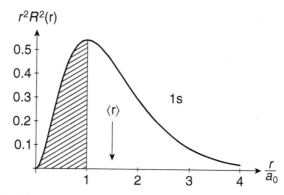

FIGURE 8 Radial probability integrand for the hydrogen $1s$ ground state. The hatched region indicates the probability $\mathcal{P}_{r \leq a_0}$ and the arrow indicates the expectation value $\langle r \rangle$.

Substituting $x = 2Zr/a_0$ and integrating gives

$$\langle r \rangle = \frac{a_0}{4Z} \int_0^\infty x^3 e^{-x}\, dx = \frac{a_0}{4Z}\left(-x^3 - 3x^2 - 6x - 6\right)e^{-x}\Big|_0^\infty$$

$$= \frac{3a_0}{2Z}. \tag{88}$$

For the hydrogen atom, the mean value of the radius is $3a_0/2$. The integrand $r^2\left|R_{n\ell}(r)\right|^2$ of the integral in Eq. (80) is plotted in Fig. The hatched area under the curve represents the probability we calculated above that the electron is measured to be in the region $0 \leq r \leq a_0$. The arrow indicates the expectation value of the radius, which is beyond the peak because the integrand is not symmetric.

Expectation values of the radial position are useful for many calculations we will do later. We quote here without proof the expectation values $\langle n\ell m | r^k | n\ell m \rangle$ for different powers:

$$\langle r \rangle = \frac{a_0}{2Z}\left[3n^2 - \ell(\ell + 1)\right]$$

$$\langle r^2 \rangle = \frac{a_0^2 n^2}{2Z^2}\left[5n^2 + 1 - 3\ell(\ell + 1)\right]$$

$$\left\langle \frac{1}{r} \right\rangle = \frac{Z}{a_0 n^2} \tag{89}$$

$$\left\langle \frac{1}{r^2} \right\rangle = \frac{Z^2}{a_0^2 n^3 \left(\ell + \frac{1}{2}\right)}$$

$$\left\langle \frac{1}{r^3} \right\rangle = \frac{Z^3}{a_0^3 n^3 \ell \left(\ell + \frac{1}{2}\right)(\ell + 1)}.$$

The result in Example 1 agrees with the general expression in the first equation above.

6 ■ SUPERPOSITION STATES

Having solved the energy eigenvalue equation for the hydrogen atom and found the allowed energies and allowed wave functions, we can now use them to find the time evolution of the atom with arbitary initial conditons using the Schrödinger time-evolution recipe. If the atom starts in one of the energy eigenstates, then the time evolution of the system is

$$|\psi(t)\rangle \doteq \psi(r,\theta,\phi,t) = R_{n\ell}(r)Y_\ell^m(\theta,\phi)e^{-iE_n t/\hbar}, \tag{90}$$

where E_n are the energy eigenvalues given in Eq. (39). The wave function acquires an overall time-dependent phase factor, but that does not affect any measurements we make on the system, so this is a stationary state.

More interesting time-dependent behavior occurs if the system starts in a superposition of energy eigenstates. In this case, the time evolution of the wave function is

$$|\psi(t)\rangle \doteq \psi(r,\theta,\phi,t) = \sum_{n,\ell,m} c_{n\ell m} R_{n\ell}(r)Y_\ell^m(\theta,\phi)e^{-iE_n t/\hbar}, \tag{91}$$

where the expansion coefficients are obtained from the projections of the initial state $|\psi(t=0)\rangle$ onto the energy eigenstates

$$c_{n\ell m} = \langle n\ell m|\psi(0)\rangle = \int_0^\infty r^2\,dr \int_0^\pi \sin\theta\,d\theta \int_0^{2\pi} d\phi\, R_{n\ell}^*(r)\,Y_\ell^{m*}(\theta,\phi)\,\psi(r,\theta,\phi,0). \tag{92}$$

Example 2 Find the time evolution of an equal superposition of the $1s$ ground state and the $2p_0(m=0)$ excited state:

$$|\psi(0)\rangle = \tfrac{1}{\sqrt{2}}|100\rangle + \tfrac{1}{\sqrt{2}}|210\rangle. \tag{93}$$

These states are both energy eigenstates, so the time evolution is obtained by application of the Schrödinger recipe:

$$\begin{aligned}
\psi(r,\theta,\phi,t) &= \tfrac{1}{\sqrt{2}}\psi_{100}(r,\theta,\phi)e^{-iE_1 t/\hbar} + \tfrac{1}{\sqrt{2}}\psi_{210}(r,\theta,\phi)e^{-iE_2 t/\hbar} \\[2mm]
&= \frac{1}{\sqrt{2\pi a_0^3}}e^{-r/a_0}e^{-iE_1 t/\hbar} + \frac{1}{\sqrt{\pi a_0^3}}\frac{r\cos\theta}{8a_0}e^{-r/2a_0}e^{-iE_2 t/\hbar} \\[2mm]
&= \frac{1}{\sqrt{2\pi a_0^3}}e^{-iE_1 t/\hbar}\left(e^{-r/a_0} + \frac{r\cos\theta}{4\sqrt{2}a_0}e^{-r/2a_0}e^{-i\omega_{21}t}\right),
\end{aligned} \tag{94}$$

where the Bohr frequency is $\omega_{21} = (E_2 - E_1)/\hbar$. Noting that $z = r\cos\theta$, we rewrite the wave function as

$$\psi(r,\theta,\phi,t) = \frac{1}{\sqrt{2\pi a_0^3}}e^{-iE_1 t/\hbar}\left(e^{-r/a_0} + \frac{z}{4\sqrt{2}a_0}e^{-r/2a_0}e^{-i\omega_{21}t}\right), \tag{95}$$

which emphasizes the z-dependence of the state. The probability amplitude (absolute value of the wave function) is displayed in Fig. 9(a) at time $t=0$. The electron cloud is displaced in the positive z-direction, but as time evolves, animation of Fig. 9(a) shows that the cloud moves up and down along z. This is a model of the *oscillating electric dipole moment* that is responsible for the radiation that the atom emits at the Bohr frequency (Problem 13).

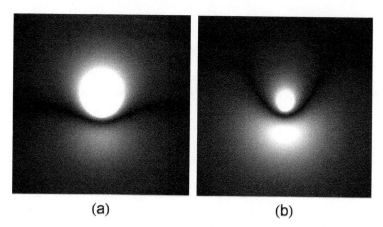

(a)   (b)

FIGURE 9 Probability amplitude (wave function) densities for (a) 1s-2p and (b) 2s-2p superposition states.

Example 3 Find the time evolution of an equal superposition of the 2s excited state and the $2p_0$ ($m = 0$) excited state:

$$|\psi(0)\rangle = \tfrac{1}{\sqrt{2}}|200\rangle + \tfrac{1}{\sqrt{2}}|210\rangle. \tag{96}$$

The time-evolved state is

$$\begin{aligned}
\psi(r,\theta,\phi,t) &= \tfrac{1}{\sqrt{2}}\psi_{200}(r,\theta,\phi)e^{-iE_2t/\hbar} + \tfrac{1}{\sqrt{2}}\psi_{210}(r,\theta,\phi)e^{-iE_2t/\hbar} \\
&= \frac{1}{2\sqrt{\pi a_0^3}}\left(1 - \frac{r}{2a_0}\right)e^{-r/2a_0}e^{-iE_2t/\hbar} + \frac{1}{\sqrt{\pi a_0^3}}\frac{r\cos\theta}{8a_0}e^{-r/2a_0}e^{-iE_2t/\hbar} \\
&= \frac{1}{2\sqrt{\pi a_0^3}}e^{-iE_2t/\hbar}\left(\left(1 - \frac{r}{2a_0}\right)e^{-r/a_0} + \frac{z}{4a_0}e^{-r/2a_0}\right).
\end{aligned} \tag{97}$$

In this case, the two states are degenerate in energy and there is no relative time-dependent phase factor. The probability amplitude (absolute value of the wave function) is displayed in Fig. 9(b) at time $t = 0$. The electron cloud is displaced in the negative z-direction in this case because of the different radial wave function for the 2s state, and as time evolves, the cloud does not move. This is a model of a *static electric dipole moment* that will be used again when studying the response of the atom to an applied electric field—the Stark effect. Such an *s-p* superposition is a hybrid orbital that can be used to explain molecular bonding. Two atoms with displaced electron clouds facing each other reduce the electrostatic repulsion of the positively charged nuclei and stabilize the system.

SUMMARY

The radial part of the energy eigenvalue equation contains the crucial physics of the Coulomb interaction that determines the energies of the bound hydrogen atom. Solving the radial differential equation yields the quantization condition on the energy. The new quantum number is the principal quantum number $n = 1, 2, 3, \ldots$. The resultant energies of the hydrogen atom states are

$$E_n = -\frac{1}{n^2} 13.6 \, \text{eV}. \tag{98}$$

The length scale of the hydrogen atom is set by the Bohr radius

$$a_0 = 0.0529 \, \text{nm}. \tag{99}$$

The radial wave functions $R_{n\ell}(r)$ combine with the spherical harmonics to give the full three-dimensional wave functions of the hydrogen atom

$$|n\ell m\rangle \doteq \psi_{n\ell m}(r, \theta, \phi) = R_{n\ell}(r) Y_\ell^m(\theta, \phi). \tag{100}$$

The allowed values of the three quantum numbers are

$$\begin{aligned}
n &= 1, 2, 3, \ldots \infty \\
\ell &= 0, 1, 2, \ldots, n - 1 \\
m &= -\ell, -\ell + 1, \ldots 0, \ldots, \ell - 1, \ell.
\end{aligned} \tag{101}$$

The hydrogen atom states $\psi_{n\ell m}(r, \theta, \phi)$ are simultaneously eigenstates of the Hamiltonian H, and the angular momentum operators $\mathbf{L}^2$ and L_z:

$$\begin{aligned}
H\psi_{n\ell m}(r, \theta, \phi) &= E_n \psi_{n\ell m}(r, \theta, \phi) \\
\mathbf{L}^2 \psi_{n\ell m}(r, \theta, \phi) &= \ell(\ell + 1)\hbar^2 \psi_{n\ell m}(r, \theta, \phi) \\
L_z \psi_{n\ell m}(r, \theta, \phi) &= m\hbar \psi_{n\ell m}(r, \theta, \phi).
\end{aligned} \tag{102}$$

RESOURCES

Activities

These activities are available at

www.physics.oregonstate.edu/qmactivities

Radial Wavefunctions: Students visualize the radial part of the probability density of the hydrogen atom.

Hydrogen Probability Densities: Students visualize the probability density of the electron in the hydrogen atom.

Further Reading

High resolution spectroscopy of the hydrogen atom is discussed in this article:
T. W. Hänsch, A. L. Schawlow, and G. W. Series, "The spectrum of atomic hydrogen," *Scientific American,* **240**(3), 94–110 (1979).

Hydrogen Atom: Problem Set

1 Calculate the coefficient c_0 that normalizes the radial wave function $R_{10}(r)$ in Eq. (61),

$$R_{10}(r) = c_0 e^{-Zr/a_0}, \tag{61}$$

and confirm the wave function shown in Table 1.

2 Use the recurrence relation for the radial wave function to construct the $n = 3$ radial states of hydrogen. Calculate the normalization constant for the $R_{32}(r)$ state.

3 Use the definition of the radial wave function in terms of the associated Laguerre polynomials [Eq. (67)],

$$R_{n\ell}(r) = -\left\{ \left(\frac{2Z}{na_0}\right)^3 \frac{(n - \ell - 1)!}{2n[(n + \ell)!]^3} \right\}^{1/2} e^{-Zr/na_0} \left(\frac{2Zr}{na_0}\right)^\ell L_{n+\ell}^{2\ell+1}(2Zr/na_0), \tag{67}$$

to construct the radial wave function $R_{42}(r)$.

4 Show that the wave functions representing the $|100\rangle$ and $|210\rangle$ states are orthogonal.

5 By direct application of the differential operators, verify that the state $|321\rangle \doteq \psi_{321}(r,\theta,\phi)$ is an eigenstate of H, $\mathbf{L}^2$, and L_z and determine the corresponding eigenvalues.

6 Calculate the probability that the electron is measured to be within one Bohr radius of the nucleus for the $n = 2$ states of hydrogen. Discuss the differences between the results for the $\ell = 0$ and $\ell = 1$ states.

7 Calculate the probability that the electron is measured to be in the classically forbidden region for the $n = 2$ states of hydrogen. Discuss the differences between the results for the $\ell = 0$ and $\ell = 1$ states.

8 Calculate by direct integration the expectation values $\langle r^2 \rangle$ and $\langle 1/r \rangle$ of the radial position for the ground state of hydrogen. Compare your results to the quoted expressions in Eq. (89),

$$\langle r \rangle = \frac{a_0}{2Z}[3n^2 - \ell(\ell + 1)]$$

$$\langle r^2 \rangle = \frac{a_0^2 n^2}{2Z^2}[5n^2 + 1 - 3\ell(\ell + 1)]$$

$$\left\langle \frac{1}{r} \right\rangle = \frac{Z}{a_0 n^2}$$

$$\left\langle \frac{1}{r^2} \right\rangle = \frac{Z^2}{a_0^2 n^3(\ell + \frac{1}{2})} \tag{89}$$

$$\left\langle \frac{1}{r^3} \right\rangle = \frac{Z^3}{a_0^3 n^3 \ell(\ell + \frac{1}{2})(\ell + 1)},$$

From Chapter 8 of *Quantum Mechanics: A Paradigms Approach*, First Edition. David H. McIntyre. Copyright © 2012 by Pearson Education, Inc. Published by Pearson Addison-Wesley. All rights reserved.

The companion websites for this text are http://physics.oregonstate.edu/portfolioswiki and http://physics.oregonstate.edu/qmactivities.

and discuss your results. Did you expect that $\langle 1/r \rangle \neq 1/\langle r \rangle$? Use your result for $\langle 1/r \rangle$ to find the expectation value of the kinetic energy of the ground state of hydrogen and discuss your result.

9 Calculate by direct integration the expectation value of the radial position for each of the $n = 3$ states of hydrogen. Compare your results to the quoted expression in Eq. (89) and discuss your results.

10 Calculate the probability that the electron in the ground state of a hydrogenic atom of nuclear charge Z is measured to be inside the nucleus. A nucleus with A nucleons (Z protons and $A-Z$ neutrons) has an approximate radius of $r \cong (1.2 \times 10^{-15} \text{ m})A^{1/3}$. Calculate the probabilities for hydrogen and uranium-238.

11 Tritium is an isotope of hydrogen, with a nucleus comprising one proton and two neutrons. The tritium nucleus (triton) is radioactive, decaying by beta (electron) emission to the helium-3 nucleus comprising two protons and one neutron. An electron is initially in the ground state of a tritium atom. After the instantaneous beta decay, what is the probability that the electron is in the ground state of the new atom?

12 Find the ground state energy, the effective Bohr radius [using Eq. (8)],

$$\boxed{a = \frac{4\pi\varepsilon_0\hbar^2}{\mu Z e^2}}, \tag{8}$$

and the Lyman-alpha wavelength of the following hydrogenic systems:

a) deuterium: electron and nucleus with one proton and one neutron

b) positive helium ion: $^4He^+$

c) positronium: electron $(q = -e, m = m_e)$ and positron $(q = +e, m = m_e)$

d) muonium: electron and antimuon $(q = +e, m = m_\mu \cong 207m_e)$

e) muonic hydrogen: muon and proton

f) hydrogen-like uranium: $^{235}U^{91+}$

13 Consider the one-dimensional probability density $\mathcal{P}(z)$ along the z-axis obtained by integrating over a plane perpendicular to the z-axis, either in Cartesian coordinates

$$\mathcal{P}(z) = \int_{-\infty}^{\infty} \int_{-\infty}^{\infty} |\psi_{n\ell m}(x,y,z)|^2 dx\,dy$$

or in cylindrical coordinates

$$\mathcal{P}(z) = \int_0^{2\pi} \int_0^{\infty} |\psi_{n\ell m}(\rho,\phi,z)|^2 \rho\,d\rho\,d\phi.$$

Calculate this probability density for the superposition states $|\psi_1\rangle = (|100\rangle + |210\rangle)/\sqrt{2}$ and $|\psi_2\rangle = (|200\rangle + |210\rangle)/\sqrt{2}$. Use these probability densities to find the expectation value of the electric dipole moment $\mathbf{d} = q\mathbf{r}$ and verify that the moments for these two states are oppositely oriented as indicated by Fig. 9. Plot and animate the probability densities to verify that one state is oscillating and one state is static.

14 A hydrogen atom is initially in the superposition state

$$|\psi(0)\rangle = \tfrac{1}{\sqrt{14}}|211\rangle - \tfrac{2}{\sqrt{14}}|32,-1\rangle + \tfrac{3i}{\sqrt{14}}|422\rangle.$$

a) What are the possible results of a measurement of the energy and with what probabilities would they occur? Plot a histogram of the measurement results. Calculate the expectation value of the energy.

b) What are the possible results of a measurement of the angular momentum operator $\mathbf{L}^2$ and with what probabilities would they occur? Plot a histogram of the measurement results. Calculate the expectation value of $\mathbf{L}^2$.

c) What are the possible results of a measurement of the angular momentum component operator L_z and with what probabilities would they occur? Plot a histogram of the measurement results. Calculate the expectation value of L_z.

d) How do the answers to (a), (b), and (c) depend upon time?

15 Consider a particle of mass m bound in an infinite square potential energy well in three dimensions:

$$V(z) = \begin{cases} 0, & 0 < x < L, 0 < y < L, 0 < z < L \\ \infty, & otherwise. \end{cases}$$

Use separation of variables in Cartesian coordinates to find the energy eigenvalues and eigenstates of this particle in a cubical box. Find the degeneracy of the first 6 energy levels.

Harmonic Oscillator

Consider what you have learned about applying the tools for analyzing the motion of particles in quantum mechanics to three important problems: (1) a particle bound in an infinite square potential energy well in one dimension, (2) a free particle in one dimension, and (3) the hydrogen atom in three dimensions. In this chapter we will solve another system with bound states in a one-dimensional potential energy well: the harmonic oscillator. This system resembles the infinite square well or particle-in-a-box system—the harmonic oscillator box just has a different shape. To solve the harmonic oscillator problem, we introduce a new method and some new tools in the process. Then we use the solutions to the harmonic oscillator problem as a means to review the fundamental tools and concepts of quantum mechanics.

1 ■ CLASSICAL HARMONIC OSCILLATOR

Let's first review the classical harmonic oscillator before we study the quantum mechanical case. A prototypical classical harmonic oscillator system is a mass m connected to a spring that is fixed to a wall at its other end. The spring force is governed by Hooke's law, which says that the force F is a restoring force and is proportional to the displacement x of the mass from equilibrium:

$$F = -kx, \tag{1}$$

where k is the spring constant. This linear restoring force is derivable from the quadratic potential energy function $V(x) = \frac{1}{2}kx^2$.

The beauty of the mass-on-a-spring system is that it is a model for many other systems in nature that behave as harmonic oscillators. To see why this is so, consider the generic potential energy curve shown in Fig. 1. We are typically interested in finding the motion in the ground state or other low energy states of the system. As the dashed line suggests, near the minimum at x_0 of the potential energy function that governs the system, the potential energy has the shape of a parabola, (i.e., it looks like a harmonic oscillator). This parabolic shape is also evident if we consider a Taylor series expansion of the function about the minimum:

$$V(x - x_0) = V(x_0) + (x - x_0)\frac{dV}{dx}\bigg|_{x=x_0} + \frac{1}{2}(x - x_0)^2 \frac{d^2V}{dx^2}\bigg|_{x=x_0} + \dots . \tag{2}$$

The leading term in Eq. (2) is the quadratic term because the first two terms are zero: (1) the potential energy offset $V(x_0)$ can be defined to be to zero because a constant potential energy does not affect the motion, and (2) the linear term is zero because the potential derivative

From Chapter 9 of *Quantum Mechanics: A Paradigms Approach*, First Edition. David H. McIntyre. Copyright © 2012 by Pearson Education, Inc. Published by Pearson Addison-Wesley. All rights reserved.

The companion websites for this text are http://physics.oregonstate.edu/portfolioswiki and http://physics.oregonstate.edu/qmactivities.

(i.e., slope) is zero at the minimum. Hence the motion of the system is that of a harmonic oscillator in the vicinity of the potential energy minimum, and we identify the spring constant k as the second derivative of the potential energy evaluated at the minimum x_0. If the motion takes the system too far from the minimum, the shape may deviate slightly from a parabola, and the motion will be altered, but we still find it useful to start by considering the motion as harmonic and then asking how that motion is perturbed. For these reasons, you will study harmonic oscillators as long as you do physics.

The motion of the classical harmonic oscillator is solved by using Newton's second law:

$$F = ma$$
$$-kx = m\frac{d^2x}{dt^2}. \tag{3}$$

It is convenient to define a new constant

$$\omega = \sqrt{\frac{k}{m}} \tag{4}$$

and rewrite the equation of motion as

$$\frac{d^2x}{dt^2} = -\omega^2 x(t). \tag{5}$$

This is a standard differential equation that you have likely encountered many times before. The solution is the sinusoidal function

$$x(t) = A\cos(\omega t + \phi), \tag{6}$$

where the amplitude A and phase constant ϕ are determined by the initial state of the motion of the system. The motion is characterized by a single angular frequency (i.e., a single harmonic—hence the name) given by ω.

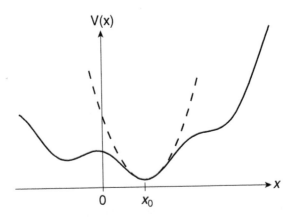

FIGURE 1 A general potential energy function (solid) is approximated by a quadratic harmonic potential (dashed) in the vicinity of the potential minimum.

2 ■ QUANTUM MECHANICAL HARMONIC OSCILLATOR

The procedure for finding the quantum mechanical Hamiltonian of any system is to first find the classical energy and then rewrite that in terms of quantum mechanical operators. The potential energy of the harmonic oscillator is

$$V(x) = \tfrac{1}{2}kx^2. \tag{7}$$

The total mechanical energy of the system is the sum of kinetic and potential energies:

$$E = \frac{p^2}{2m} + \tfrac{1}{2}kx^2. \tag{8}$$

The oscillator frequency ω plays an important role in quantum mechanics, so it is common to rewrite the potential energy using ω in place of k. From Eq. (4) we have $k = m\omega^2$, so that the quantum mechanical Hamiltonian for the harmonic oscillator is

$$\boxed{H = \frac{\hat{p}^2}{2m} + \tfrac{1}{2}m\omega^2\hat{x}^2}. \tag{9}$$

We denote the operators $\hat{x}$ and $\hat{p}$ with carets to distinguish them from the variables x and p, but we often don't use the caret notation if there is no ambiguity.

As always, our goal when presented with a new potential energy system is to solve the energy eigenvalue equation $H|E\rangle = E|E\rangle$ to find the allowed energies in the system. Then we use the energy eigenstates as the preferred basis to apply the recipe for Schrödinger time evolution. In the previous potential energy well problems, the square wells and the hydrogen atom, we expressed the energy eigenvalue equation $H|E\rangle = E|E\rangle$ as a differential equation in the wave function picture (i.e., the position representation). For the harmonic oscillator, the energy eigenvalue differential equation is

$$-\frac{\hbar^2}{2m}\frac{d^2\varphi_E(x)}{dx^2} + \frac{1}{2}m\omega^2x^2\varphi_E(x) = E\varphi_E(x). \tag{10}$$

We can solve Eq. (10) using a power series solution. Rather than do that here, we present a new method of solution that is more elegant and is known as the **operator method** or the **algebraic method**. Of course, we get the same results either way.

If you haven't seen it before, the operator method for solving the quantum mechanical harmonic oscillator problem appears to be magic. We arrive at the solution by defining some new quantities that you would not imagine would be useful and by using minimal information about what how the operators $\hat{x}$ and $\hat{p}$ behave. This operator method is also useful in describing angular momentum, and it is the basis of quantum field theory.

To make this discussion of the operator solution to the harmonic oscillator problem clearer, let's go ahead and present the energy spectrum answer to the problem. The solutions to bound state problems in different quantum mechanical systems share many features. The bound states in a potential energy well are discrete, with the ground state near, but not at, the bottom of the well. The positions of the energy levels depend upon the shape of the well. In the case of the infinite square well, the energy levels scale with n^2, where n is the quantum number labeling the energy levels $n = 1, 2, 3, \ldots$. Hence the energy level spacing in the infinite square well increases as n increases, as shown in Fig. 2(a). The hydrogen atom

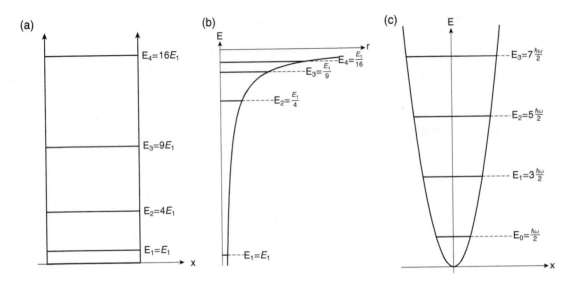

FIGURE 2   Spectra of energy eigenstates in (a) the infinite square well, (b) the hydrogen atom, and (c) the harmonic oscillator well.

has energy levels that scale as $1/n^2$ and so they get closer together as n increases, as shown in Fig. 2(b). The harmonic oscillator has a special potential energy well shape that gives rise to energy levels that scale linearly with n and hence are evenly spaced, as shown in Fig. 2(c). The energy eigenvalues of the harmonic oscillator are

$$E_n = \hbar\omega\left(n + \tfrac{1}{2}\right), \qquad n = 0, 1, 2, 3, \ldots . \tag{11}$$

The convention is to label the ground state of the harmonic oscillator as $n = 0$, rather than $n = 1$ as in most other bound state problems. In Dirac notation, the energy eigenstates $|n\rangle$ are labeled with the quantum number n and satisfy the energy eigenvalue equation

$$H|n\rangle = E_n|n\rangle = \hbar\omega\left(n + \tfrac{1}{2}\right)|n\rangle. \tag{12}$$

In the operator method of solving the harmonic oscillator problem, we define two new operators and use the properties of these operators to derive the energy eigenvalues given in Eq. (11). The new operators are the **raising and lowering operators**, $a^\dagger$ and a, respectively, and they act to change the labels n on the eigenstates. These new operators are built from the position and momentum operators, $\hat{x}$ and $\hat{p}$, that comprise the Hamiltonian in Eq. (9), and they simplify many of the calculations required in the harmonic oscillator problem.

To see where these new operators come from and why they are useful, first note that the harmonic oscillator Hamiltonian in Eq. (9) is a sum of squares. If it were a difference of squares, then we could factor it as a product of the sum and difference [i.e., $u^2 - v^2 = (u - v)(u + v)$]. But as a sum, we can still factor it if we use complex numbers, which we know are used quite often in quantum mechanics:

$$u^2 + v^2 = (u - iv)(u + iv). \tag{13}$$

Harmonic Oscillator

So let's factor the Hamiltonian in the manner of Eq. (13), and while we're at it, let's make our life easier by using dimensionless quantities. We know that Planck's constant times frequency has dimensions of energy, so we start by factoring out an energy term $\hbar\omega$ from the Hamiltonian

$$
\begin{aligned}
H &= \tfrac{1}{2}m\omega^2\left[\hat{x}^2 + \frac{\hat{p}^2}{m^2\omega^2}\right] \\
&= \hbar\omega\left\{\frac{m\omega}{2\hbar}\left[\hat{x}^2 + \frac{\hat{p}^2}{m^2\omega^2}\right]\right\}
\end{aligned}
\tag{14}
$$

such that the expression inside the curly brackets is dimensionless. We now define a new dimensionless operator, called the lowering operator, to help us factor the Hamiltonian

$$
a = \sqrt{\frac{m\omega}{2\hbar}}\left(\hat{x} + i\frac{\hat{p}}{m\omega}\right).
\tag{15}
$$

Note that the lowering operator is not Hermitian, because it is not equal to its Hermitian conjugate

$$
\begin{aligned}
a^\dagger &= \sqrt{\frac{m\omega}{2\hbar}}\left(\hat{x}^\dagger - i\frac{\hat{p}^\dagger}{m\omega}\right) \\
&= \sqrt{\frac{m\omega}{2\hbar}}\left(\hat{x} - i\frac{\hat{p}}{m\omega}\right),
\end{aligned}
\tag{16}
$$

which is the raising operator. Recall that $\hat{x}$ and $\hat{p}$ are Hermitian, $\hat{x} = \hat{x}^\dagger$ and $\hat{p} = \hat{p}^\dagger$, because they represent physical observables. Because the raising and lowering operators are not Hermitian, they do not correspond to measurable observables. Nonetheless, they are very useful.

Our attempt to factor the Hamiltonian is complicated by the fact that quantum mechanical operators do not in general commute with each other. In Eq. (13), we implicitly assumed that u and v commute with each other, so that the cross terms $-ivu$ and iuv cancel. However, the quantum mechanical operators $\hat{x}$ and $\hat{p}$ that we use to define the raising and lowering operators *do not* commute with each other. As a result, we must take care in finding the product of the two new operators:

$$
\begin{aligned}
a^\dagger a &= \frac{m\omega}{2\hbar}\left(\hat{x} - i\frac{\hat{p}}{m\omega}\right)\left(\hat{x} + i\frac{\hat{p}}{m\omega}\right) \\
&= \frac{m\omega}{2\hbar}\left(\hat{x}^2 + \frac{\hat{p}^2}{m^2\omega^2} + \frac{i}{m\omega}\left[\hat{x}\hat{p} - \hat{p}\hat{x}\right]\right) \\
&= \frac{m\omega}{2\hbar}\left(\hat{x}^2 + \frac{\hat{p}^2}{m^2\omega^2} + \frac{i}{m\omega}\left[\hat{x},\hat{p}\right]\right).
\end{aligned}
\tag{17}
$$

Hence, the product $a^\dagger a$ of the raising and lowering operators gives us what we want—the term in the curly brackets in Eq. (14)—but with an extra additive term proportional to the commutator of $\hat{x}$ and $\hat{p}$. Recall that the commutator of $\hat{x}$ and $\hat{p}$ is

$$
[\hat{x},\hat{p}] = i\hbar.
\tag{18}
$$

Substituting into Eq. (17), we obtain

$$a^{\dagger}a = \frac{m\omega}{2\hbar}\left(\hat{x}^2 + \frac{\hat{p}^2}{m^2\omega^2}\right) - \frac{1}{2}, \tag{19}$$

so that the Hamiltonian written in terms of these new operators is

$$\boxed{H = \hbar\omega\left(a^{\dagger}a + \tfrac{1}{2}\right)}. \tag{20}$$

We need one more thing before we proceed. Go back to Eq. (17) and note that if we had reversed the order of $a^{\dagger}$ and a, then we would have obtained a similar result with one difference: the commutator would be reversed in sign (Problem 1). Thus the reverse product of the raising and lowering operators is

$$aa^{\dagger} = \frac{m\omega}{2\hbar}\left(\hat{x}^2 + \frac{\hat{p}^2}{m^2\omega^2}\right) + \frac{1}{2}. \tag{21}$$

If we now subtract Eq. (19) from Eq. (21), we find the commutator of the two new operators:

$$\boxed{\left[a, a^{\dagger}\right] = aa^{\dagger} - a^{\dagger}a = 1}. \tag{22}$$

This commutator equation defines the algebra of these new operators and provides the key to finding the eigenvalue spectrum.

Armed with the commutator relation in Eq. (22), we can now demonstrate that the new operators $a^{\dagger}$ and a do act to raise and lower, respectively, the energy eigenstates, as we said at the beginning. To see how the raising and lowering operators act on energy eigenstates, we first calculate the commutator of the lowering operator with the Hamiltonian:

$$\begin{aligned}
\left[H, a\right] &= Ha - aH \\
&= \hbar\omega\left(a^{\dagger}a + \tfrac{1}{2}\right)a - a\hbar\omega\left(a^{\dagger}a + \tfrac{1}{2}\right) \\
&= \hbar\omega\left(a^{\dagger}aa - aa^{\dagger}a\right).
\end{aligned} \tag{23}$$

Now use the commutator of the raising and lowering operators to obtain

$$\begin{aligned}
\left[H, a\right] &= \hbar\omega\left(a^{\dagger}aa - \left(a^{\dagger}a + 1\right)a\right) \\
&= -\hbar\omega a.
\end{aligned} \tag{24}$$

Likewise, you can show that the commutator of the raising operator with the Hamiltonian is

$$\left[H, a^{\dagger}\right] = +\hbar\omega a^{\dagger}. \tag{25}$$

To show that the lowering operator deserves its name, act with a on an energy eigenstate $|E\rangle$, where we assume that $|E\rangle$ is a normalized energy eigenstate that satisfies the energy eigenvalue equation $H|E\rangle = E|E\rangle$, but we don't yet know the eigenvalue E. To learn about the energy of the new ket $a|E\rangle$, consider what happens when the Hamiltonian H acts on $a|E\rangle$:

$$H\left(a|E\rangle\right) = Ha|E\rangle. \tag{26}$$

Harmonic Oscillator

The commutator in Eq. (24) tells us that $Ha = aH - \hbar\omega a$, so Eq. (26) becomes

$$\begin{aligned} H\big(a|E\rangle\big) &= \big(aH - \hbar\omega a\big)|E\rangle \\ &= aH|E\rangle - \hbar\omega a|E\rangle. \end{aligned}$$ (27)

Now use the energy eigenvalue equation $H|E\rangle = E|E\rangle$ to obtain

$$\begin{aligned} H\big(a|E\rangle\big) &= \big(aE|E\rangle - \hbar\omega a|E\rangle\big) \\ &= (E - \hbar\omega)\big(a|E\rangle\big). \end{aligned}$$ (28)

This looks like algebraic gymnastics, but there is something useful buried here! Equation (28) tells us that when the new ket $a|E\rangle$ is acted on by the Hamiltonian H, the result is the same ket $a|E\rangle$ multiplied by the factor $(E - \hbar\omega)$, which means that the new ket $a|E\rangle$ is also an eigenstate of H, but with an energy eigenvalue $(E - \hbar\omega)$ that is smaller than the eigenvalue E of the original ket $|E\rangle$ by one quantum of energy $\hbar\omega$. The eigenvalue equation for this new state is

$$H|E - \hbar\omega\rangle = (E - \hbar\omega)|E - \hbar\omega\rangle.$$ (29)

So a has earned the name "lowering operator." The only tricky point is that the state $a|E\rangle$ may not be normalized (in fact it is not), assuming that the eigenstates $|E\rangle$ are normalized, so we cannot say that $a|E\rangle$ is *equal* to $|E - \hbar\omega\rangle$, merely that they are proportional.

The result is that we have now learned what happens when the operator a acts on an eigenstate $|E\rangle$ of H: it produces another eigenstate of H with the eigenvalue lowered by one quantum $\hbar\omega$. Likewise, one can show that the action of $a^\dagger$ on an eigenstate of H produces an eigenstate with the eigenvalue raised by one quantum of energy (Problem 2). Now you see why we call the operators a and $a^\dagger$ lowering and raising operators. We also refer to these operators collectively as **ladder operators** because they take us up and down a ladder of energy eigenstates, as depicted schematically in Fig. 3. We don't yet know where the rungs of the ladder are (i.e., what the energy eigenvalues are) or whether there are many interleaved ladders. But the importance of the ladder operators is that if we can find just one eigenstate $|E\rangle$, then the ladder operators can be used to find other eigenstates of the system, with each level separated by the energy quantum $\hbar\omega$.

From the discussion so far and from the schematic in Fig. 3, you probably have the impression that the ladder of energy states goes up and down symmetrically. But the commutator in Eq. (22) already gives us a hint that there is a built-in asymmetry in the ladder, which we can use to find the energy spectrum. Because a and $a^\dagger$ do not commute, we have $aa^\dagger \neq a^\dagger a$, which we can express abstractly as

$$(down)(up) \neq (up)(down).$$ (30)

But that is not how you might expect ladder operators to behave. If you stand on a rung and go up then down, you are in the same position as if you had gone down then up. The asymmetry of the harmonic oscillator is also evident if we note that the potential energy well that defines the harmonic oscillator has a minimum level at $V = 0$ from which it goes only upward. A classical particle cannot have a total energy below the potential energy minimum because kinetic energy cannot be negative. Though quantum mechanics does allow for negative kinetic energies (in the classically forbidden regions), it is also true in quantum mechanics that the total energy of a particle cannot be below the potential energy minimum (quantum mechanics may be weird, but it is not that weird). So we conclude that the ladder of energy states in Fig. 3 must not go below $E = 0$.

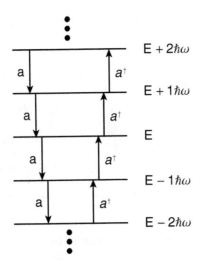

FIGURE 3 Part of the ladder of energy eigenstates, with the action of the raising and lowering operators shown.

If the ladder of energy states in Fig. 3 cannot go below zero, then there must be a lowest energy state $|E_{lowest}\rangle$. But how can that be consistent with the idea of the ladder operators? Wouldn't the lowering operator take that "lowest" state to a state with lower energy, below zero? Not if we don't let it! We do that by requiring that when we operate on the lowest possible energy state with the lowering operator we get zero:

$$a|E_{lowest}\rangle = 0. \tag{31}$$

We refer to this as the **ladder termination condition**. We now use this condition to find the energy of that lowest state. Act with the Hamiltonian H on the lowest state:

$$H|E_{lowest}\rangle = \hbar\omega\left(a^\dagger a + \tfrac{1}{2}\right)|E_{lowest}\rangle \tag{32}$$

and note that the ladder termination condition in Eq. (31) means that the first term on the right-hand side of Eq. (32) becomes zero, giving

$$H|E_{lowest}\rangle = \tfrac{1}{2}\hbar\omega|E_{lowest}\rangle. \tag{33}$$

This is nothing but the energy eigenvalue equation $H|E\rangle = E|E\rangle$ for the lowest state, so the energy is

$$E_{lowest} = \tfrac{1}{2}\hbar\omega. \tag{34}$$

Wow! This operator gymnastics has led us to the ground state energy of the quantum mechanical harmonic oscillator, using just the form of the Hamiltonian and the commutator of position and momentum. Note that the ground state does not have zero energy, in contrast to the classical harmonic oscillator. Rather, the quantum mechanical ground state has a **zero-point energy** of $\hbar\omega/2$. This is not surprising if we recall the other potential well systems we have studied such as the square well potential, where the ground state is not at the bottom of the well. The zero-point energy is also consistent with the uncertainty principle in that we expect there to be residual energy associated with the spread in momentum.

To generate the next energy eigenstate up the ladder of states, we act with the raising operator on the ground state $|E_{lowest}\rangle$, which produces a new energy eigenstate with the energy increased by one quantum $\hbar\omega$. We repeat the action of the raising operator to generate the complete ladder of energy values, as shown in Fig. 4:

$$E = \tfrac{1}{2}\hbar\omega, \tfrac{3}{2}\hbar\omega, \tfrac{5}{2}\hbar\omega, \tfrac{7}{2}\hbar\omega, \dots . \tag{35}$$

We write the energy spectrum compactly as

$$\boxed{E_n = \hbar\omega\left(n + \tfrac{1}{2}\right), \qquad n = 0, 1, 2, 3, \dots}, \tag{36}$$

which is the result we quoted at the beginning. The quantum number n is used to label the energy eigenstates $|E_n\rangle = |n\rangle$. These states satisfy the energy eigenvalue equation

$$H|n\rangle = E_n|n\rangle = \left(n + \tfrac{1}{2}\right)\hbar\omega|n\rangle, \tag{37}$$

are normalized to unity

$$\langle n|n\rangle = 1, \tag{38}$$

and are orthogonal to each other

$$\langle m|n\rangle = \delta_{mn}. \tag{39}$$

Thus we have found the complete spectrum of energy eigenstates of the harmonic oscillator, using minimal information about the operator properties.

As shown in Fig. 4, the energy eigenstates are evenly spaced by the energy quantum $\hbar\omega$. The selection rule for the quantum mechanical harmonic oscillator (coming soon in Section 8) restricts transitions to those between adjacent energy states, so the uniform spacing implies that a spectroscopy experiment would yield only one possible value for an energy difference, no matter which levels were involved. This is similar to the classical case where there is only one frequency that characterizes a harmonic oscillator.

In addition to the ladder operators, it is useful to define one more new operator that will help us "count" energy quanta. The energy eigenvalue equation for the harmonic oscillator

$$\begin{aligned} H|n\rangle &= E_n|n\rangle \\ \hbar\omega\left(a^\dagger a + \tfrac{1}{2}\right)|n\rangle &= \hbar\omega\left(n + \tfrac{1}{2}\right)|n\rangle \end{aligned} \tag{40}$$

can be simplified to obtain a new eigenvalue equation

$$a^\dagger a|n\rangle = n|n\rangle. \tag{41}$$

This equation suggests that we define the operator $a^\dagger a$ as the **number operator** N:

$$N = a^\dagger a. \tag{42}$$

The number operator N is dimensionless and obeys the eigenvalue equation

$$N|n\rangle = n|n\rangle. \tag{43}$$

The eigenvalues of the number operator are the same integers n that we use to label the energy eigenstates $|n\rangle$. We can write the harmonic oscillator Hamiltonian in terms of the number operator:

$$H = \hbar\omega\left(N + \tfrac{1}{2}\right). \tag{44}$$

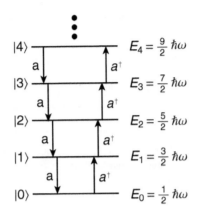

FIGURE 4 The ladder of harmonic oscillator states has its lowest rung at $n = 0$.

The number operator is Hermitian, even though the ladder operators that comprise it are not. The eigenvalues of the number operator represent the number of energy quanta $\hbar\omega$ there are in the system above the ground state.

The mathematics of the quantum mechanical harmonic oscillator system can be applied to other quantum mechanical systems, even though they do not appear to be harmonic oscillators. All that is required is that the Hamiltonian be the sum of squares of operators. For example, the Hamiltonian representing the electromagnetic field energy can be written as the sum of squares of operators representing the electric and magnetic fields (see any E&M text). Hence, when we apply quantum mechanics to the electromagnetic field, the energy eigenstate $|n\rangle$ represents a state of the system with n **photons** (particles or quanta of light), each with an energy $\hbar\omega$. The ground state $|0\rangle$ represents the state of the system with no photons, also known as the vacuum. Thus the zero-point energy represents the electromagnetic energy of the vacuum state, which is a bit surprising because we usually associate the vacuum with the absence of all "stuff." Even though spectroscopic measurements determine only energy differences, there are observable effects of this zero-point energy in the Lamb shift. Because the raising and lowering operators change the number of photons in the system, they are often referred to as **creation and annihilation operators**, respectively.

3 ■ WAVE FUNCTIONS

Though we have solved the energy eigenvalue equation, we are not quite done. We don't yet know the spatial wave functions corresponding to the energy eigenstates. That is to say, we know that the states $|n\rangle$ are the energy eigenstates, but we don't know their spatial representation $|n\rangle \doteq \varphi_n(x) = \langle x|n\rangle$. As we did for the particle in a box and the hydrogen atom, we could solve the differential equation form of the energy eigenvalue equation, which in this case is

$$-\frac{\hbar^2}{2m}\frac{d^2\varphi_n(x)}{dx^2} + \frac{1}{2}m\omega^2 x^2 \varphi_n(x) = E_n\varphi_n(x). \tag{45}$$

As we mentioned earlier, this can be solved with a power series technique that would yield the energies E_n and the states $\varphi_n(x)$. Rather, let's continue our operator approach to find the wave functions.

We said before that if we know one of the harmonic oscillator eigenstates, then we can use the ladder operators to generate the other energy eigenstates. We used this idea to discover the spectrum of energy levels by noting that the ground state is unique in that there are no states below it, which led us to the ladder termination equation

$$a|0\rangle = 0. \tag{46}$$

Let's now use this same termination condition to find the wave function representing the ground state, and then use the raising operator to generate all the other wave functions. In the x–representation, the ladder termination equation is

$$a\varphi_0(x) = 0$$

$$\sqrt{\frac{m\omega}{2\hbar}}\left(\hat{x} + i\frac{\hat{p}}{m\omega}\right)\varphi_0(x) = 0 \tag{47}$$

$$\sqrt{\frac{m\omega}{2\hbar}}\left(x + \frac{\hbar}{m\omega}\frac{d}{dx}\right)\varphi_0(x) = 0,$$

with the result

$$\frac{d}{dx}\varphi_0(x) = -\frac{m\omega}{\hbar}x\varphi_0(x). \tag{48}$$

We now have a first-order differential equation for the ground state wave function. This equation tells us that we want a function whose derivative is equal to the function itself times a constant and x. We know that the derivative of the exponential function e^x is itself, so to get the extra factor of x we need an x^2 in the exponent. To get the multiplicative factor correct, the function must be $e^{-m\omega x^2/2\hbar}$. The properly normalized solution to Eq. (48) is (Problem 3)

$$\varphi_0(x) = \left(\frac{m\omega}{\pi\hbar}\right)^{1/4}e^{-m\omega x^2/2\hbar}, \tag{49}$$

which is a Gaussian function. This ground state wave function is plotted in Fig. 5(a). The wave function has a single antinode as we expect for the ground state. A classical particle with the same energy ($\hbar\omega/2$) has classical turning points at $\pm x_0$ where the energy is all potential energy:

$$\tfrac{1}{2}\hbar\omega = \tfrac{1}{2}m\omega^2 x_0^2$$

$$x_0 = \sqrt{\frac{\hbar}{m\omega}}. \tag{50}$$

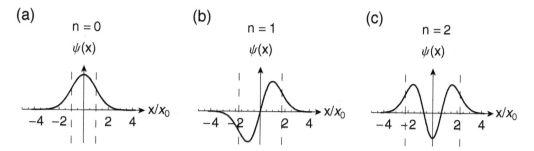

FIGURE 5   Energy eigenstate wave functions for the first three states of the harmonic oscillator. The dashed lines enclose the classically allowed region.

From the plot in Fig. 5(a), you see that there is a finite probability that the particle is in the classically forbidden region beyond $\pm x_0$ (Problem 4).

To find the other energy eigenstates we act on the ground state with the raising operator. But we have already mentioned that the ladder operators do not preserve the normalization of the energy eigenstates, so we must determine the proper scaling factor. Let's first look at the lowering operator. Consider the norm of the state $a|n\rangle$. The rules of Hermitian conjugation allows us to write the norm as

$$\left| a|n\rangle \right|^2 = \left(\langle n|a^\dagger \rangle (a|n\rangle) \right) = \langle n|a^\dagger a|n\rangle. \tag{51}$$

The product $a^\dagger a$ is the number operator N, so we get

$$\left| a|n\rangle \right|^2 = \langle n|N|n\rangle = \langle n|n|n\rangle = n\langle n|n\rangle \tag{52}$$
$$= n,$$

where we have used the normalization $\left(\langle n|n\rangle = 1 \right)$ of the energy/number eigenstates $|n\rangle$. Let c be the proportionality factor between the state $a|n\rangle$ and the eigenstate $|n-1\rangle$:

$$a|n\rangle = c|n-1\rangle. \tag{53}$$

Because both $|n\rangle$ and $|n-1\rangle$ are normalized to unity, we can use Eq. (52) to find the constant c:

$$\left| a|n\rangle \right|^2 = \left| c|n-1\rangle \right|^2 \tag{54}$$
$$n = |c|^2.$$

By convention, we choose the proportionality constant to be real and positive (an overall phase is not measurable) and obtain

$$\boxed{a|n\rangle = \sqrt{n}|n-1\rangle}. \tag{55}$$

Likewise you can show that the raising operator equation is (Problem 5)

$$\boxed{a^\dagger|n\rangle = \sqrt{n+1}|n+1\rangle}. \tag{56}$$

A simple mnemonic to remember which operator gives which factor (n or $n+1$) in Eqs. (55) and (56) is that the index under the square root is the larger value of the two eigenstates on the two sides of the equations. The different scale factors in Eqs. (55) and (56) are a reflection of the asymmetry of the raising and lowering operations that is embodied in the commutator relation in Eq. (22).

To generate states above the ground state we use Eq. (56) to formulate the raising operator equation

$$|n+1\rangle = \frac{1}{\sqrt{n+1}} a^\dagger|n\rangle. \tag{57}$$

Apply Eq. (57) to the ground state and the resulting states to obtain

$$|1\rangle = \frac{1}{\sqrt{1}} a^\dagger|0\rangle$$
$$|2\rangle = \frac{1}{\sqrt{2}} a^\dagger|1\rangle = \frac{1}{\sqrt{2 \cdot 1}} \left(a^\dagger \right)^2 |0\rangle \tag{58}$$
$$|3\rangle = \frac{1}{\sqrt{3}} a^\dagger|2\rangle = \frac{1}{\sqrt{3 \cdot 2 \cdot 1}} \left(a^\dagger \right)^3 |0\rangle$$

Harmonic Oscillator

and generalize to find

$$|n\rangle = \frac{1}{\sqrt{n!}}\left(a^\dagger\right)^n |0\rangle.$$

(59)

Projected onto the spatial basis, this general result is

$$\varphi_n(x) = \frac{1}{\sqrt{n!}}\left[\sqrt{\frac{m\omega}{2\hbar}}\left(x - \frac{\hbar}{m\omega}\frac{d}{dx}\right)\right]^n \varphi_0(x).$$

(60)

Example 1   Use the eigenstate generating expression in Eq. (60) to determine the first excited state of the harmonic oscillator.

Take Eq. (60) and set $n = 1$, which means that the raising operator acts only one time to yield the first eigenstate above the ground state:

$$
\begin{aligned}
\varphi_1(x) &= \frac{1}{\sqrt{1!}}\left[\sqrt{\frac{m\omega}{2\hbar}}\left(x - \frac{\hbar}{m\omega}\frac{d}{dx}\right)\right]\varphi_0(x) \\
&= \left[\sqrt{\frac{m\omega}{2\hbar}}\left(x - \frac{\hbar}{m\omega}\frac{d}{dx}\right)\right]\left(\frac{m\omega}{\pi\hbar}\right)^{1/4}e^{-m\omega x^2/2\hbar} \\
&= \left(\frac{m\omega}{\pi\hbar}\right)^{1/4}\sqrt{\frac{m\omega}{2\hbar}}\left[\left(x - \frac{\hbar}{m\omega}\left(-\frac{m\omega}{\hbar}x\right)\right)\right]e^{-m\omega x^2/2\hbar} \\
&= \left(\frac{m\omega}{\pi\hbar}\right)^{1/4}\sqrt{\frac{m\omega}{2\hbar}}(2x)\,e^{-m\omega x^2/2\hbar}.
\end{aligned}
$$

(61)

This result is already normalized. Note that the wave function dimensions are $1/\sqrt{length}$ to ensure that the normalization condition is dimensionless.

The general wave function expression in Eq. (60) can be difficult to use in practice because it requires n derivatives. When we apply the raising operator to the Gaussian function in $\varphi_0(x)$ n times, we obtain the Gaussian function multiplied by a polynomial of order n. The resultant polynomials are **Hermite polynomials**. To simplify the general wave function expression, it is common to write the harmonic oscillator wave functions in terms of a dimensionless variable

$$\xi \equiv \sqrt{\frac{m\omega}{\hbar}}x.$$

(62)

In this case, the ground state and the general states are written as

$$\varphi_0(x) = \left(\frac{m\omega}{\pi\hbar}\right)^{1/4}e^{-\xi^2/2}$$

(63)

and

$$\varphi_n(x) = \left(\frac{m\omega}{\pi\hbar}\right)^{1/4}\frac{1}{\sqrt{2^n n!}}H_n(\xi)e^{-\xi^2/2}.$$

(64)

309

The first several Hermite polynomials $H_n(\xi)$ are:

$$H_0(\xi) = 1$$
$$H_1(\xi) = 2\xi$$
$$H_2(\xi) = 4\xi^2 - 2 \tag{65}$$
$$H_3(\xi) = 8\xi^3 - 12\xi$$
$$H_4(\xi) = 16\xi^4 - 48\xi^2 + 12.$$

You can easily verify that for $n = 1$, Eq. (64) agrees with the result we found in Example 1.

The first three harmonic oscillator energy eigenstate wave functions are plotted in Fig. 5. As we expected, the harmonic oscillator energy eigenstates are similar in many ways to the energy eigenstates of the other bound state systems we have studied—the infinite and finite square wells and the hydrogen atom. On a superficial level, we can consider each of these bound state systems as a particle-in-a-box system—the boxes just have different shapes. Common features of these energy eigenstates are (1) the wave functions are oscillatory inside the well and exponential decaying outside the well, where the edge of the well is defined by the classical turning points; (2) the wave functions of symmetric wells are alternately even and odd with respect to inversion about the center of the well, reflecting the spatial symmetry of the well; and (3) the number of nodes and antinodes in the wave function increases with energy.

As we have done in the previous bound state problems, we combine the schematic diagrams depicting (i) the potential energy well, (ii) the energy spectrum, and (iii) the energy eigenstates in a single unified diagram, shown in Fig. 6(a). This single diagram is commonly used to represent the potential energy well problem and its quantum mechanical solution. In this unified schematic diagram, the vertical scale measures energy (i and ii) or wave function (iii), and the zero of each wave function is placed at the corresponding energy level of that state in the well.

The spatial probability density is given by the absolute square of the wave function

$$\mathcal{P}_n(x) = |\varphi_n(x)|^2. \tag{66}$$

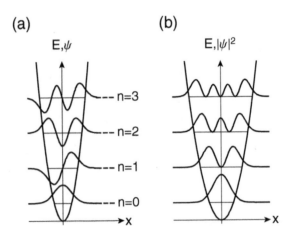

FIGURE 6 Energy eigenstate (a) wave functions and (b) probability densities of the harmonic oscillator.

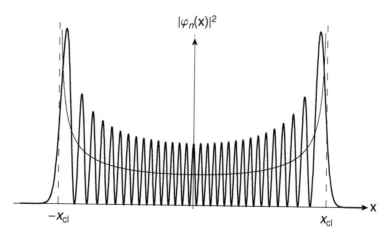

FIGURE 7 Quantum mechanical probability density for the $n = 30$ state. The classical probability distribution (thin line) peaks at the classical turning points.

In Fig. 6(b) we plot the probability densities of the first four energy eigenstates in a unified diagram. The ground state probability density is largest at the center of the well, but the location of the probability density maximum gets increasingly close to the classical turning points as the energy level increases. The probability density for a large value of the quantum number n is shown in Fig. 7. For such a high energy state, the probability density is similar, at least when locally averaged, to the probability distribution of a classical harmonic oscillator.

Let's summarize how the harmonic oscillator illustrates the first three basic postulates of quantum mechanics. The first postulate tells us that quantum states are represented by kets, such as the energy eigenstates $|n\rangle \doteq \varphi_n(x)$. The second postulate tells us that observables are represented by operators, such as the Hamiltonian H, the position $\hat{x}$ and the momentum $\hat{p}$. The third postulate tells us that the eigenvalues of an operator are the only possible results of measurements, such as the energies $E_n = (n + 1/2)\hbar\omega$.

4 ■ DIRAC NOTATION

Let's use the harmonic oscillator problem as a framework for reviewing Dirac notation. We use the Dirac kets $|n\rangle$ to represent the energy eigenstates. Recall that the labeling of the kets does not affect the properties of the kets, so we are free to use whatever labeling is most convenient. The convention is to be as brief as possible without losing specificity. We label the harmonic oscillator energy eigenstates states with the energy eigenvalue index n alone, but it is also common for φ or ψ to be used as a label with the eigenvalue index as a subscript. Or one could use the energy value itself. These are all equally valid notations:

$$
\begin{aligned}
|n\rangle &= |\varphi_n\rangle = |E_n\rangle = \left|\left(n + \tfrac{1}{2}\right)\hbar\omega\right\rangle \\
|0\rangle &= |\varphi_0\rangle = |E_0\rangle = \left|\tfrac{1}{2}\hbar\omega\right\rangle.
\end{aligned}
\tag{67}
$$

In Section 3, we found the energy eigenstate wave functions $\varphi_n(x)$. The connection between wave functions and abstract kets is expressed as

$$\varphi_n(x) = \langle x|n \rangle. \tag{68}$$

In words, Eq. (68) says that the wave function $\varphi_n(x)$ is the projection of the abstract ket $|n\rangle$ onto the position eigenstates $|x\rangle$. Or using the representation notation

$$|n\rangle \doteq \phi_n(x), \tag{69}$$

we say that $\varphi_n(x)$ is the representation of the quantum state $|n\rangle$ in the position representation.

The energy eigenstates of the harmonic oscillator obey the three important properties that we have discussed previously: normalization, orthogonality, and completeness. The normalization condition is expressed in wave function notation as

$$\int_{-\infty}^{\infty} |\varphi_n(x)|^2 dx = 1 \tag{70}$$

or in Dirac notation as

$$\langle n|n \rangle = 1. \tag{71}$$

The connection between the normalization condition in the position representation [Eq. (70)] and in abstract Dirac notation [Eq. (71)] is evident if we use the completeness relation for the position eigenstates, which form a complete continuous basis:

$$\int_{-\infty}^{\infty} |x\rangle\langle x| dx = \mathbf{1}. \tag{72}$$

Because the right hand side of Eq. (72) is the unity operator, it can be inserted into an expression without altering the value of the expression. Inserting Eq. (72) into Eq. (71) yields

$$
\begin{aligned}
1 &= \langle n|n \rangle \\
&= \langle n| \left\{ \int_{-\infty}^{\infty} |x\rangle\langle x| dx \right\} |n\rangle \\
&= \int_{-\infty}^{\infty} \langle n|x \rangle\langle x|n \rangle dx \\
&= \int_{-\infty}^{\infty} \varphi_n^*(x)\varphi_n(x)\, dx \\
&= \int_{-\infty}^{\infty} |\varphi_n(x)|^2 dx,
\end{aligned}
\tag{73}
$$

which shows that Eq. (70) and Eq. (71) are equivalent.

The energy eigenstates of the harmonic oscillator are orthogonal because they are the eigenvectors of an Hermitian operator. The orthogonality condition is expressed in wave function notation as

$$\int_{-\infty}^{\infty} \varphi_m^*(x)\varphi_n(x)\, dx = \delta_{mn} \tag{74}$$

Harmonic Oscillator

or in Dirac notation as

$$\langle m|n \rangle = \delta_{mn}. \tag{75}$$

By using a Kronecker delta, the orthogonality condition also includes the normalization, so Eqs. (74) and (75) are called the orthonormality condition. You can check that the harmonic oscillator energy eigenstate wave functions are orthogonal by doing the explicit integrals in Eq. (74) (Problem 7).

The harmonic oscillator eigenstates form a complete discrete basis, which is expressed in terms of the closure relation

$$\sum_{n=0}^{\infty} |n\rangle\langle n| = \mathbf{1}, \tag{76}$$

where the right hand side is the unity operator. Completeness of the energy basis means that any arbitrary state vector $|\psi\rangle$ can be written in terms of the energy eigenstates, either in wave function notation

$$|\psi\rangle \doteq \psi(x) = \sum_{n=0}^{\infty} c_n \varphi_n(x) \tag{77}$$

or in Dirac notation

$$|\psi\rangle = \sum_{n=0}^{\infty} c_n |n\rangle. \tag{78}$$

To find the value of a particular expansion coefficient, we use the closure relation in Eq. (76) to rewrite the state $|\psi\rangle$ in terms of the energy eigenstates:

$$\begin{aligned} |\psi\rangle &= \mathbf{1}|\psi\rangle \\ &= \left\{ \sum_{n=0}^{\infty} |n\rangle\langle n| \right\} |\psi\rangle \\ &= \sum_{n=0}^{\infty} |n\rangle\langle n|\psi\rangle. \end{aligned} \tag{79}$$

By comparing Eqs. (78) and (79), we conclude that the expansion coefficient c_n is the projection of the wave function $|\psi\rangle$ onto the particular basis state $|n\rangle$, which in Dirac notation is

$$c_n = \langle n|\psi\rangle \tag{80}$$

and in wave function notation is

$$c_n = \int_{-\infty}^{\infty} \varphi_n^*(x)\psi(x)\,dx. \tag{81}$$

The normalization requirement on the general state $|\psi\rangle \doteq \psi(x)$ in wave function notation is

$$\int_{-\infty}^{\infty} |\psi(x)|^2 dx = 1 \tag{82}$$

Harmonic Oscillator

or in Dirac notation is

$$\langle\psi|\psi\rangle = 1. \tag{83}$$

We can also use the energy eigenstate closure relation Eq. (76) to write the normalization requirement in terms of the eigenstate expansion

$$
\begin{aligned}
1 = \langle\psi|\psi\rangle &= \langle\psi|\left\{\sum_{n=0}^{\infty}|n\rangle\langle n|\right\}|\psi\rangle \\
&= \sum_{n=0}^{\infty}\langle\psi|n\rangle\langle n|\psi\rangle = \sum_{n=0}^{\infty}|\langle n|\psi\rangle|^2 \\
&= \sum_{n=0}^{\infty}|c_n|^2.
\end{aligned} \tag{84}
$$

The square of each expansion coefficient is the probability that the state $|\psi\rangle$ is measured to be in state $|n\rangle$, that is, to have energy eigenvalue E_n:

$$\mathcal{P}_{E_n} = |\langle n|\psi\rangle|^2 = |c_n|^2. \tag{85}$$

Thus the requirement that the state be normalized is a requirement that the total probability sum to unity, (i.e., there is unit probability that some value of energy is measured).

Example 2 A quantum mechanical harmonic oscillator is in the state

$$|\psi\rangle = \tfrac{\sqrt{2}}{4}|0\rangle + i\tfrac{2}{4}|1\rangle - i\tfrac{1}{4}|2\rangle + \tfrac{3}{4}e^{i\pi/3}|3\rangle. \tag{86}$$

What are the possible results of an energy measurement and with what probabilities do they occur? Find the expectation value of the energy.

The possible results of an energy measurement are the energy eigenvalues $E_n = \left(n + \tfrac{1}{2}\right)\hbar\omega$. For this superposition of four energy eigenstates, the probabilities calculated from Eq. (85) are zero except for the four energies $E_0, E_1, E_2,$ and E_3. These probabilities are

$$
\begin{aligned}
\mathcal{P}_{E_0} &= |\langle 0|\psi\rangle|^2 = \left|\langle 0|\left(\tfrac{\sqrt{2}}{4}|0\rangle + i\tfrac{2}{4}|1\rangle - i\tfrac{1}{4}|2\rangle + \tfrac{3}{4}e^{i\pi/3}|3\rangle\right)\right|^2 = \left|\tfrac{\sqrt{2}}{4}\right|^2 = \tfrac{2}{16} \\
\mathcal{P}_{E_1} &= |\langle 1|\psi\rangle|^2 = \left|\langle 1|\left(\tfrac{\sqrt{2}}{4}|0\rangle + i\tfrac{2}{4}|1\rangle - i\tfrac{1}{4}|2\rangle + \tfrac{3}{4}e^{i\pi/3}|3\rangle\right)\right|^2 = \left|i\tfrac{2}{4}\right|^2 = \tfrac{4}{16} \\
\mathcal{P}_{E_2} &= |\langle 2|\psi\rangle|^2 = \left|\langle 2|\left(\tfrac{\sqrt{2}}{4}|0\rangle + i\tfrac{2}{4}|1\rangle - i\tfrac{1}{4}|2\rangle + \tfrac{3}{4}e^{i\pi/3}|3\rangle\right)\right|^2 = \left|-i\tfrac{1}{4}\right|^2 = \tfrac{1}{16} \\
\mathcal{P}_{E_3} &= |\langle 3|\psi\rangle|^2 = \left|\langle 3|\left(\tfrac{\sqrt{2}}{4}|0\rangle + i\tfrac{2}{4}|1\rangle - i\tfrac{1}{4}|2\rangle + \tfrac{3}{4}e^{i\pi/3}|3\rangle\right)\right|^2 = \left|\tfrac{3}{4}e^{i\pi/3}\right|^2 = \tfrac{9}{16}.
\end{aligned} \tag{87}
$$

The expectation value of the energy is

$$
\begin{aligned}
\langle E\rangle = \sum_{n=0}^{\infty} E_n \mathcal{P}_{E_n} &= \left(\tfrac{1}{2}\hbar\omega\right)\tfrac{2}{16} + \left(\tfrac{3}{2}\hbar\omega\right)\tfrac{4}{16} + \left(\tfrac{5}{2}\hbar\omega\right)\tfrac{1}{16} + \left(\tfrac{7}{2}\hbar\omega\right)\tfrac{9}{16} \\
&= \tfrac{41}{16}\hbar\omega \cong 2.56\hbar\omega.
\end{aligned} \tag{88}
$$

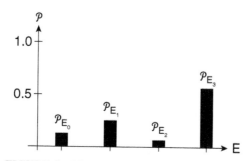

FIGURE 8 Histogram of energy measurements.

The expectation value can also be calculated as $\langle E \rangle = \langle \psi | H | \psi \rangle$, with the same result. A histogram of the energy measurements is shown in Fig. 8.

Let's continue the summary of how the harmonic oscillator illustrates the basic postulates of quantum mechanics. The fourth postulate tells us that the probability of a measurement is the complex square of the projection onto the measured eigenstate, such as the energy probability $\mathcal{P}_{E_n} = |\langle n | \psi \rangle|^2$ or the position probability density $\mathcal{P}(x) = |\psi(x)|^2$. The fifth postulate tells us that the quantum state vector after a measurement is the measured eigenstate, such as $|\psi\rangle$ collapsing to $|n\rangle$ after the energy E_n is measured. The sixth postulate tells us how to find the time evolution of states, which we'll address in Section 8.

5 ■ MATRIX REPRESENTATIONS

So far we have presented the operators and states of the harmonic oscillator in abstract Dirac notation and in wave function or position representation. However, we found a matrix representation to be useful previously, for example in the discussion of spin states. Can we use a matrix representation for the harmonic oscillator case? It turns out that we can. A matrix representation is a collection of numbers that represents states and operators in terms of a chosen basis set. So we must first choose a basis for the matrix representation. We have just solved for the energy basis states of the harmonic oscillator, so that choice seems reasonable, especially in light of the importance of the energy basis in the Schrödinger time evolution recipe. So how do we find the numbers we need to represent states and operators as matrices in the energy representation? We do it by inspection!

An operator is always diagonal in its own basis, and eigenvectors are unit vectors in their own basis. So the Hamiltonian is diagonal in the energy basis and the energy eigenstates are unit vectors in the energy basis. The diagonal elements of the Hamiltonian are the energy eigenvalues, so by inspection of our energy result in Eq. (36), we find the Hamiltonian matrix

$$H \doteq \begin{pmatrix} \frac{1}{2}\hbar\omega & 0 & 0 & 0 & \cdots \\ 0 & \frac{3}{2}\hbar\omega & 0 & 0 & \cdots \\ 0 & 0 & \frac{5}{2}\hbar\omega & 0 & \cdots \\ 0 & 0 & 0 & \frac{7}{2}\hbar\omega & \cdots \\ \vdots & \vdots & \vdots & \vdots & \ddots \end{pmatrix}, \tag{89}$$

Harmonic Oscillator

where we use the convention of ordering the rows and columns starting with the ground state energy. There are an infinite number of energy eigenstates, so the matrix representation of the Hamiltonian is infinite, but discrete. In this matrix representation, the energy basis states are the unit vectors

$$|0\rangle \doteq \begin{pmatrix} 1 \\ 0 \\ 0 \\ 0 \\ \vdots \end{pmatrix}, |1\rangle \doteq \begin{pmatrix} 0 \\ 1 \\ 0 \\ 0 \\ \vdots \end{pmatrix}, |2\rangle \doteq \begin{pmatrix} 0 \\ 0 \\ 1 \\ 0 \\ \vdots \end{pmatrix}, \cdots . \tag{90}$$

That's all there is to it!

Finding the matrix representation of other states and operators takes more work, but not too much. We already found the expansion coefficients $c_n = \langle n|\psi\rangle$ required to represent an arbitrary state $|\psi\rangle$ in terms of the energy eigenstates in Eq. (80), now we just order them in a column vector:

$$|\psi\rangle \doteq \begin{pmatrix} c_0 \\ c_1 \\ c_2 \\ c_3 \\ \vdots \end{pmatrix}. \tag{91}$$

The matrix representation of other operators requires us to know how they act upon the energy eigenstates. For the ladder operators, we learned this in Eqs. (55) and (56):

$$a|n\rangle = \sqrt{n}|n-1\rangle$$
$$a^\dagger|n\rangle = \sqrt{n+1}|n+1\rangle. \tag{92}$$

To find the individual matrix elements of the ladder operators, project each of these equations onto a different eigenstate to obtain

$$\langle m|a|n\rangle = \langle m|\sqrt{n}|n-1\rangle \quad \langle m|a^\dagger|n\rangle = \langle m|\sqrt{n+1}|n+1\rangle$$
$$= \sqrt{n}\,\delta_{m,n-1} \qquad\qquad = \sqrt{n+1}\delta_{m,n+1}. \tag{93}$$

Because the ladder operators take one state to an adjacent state, the matrix elements connect only adjacent states, as the Kronecker deltas indicate. Hence, the matrices for the ladder operators are

$$a \doteq \begin{pmatrix} 0 & \sqrt{1} & 0 & 0 & \cdots \\ 0 & 0 & \sqrt{2} & 0 & \cdots \\ 0 & 0 & 0 & \sqrt{3} & \cdots \\ 0 & 0 & 0 & 0 & \cdots \\ \vdots & \vdots & \vdots & \vdots & \ddots \end{pmatrix} \quad a^\dagger \doteq \begin{pmatrix} 0 & 0 & 0 & 0 & \cdots \\ \sqrt{1} & 0 & 0 & 0 & \cdots \\ 0 & \sqrt{2} & 0 & 0 & \cdots \\ 0 & 0 & \sqrt{3} & 0 & \cdots \\ \vdots & \vdots & \vdots & \vdots & \ddots \end{pmatrix}. \tag{94}$$

Note that these operators are dimensionless, as expected. They are each nondiagonal and they are not Hermitian. However, they are Hermitian conjugates of each other, as required by their definitions.

316

The ladder operators were defined in Eqs. (15) and (16) in terms of the position and momentum operators. Hence, the position and momentum operators are related to the ladder operators by

$$\hat{x} = \sqrt{\frac{\hbar}{2m\omega}} \left(a^\dagger + a \right)$$

$$\hat{p} = i\sqrt{\frac{\hbar m\omega}{2}} \left(a^\dagger - a \right)$$

(95)

and their matrix representations are

$$\hat{x} \doteq \sqrt{\frac{\hbar}{2m\omega}} \begin{pmatrix} 0 & \sqrt{1} & 0 & 0 & \cdots \\ \sqrt{1} & 0 & \sqrt{2} & 0 & \cdots \\ 0 & \sqrt{2} & 0 & \sqrt{3} & \cdots \\ 0 & 0 & \sqrt{3} & 0 & \cdots \\ \vdots & \vdots & \vdots & \vdots & \ddots \end{pmatrix} \qquad \hat{p} \doteq \sqrt{\frac{\hbar m\omega}{2}} \begin{pmatrix} 0 & -i\sqrt{1} & 0 & 0 & \cdots \\ i\sqrt{1} & 0 & -i\sqrt{2} & 0 & \cdots \\ 0 & i\sqrt{2} & 0 & -i\sqrt{3} & \cdots \\ 0 & 0 & i\sqrt{3} & 0 & \cdots \\ \vdots & \vdots & \vdots & \vdots & \ddots \end{pmatrix}.$$

(96)

These matrices are Hermitian, as they must be because position and momentum are observables. The position and momentum matrix elements connect only adjacent states, but in this case, states above and below. This is important in determining the selection rules for transitions, as discussed in Section 8. The position and momentum matrices are both nondiagonal in the energy basis, so they do not commute with the Hamiltonian.

Example 3   Find the expectation value of position in the ground state of the harmonic oscillator. There are three ways to calculate this.

(1) The expectation value of position is the matrix element

$$\langle \hat{x} \rangle = \langle \psi | \hat{x} | \psi \rangle.$$

(97)

The expectation value of position in the ground state is the specific matrix element

$$\langle \hat{x} \rangle = \langle 0 | \hat{x} | 0 \rangle = \hat{x}_{00}$$

(98)

which is zero by inspection of the position matrix in Eq. (96).

(2) We can also calculate the expectation value using explicit Dirac notation and the ladder operators [Eq. (95)]:

$$\langle \hat{x} \rangle = \langle 0 | \hat{x} | 0 \rangle$$

$$= \sqrt{\frac{\hbar}{2m\omega}} \langle 0 | \left(a^\dagger + a \right) | 0 \rangle.$$

(99)

The raising operator acting on the state $|0\rangle$ produces the state $|1\rangle$ in the first term and the lowering operator acting on the state $|0\rangle$ yields the value 0 in the second term. The result

$$\langle \hat{x} \rangle = \sqrt{\frac{\hbar}{2m\omega}} \left[\langle 0 | 1 \rangle + 0 \right]$$

$$= 0$$

(100)

is again zero.

(3) Finally, we can calculate the expectation value in the position representation by doing an integral

$$\langle \hat{x} \rangle = \langle 0|\hat{x}|0 \rangle$$

$$= \int_{-\infty}^{\infty} \varphi_0^*(x)\,x\varphi_0(x)\,dx$$

$$= \int_{-\infty}^{\infty} x|\varphi_0(x)|^2 dx.$$

(101)

This integral is zero because the probability density is spatially symmetric (even) about the origin and the function x is antisymmetric (odd) about the origin, yielding an antisymmetric (odd) integrand. The integral of an antisymmetric (odd) integrand over a symmetric (even) interval is zero.

This particular calculation is simple using any of these methods. More detailed calculations, such as the expectation value of the square of the position are most easily done using the operator method in Eq. (99) (Problem 9).

6 ■ MOMENTUM SPACE WAVE FUNCTION

The matrices for position and momentum in Eq. (96) have the same form, with different constants to get the dimensions correct. This suggests some symmetry between the position and momentum representation that does not exist in the other bound state problems we have solved. To explore this symmetry, let's find the momentum space representation of the energy eigenstates $|n\rangle \doteq \phi_n(p) = \langle p|n\rangle$. There are three ways we can find the momentum space wave functions.

(1) We can take the same operator approach we used above to find the position representation wave functions. We start with the ladder termination equation

$$a|0\rangle = 0$$

(102)

and express this in the momentum representation, where the position operator is a derivative with respect to momentum and the momentum operator is a multiplicative factor:

$$a\phi_0(p) = 0$$

$$\sqrt{\frac{m\omega}{2\hbar}}\left(\hat{x} + i\frac{\hat{p}}{m\omega}\right)\phi_0(p) = 0$$

$$\sqrt{\frac{m\omega}{2\hbar}}\left(i\hbar\frac{d}{dp} + \frac{i}{m\omega}p\right)\phi_0(p) = 0.$$

(103)

This leads to a differential equation

$$\frac{d}{dp}\phi_0(p) = -\frac{1}{m\omega\hbar}p\phi_0(p)$$

(104)

that has the same form as the differential equation for the ground state wave function in the position representation [see Eq. (48)]. It is a first-order differential equation whose solution is a Gaussian function [see Eq. (49)], but in this case, momentum is the argument of the function. Hence, the properly normalized ground state energy eigenstate in the momentum representation is (Problem 18):

$$\phi_0(p) = \left(\frac{1}{\pi m \omega \hbar}\right)^{1/4} e^{-p^2/2m\omega\hbar}.$$
(105)

The excited states can be found with the raising operator approach that we used in the position representation. The momentum representation result includes the same Hermite polynomials as in the position representation:

$$\phi_n(p) = \left(\frac{1}{\pi m \omega \hbar}\right)^{1/4} \frac{1}{\sqrt{2^n n!}} H_n\left(\frac{p}{\sqrt{m\omega\hbar}}\right) e^{-p^2/2m\omega\hbar}.$$
(106)

(2) We can also go back to the energy eigenvalue equation and express it in the momentum representation. In this case, we get a second-order differential equation in momentum space

$$H|n\rangle = E_n|n\rangle$$

$$\frac{1}{2m}\left[\hat{p}^2 + m^2\omega^2\hat{x}^2\right]|n\rangle = E_n|n\rangle$$

$$\frac{1}{2m}\left[p^2 - m^2\omega^2\hbar^2 \frac{d^2}{dp^2}\right]\phi_n(p) = E_n\phi_n(p)$$
(107)

$$-\frac{m\omega^2\hbar^2}{2}\frac{d^2\phi_n(p)}{dp^2} + \frac{1}{2m}p^2\phi_n(p) = E_n\phi_n(p).$$

Once again this differential equation has the same form as the spatial differential equation [see Eq. (45)] and leads to the momentum space solutions in Eq. (106) with the same functional dependence as the position representation solutions [Eq. (64)] with momentum as the argument rather than position.

(3) We can transform the position representation solutions to the momentum representation using the Fourier transform. The position representation wave function and the momentum representation wave function are connected by the Fourier transform

$$\phi(p) = \frac{1}{\sqrt{2\pi\hbar}}\int_{-\infty}^{\infty} \psi(x)e^{-ipx/\hbar}dx.$$
(108)

Because the Fourier transform of a Gaussian function is another Gaussian function, the ground state momentum space wave function is the Gaussian function in Eq. (105). The Fourier transform of an Hermite polynomial times a Gaussian function is also an Hermite polynomial times a Gaussian function, so the excited states are given by Eq. (106).

Thus we find the interesting result that the momentum space wave functions representing the energy eigenstates have the same functional dependence on momentum as the position representation wave functions have on position. This similarity is visible in the momentum space probability density for one particular energy eigenstate shown in Fig. 9. In this case, the limits $\pm p_n = \pm\sqrt{(2n+1)m\omega\hbar}$ represent the limits of the classical momentum for a particle with energy $E_n = (n + 1/2)\hbar\omega$. Note the similarity with Fig. 7.

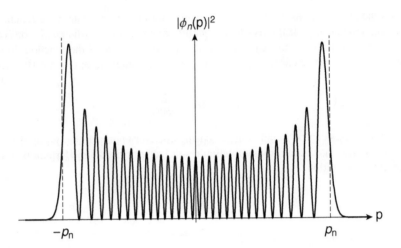

FIGURE 9   Momentum space probability density for the $n = 30$ harmonic oscillator state.

7 ■ THE UNCERTAINTY PRINCIPLE

The Heisenberg uncertainty principle places a lower limit on the product of the uncertainties of position and momentum

$$\Delta x \Delta p \geq \frac{\hbar}{2}, \tag{109}$$

where the quantum mechanical uncertainties are defined as the standard deviations

$$\Delta x = \sqrt{\langle (x - \langle x \rangle)^2 \rangle} = \sqrt{\langle x^2 \rangle - \langle x \rangle^2}$$
$$\Delta p = \sqrt{\langle (p - \langle p \rangle)^2 \rangle} = \sqrt{\langle p^2 \rangle - \langle p \rangle^2}. \tag{110}$$

Now that we know the position and momentum probability distributions, these uncertainties are straightforward to calculate by integration or by operator methods. For the ground state of the harmonic oscillator, these uncertainties can be found *by inspection* because the Gaussian functional form of the ground state wave function is a standard probability function.

The standard way of writing a Gaussian function for use in probability analysis is

$$f(x) = \frac{1}{\sqrt{2\pi}\sigma} e^{-(x - \bar{x})^2 / 2\sigma^2}. \tag{111}$$

where $\bar{x}$ is the mean or average of the distribution and σ is the standard deviation of the distribution. For the harmonic oscillator ground state, the spatial probability density distribution is

$$\mathcal{P}_0(x) = |\varphi_0(x)|^2 = \sqrt{\frac{m\omega}{\pi\hbar}} e^{-m\omega x^2 / \hbar}. \tag{112}$$

This is identical to the standard form in Eq. (111). By comparing the quantum mechanical probability density in Eq. (112) and the standard probability expression in Eq. (111), we find by inspection that the mean and standard deviation are

$$\bar{x} = 0$$

$$\sigma = \sqrt{\frac{\hbar}{2m\omega}}. \tag{113}$$

The mean or average is what we call the expectation value $\langle x \rangle$ in quantum mechanics, and the standard deviation is the quantum mechanical uncertainty Δx. Hence, we have the results for the ground state

$$\langle x \rangle = 0$$

$$\Delta x = \sqrt{\frac{\hbar}{2m\omega}}. \tag{114}$$

We already found that the expectation value $\langle x \rangle$ is zero in Example 3, and now we have found the uncertainty Δx by inspection.

The momentum probability density distribution also has a Gaussian form for the harmonic oscillator ground state

$$\mathcal{P}_0(p) = |\phi_0(p)|^2 = \sqrt{\frac{1}{\pi m \omega \hbar}} e^{-p^2/m\omega\hbar}. \tag{115}$$

If we also compare this to the standard Gaussian function, we find by inspection that the expectation value $\langle p \rangle$ and the uncertainty Δp are

$$\langle p \rangle = 0$$

$$\Delta p = \sqrt{\frac{m\omega\hbar}{2}}. \tag{116}$$

We expect the expectation value $\langle p \rangle$ to be zero, based upon inspection of the momentum matrix in Eq. (96).

We can now check that the uncertainty principle is obeyed. Using the results in Eqs. (114) and (116), we obtain

$$\Delta x \Delta p = \sqrt{\frac{\hbar}{2m\omega}}\sqrt{\frac{m\omega\hbar}{2}} = \frac{\hbar}{2}. \tag{117}$$

Not only is the uncertainty principle obeyed, but the uncertainty product has its minimum value, so we refer to the harmonic oscillator ground state as a minimum uncertainty state. The Gaussian wave packet for a free particle is also a minimum uncertainty state. However, the free particle wave packet evolves with time in a way that causes it to spread out in space, and so it is only a minimum uncertainty state at one time. The harmonic oscillator ground state is an energy eigenstate and so its time evolution produces only a multiplicative overall phase factor, which does not change the probability density in position or momentum space. Hence, the harmonic oscillator ground state remains a minimum uncertainty state for all time. The shape of the harmonic oscillator potential energy well is just right to counter the spreading of the wave packet.

8 ■ TIME DEPENDENCE

Now let's study some examples of time dependence in the harmonic oscillator. These examples demonstrate the manifestation of the sixth postulate regarding Schrödinger time evolution. They also illustrate the power of the operator approach for the harmonic oscillator, in contrast with the wave function approach. A general state of the system is expressed as a superposition of energy eigenstates

$$|\psi(0)\rangle = \sum_{n=0}^{\infty} c_n |n\rangle. \tag{118}$$

In the energy basis, the Schrödinger time evolution recipe tells us that the time dependence is found by multiplying each energy eigenstate coefficient by an energy dependent phase factor, giving:

$$
\begin{aligned}
|\psi(t)\rangle &= \sum_{n=0}^{\infty} c_n e^{-iE_n t/\hbar} |n\rangle \\
&= \sum_{n=0}^{\infty} c_n e^{-i(n+\frac{1}{2})\omega t} |n\rangle \\
&= e^{-i\omega t/2} \sum_{n=0}^{\infty} c_n e^{-in\omega t} |n\rangle.
\end{aligned} \tag{119}
$$

Thus we see that each successive term acquires an additional relative phase of $e^{-i\omega t}$ from the Schrödinger time evolution.

Example 4   A harmonic oscillator system starts in an equal superposition of the ground state and the first excited state

$$|\psi(0)\rangle = \tfrac{1}{\sqrt{2}}|0\rangle + \tfrac{1}{\sqrt{2}}|1\rangle. \tag{120}$$

Find the probability as a function of time of measuring the system to have energy $\hbar\omega/2$, the probability density as a function of time, and the expectation value of position.

The time-evolved state function is found from the Schrödinger recipe:

$$|\psi(t)\rangle = e^{-i\omega t/2}\Big[\tfrac{1}{\sqrt{2}}|0\rangle + \tfrac{1}{\sqrt{2}}e^{-i\omega t}|1\rangle\Big], \tag{121}$$

where we factor out the common phase because only the relative phase is important. The probability of finding the oscillator in the ground state is

$$
\begin{aligned}
\mathcal{P}_0 &= \big|\langle 0|\psi(t)\rangle\big|^2 = \Big|\langle 0|e^{-i\omega t/2}\big[\tfrac{1}{\sqrt{2}}|0\rangle + \tfrac{1}{\sqrt{2}}e^{-i\omega t}|1\rangle\big]\Big|^2 \\
&= \Big|e^{-i\omega t/2}\tfrac{1}{\sqrt{2}}\langle 0|0\rangle + e^{-i\omega t/2}\tfrac{1}{\sqrt{2}}e^{-i\omega t}\langle 0|1\rangle\Big|^2 \\
&= \Big|e^{-i\omega t/2}\tfrac{1}{\sqrt{2}}\Big|^2 \\
&= \tfrac{1}{2}.
\end{aligned} \tag{122}
$$

This probability is time independent, as is the probability of making any particular measurement of the energy. This is why we refer to energy states as stationary states.

The spatial probability density of this two-state superposition is

$$\mathcal{P}(x,t) = |\langle x|\psi(t)\rangle|^2 = |\psi(x,t)|^2 = \left|\left\langle x\left|e^{-i\omega t/2}\left[\tfrac{1}{\sqrt{2}}|0\rangle + \tfrac{1}{\sqrt{2}}e^{-i\omega t}|1\rangle\right]\right.\right\rangle\right|^2$$
$$= \tfrac{1}{2}\left|\varphi_0(x) + e^{-i\omega t}\varphi_1(x)\right|^2 \tag{123}$$
$$= \tfrac{1}{2}\left[|\varphi_0(x)|^2 + |\varphi_1(x)|^2 + \varphi_0(x)\varphi_1^*(x)e^{+i\omega t} + \varphi_0^*(x)\varphi_1(x)e^{-i\omega t}\right].$$

If the position is measured, then the result is time dependent because the position operator does not commute with the Hamiltonian. For the harmonic oscillator, the wave functions are real and Eq. (123) simplifies to

$$\mathcal{P}(x,t) = \tfrac{1}{2}\left[\varphi_0^2(x) + \varphi_1^2(x) + 2\varphi_0(x)\varphi_1(x)\cos\omega t\right]. \tag{124}$$

This probability density oscillates with time, as depicted in the animation frames shown in Fig. 10, where the constant τ is the oscillation period $\tau = 2\pi/\omega$ of the harmonic oscillator (see the activity on time evolution of harmonic oscillator states). The probability distribution of this superposition sloshes back and forth in the well.

We calculate the expectation value of the position using the raising and lowering operators [see Eq. (99)]

$$\langle\hat{x}\rangle = \langle\psi(t)|\hat{x}|\psi(t)\rangle = \sqrt{\frac{\hbar}{2m\omega}}\langle\psi(t)|a^\dagger + a|\psi(t)\rangle$$
$$= \sqrt{\frac{\hbar}{2m\omega}}\left[\tfrac{1}{\sqrt{2}}\langle 0| + \tfrac{1}{\sqrt{2}}e^{+i\omega t}\langle 1|\right]\left(a^\dagger + a\right)\left[\tfrac{1}{\sqrt{2}}|0\rangle + \tfrac{1}{\sqrt{2}}e^{-i\omega t}|1\rangle\right]$$
$$= \frac{1}{2}\sqrt{\frac{\hbar}{2m\omega}}\left[\langle 0|(a^\dagger + a)|1\rangle e^{-i\omega t} + \langle 1|(a^\dagger + a)|0\rangle e^{+i\omega t}\right] \tag{125}$$
$$= \frac{1}{2}\sqrt{\frac{\hbar}{2m\omega}}\left[\left(\langle 0|a^\dagger|1\rangle + \langle 0|a|1\rangle\right)e^{-i\omega t} + \left(\langle 1|a^\dagger|0\rangle + \langle 1|a|0\rangle\right)e^{+i\omega t}\right].$$

Superposition of n=0 and n=1 states

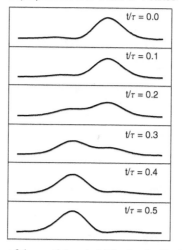

FIGURE 10 Time dependence of the spatial probability density for the superposition state composed of equal probabilities of $n = 0$ and 1 states. The frames represent half of the oscillation period τ.

Each matrix element is found using the ladder operator matrix elements in Eq. (93) or by inspection of the matrix in Eq. (94), yielding

$$\langle \hat{x} \rangle = \frac{1}{2}\sqrt{\frac{\hbar}{2m\omega}}\Big[\big(\langle 0|2\rangle\sqrt{2} + \langle 0|0\rangle\sqrt{1}\big)e^{-i\omega t} + \big(\langle 1|1\rangle\sqrt{1} + 0\big)e^{+i\omega t}\Big]$$

$$= \frac{1}{2}\sqrt{\frac{\hbar}{2m\omega}}\Big[e^{-i\omega t} + e^{+i\omega t}\Big] \tag{126}$$

$$= \sqrt{\frac{\hbar}{2m\omega}}\cos\omega t.$$

Hence, the expectation value of position oscillates with time, which is evident in the animation frames shown in Fig. 10. This calculation of matrix elements was simplified greatly by using the ladder operators. If we were to use wave functions, then we would need to calculate spatial integrals. The moral of the story is: use the ladder operators wherever you can and do not do an integral if you don't have to.

Now consider a general two-state superposition, such as

$$|\psi(0)\rangle = c_m|m\rangle + c_n|n\rangle. \tag{127}$$

In this case, the expectation value of x is equal to zero if the states $|m\rangle$ and $|n\rangle$ that comprise the superposition are not adjacent energy states because the $\hat{x}$ matrix [Eq. (96)] only connects adjacent states. This means that a measurement of $\langle x \rangle$ can oscillate only at the frequency ω, not at 2ω, 3ω, etc. This result is similar to the classical oscillator where only a single harmonic is observed. Thus it is true in both quantum mechanics and classical mechanics that a linear oscillator has no higher harmonics. We need nonlinearity in the restoring force to achieve anharmonicity and to observe other frequencies.

Note, however, that the probability density *does* exhibit higher harmonics. For example, the probability density of the state $|\psi\rangle = \frac{1}{\sqrt{2}}\big(|0\rangle + |2\rangle\big)$ oscillates with time at the frequency 2ω, but it does so in a manner that preserves the zero value of $\langle x \rangle$. As shown in the animation frames in Fig. 11(a), the probability distribution "breathes" symmetrically such that $\langle x \rangle = 0$. For the state $|\psi\rangle = \frac{1}{\sqrt{2}}\big(|0\rangle + |3\rangle\big)$, the probability distribution [Fig. 11(b)] has two lobes that pass through each other at frequency 3ω, while preserving $\langle x \rangle = 0$.

The presence of only a single Bohr frequency in the expectation value of the position is related to the selection rule for transitions between energy levels. We know that the probability for a system to make a transition is proportional to the matrix element of the interaction between the two states. Assuming that the bound particle has a charge q, then the relevant electric dipole interaction is governed by the matrix element $\langle n_i|q\hat{x}|n_f\rangle$ of the electric dipole operator $\hat{d} = q\hat{x}$. Because the matrix for position connects only adjacent states, the matrix elements are

$$\langle n_i|q\hat{x}|n_f\rangle \propto \delta_{n_i, n_f \pm 1} \tag{128}$$

and the selection rule for harmonic oscillator transitions is

$$\Delta n = n_f - n_i = \pm 1. \tag{129}$$

Now consider measurements of the momentum of a superposition state of the harmonic oscillator. The similarity of the position and momentum operators means that the momentum probability distribution and the expectation value of momentum $\langle p \rangle$ show similar results to those for position obtained above (Problem 11). In particular, the expectation values of position and momentum follow Ehrenfest's theorem, which tells us that expectation values obey classical laws. The classical relation between position and momentum is $p = mv = mdx/dt$, so the quantum mechanical superposition states obey the relation:

$$\langle p \rangle = m\frac{d\langle x \rangle}{dt}. \tag{130}$$

Though the superposition state presented in Fig. 10 exhibits the classical behavior of Eq. (130), the time evolution does not really "look" classical. Classically, we expect to see a well-localized "particle" oscillate between the turning points. We saw in Fig. 7 that higher energy states exhibit more classical behavior, so we might ask if the time evolution would appear more classical if the states $|m\rangle$ and $|n\rangle$ that comprise the superposition were higher in energy. An example of this is shown in Fig. 12. The wave is more localized but now exhibits interference fringes that would not be expected for a classical particle. One way to make the time evolution appear classical is to build a superposition state known as a **coherent state**.

A coherent state is a wave packet that moves within the quadratic harmonic oscillator potential in such a way that it retains its shape, unlike the two-state superpositions in Figs. 10, 11, and 12. Wave packets in free space distort as they propagate, so this is a new phenomenon. The coherent state is an infinite superposition of harmonic oscillator energy eigenstates with a particular choice of amplitudes and phases (hence the name coherent). The form of these coefficients is not so important for now, but what is interesting is that the wave function of the coherent state is identical to the ground state Gaussian wave function, except that it is not centered at the origin. As shown in Fig. 13(a), this displaced Gaussian state oscillates about the origin and does not change its shape (see the activity on time evolution of harmonic oscillator states). Because the ground state has a minimum uncertainty product, the coherent states also minimize the uncertainty product and do so even as they move. Figure 13(b) shows that if we choose a displaced Gaussian wave packet with the wrong width it does not move without distortion. It remains a Gaussian, but changes it size (it breathes as it moves).

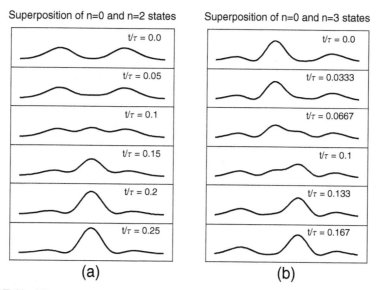

Superposition of n=0 and n=2 states | Superposition of n=0 and n=3 states

$t/\tau = 0.0$ $t/\tau = 0.0$
$t/\tau = 0.05$ $t/\tau = 0.0333$
$t/\tau = 0.1$ $t/\tau = 0.0667$
$t/\tau = 0.15$ $t/\tau = 0.1$
$t/\tau = 0.2$ $t/\tau = 0.133$
$t/\tau = 0.25$ $t/\tau = 0.167$

(a)   (b)

FIGURE 11 Time dependence of the spatial probability density for the superposition states composed of equal probabilities of (a) the $n = 0$ and 2 states, and (b) the $n = 0$ and 3 states.

Superposition of n=19 and n=20 states

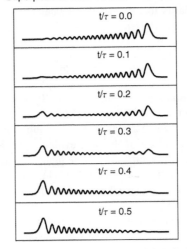

FIGURE 12 Time dependence of the spatial probability density for the superposition state composed of equal probabilities of the $n = 19$ and 20 states.

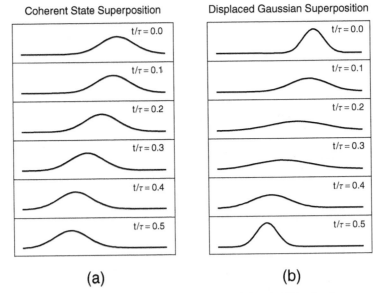

(a) (b)

FIGURE 13 Time dependence of the spatial probability density (a) for a coherent state and (b) for a displaced Gaussian state that is not the ground state.

9 ■ MOLECULAR VIBRATIONS

One of the most common applications of the quantum mechanical harmonic oscillator is found in the vibrations of the nuclei of molecules. In a diatomic molecule, the Coulomb attraction between the nuclei and the electrons is balanced by the Coulomb repulsion between the nuclei in a way that results in the potential energy diagram shown in Fig. 14. This diagram shows the Coulomb potential energy of a diatomic molecule as a function of the nuclear separation for a given electron configuration (in this case, the ground state). The minimum of the potential energy $-D_e$ occurs at the bond length R_0 of the diatomic molecule, and the zero of potential energy represents the separation of the two atoms to infinite separation, (i.e., the dissociation of the molecule). This potential energy curve determines the motion of the nuclei with respect to each other. Because this curve resembles a parabola near the minimum energy, the motion of the nuclei resembles the motion of a quantum mechanical harmonic oscillator.

The harmonic oscillator potential energy that approximates the molecular potential energy is

$$V_{HO}(R) = -D_e + \tfrac{1}{2}\mu\omega^2(R - R_0)^2, \tag{131}$$

where μ is the reduced mass of the two nuclei. However, the molecular potential energy curve resembles a parabola only near the minimum, as shown in Fig. 15. As the energy level approaches the dissociation limit, the difference between the parabolic harmonic oscillator potential and the true molecular potential becomes quite dramatic. A better approximation to the molecular potential is given by the Morse potential

$$V_M(R) = D_e\big(e^{-2\alpha(R-R_0)} - 2e^{-\alpha(R-R_0)}\big), \tag{132}$$

where the constant α is

$$\alpha = \omega\sqrt{\frac{\mu}{2D_e}}. \tag{133}$$

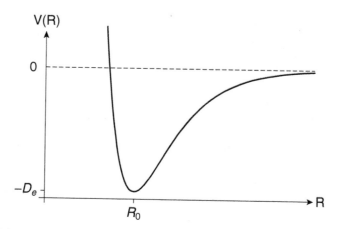

FIGURE 14   Potential energy of a diatomic molecule as a function of the nuclear separation.

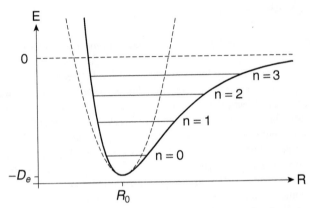

FIGURE 15   Vibrational energy states of the nuclear motion in the molecular potential. The dashed line is the approximate harmonic potential and the solid line is the more accurate Morse potential.

The energy levels shown in Fig. 15 are the solutions to the motion of the nuclei in the Morse potential and show a marked deviation from the levels of an ideal harmonic oscillator. The Morse energy levels become closer together near the top of the well, in contrast to the uniform spacing of the harmonic oscillator. This difference has a clear signature in the spectra of molecular vibrations. An ideal harmonic oscillator has transitions only between adjacent energy levels ($\Delta n = \pm 1$ selection rule from Section 8), and all those possible transitions have the same energy difference $\hbar\omega$. The transitions in a Morse oscillator exhibit a progression from the $n = 0 \leftrightarrow 1$ transition at energy $\hbar\omega$ to smaller energies as we progress up the potential well. In addition, a Morse oscillator has allowed transitions between nonadjacent states ($\Delta n = \pm 2, 3, ...$) at higher energies near to multiples of the harmonic energy $\hbar\omega$. The $\Delta n = \pm 1$ selection rule is not obeyed because of the anharmonicity of the well, though these transitions are typically weaker than the $\Delta n = \pm 1$ transitions.

The spectra observed in molecules are further complicated by the rotation of the molecule, and by transitions between different electronic levels, similar to the transitions in the hydrogen atom. The transitions due to changes in electronic, vibrational, and rotational levels are each characterized by a different energy scale. Electronic transitions are typically in the 1–5 eV range, vibrational transitions are typically 500-5000 cm^{-1} (0.06–0.6 eV), and rotational transitions are typically 0.2–60 cm^{-1} (0.02–7 meV). Thus rotational transitions represent finer structure compared to vibrational transitions, and vibrational transitions represent finer structure compared to electronic transitions. A schematic of these different energy scales is shown in Fig. 16.

Consider how the rotational spectrum of the hydrogen chloride molecule is affected by the vibrational motion. We can explain this using Fig. 15. As a molecule vibrates, it occupies higher lying vibrational levels within the potential energy well shown in Fig. 15. Because the Morse potential is asymmetric, the average value of the nuclear separation (the "bond length") deviates from the equilibrium value R_0, with the deviation growing as the energy increases. The deviation is always positive in the Morse potential, which implies that the moment of inertia of the diatomic molecule $I = \mu R^2$ increases and the rotational constant $\hbar^2/2I$ decreases. This negative shift of the rotational constant explains the discrepancy between the calculated and observed spectra. Note that this **rotation-vibration coupling** is present even in the $n = 0$ vibrational ground state, where one might be tempted to think that the molecule is not vibrating. This effect is another example of the effect of the zero-point energy of the harmonic oscillator.

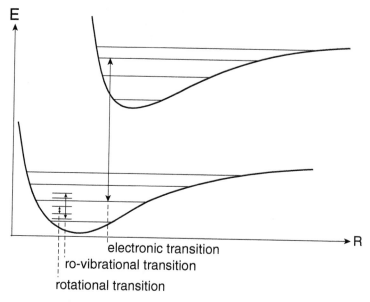

FIGURE 16 Transitions in a diatomic molecule.

SUMMARY

We solved the quantum mechanical harmonic oscillator problem using an operator approach. We defined the lowering and raising operators

$$a = \sqrt{\frac{m\omega}{2\hbar}}\left(\hat{x} + i\frac{\hat{p}}{m\omega}\right) \tag{134}$$

and

$$a^\dagger = \sqrt{\frac{m\omega}{2\hbar}}\left(\hat{x} - i\frac{\hat{p}}{m\omega}\right), \tag{135}$$

respectively. Using these operators, we expressed the Hamiltonian as

$$H = \frac{\hat{p}^2}{2m} + \tfrac{1}{2}m\omega^2\hat{x}^2 = \hbar\omega\left(a^\dagger a + \tfrac{1}{2}\right). \tag{136}$$

We solved the energy eigenvalue problem to find

$$E_n = \hbar\omega\left(n + \tfrac{1}{2}\right), \qquad n = 0, 1, 2, 3, \dots . \tag{137}$$

We used the quantum mechanical harmonic oscillator to review the fundamental ideas of quantum mechanics. Table 1 summarizes the manifestations of the quantum mechanical postulates in different systems.

Table 1   Manifestations of Quantum Mechanical Postulates

Postulates	Spin 1/2	Hydrogen atom	Harmonic Oscillator
1) State defined by ket	$|+\rangle$, $|-\rangle$	$\psi_{nlm}(r,\theta,\phi) = R_{nl}(r)Y_l^m(\theta,\phi)$	$|n\rangle, \varphi_n(x), \phi_n(p)$
2) Observables as operators	$S_z, \mathbf{S}^2, H$	$H, \mathbf{L}^2, L_z$	$H, \hat{x}, \hat{p}$
3) Measure eigen-values	$S_z = \pm\hbar/2$	$E_n = -\dfrac{Z^2 R}{n^2}$ $L^2 = \ell(\ell+1)\hbar^2, L_z = m\hbar$	$E_n = \hbar\omega\left(n + \frac{1}{2}\right)$
4) Probability (density)	$|\langle+|\psi\rangle|^2$	$|\langle nlm|\psi\rangle|^2$, $|\psi_{nlm}(r,\theta,\phi)|^2$	$|\langle n|\psi\rangle|^2$, $|\varphi_n(x)|^2$
5) State reduction	$|\psi\rangle \rightarrow |+\rangle$	$|\psi\rangle \rightarrow |nlm\rangle$, $|\psi\rangle \rightarrow |E_n\rangle$	$|\psi\rangle \rightarrow |n\rangle$
6) Schrödinger time evolution	Larmor precession	Dipole oscillation	Superposition oscillation

RESOURCES

Activities

These activities are available at

www.physics.oregonstate.edu/qmactivities

Harmonic Oscillator Basis States: Students express the normalization, orthogonality, and completeness conditions for harmonic oscillator states in Dirac notation and in wave function notation.

Time Evolution of Harmonic Oscillator States: Students animate wave functions consisting of linear combinations of eigenstates.

Further Reading

More details on treating light as a harmonic oscillator and coherent states of light can be found in these texts:

Mark Fox, *Quantum Optics: An Introduction*, Oxford: Oxford University Press, 2006.

Christopher Gerry and Peter Knight, *Introductory Quantum Optics*, Cambridge: Cambridge University Press, 2005.

Rodney Loudon, *Quantum Theory of Light*, Oxford: Oxford University Press, 2000.

Harmonic Oscillator: Problem Set

1 Show that the product of a and $a^\dagger$, in that order, is given by Eq. (21),

$$aa^\dagger = \frac{m\omega}{2\hbar}\left(\hat{x}^2 + \frac{\hat{p}^2}{m^2\omega^2}\right) + \frac{1}{2}. \tag{21}$$

2 Show that the action of $a^\dagger$ on an eigenstate of H produces an eigenstate with the eigenvalue raised by one quantum.

3 Normalize the wave function $e^{-m\omega x^2/2\hbar}$ to get the correct ground state of the harmonic oscillator, as given in Eq. (49),

$$\varphi_0(x) = \left(\frac{m\omega}{\pi\hbar}\right)^{1/4} e^{-m\omega x^2/2\hbar}. \tag{49}$$

4 Calculate the probability that a particle in the ground state of the harmonic oscillator is found in the classically forbidden region.

5 Show that the proper scale factor of the raising operation yields Eq. (56),

$$\boxed{a^\dagger|n\rangle = \sqrt{n+1}\,|n+1\rangle}: \tag{56}$$

$a^\dagger|n\rangle = \sqrt{n+1}\,|n+1\rangle.$

6 Show that the raising and lowering operators *would* commute with each other *if* their action on energy eigenstates preserved normalization. That is, assume $a|n\rangle = |n-1\rangle$ and $a^\dagger|n\rangle = |n+1\rangle$, and use that information to show that a and $a^\dagger$ commute.

7 Show by direct integration that the ground and first excited states of the harmonic oscillator are orthogonal to each other.

8 Show that the spatial probability density of a classical harmonic oscillator is

$$\mathcal{P}(x) = \frac{1}{\pi\sqrt{x_0^2 - x^2}},$$

where x_0 is the classical turning point (see Fig. 7).

9 a) For the ground state of the harmonic oscillator, calculate $\langle x\rangle$, $\langle p\rangle$, $\langle x^2\rangle$, and $\langle p^2\rangle$ by explicit spatial integration.

b) Calculate $\langle x\rangle$, $\langle p\rangle$, $\langle x^2\rangle$, and $\langle p^2\rangle$ for all the energy eigenstates $|n\rangle$ of the harmonic oscillator without doing integration (i.e., use the operators a and $a^\dagger$).

c) Check that the uncertainty principle is obeyed in both the above cases.

10 Discuss and show explicitly how Eq. (93),

$$\langle m|a|n\rangle = \langle m|\sqrt{n}|n-1\rangle \qquad \langle m|a^\dagger|n\rangle = \langle m|\sqrt{n+1}|n+1\rangle$$

$$= \sqrt{n}\,\delta_{m,n-1} \qquad\qquad = \sqrt{n+1}\,\delta_{m,n+1}, \tag{93}$$

is used to find the matrix representations of the ladder operators.

From Chapter 9 of *Quantum Mechanics: A Paradigms Approach*, First Edition. David H. McIntyre. Copyright © 2012 by Pearson Education, Inc. Published by Pearson Addison-Wesley. All rights reserved.

The companion websites for this text are http://physics.oregonstate.edu/portfolioswiki and http://physics.oregonstate.edu/qmactivities.

11 A particle in the harmonic oscillator potential has the initial state

$$|\psi(t = 0)\rangle = A\big[|0\rangle + 2e^{i\pi/2}|1\rangle\big].$$

a) Find the normalization constant A.

b) Find the time-evolved state $|\psi(t)\rangle$.

c) Calculate $\langle x \rangle$ and $\langle p \rangle$ as functions of time and verify that Ehrenfest's theorem [Eq. (130)],

$$\langle p \rangle = m\frac{d\langle x \rangle}{dt}, \tag{130}$$

is obeyed.

12 A particle is in the ground state of the harmonic oscillator potential $V_1(x) = \frac{1}{2}m\omega_1^2 x^2$ when the potential suddenly changes to $V_2(x) = \frac{1}{2}m\omega_2^2 x^2$ without initially changing the wave function.

a) What is the probability that a measurement of the particle energy yields the result $\frac{1}{2}\hbar\omega_2$?

b) Evaluate the result in (a) for the case $\omega_2 = 1.7\omega_1$.

13 Find the allowed energy levels of a particle of mass m moving in the one-dimensional potential energy well

$$V(x) = \begin{cases} \frac{1}{2}m\omega^2 x^2, & x < 0 \\ \infty, & x > 0 \end{cases}.$$

(Hint: The answer requires a qualitative argument rather than a calculation.)

14 A particle in the harmonic oscillator potential has the initial state

$$\psi(x,0) = A\left[1 - 3\sqrt{\frac{m\omega}{\hbar}}x + 2\frac{m\omega}{\hbar}x^2\right]e^{-m\omega x^2/2\hbar}$$

where A is the normalization constant.

a) Calculate the expectation value of the energy.

b) At a later time T, the wave function is

$$\psi(x,T) = B\left[3 - 3i\sqrt{\frac{m\omega}{\hbar}}x - 2\frac{m\omega}{\hbar}x^2\right]e^{-m\omega x^2/2\hbar}$$

for some constant B. What is the smallest possible value of T?

15 A measurement of the energy of a harmonic oscillator system yields the results $\hbar\omega/2$ and $3\hbar\omega/2$ with equal probability. A measurement of the position (actually measurements on an ensemble of identically prepared systems) yields the result $\langle x \rangle = -\sqrt{\hbar/2m\omega}\sin\omega t$. Calculate the expectation value of the momentum.

16 A particle is in the harmonic oscillator potential $V(x) = \frac{1}{2}m\omega^2 x^2$ and the energy is measured. The probability that the energy measurement yields $\frac{3}{2}\hbar\omega$ is 36% and the probability that the energy measurement yields $\frac{5}{2}\hbar\omega$ is 64%. The expectation value of the position $\langle x \rangle$ is a minimum at time $t = 0$.

a) Find the time-dependent wave function.

b) Calculate the expectation value $\langle p \rangle$ of the momentum for this particle, as a function of time.

c) Calculate the expectation value $\langle E \rangle$ of the energy.

17 A particle in the harmonic oscillator potential $V(x) = \frac{1}{2}m\omega^2 x^2$ starts out in the state

$$\psi(x,0) = A[\varphi_0(x) + 2\varphi_1(x) + 2\varphi_2(x)],$$

where $\varphi_n(x)$ are the normalized eigenfunctions of the Hamiltonian.

a) If you measure the energy of this particle, what values might you get, and with what probabilities?

b) Calculate the expectation value $\langle p \rangle$ of the momentum for this particle, as a function of time.

c) What is the expectation value $\langle E \rangle$ of the energy?

d) What is the standard deviation ΔE of the energy?

18 Solve the differential equation (104),

$$\frac{d}{dp}\phi_0(p) = -\frac{1}{m\omega\hbar}p\phi_0(p), \tag{104}$$

and show that the properly normalized momentum space wave function of the ground state of the harmonic oscillator is given by Eq. (105),

$$\phi_0(p) = \left(\frac{1}{\pi m\omega\hbar}\right)^{1/4} e^{-p^2/2m\omega\hbar}. \tag{105}$$

19 Find the momentum representation of the ground state of the harmonic oscillator using the Fourier transform in Eq. (108),

$$\phi(p) = \frac{1}{\sqrt{2\pi\hbar}} \int_{-\infty}^{\infty} \psi(x) e^{-ipx/\hbar} dx. \tag{108}$$

20 Use your favorite software package to study the coherent states of the harmonic oscillator. Assume that the system has the initial wave function

$$\psi(x,0) = \varphi_0(x - x_0),$$

where x_0 is a constant representing the displacement of the Gaussian ground state waveform from the origin.

a) Plot the wave function, choosing $x_0 = \sqrt{\hbar/m\omega}$

b) Calculate the overlap integrals in $c_n = \langle n|\psi(0)\rangle$ necessary to express the initial wave function in terms of energy eigenstates. Do this for the first 10 energy levels. Compare your results to the expression

$$c_n = \frac{\alpha^n}{\sqrt{n!}} e^{-\alpha^2/2},$$

where $\alpha = x_0\sqrt{m\omega/2\hbar}$. Check whether the 10 terms in the expansion are enough to properly represent the wave function. Explain.

c) Calculate the expectation value of the energy.

d) Construct the time-dependent wave function. Animate the wave function and describe its time evolution.

e) Repeat the above for $x_0 = 4\sqrt{\hbar/m\omega}$. You may need more that 10 terms!

21 Show that the Morse potential reduces to a parabolic potential for small displacements from the equilibrium bond length. Find the cubic correction term to the harmonic potential that is included in the Morse potential.

22 Imagine a quantum system with an energy spectrum $E_n = n^3 \hbar \omega$ for $n = 1, 2, 3, \ldots$. *By inspection*, write down the matrix representation of the Hamiltonian and the energy eigenstates. Write down the matrix representing the operator A in this system that is defined by $A|n\rangle = 3n^2|n + 2\rangle$.

Perturbation Theory

From Chapter 10 of *Quantum Mechanics: A Paradigms Approach*, First Edition. David H. McIntyre. Copyright © 2012 by Pearson Education, Inc. Published by Pearson Addison-Wesley. All rights reserved.

The companion websites for this text are http://physics.oregonstate.edu/portfolioswiki and http://physics.oregonstate.edu/qmactivities.

Perturbation Theory

The quantum mechanics you have studied so far has probably entailed solving a few carefully chosen problems exactly. Unfortunately, those problems represent a small fraction of the realistic problems that nature presents to us, and in most cases those exactly solvable problems are only approximations to real problems. Now we must learn to solve more realistic problems that do not admit exact solutions. The approach we take to solving these realistic problems is to make them look like problems we have already solved exactly, with an additional part that represents the new, more realistic aspect of the problem. We assume that this new part, the **perturbation**, is small so that we can use approximations to find the corrections to the exact solutions. Our focus is to discover how energies and eigenstates are affected by small additional terms in the Hamiltonian. To guide us, we will take some exactly solvable problems, solve them, and then expand the solutions. We will compare these results with the new perturbation methods that we learn.

You may have had a sneak peek at how a perturbation affects a system when studying the asymmetric square well. An additional potential energy "shelf" in the infinite square well changes the energy levels, as shown in Fig. 1. For small values V_0 of the potential energy shelf, the energy of the ground state is shifted by an amount that is linearly dependent on V_0, but as the perturbation increases, the energy begins to change quadratically. This linear-to-quadratic behavior is a common feature of perturbation theory and will be evident as we proceed. Our goal is to produce plots like Fig. 1(b) that demonstrate how energy levels shift when a perturbation is applied to a system.

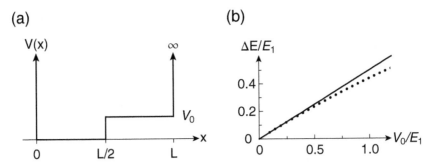

FIGURE 1   (a) Asymmetric square well and (b) energy shift of the ground state as a function of the perturbation V_0, where the points are from an exact calculation, and the straight line is from the perturbation calculation in Example 2.

1 ■ SPIN-1/2 EXAMPLE

To get a feel for what perturbation theory is and how it works, let's turn to an old standby—the spin-1/2 problem. The usual Hamiltonian of a spin-1/2 system is the potential energy of the spin magnetic moment in an applied magnetic field. For an applied magnetic field in the z-direction $\mathbf{B} = B_0\hat{\mathbf{z}}$, the Hamiltonian is

$$H_0 = -\boldsymbol{\mu}\cdot\mathbf{B} = \omega_0 S_z \doteq \frac{\hbar}{2}\begin{pmatrix} \omega_0 & 0 \\ 0 & -\omega_0 \end{pmatrix}, \tag{1}$$

where we have defined the Larmor frequency $\omega_0 = eB_0/m_e$. The subscript zero on the Hamiltonian in Eq. (1) indicates that this is the **zeroth-order** Hamiltonian (i.e., the Hamiltonian *before* we apply a perturbation). The energy eigenstates of the zeroth-order Hamiltonian are the spin up and down states $|\pm\rangle$ and the energy eigenvalues are

$$E_\pm^{(0)} = \pm\frac{\hbar\omega_0}{2}, \tag{2}$$

where the superscript zero on the energy (not an exponent) denotes the order of the solution. The energy spectrum of the zeroth-order energy eigenstates is shown in Fig. 2.

The goal of perturbation theory is to find the higher-order corrections to the energy eigenvalues and eigenstates caused by the application of a perturbation to the system. For this spin-1/2 system, we will solve the problem exactly and then expand the solutions to discover how perturbation series behave. Our exact solution should contain the zeroth-order solutions we already know [Eq. (2)] and small corrections.

The simplest way to perturb this spin system is to change the magnetic field. Any general change to the magnetic field can be decomposed into an additional component along the original field in the z-direction, and an additional component perpendicular to that, as shown in Fig. 3(a). We write the new total field as $\mathbf{B} = B_0\hat{\mathbf{z}} + B_1\hat{\mathbf{z}} + B_2\hat{\mathbf{x}}$ and characterize the two additional field components by their respective Larmor frequencies $\omega_1 = eB_1/m_e$ and $\omega_2 = eB_2/m_e$. With this notation, the new Hamiltonian is

$$H = -\boldsymbol{\mu}\cdot\mathbf{B} = \omega_0 S_z + \omega_1 S_z + \omega_2 S_x \doteq \frac{\hbar}{2}\begin{pmatrix} \omega_0+\omega_1 & \omega_2 \\ \omega_2 & -\omega_0-\omega_1 \end{pmatrix}. \tag{3}$$

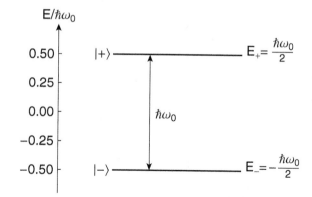

FIGURE 2 Energy levels of a spin-1/2 particle in a uniform magnetic field.

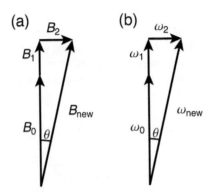

FIGURE 3   (a) Perturbing magnetic fields and (b) the resultant Larmor frequencies.

It is useful to separate the new Hamiltonian into the zeroth-order Hamiltonian H_0 and the perturbation Hamiltonian that we denote H':

$$H = H_0 + H'. \tag{4}$$

The zeroth-order Hamiltonian is given by Eq. (1) and the perturbation Hamiltonian is

$$H' \doteq \frac{\hbar}{2}\begin{pmatrix} \omega_1 & \omega_2 \\ \omega_2 & -\omega_1 \end{pmatrix}. \tag{5}$$

The perturbation Hamiltonian has terms along the diagonal and terms off the diagonal. These diagonal and off-diagonal terms play important roles in perturbation theory.

We now solve for the energy eigenvalues and eigenstates of the new Hamiltonian in Eq. (3) exactly by diagonalizing the matrix. But you may have already done this for a general spin-1/2 case of a magnetic field at an angle θ to the z-axis, where you found that the Hamiltonian is proportional to the spin component S_n along the new magnetic field direction $\hat{\mathbf{n}}$, and can be expressed in terms of the angle θ of the new field as

$$H = \omega_{new} S_n \doteq \frac{\hbar \omega_{new}}{2}\begin{pmatrix} \cos\theta & \sin\theta \\ \sin\theta & -\cos\theta \end{pmatrix}, \tag{6}$$

where

$$\tan\theta = \frac{\omega_2}{\omega_0 + \omega_1}, \tag{7}$$

as shown in Fig. 3 (b). The new Larmor frequency ω_{new} obeys the Pythagorean equation

$$\omega_{new} = \sqrt{(\omega_0 + \omega_1)^2 + \omega_2^2} \tag{8}$$

corresponding to the total field, as suggested by Fig. 3(b). The eigenstates of this new Hamiltonian are the spin states $\lvert \pm \rangle_n$ aligned along or against the new field and the eigenenergies are (Problem 1)

$$E_{new} = \pm\frac{\hbar}{2}\omega_{new} = \pm\frac{\hbar}{2}\sqrt{(\omega_0 + \omega_1)^2 + \omega_2^2}. \tag{9}$$

This is the exact solution, which we now expand in a power series.

The basic idea of perturbation theory is to assume that the new terms in the Hamiltonian are small compared to the original Hamiltonian, (i.e., the perturbation Hamiltonian H' is much smaller than the zeroth-order Hamiltonian H_0). In this spin-1/2 example, that would imply that the added fields B_1 and B_2 are small compared to the original field B_0, which means that the new Larmor frequencies ω_1 and ω_2 are small compared to the original Larmor frequency ω_0. Hence, we treat the ratios ω_1/ω_0 and ω_2/ω_0 of the new to old Larmor frequencies as small dimensionless parameters and rewrite the energy in Eq. (9) as

$$
\begin{aligned}
E_{new} &= \pm \frac{\hbar\omega_0}{2}\sqrt{\left(1 + \frac{\omega_1}{\omega_0}\right)^2 + \frac{\omega_2^2}{\omega_0^2}} \\
&= \pm \frac{\hbar\omega_0}{2}\sqrt{1 + \frac{2\omega_1}{\omega_0} + \frac{\omega_1^2}{\omega_0^2} + \frac{\omega_2^2}{\omega_0^2}}.
\end{aligned}
\tag{10}
$$

So far this is still the exact solution. Now we expand the exact energy to second order in a power series in the small parameters ω_1/ω_0 and ω_2/ω_0, so as to reach some general conclusions about perturbation theory:

$$
\begin{aligned}
E_{new} &= \pm \frac{\hbar\omega_0}{2}\left[1 + \frac{2\omega_1}{\omega_0} + \frac{\omega_1^2}{\omega_0^2} + \frac{\omega_2^2}{\omega_0^2}\right]^{1/2} \\
&= \pm \frac{\hbar\omega_0}{2}\left[1 + \frac{\omega_1}{\omega_0} + \frac{\omega_1^2}{2\omega_0^2} + \frac{\omega_2^2}{2\omega_0^2} - \frac{1}{8}\left(\frac{2\omega_1}{\omega_0} + \frac{\omega_1^2}{\omega_0^2} + \frac{\omega_2^2}{\omega_0^2}\right)^2 + ...\right] \\
&= \pm \frac{\hbar\omega_0}{2}\left[1 + \frac{\omega_1}{\omega_0} + \frac{\omega_1^2}{2\omega_0^2} + \frac{\omega_2^2}{2\omega_0^2} - \frac{\omega_1^2}{2\omega_0^2} + ...\right] \\
&\cong \pm \frac{\hbar\omega_0}{2}\left[1 + \frac{\omega_1}{\omega_0} + \frac{\omega_2^2}{2\omega_0^2}\right].
\end{aligned}
\tag{11}
$$

We now conclude that the two energies of the perturbed system, to second order in the small quantities characterizing the perturbation, are

$$
\begin{aligned}
E_+ &\cong +\frac{\hbar\omega_0}{2} + \frac{\hbar\omega_1}{2} + \frac{\hbar\omega_2^2}{4\omega_0} \\
E_- &\cong -\frac{\hbar\omega_0}{2} - \frac{\hbar\omega_1}{2} - \frac{\hbar\omega_2^2}{4\omega_0}.
\end{aligned}
\tag{12}
$$

In both energies, we identify the first term as the zeroth-order energy $E_\pm^{(0)}$ given by Eq. (2), and we note two additional terms. The first is linear or first order in the perturbation and is equal to the corresponding diagonal term $\pm\hbar\omega_1/2$ in the perturbation Hamiltonian [Eq. (5)]. The second additional term is quadratic or second order in the perturbation and is proportional to the square of the off-diagonal term $\hbar\omega_2/2$ in the perturbation Hamiltonian. This general pattern of corrections is characteristic of perturbation theory, so we denote perturbed energies as the series

$$
E_n = E_n^{(0)} + E_n^{(1)} + E_n^{(2)} + ...,
\tag{13}
$$

where the superscript indicates the order of the perturbation. We found in this spin-1/2 example that the linear corrections arose from the diagonal terms in the perturbation Hamiltonian and the quadratic terms arose from the off-diagonal terms, another characteristic pattern of general perturbation theory. In Eq. (12), the second-order energy correction due to the off-diagonal terms has a factor of ω_0 in the denominator, and it will diverge if the energy splitting $\hbar\omega_0$ is zero, (i.e., if the original levels are degenerate in energy). This divergence violates the assumption that the perturbation corrections are small, which creates a problem that we will address in Section 5.

In addition to these features of the perturbed energies, we can also draw some conclusions about the perturbation corrections to the eigenstates from our knowledge of the exact eigenstate solutions. The eigenstates of the full Hamiltonian in Eq. (6) are the spin up and down eigenstates $|\pm\rangle_n$ along the direction $\hat{\mathbf{n}}$:

$$|+\rangle_n = \cos\frac{\theta}{2}|+\rangle + \sin\frac{\theta}{2}|-\rangle$$

$$|-\rangle_n = -\sin\frac{\theta}{2}|+\rangle + \cos\frac{\theta}{2}|-\rangle. \tag{14}$$

From Fig. 3(a), it is evident that the angle θ is small for small perturbing magnetic fields, so we can also use θ as a small parameter for a series expansion:

$$|+\rangle_n \cong \left(1 - \frac{\theta^2}{8}\right)|+\rangle + \frac{\theta}{2}|-\rangle = |+\rangle + \frac{\theta}{2}|-\rangle - \frac{\theta^2}{8}|+\rangle$$

$$|-\rangle_n \cong -\frac{\theta}{2}|+\rangle + \left(1 - \frac{\theta^2}{8}\right)|-\rangle = |-\rangle - \frac{\theta}{2}|+\rangle - \frac{\theta^2}{8}|-\rangle. \tag{15}$$

To second order in the angle θ, the new eigenstates have two correction terms: a first-order term that is orthogonal to the original state, and a second-order term that is parallel (in a Hilbert space sense, not a geometric sense) to the original state. If we neglect the parallel terms (we'll see in Section 3.2 why we do this), we get:

$$|+\rangle_n \cong |+\rangle + \frac{\theta}{2}|-\rangle$$

$$|-\rangle_n \cong |-\rangle - \frac{\theta}{2}|+\rangle. \tag{16}$$

Using the schematic in Fig. 3(b), we express the small angle θ in terms of the Larmor frequencies. To first order [consistent with neglecting the second-order parallel terms in Eq. (15)], we obtain

$$\theta \cong \frac{\omega_2}{\sqrt{(\omega_0 + \omega_1)^2 + \omega_2^2}} \cong \frac{\omega_2}{\omega_0}. \tag{17}$$

Thus, we arrive at the perturbation series expansion for the perturbed states, to first order

$$|+\rangle_n \cong |+\rangle + \frac{\omega_2}{2\omega_0}|-\rangle$$

$$|-\rangle_n \cong |-\rangle - \frac{\omega_2}{2\omega_0}|+\rangle. \tag{18}$$

We conclude that the first-order eigenstate correction depends only on the off-diagonal matrix element, not on the diagonal elements. Note that the coefficient of the original state remains one, which makes it appear that the state is no longer normalized. But if we check the normalization of the perturbed state:

$$\begin{aligned}
_n\langle + | + \rangle_n &= \left[\langle + | + \frac{\omega_2}{2\omega_0} \langle - | \right]\left[| + \rangle + \frac{\omega_2}{2\omega_0} | - \rangle \right] \\
&= 1 + \left(\frac{\omega_2}{2\omega_0} \right)^2 \\
&\cong 1,
\end{aligned} \tag{19}$$

we see that it is normalized to first order in the small perturbation parameters.

2 ■ GENERAL TWO-LEVEL EXAMPLE

Continuing our introduction to perturbation theory, we consider a general two-level system that we solve exactly to learn how the solutions depend on the perturbation and to practice the notation we will use later. This example repeats the calculation of Section 1 with general notation rather than considering a specific physical system. At each step in this section, refer back to Section 1 to identify what each term is in the specific case of a perturbing magnetic field applied to a spin-1/2 system.

In the general two-level case, we assume a zeroth-order Hamiltonian of the form

$$H_0 \doteq \begin{pmatrix} E_1^{(0)} & 0 \\ 0 & E_2^{(0)} \end{pmatrix} \tag{20}$$

and a general perturbation

$$H' \doteq \begin{pmatrix} H'_{11} & H'_{12} \\ H'_{21} & H'_{22} \end{pmatrix}, \tag{21}$$

where the matrix elements of the perturbation Hamiltonian are written as

$$H'_{ij} = \langle i^{(0)} | H' | j^{(0)} \rangle. \tag{22}$$

Note that we use the energy eigenvectors of the zeroth-order Hamiltonian as the basis vectors for matrix representation of the operators. It is useful to parameterize the strength of the perturbation with a dimensionless quantity λ that allows us to keep track of the order of the perturbation in a power series solution (note that this λ is not the λ we often use as a placeholder when finding eigenvalues). In the end we will set λ equal to one, so it is used solely to keep track of the different orders in the power series. Using this parameter, the full Hamiltonian is

$$H = H_0 + \lambda H' \doteq \begin{pmatrix} E_1^{(0)} + \lambda H'_{11} & \lambda H'_{12} \\ \lambda H'_{21} & E_2^{(0)} + \lambda H'_{22} \end{pmatrix}. \tag{23}$$

Now let's find the exact eigenvalues of this Hamiltonian. To reduce the clutter in the algebra, redefine the matrix values:

$$\begin{pmatrix} E_1^{(0)} + \lambda H'_{11} & \lambda H'_{12} \\ \lambda H'_{21} & E_2^{(0)} + \lambda H'_{22} \end{pmatrix} \equiv \begin{pmatrix} a & c \\ c^* & b \end{pmatrix}, \tag{24}$$

noting that because H' is Hermitian, $H'_{12} = H'_{21}{}^*$. Using the symbol E for the energy eigenvalue, we diagonalize the Hamiltonian by finding the characteristic equation:

$$\begin{vmatrix} a - E & c \\ c^* & b - E \end{vmatrix} = 0$$

$$(a - E)(b - E) - |c|^2 = 0 \qquad (25)$$

$$E^2 - E(a + b) + ab - |c|^2 = 0$$

and solving to obtain

$$E = \tfrac{1}{2}(a + b) \pm \sqrt{\tfrac{1}{4}(a + b)^2 - ab + |c|^2}$$

$$= \tfrac{1}{2}(a + b) \pm \sqrt{\tfrac{1}{4}(a - b)^2 + |c|^2}. \qquad (26)$$

We are considering the case where the perturbation is small [i.e., $c \ll (a - b)$], so we factor and use the binomial expansion:

$$E = \tfrac{1}{2}(a + b) \pm \tfrac{1}{2}(a - b)\left[1 + \frac{4|c|^2}{(a - b)^2}\right]^{\frac{1}{2}}$$

$$\cong \tfrac{1}{2}(a + b) \pm \tfrac{1}{2}(a - b)\left[1 + \frac{2|c|^2}{(a - b)^2}\right]. \qquad (27)$$

This yields the two energies

$$E_1 \cong a + \frac{|c|^2}{(a - b)}$$

$$E_2 \cong b - \frac{|c|^2}{(a - b)}. \qquad (28)$$

Now rewrite these solutions in terms of the original parameters

$$E_1 = E_1^{(0)} + \lambda H'_{11} + \frac{\lambda^2 |H'_{12}|^2}{\left(E_1^{(0)} + \lambda H'_{11} - E_2^{(0)} - \lambda H'_{22}\right)}$$

$$E_2 = E_2^{(0)} + \lambda H'_{22} - \frac{\lambda^2 |H'_{12}|^2}{\left(E_1^{(0)} + \lambda H'_{11} - E_2^{(0)} - \lambda H'_{22}\right)} \qquad (29)$$

and expand Eq. (29) to second order in the expansion parameter λ:

$$E_1 \cong E_1^{(0)} + \lambda H'_{11} + \frac{\lambda^2 |H'_{12}|^2}{\left(E_1^{(0)} - E_2^{(0)}\right)}$$

$$E_2 \cong E_2^{(0)} + \lambda H'_{22} + \frac{\lambda^2 |H'_{21}|^2}{\left(E_2^{(0)} - E_1^{(0)}\right)}, \qquad (30)$$

where we have written the results in a way to make it clear that the two energies have the same form (they are equivalent if we swap indices $1 \leftrightarrow 2$). We have left the expansion parameter in for now to make the order of the expansion clear, but imagine it set to unity, as we will do later. The general conclusion is that an energy level E_n has a first-order correction that is the matrix element H'_{nn} of the perturbation in the state in question and a second-order correction that depends on the square of the coupling H'_{nk} to other states and inversely on the energy difference $E_n^{(0)} - E_k^{(0)}$ between states. This is the same form that we saw in the spin example above and also what we will see as we develop perturbation theory in general. Note again that degeneracy of the two states ($E_n^{(0)} - E_k^{(0)} = 0$) creates problems. For this reason we will study nondegenerate and degenerate perturbation theories separately.

3 ■ NONDEGENERATE PERTURBATION THEORY

In the examples above, we solved the problems exactly, even the "perturbed problems," to find the new energy eigenvalues and eigenstates, and then we approximated these exact solutions to draw some conclusions about the general behavior of perturbed energies and states. Now we tackle perturbed problems that are not exactly solvable, but we assume that the nonperturbed part of the problem is exactly solvable. The exactly solvable part of the problem is called the zeroth-order problem and has an energy eigenvalue equation

$$H_0 \left| n^{(0)} \right\rangle = E_n^{(0)} \left| n^{(0)} \right\rangle,\tag{31}$$

where we use a subscript on the energy to denote the quantum number and superscripts (not powers) on the energy and eigenstates to denote the order of the solution. Now suppose that this system is perturbed by the addition of a new term in the Hamiltonian that we call H'. The new perturbed problem has an energy eigenvalue equation

$$(H_0 + H') \left| n \right\rangle = E_n \left| n \right\rangle,\tag{32}$$

where E_n are the new energies and $\left| n \right\rangle$ are the new eigenstates that we seek. As discussed in the previous section, we parameterize the strength of the perturbation with a dimensionless quantity λ and rewrite the energy eigenvalue equation as

$$(H_0 + \lambda H') \left| n \right\rangle = E_n \left| n \right\rangle.\tag{33}$$

The λ parameter allows us to keep track of the order of the perturbation in a power series solution. In the end we set it equal to one, so it is here solely to keep track of the different orders in the power series.

The essence of the perturbation technique is to assume that we can write the new eigenvalues and eigenstates as power series expansions with ever-decreasing terms such that the series converge. There are some important examples where this does *not* work (e.g., superconductivity and quantum chromodynamics), but it does work in many cases. We use the dimensionless parameter λ as the expansion parameter and write the desired eigenvalues and eigenstates as

$$E_n = E_n^{(0)} + \lambda E_n^{(1)} + \lambda^2 E_n^{(2)} + \lambda^3 E_n^{(3)} + \dots$$
$$\left| n \right\rangle = \left| n^{(0)} \right\rangle + \lambda \left| n^{(1)} \right\rangle + \lambda^2 \left| n^{(2)} \right\rangle + \lambda^3 \left| n^{(3)} \right\rangle + \dots.\tag{34}$$

To find the new solutions, substitute these series into the eigenvalue equation Eq. (33) and collect terms of the same order or power of the parameter λ on each side of the equation. For the eigenvalue equation to hold for any value of λ, the coefficients of like orders on the two sides of the equation must be equal, and we can isolate an equation for each order in the expansion parameter. The result is the following set of equations: (Problem 2)

$$O\left(\lambda^0\right): \quad \left(H_0 - E_n^{(0)}\right)\left|n^{(0)}\right\rangle = 0 \tag{35}$$

$$O\left(\lambda^1\right): \quad \left(H_0 - E_n^{(0)}\right)\left|n^{(1)}\right\rangle = \left(E_n^{(1)} - H'\right)\left|n^{(0)}\right\rangle \tag{36}$$

$$O\left(\lambda^2\right): \quad \left(H_0 - E_n^{(0)}\right)\left|n^{(2)}\right\rangle = \left(E_n^{(1)} - H'\right)\left|n^{(1)}\right\rangle + E_n^{(2)}\left|n^{(0)}\right\rangle \tag{37}$$

$$O\left(\lambda^3\right): \quad \left(H_0 - E_n^{(0)}\right)\left|n^{(3)}\right\rangle = \left(E_n^{(1)} - H'\right)\left|n^{(2)}\right\rangle + E_n^{(2)}\left|n^{(1)}\right\rangle + E_n^{(3)}\left|n^{(0)}\right\rangle \tag{38}$$

and so on. At this point, the parameter λ has done its work and is not needed any more.

Equation (35) is zeroth order in the expansion parameter and is simply the original eigenvalue equation [Eq. (31)]. That's why it's called the zeroth-order equation. We assume that the zeroth-order energies $E_n^{(0)}$ and the zeroth order eigenstates $\left|n^{(0)}\right\rangle$ have been solved for and are known.

3.1 ■ First-Order Energy Correction

Equation (36) is the first-order equation and contains the first-order corrections $E_n^{(1)}$ and $\left|n^{(1)}\right\rangle$ to the eigenvalues and eigenstates, respectively, as unknowns. For a system with N energy levels (i.e., N is the dimension of the Hilbert space), Eq. (36) represents N equations for $n = 1, 2, ... N$ to be solved for each energy and each eigenstate. Moreover, for any given n, Eq. (36) is really a system of N equations because the Hamiltonian operators are represented by $N \times N$ matrices. To see our way through this morass of N^2 equations, it is helpful to examine the full matrix representation of Eq. (36) for one particular choice of n and then generalize from that result.

Of course, to use matrices, we must choose a basis for representation. Given that we have solved only the zeroth-order problem at this stage, the basis of zeroth-order energy eigenstates $\left|n^{(0)}\right\rangle$ is the most obvious basis at our disposal. So, we express each part of Eq. (36) in this basis. The matrices representing the Hamiltonians H_0 and H' do not depend on the choice of the state n and are

$$H_0 \doteq \begin{pmatrix} E_1^{(0)} & 0 & 0 & 0 & \cdots \\ 0 & E_2^{(0)} & 0 & 0 & \cdots \\ 0 & 0 & E_3^{(0)} & 0 & \cdots \\ 0 & 0 & 0 & E_4^{(0)} & \cdots \\ \vdots & \vdots & \vdots & \vdots & \ddots \end{pmatrix}$$

$$H' \doteq \begin{pmatrix} H'_{11} & H'_{12} & H'_{13} & H'_{14} & \cdots \\ H'_{21} & H'_{22} & H'_{23} & H'_{24} & \cdots \\ H'_{31} & H'_{32} & H'_{33} & H'_{34} & \cdots \\ H'_{41} & H'_{42} & H'_{43} & H'_{44} & \cdots \\ \vdots & \vdots & \vdots & \vdots & \ddots \end{pmatrix}, \tag{39}$$

where the matrix elements of the perturbation Hamiltonian are defined in the zeroth-order basis

$$H'_{ij} = \left\langle i^{(0)}\left|H'\right|j^{(0)}\right\rangle. \tag{40}$$

All of the elements of these two matrices are known quantities.

The other terms in Eq. (36) do depend on the choice of the state n. Let's choose $n = 3$ for this example, which means that the zeroth-order energy eigenstate $\left|3^{(0)}\right\rangle$ is

$$\left|3^{(0)}\right\rangle \doteq \begin{pmatrix} 0 \\ 0 \\ 1 \\ 0 \\ \vdots \end{pmatrix}. \tag{41}$$

The first-order correction to the eigenstate $\left|3^{(1)}\right\rangle$ is not yet known, and we characterize it in terms of a set of yet-to-be-found first-order coefficients $c_{3m}^{(1)} = \left\langle m^{(0)} \middle| 3^{(1)} \right\rangle$ in the zeroth-order basis

$$\left|3^{(1)}\right\rangle \doteq \begin{pmatrix} c_{31}^{(1)} \\ c_{32}^{(1)} \\ c_{33}^{(1)} \\ c_{34}^{(1)} \\ \vdots \end{pmatrix}. \tag{42}$$

The other two ingredients in Eq. (36) are the known zeroth-order energy $E_3^{(0)}$ and the unknown first-order energy correction $E_3^{(1)}$. We are now ready to construct the matrix form of Eq. (36) and solve for the unknowns for this choice of n: the first-order energy correction $E_3^{(1)}$ and the set of coefficients $c_{3m}^{(1)}$ that determine the first-order correction $\left|3^{(1)}\right\rangle$ to the eigenstate.

For the choice $n = 3$, the left-hand side of Eq. (36) is

$$\left(H_0 - E_3^{(0)}\right)\left|3^{(1)}\right\rangle \doteq \begin{pmatrix} E_1^{(0)} - E_3^{(0)} & 0 & 0 & 0 & \cdots \\ 0 & E_2^{(0)} - E_3^{(0)} & 0 & 0 & \cdots \\ 0 & 0 & \boxed{0} & 0 & \cdots \\ 0 & 0 & 0 & E_4^{(0)} - E_3^{(0)} & \cdots \\ \vdots & \vdots & \vdots & \vdots & \ddots \end{pmatrix} \begin{pmatrix} c_{31}^{(1)} \\ c_{32}^{(1)} \\ c_{33}^{(1)} \\ c_{34}^{(1)} \\ \vdots \end{pmatrix}$$

$$\doteq \begin{pmatrix} \left(E_1^{(0)} - E_3^{(0)}\right)c_{31}^{(1)} \\ \left(E_2^{(0)} - E_3^{(0)}\right)c_{32}^{(1)} \\ \boxed{0} \\ \left(E_4^{(0)} - E_3^{(0)}\right)c_{34}^{(1)} \\ \vdots \end{pmatrix}. \tag{43}$$

In the matrix and the resultant vector, we have boxed the zero element that arises from subtracting the zeroth-order energy $E_3^{(0)}$ from the zeroth-order Hamiltonian in order to highlight the importance of that element in the solution. The right-hand side of Eq. (36) is

$$
\left(E_3^{(1)} - H'\right)|3^{(0)}\rangle \doteq \begin{pmatrix} E_3^{(1)} - H'_{11} & -H'_{12} & -H'_{13} & -H'_{14} & \cdots \\ -H'_{21} & E_3^{(1)} - H'_{22} & -H'_{23} & -H'_{24} & \cdots \\ -H'_{31} & -H'_{32} & \boxed{E_3^{(1)} - H'_{33}} & -H'_{34} & \cdots \\ -H'_{41} & -H'_{42} & -H'_{43} & E_3^{(1)} - H'_{44} & \cdots \\ \vdots & \vdots & \vdots & \vdots & \ddots \end{pmatrix} \begin{pmatrix} 0 \\ 0 \\ 1 \\ 0 \\ \vdots \end{pmatrix}
$$

$$
\doteq \begin{pmatrix} -H'_{13} \\ -H'_{23} \\ \boxed{E_3^{(1)} - H'_{33}} \\ -H'_{43} \\ \vdots \end{pmatrix}.
$$

(44)

Again we have boxed in the diagonal matrix element and the resultant vector component corresponding to the state $|3^{(0)}\rangle$ that we are solving for. Equating the two sides of Eq. (36) gives

$$
\begin{pmatrix} \left(E_1^{(0)} - E_3^{(0)}\right)c_{31}^{(1)} \\ \left(E_2^{(0)} - E_3^{(0)}\right)c_{32}^{(1)} \\ \boxed{0} \\ \left(E_4^{(0)} - E_3^{(0)}\right)c_{34}^{(1)} \\ \vdots \end{pmatrix} = \begin{pmatrix} -H'_{13} \\ -H'_{23} \\ \boxed{E_3^{(1)} - H'_{33}} \\ -H'_{43} \\ \vdots \end{pmatrix}.
$$

(45)

As promised, we have N equations containing the unknown energy correction $E_3^{(1)}$ and the unknown eigenstate correction $|3^{(1)}\rangle$ represented by the coefficients $c_{3m}^{(1)}$. The third row of Eq. (45), which we have been highlighting all along, yields the solution for the first-order energy correction to the $n = 3$ state

$$
E_3^{(1)} - H'_{33} = 0
$$

$$
E_3^{(1)} = H'_{33}.
$$

(46)

We conclude that the first-order energy correction is the diagonal matrix element of the perturbation for the state in question, which agrees with the results in Sections 1 and 2. The diagonal matrix element of the perturbation is also what we call the expectation value of the perturbation. Note that no other states affect the energy correction of this state and the unperturbed states are used to find the expectation value of the perturbation; *there is no need to know the correction to the state in order to find the first-order correction to the energy.* Having solved the first-order perturbation equation for this specific case of $n = 3$, we can now infer the result for the general n. The general result of nondegenerate first-order perturbation theory is:

$$\boxed{E_n^{(1)} = H'_{nm} = \left\langle n^{(0)} \middle| H' \middle| n^{(0)} \right\rangle}. \tag{47}$$

The first-order correction to the energy is the expectation value of the perturbation in the unperturbed state. In wave function notation, the expectation value is expressed as an integral

$$\boxed{E_n^{(1)} = H'_{nn} = \int \varphi_n^{(0)*}(\mathbf{r}) H' \varphi_n^{(0)}(\mathbf{r}) dV}, \tag{48}$$

where $\varphi_n^{(0)}(\mathbf{r})$ are the energy eigenstates of the zeroth-order Hamiltonian.

That's the result. Now let's use it.

Example 1 The sodium nucleus has spin 3/2 and a magnetic moment $\boldsymbol{\mu}_{Na} = (g_{Na}e/2m_p)\mathbf{S}$, where the gyromagnetic ratio is $g_{Na} = 1.48$. The sodium nucleus is placed in a constant magnetic field in the z-direction $\mathbf{B}_0 = B_0\hat{\mathbf{z}}$. An additional, perturbative magnetic field $\mathbf{B}' = B_1\hat{\mathbf{z}}$ is applied to the system. Find the first-order energy shifts due to the perturbation.

This problem is a variation on the spin-1/2 example in Section 1. The zeroth-order Hamiltonian H_0 is determined by the potential energy of the nuclear magnetic moment in the constant field $\mathbf{B}_0 = B_0\hat{\mathbf{z}}$:

$$H_0 = -\boldsymbol{\mu} \cdot \mathbf{B}_0 = \omega_0 S_z \doteq \begin{pmatrix} \frac{3}{2}\hbar\omega_0 & 0 & 0 & 0 \\ 0 & \frac{1}{2}\hbar\omega_0 & 0 & 0 \\ 0 & 0 & -\frac{1}{2}\hbar\omega_0 & 0 \\ 0 & 0 & 0 & -\frac{3}{2}\hbar\omega_0 \end{pmatrix}, \tag{49}$$

where we have defined the Larmor frequency $\omega_0 = g_{Na}eB_0/2m_p$. The zeroth-order energies are $E_1^{(0)} = \frac{3}{2}\hbar\omega_0$, $E_2^{(0)} = \frac{1}{2}\hbar\omega_0$, $E_3^{(0)} = -\frac{1}{2}\hbar\omega_0$, and $E_4^{(0)} = -\frac{3}{2}\hbar\omega_0$, labeled in order of decreasing energy. The zeroth-order energy eigenstates are the eigenstates of the spin component operator S_z: $\left|1^{(0)}\right\rangle = \left|\frac{3}{2}\right\rangle$, $\left|2^{(0)}\right\rangle = \left|\frac{1}{2}\right\rangle$, $\left|3^{(0)}\right\rangle = \left|\frac{-1}{2}\right\rangle$, and $\left|4^{(0)}\right\rangle = \left|\frac{-3}{2}\right\rangle$, which are labeled with the magnetic quantum number m.

The perturbation Hamiltonian H' is determined by the field $\mathbf{B}' = B_1\hat{\mathbf{z}}$ and is characterized by a different Larmor frequency $\omega_1 = g_{Na}eB_1/2m_p$:

$$H' = -\boldsymbol{\mu} \cdot \mathbf{B}' = \omega_1 S_z \doteq \begin{pmatrix} \frac{3}{2}\hbar\omega_1 & 0 & 0 & 0 \\ 0 & \frac{1}{2}\hbar\omega_1 & 0 & 0 \\ 0 & 0 & -\frac{1}{2}\hbar\omega_1 & 0 \\ 0 & 0 & 0 & -\frac{3}{2}\hbar\omega_1 \end{pmatrix}. \tag{50}$$

So far, all these are quantities known from the statement of the problem. Perturbation theory tells us that the first-order correction to the energy is the expectation value of the perturbation in the unperturbed state:

$$E_n^{(1)} = H'_{nn} = \left\langle n^{(0)} \middle| H' \middle| n^{(0)} \right\rangle. \tag{51}$$

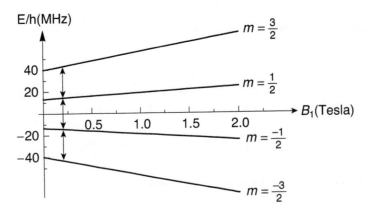

FIGURE 4 First-order corrected energies of a sodium nucleus in a perturbing magnetic field that is parallel to the constant zeroth-order field.

These are the diagonal elements of the matrix representing H' in the basis of zeroth-order energy eigenstates. The matrix in Eq. (50) thus yields the first-order energy shifts due to the perturbation:

$$
\begin{aligned}
E_1^{(1)} &= \tfrac{3}{2}\hbar\omega_1 \\
E_2^{(1)} &= \tfrac{1}{2}\hbar\omega_1 \\
E_3^{(1)} &= -\tfrac{1}{2}\hbar\omega_1 \\
E_4^{(1)} &= -\tfrac{3}{2}\hbar\omega_1.
\end{aligned}
\tag{52}
$$

These energy shifts add to the zeroth-order energies to produce the results shown in Fig. 4 as a function of the perturbing field. The new energies exhibit the linear dependence we expect for first-order corrections. The constant B_0 field is assumed to be 2.35 Tesla, which is a standard field in nuclear magnetic resonance spectroscopy because it produces a 100 MHz resonance for hydrogen nuclei. For sodium nuclei, the resonance in this field is 26.5 MHz ($\omega_0/2\pi$), indicated by the transition arrows in Fig. 4. As the perturbing field increases, the resonance shifts in frequency. When the perturbing field is produced by the local chemical environment of the nucleus, the resonance shift is called a **chemical shift**. This technique is commonly used to identify chemical microstructure.

3.2 ■ First-Order State Vector Correction

Now that we have the first-order energy correction, we proceed to find the first-order correction to the energy eigenstates. The other rows (nonhighlighted) of Eq. (45) yield equations of identical form for the coefficients $c_{3m}^{(1)}$ that determine the first-order correction to the state vector:

$$
\begin{aligned}
\left(E_m^{(0)} - E_3^{(0)}\right)c_{3m}^{(1)} &= -H_{m3}', \qquad m \neq 3 \\
c_{3m}^{(1)} &= \frac{H_{m3}'}{E_3^{(0)} - E_m^{(0)}}, \qquad m \neq 3.
\end{aligned}
\tag{53}
$$

Equation (53) determines all the coefficients for $m \neq 3$; however, there is no information about the coefficient $c_{33}^{(1)}$. This is not surprising. In solving energy eigenvalue equations before, we have always found that one eigenstate coefficient is undetermined by the equations. In those problems, we used the normalization requirement to determine the last coefficient. We do the same here.

Using Eq. (34) (with $\lambda = 1$) and Eq. (42), we write the corrected eigenstate to first order as

$$\begin{aligned}
|3\rangle &= \left|3^{(0)}\right\rangle + \left|3^{(1)}\right\rangle \\
&= \left|3^{(0)}\right\rangle + \sum_{m=1}^{N} c_{3m}^{(1)}\left|m^{(0)}\right\rangle .
\end{aligned} \tag{54}$$

Separating out the undetermined coefficient $c_{33}^{(1)}$, we obtain

$$\begin{aligned}
|3\rangle &= \left|3^{(0)}\right\rangle + c_{33}^{(1)}\left|3^{(0)}\right\rangle + \sum_{m \neq 3} c_{3m}^{(1)}\left|m^{(0)}\right\rangle \\
&= \left(1 + c_{33}^{(1)}\right)\left|3^{(0)}\right\rangle + \sum_{m \neq 3} c_{3m}^{(1)}\left|m^{(0)}\right\rangle .
\end{aligned} \tag{55}$$

Now normalize this state to determine $c_{33}^{(1)}$ [all the other coefficients are already specified by Eq. (53)]

$$\begin{aligned}
\langle 3|3\rangle &= \left\{\left(1 + c_{33}^{(1)*}\right)\left\langle 3^{(0)}\right| + \sum_{k \neq 3} c_{3k}^{(1)*}\left\langle k^{(0)}\right|\right\}\left\{\left(1 + c_{33}^{(1)}\right)\left|3^{(0)}\right\rangle + \sum_{m \neq 3} c_{3m}^{(1)}\left|m^{(0)}\right\rangle\right\} \\
&= \left(1 + c_{33}^{(1)*}\right)\left(1 + c_{33}^{(1)}\right) + \sum_{m \neq 3}\left|c_{3m}^{(1)}\right|^2 \\
&= 1 + c_{33}^{(1)} + c_{33}^{(1)*} + \left|c_{33}^{(1)}\right|^2 + \sum_{m \neq 3}\left|c_{3m}^{(1)}\right|^2 ,
\end{aligned} \tag{56}$$

where we used the orthogonality $\left\langle k^{(0)}|m^{(0)}\right\rangle = \delta_{km}$ of the zeroth-order states. We are working in the first-order perturbation approximation, so we must drop the second-order terms in the normalization equation for consistency, giving

$$\langle 3|3\rangle = 1 + c_{33}^{(1)} + c_{33}^{(1)*} . \tag{57}$$

Using our freedom to choose the overall phase of the state vector, we choose $c_{33}^{(1)}$ to be real and conclude that

$$c_{33}^{(1)} = 0 . \tag{58}$$

Hence, there is no component of the zeroth-order eigenstate $\left|3^{(0)}\right\rangle$ in the first-order eigenstate correction $\left|3^{(1)}\right\rangle$, which is the same conclusion we reached in the spin example in Eq. (15). This conclusion can be understood with an analogy between quantum state vectors and spatial vectors. Because all quantum state vectors must be normalized (in order to interpret the projections as probability amplitudes), all that really matters about a quantum state vector is its direction. Thus, as we look for changes in the vector, we must focus only on changes in direction. Figure 5 shows an analogy with spatial vectors, whereby we see that for small changes in direction, the change can be considered to be perpendicular to the original vector, and hence have no component along the original vector.

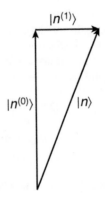

FIGURE 5 Perturbed state corrections are orthogonal to the original state.

For this $n = 3$ state, the first-order eigenstate correction is

$$|3^{(1)}\rangle \doteq \begin{pmatrix} \dfrac{H'_{13}}{E_3^{(0)} - E_1^{(0)}} \\[2ex] \dfrac{H'_{23}}{E_3^{(0)} - E_2^{(0)}} \\[2ex] 0 \\[2ex] \dfrac{H'_{43}}{E_3^{(0)} - E_4^{(0)}} \\ \vdots \end{pmatrix}, \tag{59}$$

and the corrected eigenstate to first order is

$$|3\rangle = |3^{(0)}\rangle + |3^{(1)}\rangle \doteq \begin{pmatrix} \dfrac{H'_{13}}{E_3^{(0)} - E_1^{(0)}} \\[2ex] \dfrac{H'_{23}}{E_3^{(0)} - E_2^{(0)}} \\[2ex] 1 \\[2ex] \dfrac{H'_{43}}{E_3^{(0)} - E_4^{(0)}} \\ \vdots \end{pmatrix}. \tag{60}$$

For the perturbation approach to be valid, we must have the new correction terms be small, which implies that the matrix elements of the perturbation Hamiltonian are smaller than the unperturbed energy *differences*. The absolute energies are not important because we can always shift the energy axis.

For a general state, the coefficients for the eigenstate correction in Eqs. (53) and (58) generalize to

$$c_{nm}^{(1)} = \frac{H'_{mn}}{E_n^{(0)} - E_m^{(0)}}; \qquad m \neq n$$

$$c_{nn}^{(1)} = 0. \tag{61}$$

We conclude that the first-order correction to the eigenstate is

$$\boxed{\left| n^{(1)} \right\rangle = \sum_{m \neq n} \frac{\left\langle m^{(0)} \middle| H' \middle| n^{(0)} \right\rangle}{\left(E_n^{(0)} - E_m^{(0)} \right)} \left| m^{(0)} \right\rangle}. \tag{62}$$

Note that the expansion coefficients $c_{nm}^{(1)}$ do not enter into the solution for the energy correction. This feature is true in general for perturbation theory. We need the eigenstate correction only when solving for the next order of the energy correction.

To illustrate the perturbation theory approach in the general case, let's repeat the matrix calculation we have just completed using Dirac bra-ket notation for the first-order energy correction. We start with the first-order equation:

$$\left(H_0 - E_n^{(0)} \right) \left| n^{(1)} \right\rangle = \left(E_n^{(1)} - H' \right) \left| n^{(0)} \right\rangle. \tag{63}$$

We saw in Eq. (45) that the solution for the energy correction came from isolating the row for the state of interest. In bra-ket notation, that means that we want to project Eq. (63) onto the zeroth-order n^{th} eigenstate (as a bra):

$$\left\langle n^{(0)} \middle| \left(H_0 - E_n^{(0)} \right) \middle| n^{(1)} \right\rangle = \left\langle n^{(0)} \middle| \left(E_n^{(1)} - H' \right) \middle| n^{(0)} \right\rangle. \tag{64}$$

The Hamiltonian H_0 is Hermitian, so it can act backwards on the bra $\left\langle n^{(0)} \right|$ and give the energy $\left(\left\langle n^{(0)} \middle| H_0 = \left\langle n^{(0)} \middle| E_n^{(0)} \right. \right)$, yielding zero on the left-hand side:

$$\left\langle n^{(0)} \middle| \left(E_n^{(0)} - E_n^{(0)} \right) \middle| n^{(1)} \right\rangle = E_n^{(1)} \left\langle n^{(0)} \middle| n^{(0)} \right\rangle - \left\langle n^{(0)} \middle| H' \middle| n^{(0)} \right\rangle$$

$$0 = E_n^{(1)} \left\langle n^{(0)} \middle| n^{(0)} \right\rangle - \left\langle n^{(0)} \middle| H' \middle| n^{(0)} \right\rangle. \tag{65}$$

Solving for the energy correction gives

$$E_n^{(1)} = \left\langle n^{(0)} \middle| H' \middle| n^{(0)} \right\rangle, \tag{66}$$

which is the same as we obtained with the matrix approach above.

In summary, the new energy eigenvalues and eigenstates to first order in the perturbation are

$$\boxed{\begin{aligned} E_n &= E_n^{(0)} + \left\langle n^{(0)} \middle| H' \middle| n^{(0)} \right\rangle \\ \left| n \right\rangle &= \left| n^{(0)} \right\rangle + \sum_{m \neq n} \frac{\left\langle m^{(0)} \middle| H' \middle| n^{(0)} \right\rangle}{\left(E_n^{(0)} - E_m^{(0)} \right)} \left| m^{(0)} \right\rangle}. \end{aligned}} \tag{67}$$

The eigenvalue and eigenstate corrections are independent of each other at this order. The corrections at this order will affect the corrections at the next order—the first-order eigenstate corrections lead to second-order eigenvalue corrections, etc. The matrix elements of the perturbation Hamiltonian must be smaller than the unperturbed energy differences for the perturbation approach to be valid.

Example 2 An infinite square well, shown in Fig. 6(a), is perturbed by an additional potential energy term, with the resultant well shown in Fig. 6(b). Find the first-order corrections to the energies.

Consider the zeroth-order Hamiltonian for the infinite square well. The zeroth-order eigenvalues and eigenstates are

$$E_n^{(0)} = n^2 \frac{\pi^2 \hbar^2}{2mL^2}$$

$$|n^{(0)}\rangle \doteq \varphi_n^{(0)}(x) = \sqrt{\frac{2}{L}} \sin\left(\frac{n\pi x}{L}\right).$$

$$(68)$$

In the perturbed case, a potential energy shelf of value V_0 is added to the right half of the well. This is an asymmetric square well problem. Now we solve it using our new perturbation theory tools and compare to the exact result. The shift in energy to first order is the expectation value of the perturbation Hamiltonian in the unperturbed eigenstates:

$$E_n^{(1)} = \langle n^{(0)} | H' | n^{(0)} \rangle.$$

$$(69)$$

The perturbation Hamiltonian $H' = V(x)$ has spatial dependence in this problem, and we must use the wave function form of the first-order energy correction in Eq. (48) involving a spatial integral—we cannot simply use bra-ket notation. More formally, we do not know how this new perturbation acts on kets. The first-order energy correction is

$$E_n^{(1)} = \int_{-\infty}^{\infty} \varphi_n^{(0)*}(x) V(x) \varphi_n^{(0)}(x) dx.$$

$$(70)$$

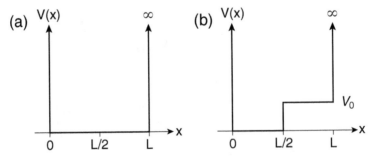

FIGURE 6 (a) An infinite square potential energy well perturbed by (b) a potential energy shelf in the right half of the well.

The perturbation is different in the two halves of the well, so we break the integral into two pieces, with the perturbation Hamiltonian equal to zero in the left half and V_0 in the right half:

$$
\begin{aligned}
E_n^{(1)} &= \int_0^{L/2} \varphi_n^{(0)*}(x)\, 0\, \varphi_n^{(0)}(x)dx + \int_{L/2}^{L} \varphi_n^{(0)*}(x) V_0 \varphi_n^{(0)}(x)dx \\
&= V_0 \int_{L/2}^{L} \left|\varphi_n^{(0)}(x)\right|^2 dx.
\end{aligned}
\tag{71}
$$

The remaining spatial integral is the integral of the probability density over the right half of the well. All the energy eigenstate probability densities are symmetric about the middle of the well, so the integral is 1/2, yielding (Problem 4)

$$
E_n^{(1)} = \frac{V_0}{2}
\tag{72}
$$

for all states. This is the result we included as the perturbation theory prediction of the ground state energy in Fig. 1, which shows that the first-order perturbation correction is not exact. This perturbation involves higher-order terms because the off-diagonal matrix elements are not zero, leading to eigenstate corrections [Eq. (62)] (Problem 5), which lead to second-order eigenvalue corrections as we'll see in the next section.

4 ■ SECOND-ORDER NONDEGENERATE PERTURBATION THEORY

Now let's proceed and find the second-order energy correction in nondegenerate perturbation theory. The second-order perturbation equation (37) is

$$
\left(H_0 - E_n^{(0)}\right)\left|n^{(2)}\right\rangle = \left(E_n^{(1)} - H'\right)\left|n^{(1)}\right\rangle + E_n^{(2)}\left|n^{(0)}\right\rangle.
\tag{73}
$$

First, we'll use the matrix approach to solve this. The matrices representing the Hamiltonians H_0 and H' are again given by Eq. (39). The first-order correction to the eigenstate $\left|3^{(1)}\right\rangle$ is now known, and the second-order correction $\left|3^{(2)}\right\rangle$ is unknown, which we again characterize in terms of a set of coefficients $c_{3m}^{(2)}$ in the zeroth-order basis. The corrections to the unperturbed $n = 3$ state are

$$
\left|3^{(1)}\right\rangle \doteq \begin{pmatrix} c_{31}^{(1)} \\ c_{32}^{(1)} \\ 0 \\ c_{34}^{(1)} \\ \vdots \end{pmatrix}, \qquad \left|3^{(2)}\right\rangle \doteq \begin{pmatrix} c_{31}^{(2)} \\ c_{32}^{(2)} \\ c_{33}^{(2)} \\ c_{34}^{(2)} \\ \vdots \end{pmatrix}.
\tag{74}
$$

The left-hand side of Eq. (73) is

$$\left(H_0 - E_3^{(0)}\right)\big|3^{(2)}\big\rangle \doteq \begin{pmatrix} E_1^{(0)} - E_3^{(0)} & 0 & 0 & 0 & \cdots \\ 0 & E_2^{(0)} - E_3^{(0)} & 0 & 0 & \cdots \\ 0 & 0 & \boxed{0} & 0 & \cdots \\ 0 & 0 & 0 & E_4^{(0)} - E_3^{(0)} & \cdots \\ \vdots & \vdots & \vdots & \vdots & \ddots \end{pmatrix}\begin{pmatrix} c_{31}^{(2)} \\ c_{32}^{(2)} \\ c_{33}^{(2)} \\ c_{34}^{(2)} \\ \vdots \end{pmatrix}$$

$$\doteq \begin{pmatrix} \left(E_1^{(0)} - E_3^{(0)}\right)c_{31}^{(2)} \\ \left(E_2^{(0)} - E_3^{(0)}\right)c_{32}^{(2)} \\ \boxed{0} \\ \left(E_4^{(0)} - E_3^{(0)}\right)c_{34}^{(2)} \\ \vdots \end{pmatrix},$$

(75)

where we have again boxed the zero matrix element and the resultant vector component to highlight their importance in the solution. The first term on the right-hand side of Eq. (73) is

$$\left(E_3^{(1)} - H'\right)\big|3^{(1)}\big\rangle \doteq \begin{pmatrix} E_3^{(1)} - H'_{11} & -H'_{12} & -H'_{13} & -H'_{14} & \cdots \\ -H'_{21} & E_3^{(1)} - H'_{22} & -H'_{23} & -H'_{24} & \cdots \\ -H'_{31} & -H'_{32} & \boxed{E_3^{(1)} - H'_{33}} & -H'_{34} & \cdots \\ -H'_{41} & -H'_{42} & -H'_{43} & E_3^{(1)} - H'_{44} & \cdots \\ \vdots & \vdots & \vdots & \vdots & \ddots \end{pmatrix}\begin{pmatrix} c_{31}^{(1)} \\ c_{32}^{(1)} \\ \boxed{0} \\ c_{34}^{(1)} \\ \vdots \end{pmatrix}$$

(76)

$$\doteq \begin{pmatrix} \left(E_3^{(1)} - H'_{11}\right)c_{31}^{(1)} - H'_{12}c_{32}^{(1)} - H'_{14}c_{34}^{(1)} - \cdots \\ -H'_{21}c_{31}^{(1)} + \left(E_3^{(1)} - H'_{22}\right)c_{32}^{(1)} - H'_{24}c_{34}^{(1)} - \cdots \\ \boxed{-H'_{31}c_{31}^{(1)} - H'_{32}c_{32}^{(1)} - H'_{34}c_{34}^{(1)} - \cdots} \\ -H'_{41}c_{31}^{(1)} - H'_{42}c_{32}^{(1)} + \left(E_3^{(1)} - H'_{44}\right)c_{34}^{(1)} \\ \vdots \end{pmatrix}.$$

Again we have boxed in the diagonal matrix element and the resultant vector component corresponding to the state $\left|3^{(0)}\right\rangle$ that we are solving for. The second term on the right-hand side of Eq. (73) is

$$
E_3^{(2)}\left|3^{(0)}\right\rangle \doteq E_3^{(2)} \begin{pmatrix} 0 \\ 0 \\ 1 \\ 0 \\ \vdots \end{pmatrix} = \begin{pmatrix} 0 \\ 0 \\ \boxed{E_3^{(2)}} \\ 0 \\ \vdots \end{pmatrix}.
\tag{77}
$$

Equating the two sides of Eq. (73) gives

$$
\begin{pmatrix} \left(E_1^{(0)} - E_3^{(0)}\right)c_{31}^{(2)} \\ \left(E_2^{(0)} - E_3^{(0)}\right)c_{32}^{(2)} \\ \boxed{0} \\ \left(E_4^{(0)} - E_3^{(0)}\right)c_{34}^{(2)} \\ \vdots \end{pmatrix} = \begin{pmatrix} \left(E_3^{(1)} - H'_{11}\right)c_{31}^{(1)} - H'_{12}c_{32}^{(1)} - H'_{14}c_{34}^{(1)} - \cdots \\ -H'_{21}c_{31}^{(1)} + \left(E_3^{(1)} - H'_{22}\right)c_{32}^{(1)} - H'_{24}c_{34}^{(1)} - \cdots \\ \boxed{-H'_{31}c_{31}^{(1)} - H'_{32}c_{32}^{(1)} - H'_{34}c_{34}^{(1)} - \cdots} \\ -H'_{41}c_{31}^{(1)} - H'_{42}c_{32}^{(1)} + \left(E_3^{(1)} - H'_{44}\right)c_{34}^{(1)} \\ \vdots \end{pmatrix} + \begin{pmatrix} 0 \\ 0 \\ \boxed{E_3^{(2)}} \\ 0 \\ \vdots \end{pmatrix}.
\tag{78}
$$

As in the first-order calculation, the highlighted elements yield the solution for the second-order energy correction

$$
\begin{aligned}
E_3^{(2)} &= H'_{31}c_{31}^{(1)} + H'_{32}c_{32}^{(1)} + H'_{34}c_{34}^{(1)} + \dots \\
&= \sum_{m \neq 3} H'_{3m}c_{3m}^{(1)}.
\end{aligned}
\tag{79}
$$

As we said earlier, the second-order energy correction depends on the first-order state vector correction through the coefficients $c_{3m}^{(1)}$. We substitute for the coefficients from Eq. (53) to get

$$
\begin{aligned}
E_3^{(2)} &= \sum_{m \neq 3} H'_{3m} \frac{H'_{m3}}{E_3^{(0)} - E_m^{(0)}} \\
&= \sum_{m \neq 3} \left\langle 3^{(0)}\middle|H'\middle|m^{(0)}\right\rangle \frac{\left\langle m^{(0)}\middle|H'\middle|3^{(0)}\right\rangle}{\left(E_3^{(0)} - E_m^{(0)}\right)} \\
&= \sum_{m \neq 3} \frac{\left|\left\langle 3^{(0)}\middle|H'\middle|m^{(0)}\right\rangle\right|^2}{\left(E_3^{(0)} - E_m^{(0)}\right)}.
\end{aligned}
\tag{80}
$$

Having solved for the specific $n = 3$ case, we now generalize this result to

$$
\boxed{E_n^{(2)} = \sum_{m \neq n} \frac{\left|\left\langle n^{(0)}\middle|H'\middle|m^{(0)}\right\rangle\right|^2}{\left(E_n^{(0)} - E_m^{(0)}\right)}.}
\tag{81}
$$

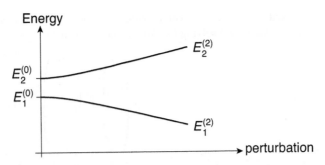

FIGURE 7   Energy levels repel each other in second-order perturbation theory.

The second-order energy correction is proportional to the squares of matrix elements connecting states and inversely proportional to the energy differences between those states. Hence, states that are nearby in energy generally have a stronger influence on the perturbation, and because the connecting matrix elements are squared, the sign of the energy shift is determined solely by the sign of the energy difference in the denominator. Energy levels m that lie above the state n give a negative contribution and hence push the energy level n down, away from the states m. Energy levels m that lie below the state n give a positive contribution and hence push the energy level n up, also away from the states m. The take-away message is that in second order, energy levels tend to repel each other, as shown in Fig. 7. This result has the quadratic form we expected from our examples on two-level problems at the beginning of the chapter.

Example 3   A sodium nucleus in a constant magnetic field in the z-direction $\mathbf{B}_0 = B_0\hat{\mathbf{z}}$ is subject to a perturbation caused by an additional magnetic field $\mathbf{B}' = B_2\hat{\mathbf{x}}$ applied to the system. Find the second-order energy shifts due to the perturbation and the state vectors correct to first order.

This problem is a variation on the spin-3/2 problem in Example 1 and also parallels the spin-1/2 problem in Section 1. Here, the perturbing field is perpendicular to, rather than parallel to, the zeroth-order field $\mathbf{B}_0 = B_0\hat{\mathbf{z}}$. As in Example 1, the zeroth-order Hamiltonian H_0 is determined by the potential energy of the nuclear magnetic moment in the uniform field $\mathbf{B}_0 = B_0\hat{\mathbf{z}}$:

$$H_0 = -\boldsymbol{\mu}\cdot\mathbf{B}_0 = \omega_0 S_z \doteq \begin{pmatrix} \frac{3}{2}\hbar\omega_0 & 0 & 0 & 0 \\ 0 & \frac{1}{2}\hbar\omega_0 & 0 & 0 \\ 0 & 0 & -\frac{1}{2}\hbar\omega_0 & 0 \\ 0 & 0 & 0 & -\frac{3}{2}\hbar\omega_0 \end{pmatrix}, \tag{82}$$

where we have defined the Larmor frequency $\omega_0 = g_{Na}eB_0/2m_p$. The zeroth-order energies are $E_1^{(0)} = \frac{3}{2}\hbar\omega_0$, $E_2^{(0)} = \frac{1}{2}\hbar\omega_0$, $E_3^{(0)} = -\frac{1}{2}\hbar\omega_0$, and $E_4^{(0)} = -\frac{3}{2}\hbar\omega_0$, using the same state labeling as in Example 1.

The perturbation Hamiltonian H' is determined by the field $\mathbf{B}' = B_1\hat{\mathbf{x}}$ and is characterized by a different Larmor frequency $\omega_2 = g_{Na}eB_2/2m_p$:

$$H' = -\boldsymbol{\mu}\cdot\mathbf{B}' = \omega_2 S_x \doteq \begin{pmatrix} 0 & \frac{\sqrt{3}}{2}\hbar\omega_2 & 0 & 0 \\ \frac{\sqrt{3}}{2}\hbar\omega_2 & 0 & \frac{\sqrt{4}}{2}\hbar\omega_2 & 0 \\ 0 & \frac{\sqrt{4}}{2}\hbar\omega_2 & 0 & \frac{\sqrt{3}}{2}\hbar\omega_2 \\ 0 & 0 & \frac{\sqrt{3}}{2}\hbar\omega_2 & 0 \end{pmatrix}. \tag{83}$$

This perturbation Hamiltonian has no diagonal elements, so there are no first-order energy corrections, in contrast to Example 1. The off-diagonal elements give first-order state vector corrections [Eq. (62)] and second-order energy corrections [Eq. (81)]. We'll calculate the second-order energy corrections first.

The second-order correction to the energy is proportional to the squares of matrix elements connecting states and inversely proportional to the energy differences between those states:

$$E_n^{(2)} = \sum_{m\neq n} \frac{\left|\left\langle n^{(0)}\middle|H'\middle|m^{(0)}\right\rangle\right|^2}{\left(E_n^{(0)} - E_m^{(0)}\right)}. \tag{84}$$

For the $\left|1^{(0)}\right\rangle$ state, the energy shift is given by a sum, but there is only one term in the sum because only $H'_{12} \neq 0$:

$$\begin{aligned} E_1^{(2)} &= \sum_{m\neq n} \frac{\left|\left\langle 1^{(0)}\middle|H'\middle|m^{(0)}\right\rangle\right|^2}{\left(E_1^{(0)} - E_m^{(0)}\right)} = \frac{\left|\left\langle 1^{(0)}\middle|H'\middle|2^{(0)}\right\rangle\right|^2}{\left(E_1^{(0)} - E_2^{(0)}\right)} \\ &= \frac{\left|\frac{\sqrt{3}}{2}\hbar\omega_2\right|^2}{\left(\frac{3}{2}\hbar\omega_0 - \frac{1}{2}\hbar\omega_0\right)} \\ &= \frac{3\hbar\omega_2^2}{4\omega_0}. \end{aligned} \tag{85}$$

For the $\left|2^{(0)}\right\rangle$ state, the energy shift is

$$\begin{aligned} E_2^{(2)} &= \sum_{m\neq n} \frac{\left|\left\langle 2^{(0)}\middle|H'\middle|m^{(0)}\right\rangle\right|^2}{\left(E_2^{(0)} - E_m^{(0)}\right)} = \frac{\left|\left\langle 2^{(0)}\middle|H'\middle|1^{(0)}\right\rangle\right|^2}{\left(E_2^{(0)} - E_1^{(0)}\right)} + \frac{\left|\left\langle 2^{(0)}\middle|H'\middle|3^{(0)}\right\rangle\right|^2}{\left(E_2^{(0)} - E_3^{(0)}\right)} \\ &= \frac{\left|\frac{\sqrt{3}}{2}\hbar\omega_2\right|^2}{\left(\frac{1}{2}\hbar\omega_0 - \frac{3}{2}\hbar\omega_0\right)} + \frac{\left|\frac{\sqrt{4}}{2}\hbar\omega_2\right|^2}{\left(\frac{1}{2}\hbar\omega_0 - \frac{-1}{2}\hbar\omega_0\right)} \\ &= \frac{\hbar\omega_2^2}{4\omega_0}. \end{aligned} \tag{86}$$

Similarly, the shifts for the $\left|3^{(0)}\right\rangle$ and $\left|4^{(0)}\right\rangle$ state are:

$$E_3^{(2)} = -\frac{\hbar\omega_2^2}{4\omega_0}$$

$$E_4^{(2)} = -\frac{3\hbar\omega_2^2}{4\omega_0}.$$

(87)

Adding these energy shifts to the zeroth-order energies gives the perturbed energies shown in Fig. 8 as a function of the perturbing field magnitude B_2. The new energies exhibit the quadratic dependence we expect for second-order shifts and also illustrate the repulsion of levels that we expect. The NMR transitions are indicated by the arrows in Fig. 8. The resonance shifts in this case are different from the shifts in Fig. 4, because the perturbing field is perpendicular to, rather than parallel to, the constant B_0 field. Hence chemical shifts also provide information about the spatial alignment of the system with respect to the constant B_0 field.

The first-order state vector correction is

$$\left|n^{(1)}\right\rangle = \sum_{m \neq n} \frac{\left\langle m^{(0)}\left|H'\right|n^{(0)}\right\rangle}{\left(E_n^{(0)} - E_m^{(0)}\right)}\left|m^{(0)}\right\rangle.$$

(88)

For the $\left|1^{(0)}\right\rangle$ state, the first-order correction again has only one term in the sum because only $H'_{12} \neq 0$:

$$\begin{aligned}
\left|1^{(1)}\right\rangle &= \sum_{m \neq n} \frac{\left\langle m^{(0)}\left|H'\right|1^{(0)}\right\rangle}{\left(E_1^{(0)} - E_m^{(0)}\right)}\left|m^{(0)}\right\rangle = \frac{\left\langle 2^{(0)}\left|H'\right|1^{(0)}\right\rangle}{\left(E_1^{(0)} - E_2^{(0)}\right)}\left|2^{(0)}\right\rangle \\
&= \frac{\frac{\sqrt{3}}{2}\hbar\omega_2}{\left(\frac{3}{2}\hbar\omega_0 - \frac{1}{2}\hbar\omega_0\right)}\left|2^{(0)}\right\rangle \\
&= \frac{\sqrt{3}\omega_2}{2\omega_0}\left|2^{(0)}\right\rangle.
\end{aligned}$$

(89)

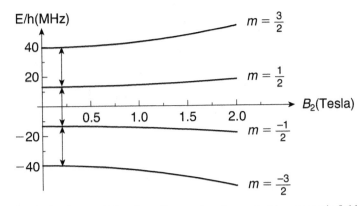

FIGURE 8 Energy shifts of a sodium nucleus in a perturbing magnetic field that is perpendicular to the constant zeroth-order field.

The state vector correct to first order includes the zeroth-order state:

$$|1\rangle = \left|1^{(0)}\right\rangle + \frac{\sqrt{3}\omega_2}{2\omega_0}\left|2^{(0)}\right\rangle. \tag{90}$$

Similarly, the other corrected states to first order are (Problem 6)

$$|2\rangle = \left|2^{(0)}\right\rangle - \frac{\sqrt{3}\omega_2}{2\omega_0}\left|1^{(0)}\right\rangle + \frac{\omega_2}{\omega_0}\left|3^{(0)}\right\rangle$$

$$|3\rangle = \left|3^{(0)}\right\rangle - \frac{\omega_2}{\omega_0}\left|2^{(0)}\right\rangle + \frac{\sqrt{3}\omega_2}{2\omega_0}\left|4^{(0)}\right\rangle \tag{91}$$

$$|4\rangle = \left|4^{(0)}\right\rangle - \frac{\sqrt{3}\omega_2}{2\omega_0}\left|3^{(0)}\right\rangle.$$

To conclude, we repeat the matrix calculation of the second-order energy correction using Dirac bra-ket notation. As before, we project out the desired state by taking the inner product of the second-order equation (37) with the nth zero-order eigenstate and get

$$\left\langle n^{(0)}\right|\left(H_0 - E_n^{(0)}\right)\left|n^{(2)}\right\rangle = \left\langle n^{(0)}\right|\left(E_n^{(1)} - H'\right)\left|n^{(1)}\right\rangle + \left\langle n^{(0)}\right|E_n^{(2)}\left|n^{(0)}\right\rangle. \tag{92}$$

The Hamiltonian H_0 is Hermitian, so it can act backwards on the bra $\left\langle n^{(0)}\right|$ to give the energy $\left(\left\langle n^{(0)}\right|H_0 = \left\langle n^{(0)}\right|E_n^{(0)}\right)$, giving zero on the left-hand side:

$$\left\langle n^{(0)}\right|\left(E_n^{(0)} - E_n^{(0)}\right)\left|n^{(2)}\right\rangle = \left\langle n^{(0)}\right|\left(E_n^{(1)} - H'\right)\left|n^{(1)}\right\rangle + E_n^{(2)}$$

$$0 = E_n^{(1)}\left\langle n^{(0)}\middle|n^{(1)}\right\rangle - \left\langle n^{(0)}\middle|H'\middle|n^{(1)}\right\rangle + E_n^{(2)}. \tag{93}$$

The first-order state vector correction $\left|n^{(1)}\right\rangle$ is orthogonal to the original state $\left|n^{(0)}\right\rangle$, making the first term on the right-hand side zero. Now solve for the second-order energy correction

$$0 = 0 - \left\langle n^{(0)}\middle|H'\middle|n^{(1)}\right\rangle + E_n^{(2)}$$

$$E_n^{(2)} = \left\langle n^{(0)}\middle|H'\middle|n^{(1)}\right\rangle. \tag{94}$$

Use the previous result for the first-order state vector correction to get the second-order energy correction

$$E_n^{(2)} = \sum_{m \neq n} c_{mn}\left\langle n^{(0)}\middle|H'\middle|m^{(0)}\right\rangle$$

$$E_n^{(2)} = \sum_{m \neq n} \frac{\left\langle m^{(0)}\middle|H'\middle|n^{(0)}\right\rangle}{\left(E_n^{(0)} - E_m^{(0)}\right)}\left\langle n^{(0)}\middle|H'\middle|m^{(0)}\right\rangle \tag{95}$$

$$E_n^{(2)} = \sum_{m \neq n} \frac{\left|\left\langle n^{(0)}\middle|H'\middle|m^{(0)}\right\rangle\right|^2}{\left(E_n^{(0)} - E_m^{(0)}\right)},$$

which is the general result we found in Eq. (81). We haven't bothered to find the second-order corrections to the eigenstates, because we are primarily concerned with energy corrections. If you are so inclined, you can derive them from the $m \neq 3$ rows of Eq. (78).

5 ■ DEGENERATE PERTURBATION THEORY

As we have pointed out several times, states that are degenerate in energy with respect to the zeroth-order Hamiltonian create a problem in perturbation theory. If two states have the same zeroth-order energy, then the term $E_n^{(0)} - E_m^{(0)}$ in the denominator of the first-order state vector correction in Eq. (67) becomes zero and the correction is no longer small, but rather diverges. This same problematic denominator appears in the second-order energy correction in Eq. (81). Though degeneracy creates no problem with the first-order energy correction, these divergences still call into question our overall approach to the problem. So we must explicitly address systems with energy degeneracy.

If we look back at the matrix solution to the first-order perturbation equation in Section 3, we can identify the source of the divergence problem and decide how to proceed. The terms that cause the divergence are the diagonal terms $E_n^{(0)} - E_3^{(0)}$ in the matrix representing $H_0 - E_3^{(0)}$ in Eq. (43). We knew that the term $E_3^{(0)} - E_3^{(0)}$ was zero and we used that fact to find the first-order energy correction $E_3^{(1)}$, as we indicated with the boxed parts of the matrix equations. However, we didn't expect any of the other diagonal terms to be zero and so we ended up dividing by them in Eq. (53). Let's identify which diagonal terms are zero *before* we start the solution and then we can avoid the division-by-zero problem.

Again, it helps to choose a specific example to illustrate the basic idea and then generalize at the end. Let's assume that the $n = 2$ and $n = 3$ states of a system are degenerate with the same energy $E_2^{(0)}$. The zeroth-order Hamiltonian in that case is

$$H_0 \doteq \begin{pmatrix} E_1^{(0)} & 0 & 0 & 0 & \cdots \\ 0 & E_2^{(0)} & 0 & 0 & \cdots \\ 0 & 0 & E_2^{(0)} & 0 & \cdots \\ 0 & 0 & 0 & E_4^{(0)} & \cdots \\ \vdots & \vdots & \vdots & \vdots & \ddots \end{pmatrix}. \tag{96}$$

The first-order perturbation equation we want to solve is [see Eq. (36)]

$$\left(H_0 - E_n^{(0)} \right) \left| n^{(1)} \right\rangle = \left(E_n^{(1)} - H' \right) \left| n^{(0)} \right\rangle, \tag{97}$$

where we are trying to find the correction $E_2^{(1)}$. The matrix $\left(H_0 - E_2^{(0)} \right)$ on the left-hand side of Eq. (97) is then

$$\left(H_0 - E_2^{(0)} \right) \doteq \begin{pmatrix} E_1^{(0)} - E_2^{(0)} & 0 & 0 & 0 & \cdots \\ 0 & \boxed{\begin{matrix} 0 & 0 \end{matrix}} & 0 & \cdots \\ 0 & \boxed{\begin{matrix} 0 & 0 \end{matrix}} & 0 & \cdots \\ 0 & 0 & 0 & E_4^{(0)} - E_2^{(0)} & \cdots \\ \vdots & \vdots & \vdots & \vdots & \ddots \end{pmatrix}. \tag{98}$$

Now we have two zeros along the diagonal instead of one. More important, there is a whole submatrix, indicated by the central boxed item, that is equal to zero, instead of a single number [Eq. (43)], and that submatrix is isolated from the rest of the matrix by virtue of the zeros in all the corresponding rows and columns.

Turning now to the right-hand side of Eq. (97), the matrix $\left(E_2^{(1)} - H'\right)$ is

$$\left(E_2^{(1)} - H'\right) \doteq \begin{pmatrix} E_2^{(1)} - H'_{11} & -H'_{12} & -H'_{13} & -H'_{14} & \cdots \\ -H'_{21} & \boxed{\begin{matrix} E_2^{(1)} - H'_{22} & -H'_{23} \end{matrix}} & -H'_{24} & \cdots \\ -H'_{31} & \boxed{\begin{matrix} -H'_{32} & E_2^{(1)} - H'_{33} \end{matrix}} & -H'_{34} & \cdots \\ -H'_{41} & -H'_{42} & -H'_{43} & E_2^{(1)} - H'_{44} & \cdots \\ \vdots & \vdots & \vdots & \vdots & \ddots \end{pmatrix},$$

(99)

where we have identified the submatrix corresponding to the zero submatrix in Eq. (98). In the non-degenerate case, we equated the two sides of Eq. (97) and found the solution for the first-order energy correction in the row corresponding to the energy level of interest [Eq. (45)]. But now the energy level of interest is degenerate and corresponds to two rows and two columns of the matrices, as indicated in Eqs. (98) and (99). So instead of a single equation for the energy correction, we have a matrix equation. To find this matrix equation, we must include the column vectors representing the states in Eq. (97). On the left-hand side is the unknown state correction $\left|2^{(1)}\right\rangle$ or $\left|3^{(1)}\right\rangle$:

$$\left|2^{(1)}\right\rangle \doteq \begin{pmatrix} c_{21}^{(1)} \\ c_{22}^{(1)} \\ c_{23}^{(1)} \\ c_{24}^{(1)} \\ \vdots \end{pmatrix}, \quad \left|3^{(1)}\right\rangle \doteq \begin{pmatrix} c_{31}^{(1)} \\ c_{32}^{(1)} \\ c_{33}^{(1)} \\ c_{34}^{(1)} \\ \vdots \end{pmatrix}.$$

(100)

On the right-hand side is the known eigenstate $\left|2^{(0)}\right\rangle$, or its degenerate partner $\left|3^{(0)}\right\rangle$:

$$\left|2^{(0)}\right\rangle \doteq \begin{pmatrix} 0 \\ 1 \\ 0 \\ 0 \\ \vdots \end{pmatrix}, \quad \left|3^{(0)}\right\rangle \doteq \begin{pmatrix} 0 \\ 0 \\ 1 \\ 0 \\ \vdots \end{pmatrix}.$$

(101)

But the energy degeneracy of these two states creates an ambiguity. Both $\left|2^{(0)}\right\rangle$ and $\left|3^{(0)}\right\rangle$ satisfy the zeroth-order energy eigenvalue equation for the energy $E_2^{(0)}$, but so does any linear combination of the two states. If we are trying to find the energy correction to the state with zeroth-order energy $E_2^{(0)}$, how do we know whether to use the state $\left|2^{(0)}\right\rangle$ or the state $\left|3^{(0)}\right\rangle$ in the perturbation equation? We don't know which one to use. We have no information that would help us decide which linear combination is "correct," so we let the solution to the problem tell us! We leave the state unspecified and write it as

$$
\left|2_{new}^{(0)}\right\rangle \doteq \begin{pmatrix} 0 \\ \alpha \\ \beta \\ 0 \\ \vdots \end{pmatrix}. \tag{102}
$$

This ambiguity turns out to be the answer to our degeneracy problem in perturbation theory.

Now the left-hand side of Eq. (97) is

$$
\left(H_0 - E_n^{(0)}\right)\left|n^{(1)}\right\rangle \doteq \begin{pmatrix} E_1^{(0)} - E_2^{(0)} & 0 & 0 & 0 & \cdots \\ 0 & \boxed{\begin{matrix} 0 & 0 \\ 0 & 0 \end{matrix}} & 0 & \cdots \\ 0 & 0 & 0 & E_4^{(0)} - E_2^{(0)} & \cdots \\ \vdots & \vdots & \vdots & \vdots & \ddots \end{pmatrix} \begin{pmatrix} c_{21}^{(1)} \\ c_{22}^{(1)} \\ c_{23}^{(1)} \\ c_{24}^{(1)} \\ \vdots \end{pmatrix}
$$

$$
\doteq \begin{pmatrix} \left(E_1^{(0)} - E_3^{(0)}\right)c_{21}^{(1)} \\ \boxed{\begin{matrix} 0 \\ 0 \end{matrix}} \\ \left(E_4^{(0)} - E_3^{(0)}\right)c_{24}^{(1)} \\ \vdots \end{pmatrix} \tag{103}
$$

and the right-hand side is

$$
\left(E_n^{(1)} - H'\right)\left|n^{(0)}\right\rangle \doteq \begin{pmatrix} E_2^{(1)} - H_{11}' & -H_{12}' & -H_{13}' & -H_{14}' & \cdots \\ -H_{21}' & \boxed{E_2^{(1)} - H_{22}'} & -H_{23}' & -H_{24}' & \cdots \\ -H_{31}' & -H_{32}' & E_2^{(1)} - H_{33}' & -H_{34}' & \cdots \\ -H_{41}' & -H_{42}' & -H_{43}' & E_2^{(1)} - H_{44}' & \cdots \\ \vdots & \vdots & \vdots & \vdots & \ddots \end{pmatrix} \begin{pmatrix} 0 \\ \alpha \\ \beta \\ 0 \\ \vdots \end{pmatrix}
$$

$$
\doteq \begin{pmatrix} -H_{12}'\alpha - H_{13}'\beta \\ \boxed{\begin{matrix} \left(E_2^{(1)} - H_{22}'\right)\alpha - H_{23}'\beta \\ -H_{32}'\alpha + \left(E_2^{(1)} - H_{33}'\right)\beta \end{matrix}} \\ -H_{42}'\alpha - H_{43}'\beta \\ \vdots \end{pmatrix}. \tag{104}
$$

We equate the two rows of interest to get the set of equations

$$\left(E_2^{(1)} - H_{22}'\right)\alpha - H_{23}'\beta = 0$$
$$-H_{32}'\alpha + \left(E_2^{(1)} - H_{33}'\right)\beta = 0. \tag{105}$$

We write these equations in matrix form

$$\begin{pmatrix} E_2^{(1)} - H_{22}' & -H_{23}' \\ -H_{32}' & E_2^{(1)} - H_{33}' \end{pmatrix}\begin{pmatrix} \alpha \\ \beta \end{pmatrix} = 0, \tag{106}$$

which shows that we have isolated the submatrix of the full perturbation equation corresponding to the two degenerate levels. Now rewrite Eq. (106) in a simpler form

$$\begin{pmatrix} H_{22}' & H_{23}' \\ H_{32}' & H_{33}' \end{pmatrix}\begin{pmatrix} \alpha \\ \beta \end{pmatrix} = E_2^{(1)}\begin{pmatrix} \alpha \\ \beta \end{pmatrix}. \tag{107}$$

This equation looks surprisingly like a standard energy eigenvalue equation. However, this equation is *limited to only the two states comprising the degenerate energies*, with the perturbation Hamiltonian playing the role of the Hamiltonian, while the energy eigenvalue is the first-order correction that we are seeking. We commonly refer to this isolated subspace of the whole system as the **degenerate subspace**.

We solve Eq. (107) by the standard procedure of diagonalization for eigenvalue equations, which yields two eigenvalues and two eigenstates. The eigenvalues are the two corrections $E_2^{(1)}$ to the zeroth-order energy $E_2^{(0)}$. If we label the two energy solutions $E_{2a}^{(1)}$ and $E_{2b}^{(1)}$, then the energies correct to first order are

$$E_{2a} = E_2^{(0)} + E_{2a}^{(1)}$$
$$E_{2b} = E_2^{(0)} + E_{2b}^{(1)}. \tag{108}$$

The two sets of α and β coefficients from solving Eq. (107) give the two eigenstate solutions $\left|2_a\right\rangle$ and $\left|2_b\right\rangle$ that form a new basis in the degenerate subspace that was originally defined by $\left|2^{(0)}\right\rangle$ and $\left|3^{(0)}\right\rangle$. In this new basis, the perturbation Hamiltonian is diagonal.

Now let's generalize our specific solution. The result of the twofold degenerate example was the eigenvalue equation (107) for the perturbation Hamiltonian within the degenerate subspace. The perturbation corrections are found by solving that eigenvalue equation through the diagonalization procedure we use throughout quantum mechanics. So there is no silver bullet formula for degenerate perturbation theory. There is just the mantra:

Diagonalize the perturbation Hamiltonian in the degenerate subspace.

That's it! Let's see how it works.

Example 4 An electron is bound to move on the surface of a sphere. Find the energy corrections caused by a perturbing magnetic field $\mathbf{B}' = B_1\hat{\mathbf{x}}$, limiting your consideration to the first two energy levels.

Perturbation Theory

The zeroth-order Hamiltonian of a particle on a sphere is the kinetic energy:

$$H_{sphere} = \frac{\mathbf{L}^2}{2I}.$$

(109)

The zeroth-order eigenstates are the angular momentum eigenstates

$$|\ell m\rangle \doteq Y_\ell^m(\theta, \phi)$$

(110)

and the zeroth-order energies are

$$E_\ell = \frac{\hbar^2}{2I}\ell(\ell + 1),$$

(111)

as illustrated in the energy spectrum. The energy is independent of the magnetic quantum number m, so each energy level is degenerate except the $\ell = 0$ ground state, with $(2\ell + 1)$ possible m states for a given ℓ. Hence the need for degenerate perturbation theory.

The perturbation Hamiltonian is the potential energy of interaction $H' = -\boldsymbol{\mu}_L \cdot \mathbf{B}'$ between the applied magnetic field and the magnetic moment of the electron due to its orbital angular momentum (we ignore spin angular momentum here). The electron magnetic moment associated with the orbital motion is

$$\boldsymbol{\mu}_L = -\frac{e}{2m_e}\mathbf{L}$$

(112)

and the resultant perturbation Hamiltonian is

$$H' = \frac{e}{2m_e}\mathbf{L} \cdot \mathbf{B}' = \frac{e}{2m_e}B_1 L_x$$

(113)

$$= \omega_1 L_x.$$

The Larmor frequency in this case is $\omega_1 = eB_1/2m_e$.

We limit ourselves to the first two energy levels: $E_0^{(0)} = 0$ and $E_1^{(0)} = \hbar^2/I$. The ground state is nondegenerate and the first excited state is threefold degenerate, with the zeroth-order Hamiltonian for these states

$$H_0 \doteq \begin{pmatrix} 0 & 0 & 0 & 0 \\ 0 & \hbar^2/I & 0 & 0 \\ 0 & 0 & \hbar^2/I & 0 \\ 0 & 0 & 0 & \hbar^2/I \end{pmatrix} \begin{matrix} \ell & m \\ 0 & 0 \\ 1 & 1 \\ 1 & 0 \\ 1 & -1 \end{matrix}.$$

(114)

Using the matrix representation of L_x for $\ell = 1$, we find the perturbation Hamiltonian:

$$H' \doteq \begin{pmatrix} 0 & 0 & 0 & 0 \\ 0 & 0 & \hbar\omega_1/\sqrt{2} & 0 \\ 0 & \hbar\omega_1/\sqrt{2} & 0 & \hbar\omega_1/\sqrt{2} \\ 0 & 0 & \hbar\omega_1/\sqrt{2} & 0 \end{pmatrix} \begin{matrix} \ell & m \\ 0 & 0 \\ 1 & 1 \\ 1 & 0 \\ 1 & -1 \end{matrix}.$$

(115)

The $\ell = 0$ level is nondegenerate, but the diagonal and off-diagonal matrix elements for $\ell = 0$ are zero, so there is neither a first-order nor a second-order correction to that energy. The $\ell = 1$ level is threefold degenerate, so we must diagonalize the perturbation Hamiltonian in the degenerate subspace:

$$H'_{\ell=1} \doteq \begin{pmatrix} 0 & \hbar\omega_1/\sqrt{2} & 0 \\ \hbar\omega_1/\sqrt{2} & 0 & \hbar\omega_1/\sqrt{2} \\ 0 & \hbar\omega_1/\sqrt{2} & 0 \end{pmatrix}. \tag{116}$$

The characteristic equation is

$$0 = \begin{vmatrix} \lambda & -\hbar\omega_1/\sqrt{2} & 0 \\ -\hbar\omega_1/\sqrt{2} & \lambda & -\hbar\omega_1/\sqrt{2} \\ 0 & -\hbar\omega_1/\sqrt{2} & \lambda \end{vmatrix}$$

$$= \lambda(\lambda^2 - \hbar^2\omega_1^2/2) - (-\hbar\omega_1/\sqrt{2})(-\hbar\omega_1/\sqrt{2})\lambda \tag{117}$$

$$= \lambda(\lambda^2 - \hbar^2\omega_1^2)$$

with solutions

$$\lambda = \hbar\omega_1, 0, -\hbar\omega_1. \tag{118}$$

This result is to be expected because the eigenvalues of L_x for $\ell = 1$ are $\hbar, 0, -\hbar$ and the perturbation is $H' = \omega_1 L_x$. The resultant energy shifts are

$$E_{1a}^{(1)} = \hbar\omega_1$$
$$E_{1b}^{(1)} = 0 \tag{119}$$
$$E_{1c}^{(1)} = -\hbar\omega_1.$$

The perturbed energy spectrum of the first two levels is shown in Fig. 9.

The eigenstates of the perturbation Hamiltonian are the L_x eigenstates $|1m_x\rangle$ because the perturbation is $H' = \omega_1 L_x$. If we had written the perturbation Hamiltonian in the L_x basis instead of the usual L_z basis, then the matrix representing the perturbation Hamiltonian would have already been diagonal and the problem would be solved by inspection. The L_x eigenstates are thus the "correct" basis for the perturbation problem. The solution for higher-order states now becomes clear. Each energy state is split into the $(2\ell + 1)$ possible m_x states for that ℓ state.

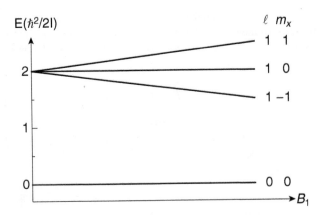

FIGURE 9   Perturbed energies of an electron bound to a sphere with an applied magnetic field.

As we pointed out in the example above, if the perturbation Hamiltonian is already diagonal in the degenerate subspace, then the solution is obtained by inspection of the perturbation matrix: the energy corrections are the diagonal elements $H'_{nn} = \langle n^{(0)}|H'|n^{(0)}\rangle$. But this is exactly what first-order nondegenerate perturbation theory tells us to do! So if the perturbation is diagonal in the degenerate subspace, then degenerate perturbation theory reduces to nondegenerate theory. In this case, the problem with the divergent denominators fades because the off-diagonal elements that appear in those same numerators [Eqs. (67) and (81)] are now zero. If the perturbation is not diagonal, then we make it diagonal by applying the diagonalization procedure to solve Eq. (107). The resultant eigenvalues (i.e., the diagonal elements in the new basis) are the desired energy corrections and the resultant eigenstates form the "correct" basis that avoids the divergence problems.

Given the ambiguity of the zeroth-order eigenstates in the degenerate subspace, we can try to be clever enough to start the problem by choosing the "correct" or "good" basis that makes the perturbation diagonal. We can do that by using eigenstates of some operator that commutes with both the zeroth-order Hamiltonian and the perturbation Hamiltonian. In Example 4, the L_x basis is the "correct" basis because the perturbation Hamiltonian is diagonal in that basis.

Let's conclude with some remarks about what is really going on with degenerate perturbation theory. We know that the general method for finding the energy eigenvalues of a system is to diagonalize the Hamiltonian. When we add a perturbation to a system, we must rediagonalize the full Hamiltonian. If that is possible, by all means do it and you will have the exact answer to the problem. But perturbation theory is designed to tackle problems where we cannot, for whatever reason, diagonalize the full Hamiltonian. So we diagonalize the zeroth-order Hamiltonian and then try to find a way to account for the perturbation Hamiltonian as best we can.

In the case of degenerate energy levels, we found that the nondegenerate perturbation theory developed in Section 3 led to divergences when the degenerate energy states were involved. The solution we presented above is to diagonalize the perturbation Hamiltonian within the degenerate subspace. However, one might ask whether we are justified in ignoring the original Hamiltonian and only diagonalizing the perturbing Hamiltonian because the diagonalization procedure amounts to a transformation of bases, which one would expect to disturb the original basis and hence "undiagonalize" the original Hamiltonian. But the original Hamiltonian is degenerate within the subspace corresponding to the degenerate energy, so it is proportional to the identity matrix within that subspace [Eq. (96)], and a transformation of the identity matrix leaves it unchanged. This is the mathematical consequence of the arbitrariness of choice of basis in the original problem. Hence, we are able to diagonalize the perturbation Hamiltonian within the degenerate subspace without undiagonalizing the zeroth-order Hamiltonian.

In some cases, the perturbing Hamiltonian is already diagonal, in which case there is not much work to do. The first-order energy corrections are obtained by inspection of the matrix as the diagonal elements H'_{nn}, which are the expectation values of the perturbation in the degenerate subspace. This result is the same as we obtained with nondegenerate perturbation theory, so if we choose the original basis correctly, then degenerate and nondegenerate perturbation theory are the same.

If the perturbing Hamiltonian is not diagonal, then we must go through the diagonalization procedure to find the new eigenvalues and eigenstates. The energy results are the same that we would have obtained if we had done nondegenerate perturbation theory using the "correct" basis, (i.e., the one we have found to diagonalize the perturbation). So in some sense we have merely found the "right" basis in which nondegenerate perturbation theory is valid.

You might ask whether we have found the exact solution and not just an approximation. The answer is no. By diagonalizing the perturbation Hamiltonian only within the degenerate subspace, we neglect other terms in the perturbation Hamiltonian that connect the degenerate states with other states in the system [Eq. (104)]. That we can safely neglect these other states in degenerate perturbation theory is suggested by the second-order energy correction in Eq. (81), which says that states farther away contribute less to perturbation. Degenerate states are the closest to each other and hence contribute the most to the corrections.

6 ■ MORE EXAMPLES

Let's apply perturbation theory to some of our favorite systems.

6.1 ■ Harmonic Oscillator

The harmonic oscillator has zeroth-order Hamiltonian

$$H_0 = \frac{\hat{p}^2}{2m} + \tfrac{1}{2}m\omega^2\hat{x}^2 = \hbar\omega\big(a^\dagger a + \tfrac{1}{2}\big), \tag{120}$$

where we have written it using ladder operators because that makes the calculations easier. Now consider adding a perturbation to the Hamiltonian of the form

$$H' = \varepsilon\tfrac{1}{2}m\omega^2\hat{x}^2, \tag{121}$$

where ε is a small dimensionless term parameterizing the strength of the perturbation. This perturbation has a parabolic spatial dependence, which is the same as the zeroth-order Hamiltonian, so the solution is known exactly, but we proceed with the example to see how the method is applied. For a positive value of ε, the strength of the harmonic well is increased, which confines the particle to a smaller region of space. The uncertainty principle then leads us to expect an increase in the energy.

The energy levels of the harmonic oscillator are nondegenerate, so we use nondegenerate perturbation theory. The first-order correction to the energy is the expectation value

$$E_n^{(1)} = \langle n^{(0)} | H' | n^{(0)} \rangle. \tag{122}$$

To calculate this, it is most convenient to express the perturbation Hamiltonian using ladder operators:

$$H' = \varepsilon \tfrac{1}{2} m \omega^2 \left(\frac{\hbar}{2m\omega} \right) \left(a^\dagger + a \right)^2 \tag{123}$$

$$H' = \varepsilon \tfrac{1}{4} \hbar \omega \left(a^\dagger a^\dagger + a^\dagger a + a a^\dagger + a a \right).$$

The expectation value of the perturbation is

$$E_n^{(1)} = \varepsilon \tfrac{1}{4} \hbar \omega \langle n^{(0)} | \left(a^\dagger a^\dagger + a^\dagger a + a a^\dagger + a a \right) | n^{(0)} \rangle. \tag{124}$$

The operators $a^\dagger a^\dagger$ and aa contribute zero because they raise or lower the state $|n^{(0)}\rangle$ twice and produce a new state that is orthogonal to $|n^{(0)}\rangle$. The remaining terms are calculated using $a|n\rangle = \sqrt{n}|n-1\rangle$ and $a^\dagger|n\rangle = \sqrt{n+1}|n+1\rangle$:

$$
\begin{aligned}
E_n^{(1)} &= \varepsilon \tfrac{1}{4} \hbar \omega \langle n^{(0)} | \left(a^\dagger a + a a^\dagger \right) | n^{(0)} \rangle \\
&= \varepsilon \tfrac{1}{4} \hbar \omega \langle n^{(0)} | \left(\sqrt{n}\sqrt{n} + \sqrt{n+1}\sqrt{n+1} \right) | n^{(0)} \rangle \\
&= \varepsilon \tfrac{1}{4} \hbar \omega (n + n + 1) \\
&= \varepsilon \tfrac{1}{2} \hbar \omega \left(n + \tfrac{1}{2} \right).
\end{aligned}
\tag{125}
$$

The resultant energy of level n to first order in the perturbation is

$$
\begin{aligned}
E_n &= E_n^{(0)} + E_n^{(1)} \\
&= \hbar \omega \left(n + \tfrac{1}{2} \right) + \varepsilon \tfrac{1}{2} \hbar \omega \left(n + \tfrac{1}{2} \right) \\
&= \hbar \omega \left(n + \tfrac{1}{2} \right) \left(1 + \tfrac{1}{2} \varepsilon \right).
\end{aligned}
\tag{126}
$$

Each state is shifted upwards, with the shift larger for larger states. The original and first-order perturbed energy levels are shown in Fig. 10(a).

Now consider the second-order energy correction

$$E_n^{(2)} = \sum_{m \neq n} \frac{\left| \langle n^{(0)} | H' | m^{(0)} \rangle \right|^2}{\left(E_n^{(0)} - E_m^{(0)} \right)}. \tag{127}$$

This looks like an infinite sum, which would be problematic, but we plow ahead and find that the sum is reduced for the harmonic oscillator case. The matrix elements are

$$
\begin{aligned}
\langle n^{(0)} | H' | m^{(0)} \rangle &= \varepsilon \tfrac{1}{4} \hbar \omega \langle n^{(0)} | \left(a^\dagger a^\dagger + a^\dagger a + a a^\dagger + a a \right) | m^{(0)} \rangle \\
&= \varepsilon \tfrac{1}{4} \hbar \omega \left[\begin{array}{l} \sqrt{m+1}\sqrt{m+2}\,\delta_{n,m+2} + \sqrt{m}\sqrt{m}\,\delta_{n,m} \\ + \sqrt{m+1}\sqrt{m+1}\,\delta_{n,m} + \sqrt{m}\sqrt{m-1}\,\delta_{n,m-2} \end{array} \right].
\end{aligned}
\tag{128}
$$

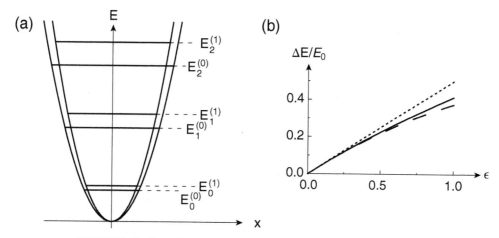

FIGURE 10 Perturbation of the harmonic oscillator. (a) Shifts of the first three energy levels. (b) Dependence of the shift of the ground state energy on the perturbation strength to first order (dotted), second order (dashed), and exact (solid).

For a given energy level n, only two terms in the sum ($m \neq n$) contribute, yielding

$$
\begin{aligned}
E_n^{(2)} &= \frac{\left[\frac{1}{4}\varepsilon\hbar\omega\sqrt{n-1}\sqrt{n}\right]^2}{E_n^{(0)} - E_{n-2}^{(0)}} + \frac{\left[\frac{1}{4}\varepsilon\hbar\omega\sqrt{n+2}\sqrt{n+1}\right]^2}{E_n^{(0)} - E_{n+2}^{(0)}} \\
&= \left(\tfrac{1}{4}\varepsilon\hbar\omega\right)^2\left[\frac{n(n-1)}{2\hbar\omega} + \frac{(n+1)(n+2)}{-2\hbar\omega}\right] \\
&= \tfrac{1}{32}\varepsilon^2\hbar\omega\left[n^2 - n - \left(n^2 + 3n + 2\right)\right] \\
&= -\tfrac{1}{8}\varepsilon^2\hbar\omega\left(n + \tfrac{1}{2}\right).
\end{aligned}
\tag{129}
$$

Note that the second-order contribution is negative. Only the two levels $m = n + 2$ and $m = n - 2$ contribute to the energy correction in Eq. (129). They each have the same magnitude energy denominators, but the matrix element is larger for the $m = n + 2$ state above the state of interest, so the level is pushed down. The resultant energy of level n to second order in the perturbation is

$$
\begin{aligned}
E_n &= E_n^{(0)} + E_n^{(1)} + E_n^{(2)} \\
&= \hbar\omega\left(n + \tfrac{1}{2}\right)\left(1 + \tfrac{1}{2}\varepsilon - \tfrac{1}{8}\varepsilon^2\right).
\end{aligned}
\tag{130}
$$

The perturbed energies to first and second order and the exact result are plotted in Fig. 10(b) as a function of the perturbation strength.

Perturbation Theory

In this example, we can find the exact answer, so we can check the perturbation result and confirm that perturbation theory works. The exact Hamiltonian is

$$
\begin{aligned}
H &= H_0 + H' \\
&= \frac{\hat{p}^2}{2m} + \tfrac{1}{2}m\omega^2\hat{x}^2 + \varepsilon\tfrac{1}{2}m\omega^2\hat{x}^2 \\
&= \frac{\hat{p}^2}{2m} + \tfrac{1}{2}m\omega^2\hat{x}^2(1 + \varepsilon) \\
&= \frac{\hat{p}^2}{2m} + \tfrac{1}{2}m\omega_p^2\hat{x}^2,
\end{aligned}
\tag{131}
$$

where we have defined a new perturbed harmonic frequency

$$
\omega_p = \omega\sqrt{1 + \varepsilon}.
\tag{132}
$$

This new Hamiltonian has the same form as the original harmonic oscillator problem we have already solved, but with a new characteristic frequency. Hence, we know the energy eigenvalues exactly. They are

$$
E_n = \left(n + \tfrac{1}{2}\right)\hbar\omega_p = \left(n + \tfrac{1}{2}\right)\hbar\omega\sqrt{1 + \varepsilon}.
\tag{133}
$$

The perturbation theory result in Eq. (130) was obtained to second order in the perturbation parameter ε, so we must compare it to the exact result at this same order. Expanding the exact result in powers of ε gives

$$
\begin{aligned}
E_n &= \left(n + \tfrac{1}{2}\right)\hbar\omega(1 + \varepsilon)^{1/2} \\
&= \left(n + \tfrac{1}{2}\right)\hbar\omega\left(1 + \tfrac{1}{2}\varepsilon - \tfrac{1}{8}\varepsilon^2 + \ldots\right).
\end{aligned}
\tag{134}
$$

Thus we see that the two results agree, at least to second order.

Note that the operator approach made our life very easy here—there was no need to do any spatial integrals. However, this is not always the case. For the harmonic oscillator problem, one can always use the operator approach because the spatial dependence of the perturbing potential energy, no matter how complicated, can be expressed as a polynomial in x and written in terms of the ladder operators. But for other potential wells, we do not know how to write the spatial function in terms of any simple operators and a spatial integral is often required.

6.2 ■ Stark Effect in Hydrogen

Now consider a perturbation of the hydrogen atom. The **Stark effect** is the perturbation of energies caused by an external electric field. For hydrogen, this example gives us a chance to practice degenerate perturbation theory. The unperturbed Hamiltonian is the sum of kinetic and Coulomb potential energies:

$$
\begin{aligned}
H_0 &= \frac{\mathbf{p}^2}{2m} + V(r) \\
&= \frac{\mathbf{p}^2}{2m} - \frac{Ze^2}{4\pi\varepsilon_0 r}.
\end{aligned}
\tag{135}
$$

The eigenstate solutions to this zeroth-order problem are labeled with quantum numbers $n\ell m$

$$\left|\psi^{(0)}\right\rangle = \left|n\ell m^{(0)}\right\rangle \doteq \psi_{n\ell m}^{(0)}(r,\theta,\phi) = R_{n\ell}(r)Y_\ell^m(\theta,\phi) \tag{136}$$

and the eigenenergies are

$$E_n^{(0)} = -\frac{Z^2}{n^2}Ryd. \tag{137}$$

These energy levels are degenerate because the energy is not a function of ℓ and m. Each energy level has n^2 states, so only the ground state with $n = 1$ is nondegenerate. Thus, we expect to have to use both nondegenerate and degenerate perturbation theory.

To perturb the system, we apply a uniform electric field of magnitude $\mathcal{E}$. When solving the hydrogen atom problem, we use spherical coordinates because of the spherical symmetry of the problem. The applied electric field has a specific direction in space and breaks the spherical symmetry of the problem, but we continue to use spherical coordinates because we use the original basis states in the perturbation solutions. Because the z-axis in spherical coordinates is special (the polar angle is measured from it and the azimuthal angle is measured about it), it is simplest to assume that the applied field is aligned along the z-axis: $\mathbf{E} = \mathcal{E}\hat{\mathbf{z}}$. The perturbation Hamiltonian is the potential energy of the hydrogen atom in the applied field. The electron and nucleus form an electric dipole, which the field tries to orient along its direction. An electric dipole $\mathbf{d}$ has a magnitude given by the product of the charge (the positive and negative charges are assumed equal) and the displacement between the charges, and a direction pointing from negative to positive charge. We have placed the origin of our coordinate system at the nucleus, so $\mathbf{r}$ represents the location of the electron with respect to the nucleus. Thus the dipole moment of the atom is

$$\mathbf{d} = -e\mathbf{r}. \tag{138}$$

The classical potential energy of an electric dipole in an electric field is

$$U = -\mathbf{d}\cdot\mathbf{E}. \tag{139}$$

The quantum mechanical potential energy is obtained by using this same expression as long as we clarify what the proper operators are. In this case only the position $\mathbf{r}$ is an operator. The charge and the applied electric field are parameters. Thus the Hamiltonian representing the perturbation is

$$\begin{aligned} H' &= -\mathbf{d}\cdot\mathbf{E} \\ &= -(-e\mathbf{r})\cdot\mathcal{E}\hat{\mathbf{z}} \\ &= e\mathcal{E}z \\ &= e\mathcal{E}r\cos\theta. \end{aligned} \tag{140}$$

Let's first consider the ground state of hydrogen. This state is nondegenerate, so we use nondegenerate perturbation theory. The first-order perturbed energy is the expectation value of the perturbation in the state:

$$\begin{aligned} E_1^{(1)} &= \left\langle 100^{(0)}\right|H'\left|100^{(0)}\right\rangle \\ &= \left\langle 100^{(0)}\right|e\mathcal{E}z\left|100^{(0)}\right\rangle \\ &= e\mathcal{E}\left\langle 100^{(0)}\right|z\left|100^{(0)}\right\rangle \\ &= e\mathcal{E}\int z\left|\psi_{100}^{(0)}(r,\theta,\phi)\right|^2dV. \end{aligned} \tag{141}$$

The expectation value of z is zero in the ground state because the function z has odd parity and the square of the wave function has even parity. The resultant integrand has odd parity and so yields zero when integrated over all space. To formally do the integral, one would use the substitution $z = r\cos\theta$ because the wave functions are in r, θ, ϕ, coordinates. The theta integral is the one that is zero, because $\cos\theta$ is odd with respect to $\theta = \pi/2$ (Problem 12).

The result of this calculation is that there is no first-order (i.e., linear) Stark effect in the ground state of hydrogen. All hydrogen atom eigenstates have definite parity, odd or even, yielding even wave function squares and zero expectation values of the electric dipole perturbation. However, the degeneracy in the excited states of hydrogen means that a given energy state includes states of differing parity, which permits a linear Stark effect, as we will see shortly. The absence of a linear Stark effect in the ground state implies that the atom does not have a permanent electric dipole moment in its ground state, because the expectation value of the perturbation that we calculated in Eq. (141) is just the expectation value of the dipole moment $\mathbf{d} = -e\mathbf{r}$ times the value of the applied field. Given the calculation in Eq. (141), we attribute that lack of dipole moment to the definite parity of the atomic wave function, which arises from the symmetry of the atomic system. We can now turn this whole argument on its end and say that if we measure the atom to have a permanent electric dipole moment (by observing a linear Stark effect or other means), then we can conclude that parity is not an obeyed property of the atom. There is a whole cottage industry of experiments designed to search for such effects because they indicate "parity violation." Parity violating effects are attributed to the weak nuclear interaction and are usually studied in high-energy particle collision experiments. Atomic parity violation experiments provide a unique opportunity for "low-energy" physicists to do "high-energy" measurements.

There is a second-order (i.e., quadratic) Stark effect in the ground state of hydrogen, but the calculation is tedious because it involves an infinite sum. We'll skip that calculation and move on to excited hydrogen states that require degenerate perturbation theory.

The $n = 2$ state of the hydrogen atom is fourfold degenerate, with one $2s$ state and three $2p$ states. Degenerate perturbation theory tells us to *diagonalize the perturbation Hamiltonian in the degenerate subspace*. To do this, we first need to find the matrix representing the Stark effect perturbation within the subspace of the four degenerate states. The four $n = 2$ states of hydrogen are

$$|200\rangle \doteq \psi_{200}^{(0)}(r,\theta,\phi) = R_{20}(r)Y_0^0(\theta,\phi) = \frac{2}{(2a_0)^{3/2}}\left(1 - \frac{r}{a_0}\right)e^{-r/2a_0}\frac{1}{\sqrt{4\pi}}$$

$$|210\rangle \doteq \psi_{210}^{(0)}(r,\theta,\phi) = R_{21}(r)Y_1^0(\theta,\phi) = \frac{1}{\sqrt{3}(2a_0)^{3/2}}\frac{r}{a_0}e^{-r/2a_0}\sqrt{\frac{3}{4\pi}}\cos\theta \qquad (142)$$

$$|21,\pm1\rangle \doteq \psi_{21\pm1}^{(0)}(r,\theta,\phi) = R_{21}(r)Y_1^{\pm1}(\theta,\phi) = \frac{\pm1}{\sqrt{3}(2a_0)^{3/2}}\frac{r}{a_0}e^{-r/2a_0}\sqrt{\frac{3}{8\pi}}e^{\pm i\phi}\sin\theta,$$

and we need to calculate the 16 matrix elements

$$\langle 2\ell m^{(0)}|H'|2\ell'm'^{(0)}\rangle \qquad (143)$$

to construct the matrix of the perturbation in the degenerate subspace.

As we saw in the first-order ground state calculation above, the consideration of parity is important in evaluating the required matrix elements. The parity of the hydrogen atom wave functions is determined by the parity of the spherical harmonics Y_ℓ^m, which is $(-1)^\ell$, independent of m. The Hamiltonian for the perturbation has odd parity, so the matrix elements between states of the same parity give an integrand that is odd and hence a zero integral. The only nonzero matrix elements are those between states of different parity, which are the s and p states. Thus we expect to do three integrals, between the s state and each of the three p states. However, we can reduce our task even further by considering the ϕ part of the integrals for these cases. There is no ϕ dependence in the perturbation Hamiltonian, so the matrix elements in Eq. (143) have azimuthal integrals

$$\int_0^{2\pi} e^{-im\phi}e^{im'\phi}d\phi = \int_0^{2\pi} e^{i(m'-m)\phi}d\phi. \tag{144}$$

This integral is zero unless the magnetic quantum numbers m and m' are the same, which only happens for the matrix element between the $2s$ state and the $2p_0$ state. Thus the only nonzero matrix element in the degenerate subspace is

$$\langle 210^{(0)}|H'|200^{(0)}\rangle \neq 0, \tag{145}$$

where the ℓ's are different but the m's are the same. Thus the matrix representing the perturbation Hamiltonian in the degenerate subspace has the form

$$
\begin{array}{cccc}
n & 2 & 2 & 2 & 2 \\
\ell & 0 & 1 & 1 & 1 \\
m & 0 & 1 & 0 & -1
\end{array}
$$

$$H' \doteq \begin{pmatrix} 0 & 0 & \Box & 0 \\ 0 & 0 & 0 & 0 \\ \Box & 0 & 0 & 0 \\ 0 & 0 & 0 & 0 \end{pmatrix}, \tag{146}$$

where the columns are labeled with $n\ell m$ (of course one must use the same labeling order for both rows and columns), and the nonzero elements are boxed.

Now we do the integral to find the nonzero matrix elements

$$\langle 200^{(0)}|H'|210^{(0)}\rangle = \int \psi_{200}^{(0)*}(r,\theta,\phi)e\mathcal{E}r\cos\theta\,\psi_{210}^{(0)}(r,\theta,\phi)r^2\sin\theta\,dr\,d\theta\,d\phi$$

$$= e\mathcal{E}\frac{2}{(2a_0)^{3/2}}\frac{1}{\sqrt{4\pi}}\frac{1}{\sqrt{3}(2a_0)^{3/2}}\sqrt{\frac{3}{4\pi}}\int_0^\infty \left(1-\frac{r}{a_0}\right)e^{-r/a_0}r^4dr$$

$$\int_0^\pi \cos^2\theta\sin\theta\,d\theta \int_0^{2\pi} d\phi. \tag{147}$$

The θ and ϕ angular integrals are straightforward and give $2/3$ and 2π, respectively (Problem 13). Doing the radial integral yields the final result

$$\langle 200|H'|210\rangle] = e\mathcal{E}\frac{2}{(2a_0)^3}\frac{1}{4\pi}\frac{2}{3}2\pi\left[\int_0^\infty r^4e^{-r/a_0}dr - \frac{1}{2a_0}\int_0^\infty r^5e^{-r/a_0}dr\right]$$

$$= e\mathcal{E}\frac{1}{6a_0^2}\left[4!a_0^5 - \frac{1}{2a_0}5!a_0^6\right]$$

$$= -3e\mathcal{E}a_0. \tag{148}$$

Now we have the matrix representing the perturbation Hamiltonian in the original basis within the $n = 2$ subspace, and the recipe we have for degenerate perturbation theory tells us to diagonalize this matrix. It is convenient to reorder the rows and columns of the matrix in a way that makes the mathematics of diagonalization easier and the physics of the perturbation more obvious:

$$H' \doteq \begin{pmatrix} 0 & -3e\mathcal{E}a_0 & 0 & 0 \\ -3e\mathcal{E}a_0 & 0 & 0 & 0 \\ 0 & 0 & 0 & 0 \\ 0 & 0 & 0 & 0 \end{pmatrix} \begin{matrix} 200 \\ 210 \\ 211 \\ 21,-1 \end{matrix}. \tag{149}$$

Be careful to note the new labeling of rows and columns. Only the $2s$ and $2p_0$ states are connected by the perturbation; the $2p_{\pm 1}$ states are not affected by the perturbation and their energies are unchanged. We diagonalize the perturbation Hamiltonian to get the energies and states:

$$\begin{vmatrix} -\lambda & -3e\mathcal{E}a_0 & 0 & 0 \\ -3e\mathcal{E}a_0 & -\lambda & 0 & 0 \\ 0 & 0 & -\lambda & 0 \\ 0 & 0 & 0 & -\lambda \end{vmatrix} = 0 \tag{150}$$

$$\left[\lambda^2 - \left(3e\mathcal{E}a_0\right)^2\right]\lambda^2 = 0$$

$$\lambda = \pm 3e\mathcal{E}a_0, 0, 0.$$

As we said, the $2p_{\pm 1}$ states are not shifted, and those eigenstates remain the same. The $2s$ and $2p_0$ states are mixed by the perturbation, with the normalized states from the diagonalization being (Problem 14):

$$\left|\psi_+\right\rangle = \tfrac{1}{\sqrt{2}}\left[\left|200\right\rangle - \left|210\right\rangle\right]$$

$$\left|\psi_-\right\rangle = \tfrac{1}{\sqrt{2}}\left[\left|200\right\rangle + \left|210\right\rangle\right], \tag{151}$$

where the $\pm$ subscript on the states corresponds to the energies $E_\pm = \pm 3e\mathcal{E}a_0$. The perturbed energy states are shown in Fig. 11. Note that the perturbation has lifted some of the degeneracy, but not all of it; two states remain degenerate.

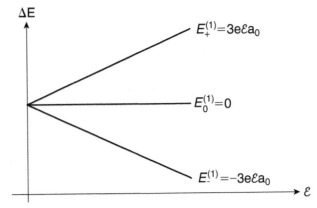

FIGURE 11   Stark effect in the hydrogen $n = 2$ state.

The shifts of the two superposition states in Eq. (151) are linear in the applied field because the combined s and p state has an electric dipole moment. This is allowed because it is not a state of definite parity. The $|\psi_-\rangle$ state of lower energy is the state we studied in Fig. 8.9(b), which has an electric dipole moment pointing in the field direction (Problem 15). This is what we expect from the classical model of an electric dipole moment that aligns with the electric field in its lowest energy state.

SUMMARY

Perturbation theory allows us to calculate the effects of adding new terms to the Hamiltonian of a system we have already solved exactly. The zeroth-order Hamiltonian with exact solutions obeys the eigenvalue equation

$$H_0\left|n^{(0)}\right\rangle = E_n^{(0)}\left|n^{(0)}\right\rangle. \tag{152}$$

The system is perturbed by the addition of a new term H', and the new Hamiltonian has the energy eigenvalue equation

$$\left(H_0 + H'\right)|n\rangle = E_n|n\rangle. \tag{153}$$

The approximate solutions to this equation are expressed as a series in increasing orders of the strength of the perturbation:

$$
\begin{aligned}
E_n &= E_n^{(0)} + E_n^{(1)} + E_n^{(2)} + ... \\
|n\rangle &= \left|n^{(0)}\right\rangle + \left|n^{(1)}\right\rangle + \left|n^{(2)}\right\rangle + ...
\end{aligned}
\tag{154}
$$

The first-order energy correction in nondegenerate perturbation theory is the expectation value of the perturbation in the state

$$E_n^{(1)} = H'_{nn} = \left\langle n^{(0)}\left|H'\right|n^{(0)}\right\rangle. \tag{155}$$

In wave function notation, the expectation value is expressed as an integral

$$E_n^{(1)} = H'_{nn} = \int \varphi_n^{(0)*}(\mathbf{r})\, H'\varphi_n^{(0)}(\mathbf{r})dV, \tag{156}$$

where $\varphi_n^{(0)}(\mathbf{r})$ are the energy eigenstates of the zeroth-order Hamiltonian. The first-order eigenstate correction is

$$\left|n^{(1)}\right\rangle = \sum_{m \neq n} \frac{\left\langle m^{(0)}\left|H'\right|n^{(0)}\right\rangle}{\left(E_n^{(0)} - E_m^{(0)}\right)}\left|m^{(0)}\right\rangle. \tag{157}$$

The second-order energy correction is

$$E_n^{(2)} = \sum_{m \neq n} \frac{\left|\left\langle n^{(0)}\left|H'\right|m^{(0)}\right\rangle\right|^2}{\left(E_n^{(0)} - E_m^{(0)}\right)}. \tag{158}$$

For degenerate states, we must use degenerate perturbation theory, which tells us to **diagonalize the perturbation Hamiltonian in the degenerate subspace**.

Perturbation Theory: Problem Set

1 Diagonalize the Hamiltonian in Eq. (3),

$$H = -\boldsymbol{\mu}\cdot\mathbf{B} = \omega_0 S_z + \omega_1 S_z + \omega_2 S_x \doteq \frac{\hbar}{2}\begin{pmatrix} \omega_0+\omega_1 & \omega_2 \\ \omega_2 & -\omega_0-\omega_1 \end{pmatrix}, \tag{3}$$

and confirm the energy eigenvalues in Eq. (9),

$$E_{new} = \pm\frac{\hbar}{2}\omega_{new} = \pm\frac{\hbar}{2}\sqrt{(\omega_0+\omega_1)^2 + \omega_2^2}. \tag{9}$$

2 Show that the assumed power series expansions in Eq. (34),

$$E_n = E_n^{(0)} + \lambda E_n^{(1)} + \lambda^2 E_n^{(2)} + \lambda^3 E_n^{(3)} + \dots$$

$$|n\rangle = |n^{(0)}\rangle + \lambda|n^{(1)}\rangle + \lambda^2|n^{(2)}\rangle + \lambda^3|n^{(3)}\rangle + \dots. \tag{34}$$

lead to the set of equations (35),

$$O(\lambda^0): \quad \left(H_0 - E_n^{(0)}\right)|n^{(0)}\rangle = 0 \tag{35}$$

$$O(\lambda^1): \quad \left(H_0 - E_n^{(0)}\right)|n^{(1)}\rangle = \left(E_n^{(1)} - H'\right)|n^{(0)}\rangle \tag{36}$$

$$O(\lambda^2): \quad \left(H_0 - E_n^{(0)}\right)|n^{(2)}\rangle = \left(E_n^{(1)} - H'\right)|n^{(1)}\rangle + E_n^{(2)}|n^{(0)}\rangle \tag{37}$$

through (38),

$$O(\lambda^3): \quad \left(H_0 - E_n^{(0)}\right)|n^{(3)}\rangle = \left(E_n^{(1)} - H'\right)|n^{(2)}\rangle + E_n^{(2)}|n^{(1)}\rangle + E_n^{(3)}|n^{(0)}\rangle. \tag{38}$$

3 Assume a 3-state quantum mechanical system and use the matrix approach of Section 3 to explicitly show that the first-order energy shift of the $n=2$ state is given by $E_2^{(1)} = H_{22}' = \langle 2^{(0)}|H'|2^{(0)}\rangle$.

4 Do the explicit integral in Eq. (71),

$$E_n^{(1)} = \int_0^{L/2} \varphi_n^{(0)*}(x)\, 0\, \varphi_n^{(0)}(x)dx + \int_{L/2}^L \varphi_n^{(0)*}(x) V_0 \varphi_n^{(0)}(x)dx$$

$$= V_0 \int_{L/2}^L |\varphi_n^{(0)}(x)|^2 dx, \tag{71}$$

to confirm the result in Eq. (72),

$$E_n^{(1)} = \frac{V_0}{2}. \tag{72}$$

5 Find the first-order eigenstate corrections to the ground state of the asymmetric square well of Example 2.

The companion websites for this text are http://physics.oregonstate.edu/portfolioswiki and http://physics. oregonstate.edu/qmactivities.

6 Show that the eigenstates correct to first order in Example 3 are given by Eq. (91),

$$|2\rangle = |2^{(0)}\rangle - \frac{\sqrt{3}\omega_2}{2\omega_0}|1^{(0)}\rangle + \frac{\omega_2}{\omega_0}|3^{(0)}\rangle$$

$$|3\rangle = |3^{(0)}\rangle - \frac{\omega_2}{\omega_0}|2^{(0)}\rangle + \frac{\sqrt{3}\omega_2}{2\omega_0}|4^{(0)}\rangle \tag{91}$$

$$|4\rangle = |4^{(0)}\rangle - \frac{\sqrt{3}\omega_2}{2\omega_0}|3^{(0)}\rangle.$$

7 The nitrogen nucleus has spin 1 and a gyromagnetic ratio $g_N = 0.404$. A nitrogen nucleus is placed in a constant magnetic field in the z-direction $\mathbf{B}_0 = B_0\hat{\mathbf{z}}$. An additional, perturbative magnetic field $\mathbf{B}' = B_1\hat{\mathbf{z}}$ is applied to the system. Find the first-order energy shifts due to the perturbation. Plot your results as a function of the perturbing field strength, assuming that the constant field is $B_0 = 2.35$ Tesla.

8 The nitrogen nucleus has spin 1 and a gyromagnetic ratio $g_N = 0.404$. A nitrogen nucleus is placed in a constant magnetic field in the z-direction $\mathbf{B}_0 = B_0\hat{\mathbf{z}}$. An additional, perturbative magnetic field $\mathbf{B}' = B_2\hat{\mathbf{x}}$ is applied to the system. Find the second-order energy shifts due to the perturbation. Plot your results as a function of the perturbing field strength, assuming that the constant field is $B_0 = 2.35$ Tesla.

9 An electron is bound to move on the surface of a sphere. Find the energy corrections caused by a perturbing magnetic field $\mathbf{B}' = B_1\hat{\mathbf{y}}$. Identify the "correct" zeroth-order basis.

10 Consider a particle bound in the harmonic oscillator potential $V(x) = \frac{1}{2}m\omega^2 x^2$. A perturbation $H' = \gamma x^3$ is applied to the system.

a) Calculate the first-order corrections to the energies.

b) Calculate the second-order corrections to the first three energy levels.

c) Find the first-order corrections to the eigenstates for these three states.

11 Consider a particle bound in the harmonic oscillator potential $V(x) = \frac{1}{2}m\omega^2 x^2$. A perturbation $H' = \eta x^4$ is applied to the system. Calculate the first-order corrections to the energies.

12 Confirm by explicit integration of Eq. (141),

$$\begin{aligned} E_1^{(1)} &= \langle 100^{(0)}|H'|100^{(0)}\rangle \\ &= \langle 100^{(0)}|e\mathcal{E}z|100^{(0)}\rangle \\ &= e\mathcal{E}\langle 100^{(0)}|z|100^{(0)}\rangle \\ &= e\mathcal{E}\int z|\psi_{100}^{(0)}(r,\theta,\phi)|^2 dV, \end{aligned} \tag{141}$$

that the linear Stark shift of the hydrogen ground state is zero.

13 Do the angular integrals in Eq. (147),

$$\langle 200^{(0)}|H'|210^{(0)}\rangle = \int \psi_{200}^{(0)*}(r,\theta,\phi)e\mathcal{E}r\cos\theta\,\psi_{210}^{(0)}(r,\theta,\phi)r^2\sin\theta\,dr\,d\theta\,d\phi$$

$$= e\mathcal{E}\frac{2}{(2a_0)^{3/2}}\frac{1}{\sqrt{4\pi}}\frac{1}{\sqrt{3}(2a_0)^{3/2}}\sqrt{\frac{3}{4\pi}}\int_0^\infty \left(1 - \frac{r}{a_0}\right)e^{-r/a_0}r^4 dr \tag{147}$$

$$\int_0^\pi \cos^2\theta\sin\theta\,d\theta\int_0^{2\pi}d\phi,$$

and confirm the results quoted in the text.

14 Find the eigenstates of the perturbation Hamiltonian in Eq. (149),

$$H' \doteq \begin{pmatrix} 0 & -3e\mathcal{E}a_0 & 0 & 0 \\ -3e\mathcal{E}a_0 & 0 & 0 & 0 \\ 0 & 0 & 0 & 0 \\ 0 & 0 & 0 & 0 \end{pmatrix} \begin{matrix} 200 \\ 210 \\ 211 \\ 21,-1 \end{matrix} , \tag{149}$$

and verify the results in Eq. (151),

$$|\psi_+\rangle = \tfrac{1}{\sqrt{2}}\big[|200\rangle - |210\rangle\big]$$

$$|\psi_-\rangle = \tfrac{1}{\sqrt{2}}\big[|200\rangle + |210\rangle\big]. \tag{151}$$

15 Calculate the expectation value of the electric dipole moment for the lower energy state $|\psi_-\rangle$ in Eq. (151) and verify that the moment is aligned with the field.

16 Consider the infinite square well with the shelf perturbation shown in Fig. 6(b),
Calculate the second-order energy shift of the ground state.

17 Consider the infinite square well shown in Fig. 6(a). Add a linear "ramp" perturbation $H' = V(x) = \beta x$ for $0 < x < L$ to the system and find the first-order energy shift of the ground state.

18 Consider an infinite square well potential with walls at $x = 0$ and $x = L$; that is, $V(x) = 0$ for $0 < x < L$; $V(x) = \infty$ otherwise. Now impose a perturbation on this potential of the form $H' = L V_0 \delta(x - L/2)$, where $\delta(x)$ is the Dirac delta function.

a) Calculate the first-order correction to the energy of the nth state of the infinite well.

b) Give some physical insight into why your answer is different for even and odd values of n.

c) The ground state wave function is modified under the influence of the perturbation. Calculate the largest contribution to the first-order correction. (In other words, which state is mixed in the most?)

Now consider the case where we impose a perturbation on the infinite square well potential as shown in Fig. 12, with ε a small number.

d) Calculate the first-order correction to the energy of the ground state of the infinite well.

e) In the limit where ε goes to zero, compare your answer to (d) with the answer in (a). Discuss.

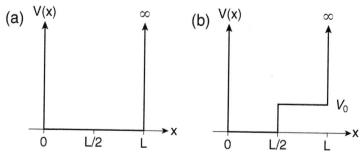

FIGURE 6 (a) An infinite square potential energy well perturbed by (b) a potential energy shelf in the right half of the well.

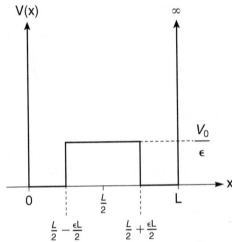

FIGURE 12 Perturbed square well.

19 Calculate the first-order energy corrections for all levels of an infinite square well potential with a perturbation $H' = V_0 \sin(\pi x/L)$.

20 Calculate the first-order energy corrections for all levels of an infinite square well potential with a perturbation $H' = \gamma x(L - x)$.

21 Consider a charged particle bound in the harmonic oscillator potential $V(x) = \frac{1}{2}m\omega^2 x^2$. A weak electric field $\mathcal{E}$ is applied to the system such that the potential energy is shifted by an amount $H' = -q\mathcal{E}x$.

   a) Calculate the energy levels of the perturbed system to second order in the small perturbation.

   b) Show that the perturbed system can be solved exactly by completing the square in the Hamiltonian. Compare the exact energies with the perturbation results found in (a).

22 Extend the Stark effect calculation in Section 6.2 to the $n = 3$ state of hydrogen. The symmetry and azimuthal integral arguments allow you to reduce the $81 = 9 \times 9$ required matrix elements to only 8 non-zero matrix elements and 4 necessary integrals. Find the perturbed energies and the new preferred basis. Discuss the electric dipole moments of the new states.

23 Consider a quantum system with three states and a Hamiltonian given by

$$H \doteq V_0 \begin{pmatrix} 1 & 2\varepsilon & 0 \\ 2\varepsilon & 1 & 3\varepsilon \\ 0 & 3\varepsilon & 4 \end{pmatrix},$$

   where V_0 is a constant and ε is a small number ($\varepsilon \ll 1$) that characterizes the perturbation of the system.

   a) Write down the eigenvectors and eigenvalues of the unperturbed Hamiltonian ($\varepsilon = 0$).

   b) Find the leading correction to the energy of the state that is nondegenerate in the zeroth-order Hamiltonian.

   c) Use degenerate perturbation theory to find the first-order corrections to the two initially degenerate energies.

   d) Plot the results of (b) and (c) as a function of the parameter ε and discuss your results.

Perturbation Theory: Problem Set

24 Consider a quantum system with four states and a Hamiltonian given by

$$H \doteq V_0 \begin{pmatrix} 3 & \varepsilon & 0 & 0 \\ \varepsilon & 3 & 2\varepsilon & 0 \\ 0 & 2\varepsilon & 5 & \varepsilon \\ 0 & 0 & \varepsilon & 7 \end{pmatrix},$$

where V_0 is a constant and ε is a small number ($\varepsilon \ll 1$) that characterizes the perturbation of the system.

a) Write down the eigenvectors and eigenvalues of the unperturbed Hamiltonian ($\varepsilon = 0$).

b) Use perturbation theory to find corrections to the energy of each energy eigenstate. Find the first nonvanishing order for each state.

Hyperfine Structure and the Addition of Angular Momenta

Spectroscopy of the hydrogen atom reveals structure in the energy levels beyond the $1/n^2$ pattern determined by the Coulomb interaction between the electron and proton. These additional energy levels arise from a variety of perturbations to the zeroth-order Coulomb interaction Hamiltonian. In this chapter, we focus on the **hyperfine structure**, so named because its effects are smaller than another effect called the fine structure. Studying hyperfine structure in the hydrogen atom gives us a chance to use perturbation theory to calculate an important energy and also gives us a chance to learn some new angular momentum tools. We can solve the problem more easily if we choose the "correct" basis at the start of the problem. The "correct" basis is not so much correct as it is convenient because the perturbation Hamiltonian is already diagonal in that basis and we avoid the tedious diagonalization required by degenerate perturbation theory. The hyperfine structure calculation presents us with a similar scenario, but not yet knowing how to choose the most convenient basis, we will solve the hyperfine problem by brute force in the "inconvenient" basis and then analyze the results to learn how to choose bases. The two bases for the hyperfine problem are the **uncoupled** and **coupled** bases, which refer to the coupling or **addition of angular momenta.** The theory of the addition of angular momenta complements perturbation theory to allow us to more easily solve for the many rich details in the hydrogen atom.

1 ■ HYPERFINE INTERACTION

The **hyperfine interaction** between the electron and the nucleus arises from higher electromagnetic multipole moments of the nucleus, beyond the electric monopole moment (i.e., charge) that is already included in the Coulomb interaction. The dominant hyperfine effect is due to the magnetic moment of the nucleus and its interaction with the internal magnetic fields in the atom caused by the electron's orbital motion and by the electron's spin magnetic moment. The intrinsic magnetic moment of the electron associated with its spin is

$$\boldsymbol{\mu}_e = -g_e \frac{e}{2m_e} \mathbf{S} = -g_e \mu_B \frac{\mathbf{S}}{\hbar}, \tag{1}$$

where the gyromagnetic ratio g_e is approximately 2 and the **Bohr magneton** is $\mu_B = e\hbar/2m_e$. The proton is also a spin-1/2 particle and has an associated magnetic moment. We label the proton spin, and nuclear spin in general, as **I**, so the intrinsic magnetic moment of the proton is

$$\boldsymbol{\mu}_p = g_p \frac{e}{2m_p} \mathbf{I} = g_p \mu_N \frac{\mathbf{I}}{\hbar}, \tag{2}$$

From Chapter 11 of *Quantum Mechanics: A Paradigms Approach*, First Edition. David H. McIntyre. Copyright © 2012 by Pearson Education, Inc. Published by Pearson Addison-Wesley. All rights reserved.

The companion websites for this text are http://physics.oregonstate.edu/portfolioswiki and http://physics. oregonstate.edu/qmactivities.

where the nuclear magneton is $\mu_N = e\hbar/2m_p$. The gyromagnetic ratio g_p of the proton is 5.59, which arises from the composite quark structure of the proton. The proton mass is 1836 times larger than the electron mass, so the proton magnetic moment is approximately three orders of magnitude smaller than the electron magnetic moment. This factor is responsible for the small scale of the hyperfine structure.

The hyperfine interaction Hamiltonian is

$$H'_{hf} = \boldsymbol{\mu}_p \cdot \frac{\mu_0}{4\pi} \frac{e\mathbf{L}}{mr^3} + \frac{\mu_0}{4\pi} \frac{1}{r^3} \left[\boldsymbol{\mu}_e \cdot \boldsymbol{\mu}_p - 3 \frac{(\boldsymbol{\mu}_e \cdot \mathbf{r})(\boldsymbol{\mu}_p \cdot \mathbf{r})}{r^2} \right] - \frac{\mu_0}{4\pi} \frac{8\pi}{3} \boldsymbol{\mu}_e \cdot \boldsymbol{\mu}_p \delta(\mathbf{r}). \tag{3}$$

The first term represents the interaction between the proton magnetic moment and the magnetic field arising from the electron's orbital angular momentum. The second term is the interaction between the two magnetic dipoles for the case $r \neq 0$. The third term is the same dipole-dipole interaction for the case $r = 0$ and is often called the Fermi contact interaction. Substituting the electron and proton spin operators into Eq. (3), we obtain the hyperfine Hamiltonian for the hydrogen atom:

$$H'_{hf} = \frac{\mu_0}{4\pi} \frac{g_e \mu_B g_p \mu_N}{\hbar^2} \left[\frac{1}{r^3} \mathbf{I} \cdot \mathbf{L} - \frac{1}{r^3} \mathbf{S} \cdot \mathbf{I} + \frac{3}{r^5} (\mathbf{S} \cdot \mathbf{r})(\mathbf{I} \cdot \mathbf{r}) + \frac{8\pi}{3} \mathbf{S} \cdot \mathbf{I} \delta(\mathbf{r}) \right]. \tag{4}$$

We limit our discussion to the $1s$ ground state of hydrogen. For s states, the first three terms of Eq. (4) are zero, and only the Fermi contact term of the hyperfine Hamiltonian need be considered. Hence, the hyperfine Hamiltonian for the ground state of hydrogen is

$$H'_{hf} = \frac{\mu_0}{4\pi} \frac{g_e \mu_B g_p \mu_N}{\hbar^2} \frac{8\pi}{3} \mathbf{S} \cdot \mathbf{I} \delta(\mathbf{r}). \tag{5}$$

Perturbation theory requires us to take matrix elements of the perturbation Hamiltonian. The hyperfine Hamiltonian has space and spin dependence, so the matrix elements have the form

$$\langle space | \langle spin | \frac{\mu_0}{4\pi} \frac{g_e \mu_B g_p \mu_N}{\hbar^2} \frac{8\pi}{3} \mathbf{S} \cdot \mathbf{I} \delta(\mathbf{r}) | spin \rangle | space \rangle, \tag{6}$$

which can be factored into spin and space parts

$$\frac{\mu_0}{4\pi} \frac{g_e \mu_B g_p \mu_N}{\hbar^2} \frac{8\pi}{3} \langle space | \delta(\mathbf{r}) | space \rangle \langle spin | \mathbf{S} \cdot \mathbf{I} | spin \rangle. \tag{7}$$

The spatial matrix element in the ground state of hydrogen

$$\langle space | \delta(\mathbf{r}) | space \rangle = \int_{space} \psi_{1s}^*(r,\theta,\phi) \delta(\mathbf{r}) \psi_{1s}(r,\theta,\phi) d^3 r$$

$$= |\psi_{1s}(0)|^2 \tag{8}$$

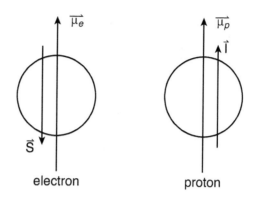

FIGURE 1 Hyperfine interaction between electron and proton magnetic moments.

results in the probability density at the origin. But we don't know how to calculate the spin matrix elements because we neglected to include the spins of the electron and proton in the solution of the energy eigenstates. Developing the tools to find these spin matrix elements is one of the goals of this chapter.

Using the result in Eq. (8), we simplify the hyperfine Hamiltonian for the ground state of hydrogen to just the spin aspect

$$H'_{hf} = \frac{A}{\hbar^2} \mathbf{S} \cdot \mathbf{I} \,, \tag{9}$$

where the constant A has dimensions of energy and includes the spatial integral:

$$A = \frac{2\mu_0}{3} g_e \mu_B g_p \mu_N |\psi_{1s}(0)|^2. \tag{10}$$

For hydrogen, A is less than one-millionth of the Rydberg energy. The hyperfine interaction Hamiltonian in Eq. (9) has the form you might expect classically. Two classical magnetic dipoles tend to align themselves in the same direction when you put them on top of each other, as depicted in Fig. 1. The electron magnetic moment is opposite to its spin, so the aligned magnetic dipoles correspond to antialigned electron and proton spins, which according to the Hamiltonian in Eq. (9) lowers the energy.

2 ■ ANGULAR MOMENTUM REVIEW

Before we embark on finding the matrix elements of the hyperfine Hamiltonian, a quick review of angular momentum is in order. You have studied spin angular momentum $\mathbf{S}$ and orbital angular momentum $\mathbf{L}$. They have different physical origins—spin angular momentum is an intrinsic property of fundamental particles while orbital angular momentum depends on the state of motion of a particle—but they share many similarities. There are many instances where the physical origin of the angular momentum is not important, and we refer to a generalized angular momentum, which we symbolize by $\mathbf{J}$.

The eigenvalue equations for a generalized angular momentum have the same form as spin and orbital angular momentum eigenvalue equations

$$\boxed{\begin{aligned} \mathbf{J}^2|jm_j\rangle &= j(j+1)\hbar^2|jm_j\rangle \\ J_z|jm_j\rangle &= m_j\hbar|jm_j\rangle \end{aligned}}, \tag{11}$$

where $|jm_j\rangle$ are simultaneous eigenstates of the commuting operators $\mathbf{J}^2$ and J_z and are labeled with the respective eigenvalues. The angular momentum quantum number j can be any integer or half integer. The magnetic quantum number m_j is restricted to the values

$$m_j = -j, -j+1, \ldots, j-1, j \tag{12}$$

for a given value of j. This yields $2j+1$ possible m_j states for each j value. Because all angular momenta obey the eigenvalue equations (11), they exhibit the same spectra of angular momentum quantum numbers. For example, $s=1$ and $\ell=1$ both have three possible component states $m_s = 1,0,-1$ and $m_\ell = 1,0,-1$. In the general case, a given value of j yields a spectrum or **manifold** of m_j states, as shown in Fig. 2.

The mathematical rules for generalized angular momentum are the same as those we have learned for spin and orbital angular momentum. Specifically, the rectangular components of angular momentum do not commute with each other:

$$\begin{aligned} \left[J_x, J_y\right] &= i\hbar J_z \\ \left[J_y, J_z\right] &= i\hbar J_x \\ \left[J_z, J_x\right] &= i\hbar J_y. \end{aligned} \tag{13}$$

Note that these commutation relations are cyclic in xyz. The angular momentum commutation relations imply that we cannot measure two different components simultaneously, so we cannot know the direction of the angular momentum vector. We can, however, know the square of its magnitude $\mathbf{J}^2$. The operator $\mathbf{J}^2$ commutes with each of the angular momentum components

$$\left[\mathbf{J}^2, J_x\right] = \left[\mathbf{J}^2, J_y\right] = \left[\mathbf{J}^2, J_z\right] = 0 \tag{14}$$

so we can simultaneously measure the magnitude of the vector and its projection along one axis.

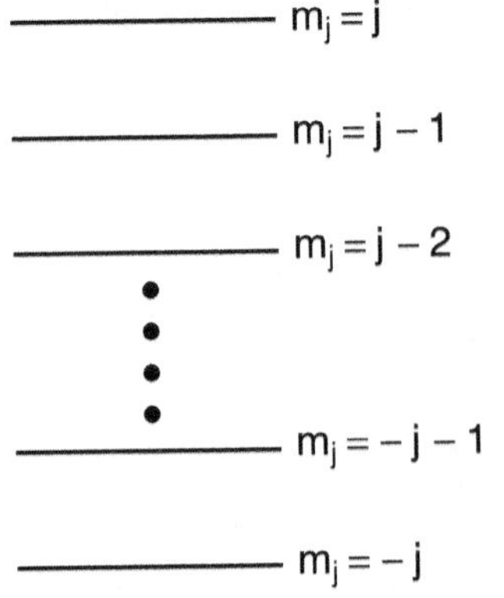

FIGURE 2 Manifold of angular momentum component eigenstates for a given j.

We can represent angular momentum operators as matrices in the angular momentum basis (vs. the position or momentum basis). It is the standard convention to write separate matrices for each particular value of j (i.e., each j subspace), and use the eigenstates of the angular momentum component operator J_z as the basis. Each j matrix has $2j+1$ rows and columns, corresponding to the number of possible m_j component states. The matrices do not distinguish between spin and orbital angular momentum. Thus we get, for example:

$$
j = \tfrac{1}{2} \Rightarrow \mathbf{J}^2 \doteq \frac{3}{4}\hbar^2 \begin{pmatrix} 1 & 0 \\ 0 & 1 \end{pmatrix}, \qquad J_z \doteq \frac{\hbar}{2}\begin{pmatrix} 1 & 0 \\ 0 & -1 \end{pmatrix}
$$

$$
j = 1 \Rightarrow \mathbf{J}^2 \doteq 2\hbar^2 \begin{pmatrix} 1 & 0 & 0 \\ 0 & 1 & 0 \\ 0 & 0 & 1 \end{pmatrix}, \; J_z \doteq \hbar \begin{pmatrix} 1 & 0 & 0 \\ 0 & 0 & 0 \\ 0 & 0 & -1 \end{pmatrix}.
$$

(15)

3 ■ ANGULAR MOMENTUM LADDER OPERATORS

The manifold of angular momentum component states in Fig. 2 is very similar to the harmonic oscillator problem, where the energy levels are labeled with n, which is the eigenvalue of the number operator N. Similarly, the angular momentum states in Fig. 2 differ by one unit of the magnetic quantum number m_j (we don't know anything about the energy in the angular momentum case yet). In the harmonic oscillator problem, we found a pair of ladder operators that connected the different energy states and that proved very useful. For angular momentum, there are similar ladder operators that connect the states within a given j manifold. The angular momentum ladder operators are defined as

$$
\boxed{\begin{aligned} J_+ &= J_x + iJ_y \\ J_- &= J_x - iJ_y \end{aligned}}.
$$

(16)

These new operators are analogous to the raising and lowering operators $a^\dagger$ and a of the harmonic oscillator. Like $a^\dagger$ and a, J_+ and J_- are not Hermitian, so they do not represent physical observables. They are Hermitian conjugates of each other

$$
J_+ = J_-^\dagger,
$$

(17)

and they do not commute with each other:

$$
[J_+, J_-] = 2\hbar J_z,
$$

(18)

but they do commute with $\mathbf{J}^2$:

$$
[\mathbf{J}^2, J_\pm] = 0.
$$

(19)

The important commutation relations for these new angular momentum ladder operators are (Problem 1)

$$
\begin{aligned} [J_z, J_+] &= +\hbar J_+ \\ [J_z, J_-] &= -\hbar J_-, \end{aligned}
$$

(20)

which are analogous to the relations

$$[H, a^\dagger] = +\hbar\omega a^\dagger$$
$$[H, a] = -\hbar\omega a \tag{21}$$

from a given harmonic oscillator problem.

In the harmonic oscillator problem, we use the commutation relations in Eq. (21) to show that $a^\dagger$ and a raise and lower, respectively, the energy by one energy quantum $\hbar\omega$ and hence change the label n. The physical requirement that the energy of the harmonic oscillator cannot be negative yielded the termination condition for the ladder, $a|0\rangle = 0$, which resulted in the energy spectrum $E_n = \left(n + \frac{1}{2}\right)\hbar\omega$. In the angular momentum case, the commutation relations in Eq. (20) similarly imply that J_+ and J_- raise and lower, respectively, the angular momentum component by one quantum $\hbar$ and hence change the label m_j (Problem 2). The physical condition that limits the extent of the angular momentum ladder of states is that the angular momentum component J_z cannot be greater than the magnitude of $\mathbf{J}$, which is the square root of $\mathbf{J}^2$. This physical condition leads to the conclusion that the top and bottom states of the angular momentum manifold for a given j are $m_j = \pm j$, with the termination equations (Problem 3)

$$J_+|jj\rangle = 0$$
$$J_-|j,-j\rangle = 0. \tag{22}$$

In the angular momentum case, the operator $\mathbf{J}^2$ provides an additional label j, in contrast to the single label n for the harmonic oscillator states. But the ladder operators J_+ and J_- commute with $\mathbf{J}^2$ [Eq. (19)], so their action does not change the j label, only the m_j label. Hence, the ladder operators do not connect manifolds with different j values. That is why we commonly restrict our attention to a manifold of m_j states for a given j, such as in Fig. 2. The actions of the ladder operators are summarized by the equation (Problem 2):

$$\boxed{J_\pm|jm_j\rangle = \hbar[j(j+1) - m_j(m_j \pm 1)]^{1/2}|j, m_j \pm 1\rangle.} \tag{23}$$

Similar to the harmonic oscillator ladder operators, the angular momentum ladder operators do not preserve the normalization of states. In addition, the angular momentum ladder operators have dimensions of $\hbar$, as evidenced in Eq. (23). An example of the manifold or ladder of angular momentum states for $j = 2$ is shown in Fig. 3. This view of the ladder of angular momentum states will be useful when we apply perturbation theory to these states.

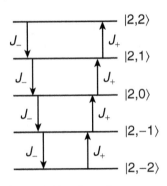

FIGURE 3   Manifold or ladder of angular momentum states for $j = 2$.

4 ■ DIAGONALIZATION OF THE HYPERFINE PERTURBATION

We are now ready to find the matrix elements of the hyperfine Hamiltonian that we need in order to apply perturbation theory to the ground state of hydrogen. The full quantum state vector includes the spatial wave function and the spin vectors for the electron and proton. For example, if the electron spin is up and the proton spin is down, then the atomic state vector is

$$|\psi_{1s}\rangle \doteq \psi_{1s}(r,\theta,\phi)\,|+\rangle_e\,|-\rangle_p, \tag{24}$$

where subscripts distinguish the electron and proton spin vectors. We have already used the spatial wave function to reduce the hyperfine Hamiltonian to a simple form in Eq. (9), so we limit our discussion to the spin vectors. The electron ($s = 1/2$) and proton ($I = 1/2$) are both spin-1/2 particles, so the individual spin states satisfy the eigenvalue equations:

$$S_z|\pm\rangle_e = \pm\frac{\hbar}{2}|\pm\rangle_e, \quad \mathbf{S}^2|\pm\rangle_e = \frac{3\hbar^2}{4}|\pm\rangle_e$$

$$I_z|\pm\rangle_p = \pm\frac{\hbar}{2}|\pm\rangle_p, \quad \mathbf{I}^2|\pm\rangle_p = \frac{3\hbar^2}{4}|\pm\rangle_p. \tag{25}$$

Due to the flexibility of Dirac notation, we can write the state $|+\rangle_e\,|-\rangle_p$ many equivalent ways—what you put inside the ket symbol is just a mnemonic label. We can specify all the quantum numbers in each ket:

$$|+\rangle_e\,|-\rangle_p = \left|s = \tfrac{1}{2}, m_s = \tfrac{1}{2}\right\rangle\left|I = \tfrac{1}{2}, m_I = -\tfrac{1}{2}\right\rangle \tag{26}$$

or we can write a single ket for the whole system, with all quantum numbers specified:

$$|+\rangle_e\,|-\rangle_p = \left|s = \tfrac{1}{2}, m_s = \tfrac{1}{2}, I = \tfrac{1}{2}, m_I = -\tfrac{1}{2}\right\rangle$$

$$= \left|s = \tfrac{1}{2}, I = \tfrac{1}{2}, m_s = \tfrac{1}{2}, m_I = -\tfrac{1}{2}\right\rangle \tag{27}$$

or we can suppress the spin quantum numbers s and I because we know that they do not change:

$$|+\rangle_e\,|-\rangle_p = \left|m_s = \tfrac{1}{2}, m_I = -\tfrac{1}{2}\right\rangle$$

$$= |+-\rangle. \tag{28}$$

In the last case, we use the first symbol for the electron and the second symbol for the proton, so that $|+-\rangle$ and $|-+\rangle$ are distinct states.

The electron-proton spin states exist in a new vector space obtained by combining the spaces for the spins of the two individual particles. There are four possible ways to combine the electron and proton spin states, so this new vector space is spanned by four basis states:

$$|++\rangle,\ |+-\rangle,\ |-+\rangle,\ |--\rangle. \tag{29}$$

This basis, in which the states are eigenstates of both S_z and I_z, is called the "uncoupled" basis. The reason for its name will become clearer in the next section when we learn about the alternative, "coupled" basis. The four possible spin combinations in Eq. (29) imply that the zeroth-order hydrogen ground state is *not* nondegenerate, but rather is fourfold degenerate. Hence, in order to use perturbation theory to find the effect of the hyperfine interaction, we must use degenerate perturbation theory, which requires us to diagonalize a 4×4 matrix.

Hyperfine Structure and the Addition of Angular Momenta

Let's first clarify how the spin operators act in this new four-dimensional vector space. Because each spin operator is associated with a specific particle, each operator acts only on those aspects of the system kets that are associated with that particle. For example, S_z is associated with electron spin only:

$$S_z|+-\rangle = S_z|+\rangle_e|-\rangle_p = \{S_z|+\rangle_e\}|-\rangle_p = \left\{+\frac{\hbar}{2}|+\rangle_e\right\}|-\rangle_p = \frac{\hbar}{2}|+-\rangle. \tag{30}$$

In general, the spin component eigenvalue equations in the four-dimensional vector space are

$$S_z|m_s m_I\rangle = m_s\hbar|m_s m_I\rangle$$
$$I_z|m_s m_I\rangle = m_I\hbar|m_s m_I\rangle, \tag{31}$$

where the allowed magnetic quantum numbers are $m_s = \pm 1/2$ and $m_I = \pm 1/2$. Because these spin operators act only on their own parts of the states, they commute with each other (Problem 5).

Perhaps you have represented spin operators as 2×2 matrices. In this example, we have four basis states, so we need 4×4 matrices. Using the eigenvalue equations (1), the new matrices representing the spin component operators are straightforward to derive (Problem 6 and activity on system of two spin-1/2 particles):

$$S_z \doteq \frac{\hbar}{2}\begin{pmatrix} 1 & 0 & 0 & 0 \\ 0 & 1 & 0 & 0 \\ 0 & 0 & -1 & 0 \\ 0 & 0 & 0 & -1 \end{pmatrix}\begin{matrix} ++ \\ +- \\ -+ \\ -- \end{matrix}$$

$$I_z \doteq \frac{\hbar}{2}\begin{pmatrix} 1 & 0 & 0 & 0 \\ 0 & -1 & 0 & 0 \\ 0 & 0 & 1 & 0 \\ 0 & 0 & 0 & -1 \end{pmatrix}\begin{matrix} ++ \\ +- \\ -+ \\ -- \end{matrix}, \tag{32}$$

where we have been explicit about labeling the rows, and by inference the columns, with the four basis states of the two-particle system using the labeling convention in Eq. (29).

The hyperfine Hamiltonian is proportional to the operator

$$\mathbf{S}\cdot\mathbf{I} = S_x I_x + S_y I_y + S_z I_z. \tag{33}$$

The matrix representing this operator is off-diagonal because the S_x, S_y, I_x, and I_x operators are off-diagonal. To make the matrix elements easier to calculate, it helps to rewrite $\mathbf{S}\cdot\mathbf{I}$ using the angular momentum ladder operators (Problem 7):

$$\mathbf{S}\cdot\mathbf{I} = \tfrac{1}{2}\left(S_+I_- + S_-I_+\right) + S_z I_z. \tag{34}$$

Recall that the ladder operators yield zero when acting on the extreme states; for example

$$S_+|++\rangle = 0$$
$$I_-|+-\rangle = 0. \tag{35}$$

Thus, the action of the ladder operators on the basis states yields only a few nonzero results. For example, using Eq. (23), we find (Problem 8)

$$
\begin{aligned}
S_+|-+\rangle &= \hbar\left[s(s+1) - m_s(m_s+1)\right]^{1/2}|++\rangle \\
&= \hbar\left[\tfrac{1}{2}\tfrac{3}{2} - \left(-\tfrac{1}{2}\right)\left(-\tfrac{1}{2}+1\right)\right]^{1/2}|++\rangle \\
&= \hbar\left[\tfrac{3}{4}+\tfrac{1}{4}\right]^{1/2}|++\rangle \\
&= \hbar|++\rangle.
\end{aligned}
\tag{36}
$$

The action of $\mathbf{S}\cdot\mathbf{I}$ on the basis states $|m_s m_I\rangle$ is:

$$
\begin{aligned}
\mathbf{S}\cdot\mathbf{I}|++\rangle &= \left\{\tfrac{1}{2}\left(S_+I_- + S_-I_+\right) + S_z I_z\right\}|++\rangle \\
&= \left\{\tfrac{1}{2}(0+0) + \tfrac{1}{2}\hbar\,\tfrac{1}{2}\hbar\right\}|++\rangle \\
&= \tfrac{1}{4}\hbar^2|++\rangle \\
\mathbf{S}\cdot\mathbf{I}|--\rangle &= \left\{\tfrac{1}{2}(0+0) + \left(\tfrac{-1}{2}\right)\hbar\left(\tfrac{-1}{2}\right)\hbar\right\}|--\rangle \\
&= \tfrac{1}{4}\hbar^2|--\rangle \\
\mathbf{S}\cdot\mathbf{I}|+-\rangle &= 0 + \tfrac{1}{2}\hbar\hbar|-+\rangle + \tfrac{1}{2}\hbar\left(\tfrac{-1}{2}\right)\hbar|+-\rangle \\
&= \tfrac{1}{4}\hbar^2[2|-+\rangle - |+-\rangle] \\
\mathbf{S}\cdot\mathbf{I}|-+\rangle &= 0 + \tfrac{1}{2}\hbar\hbar|+-\rangle + \tfrac{1}{2}\hbar\left(\tfrac{-1}{2}\right)\hbar|-+\rangle \\
&= \tfrac{1}{4}\hbar^2[2|+-\rangle - |-+\rangle].
\end{aligned}
\tag{37}
$$

Projecting these results onto the basis states yields the matrix representation

$$
\mathbf{S}\cdot\mathbf{I} \doteq \frac{\hbar^2}{4}\begin{pmatrix} 1 & 0 & 0 & 0 \\ 0 & -1 & 2 & 0 \\ 0 & 2 & -1 & 0 \\ 0 & 0 & 0 & 1 \end{pmatrix}\begin{matrix} ++ \\ +- \\ -+ \\ -- \end{matrix}.
\tag{38}
$$

The operator $\mathbf{S}\cdot\mathbf{I}$ is not diagonal in the $|m_s m_I\rangle$ (uncoupled) basis, so the $|m_s m_I\rangle$ states are not eigenstates of $\mathbf{S}\cdot\mathbf{I}$. The two extreme states $|++\rangle$ and $|--\rangle$ are eigenstates of $\mathbf{S}\cdot\mathbf{I}$, but the states $|+-\rangle$ and $|-+\rangle$ are not.

Using the result in Eq. (38), the hyperfine perturbation Hamiltonian becomes

$$
H'_{hf} \doteq \frac{A}{4}\begin{pmatrix} 1 & 0 & 0 & 0 \\ 0 & -1 & 2 & 0 \\ 0 & 2 & -1 & 0 \\ 0 & 0 & 0 & 1 \end{pmatrix}\begin{matrix} ++ \\ +- \\ -+ \\ -- \end{matrix}.
\tag{39}
$$

Degenerate perturbation theory tells us to *diagonalize the perturbation Hamiltonian in the degenerate subspace*. The hyperfine Hamiltonian is block diagonal, so we know two eigenvalues and eigenstates by inspection:

$$
\begin{aligned}
E_1 &= A/4, \quad |E_1\rangle = |++\rangle \\
E_2 &= A/4, \quad |E_2\rangle = |--\rangle.
\end{aligned}
\tag{40}
$$

The other two eigenvalues are found by diagonalizing the submatrix indicated by the box in Eq. (39):

$$
\begin{aligned}
\begin{vmatrix} -A/4-\lambda & A/2 \\ A/2 & -A/4-\lambda \end{vmatrix} &= 0 \\
(-A/4 - \lambda)^2 - (A/2)^2 &= 0 \\
(-A/4 - \lambda) &= \pm(A/2) \\
\lambda &= -A/4 \pm A/2 \\
\lambda &= \begin{cases} A/4 \\ -3A/4. \end{cases}
\end{aligned}
\tag{41}
$$

The resultant eigenstates are superpositions of the two states $|+-\rangle$ and $|-+\rangle$:

$$
\begin{aligned}
E_3 &= A/4, \quad |E_3\rangle = \tfrac{1}{\sqrt{2}}[|+-\rangle + |-+\rangle] \\
E_4 &= -3A/4, \quad |E_4\rangle = \tfrac{1}{\sqrt{2}}[|+-\rangle - |-+\rangle].
\end{aligned}
\tag{42}
$$

The energy level diagram of this perturbation is shown in Fig. 4. The degeneracy has been partially lifted. The two spin-aligned states $|++\rangle$ and $|--\rangle$ have the same positive energy shift, as you might expect because the magnetic moments are anti-aligned. Perhaps surprisingly, the spin-anti-aligned states $|+-\rangle$ and $|-+\rangle$ combine into two different superposition states with different energy shifts. There must be something different about those two superposition states, $|E_3\rangle$ and $|E_4\rangle$, that is not yet obvious. We will address this in the next section. The energy difference between the two hyperfine levels is A, so that [using Eq. (10)]

$$
\Delta E_{hf} = A = \frac{2\mu_0}{3} g_e \mu_B g_p \mu_N |\psi_{1s}(0)|^2.
\tag{43}
$$

The square of the hydrogen $1s$ wave function at the origin is

$$
|\psi_{1s}(0)|^2 = \frac{1}{\pi a_0^3},
\tag{44}
$$

where a_0 is the Bohr radius. Hence, the hyperfine splitting of the hydrogen ground state is

$$
\Delta E_{hf} = \frac{2\mu_0}{3} \frac{g_e \mu_B g_p \mu_N}{\pi a_0^3} = \alpha^4 m_e c^2 \frac{4}{3} g_e g_p \left(\frac{m_e}{m_p}\right)
\tag{45}
$$

$$
= 5.88 \times 10^{-6} \, \text{eV} = h \times 1420.4057517667(9) \, \text{MHz}.
$$

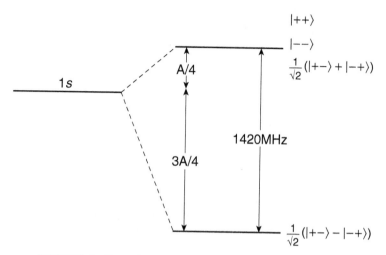

FIGURE 4 Hyperfine structure of the ground state of hydrogen.

The energy scale in hydrogen is set by the Rydberg energy $13.6\,\text{eV} = h \times 3.285 \times 10^{15}\,\text{Hz}$, so the hyperfine splitting is about a million times smaller. The transition between the two hyperfine states is a magnetic dipole transition in the microwave region of the spectrum. The electric dipole transition is forbidden because the matrix element is zero due to parity (both states have the same $1s$ spatial wave function). The transition between the two hyperfine states has a wavelength of 21 cm, and has played a pivotal role in radio astronomy. Because most of the elemental matter in the universe is in the form of hydrogen, observation of the 21-cm line is used to map the matter distribution in our galaxy and in the universe. The hydrogen hyperfine transition is also observed in the laboratory, where it is used as the active transition in the hydrogen maser, which permits the extremely precise frequency measurements indicated by the precision of the energy separation quoted above. An analogous transition in cesium is the basis of the atomic clock used in national standards laboratories.

5 ■ THE COUPLED BASIS

Let's return to the question posed in the last section: What distinguishes the two states $|E_3\rangle = [|+-\rangle + |-+\rangle]/\sqrt{2}$ and $|E_4\rangle = [|+-\rangle - |-+\rangle]/\sqrt{2}$ from each other? How can that little minus sign play such a large role in the energy of the two states? The answer to these questions comes from considering what we do in applying degenerate perturbation theory. In the new basis of hyperfine energy eigenstates, the hyperfine Hamiltonian is diagonal. As we discussed at the start of the chapter, if we are clever enough to choose the right basis for representing the perturbation Hamiltonian at the start of a problem, then the matrix is already diagonal and the problem is solved. So the question we really want to answer is: What is special about the new hyperfine basis states, and how should we have known to choose that basis to start the problem rather than the (uncoupled) basis we did choose?

When two classical magnetic dipoles interact, they exert torques on each other that try to align the magnetic moments. Because of the torque, the angular momentum of each particle is not conserved. The magnitude of each particle's angular momentum stays the same, but the direction changes. The quantum mechanical manifestation of this is that the electron and proton spin observables $\mathbf{S}^2$ and $\mathbf{I}^2$

commute with the hyperfine Hamiltonian and the component observables S_z and I_z do not (Problem 9). The quantum numbers s and I are thus "good" quantum numbers, but m_s and m_I are not good quantum numbers, which is evident in Eq. (42) because the $|E_3\rangle$ and $|E_4\rangle$ hyperfine eigenstates involve superpositions of eigenstates of the original $|m_s m_I\rangle$ basis—the *uncoupled basis*. To find the good quantum numbers for this problem and hence the "correct" or convenient basis, we must look for a conserved quantity.

The hyperfine interaction between the electron and proton arises from the torques the particles exert on each other. This is an internal torque, so the total angular momentum of the system is conserved. Hence, the basis of eigenstates of the total angular momentum of the system of the two particles is the basis in which the hyperfine Hamiltonian is diagonal. If we had chosen that basis to start the problem, then the hyperfine Hamiltonian would already be diagonal and the perturbation results would come by inspection. Let's now show this.

In the hydrogen ground state, the total angular momentum of the system is the sum of the spin angular momentum of the electron and the spin angular momentum of the proton because there is no orbital angular momentum. For historical reasons, we label the total angular momentum $\mathbf{F}$:

$$\mathbf{F} = \mathbf{S} + \mathbf{I}. \tag{46}$$

This new total spin operator behaves like an angular momentum because it is a sum (or coupling) of two angular momenta, and obeys the commutation relations of an angular momentum. For example,

$$\begin{aligned}
\left[F_x, F_y\right] &= \left[S_x + I_x, S_y + I_y\right] \\
&= \left[S_x, S_y\right] + \left[S_x, I_y\right] + \left[I_x, S_y\right] + \left[I_x, I_y\right] \\
&= i\hbar S_z + 0 + 0 + i\hbar I_z \\
&= i\hbar F_z,
\end{aligned} \tag{47}$$

where we have used the fact that the operators for the electron and the proton commute with each other. Because the total angular momentum behaves like all other angular momenta, it must have a set of basis kets $|FM_F\rangle$ that are eigenstates of the total angular momentum operators $\mathbf{F}^2$ and F_z. The quantum number F is the total angular momentum quantum number of the two-particle system. The quantum number M_F is the total magnetic quantum number of the two-particle system. We refer to these new states $|FM_F\rangle$ as the *coupled basis* because they arise from coupling or adding together two angular momenta. We refer to the original $|m_s m_I\rangle$ basis as the *uncoupled basis* because it uses quantum numbers from the individual angular momenta before we consider their coupling or addition.

We are familiar with the uncoupled basis $|m_s m_I\rangle$, which means that we know the single-particle quantum numbers s, I, m_s, and m_I. But we do not yet know the quantum numbers F and M_F of the coupled basis, which characterize the two-particle system. How do we find them? Well, how do we find any eigenstates and eigenvalues? *We solve the eigenvalue equation.* This will also tell us how the coupled basis eigenstates $|FM_F\rangle$ relate to the uncoupled basis eigenstates $|m_s m_I\rangle$.

So our task is to find the eigenstates and eigenvalues of the total angular momentum operators $\mathbf{F}^2$ and F_z. We do this by *diagonalizing the matrices* representing these physical observables, so we need to find the matrices first. We have already written down the matrices for S_z and I_z above, in the uncoupled basis we started with—the eigenstates $|m_s m_I\rangle$ of the two individual particles. We'll start with that approach and find the matrix representations of the total angular momentum operators in this basis. Let's first consider the total angular momentum component operator F_z, which is

$$F_z = S_z + I_z. \tag{48}$$

To find the matrix for F_z, we add the matrices in Eq. (32) to get

$$F_z \doteq \hbar \begin{pmatrix} 1 & 0 & 0 & 0 \\ 0 & \boxed{\begin{matrix} 0 & 0 \\ 0 & 0 \end{matrix}} & 0 \\ 0 & & & 0 \\ 0 & 0 & 0 & -1 \end{pmatrix} \begin{matrix} ++ \\ +- \\ -+ \\ -- \end{matrix} . \tag{49}$$

The F_z operator is already diagonal in the uncoupled $|m_s m_I\rangle$ basis—that was easy! This immediately tells us that the states $|m_s m_I\rangle$ are eigenstates of F_z. This is also clear if we operate with F_z on the $|m_s m_I\rangle$ states:

$$\begin{aligned} F_z |m_s m_I\rangle &= (S_z + I_z)|m_s m_I\rangle \\ &= (m_s + m_I)\hbar|m_s m_I\rangle. \end{aligned} \tag{50}$$

The eigenvalue equation for F_z in the coupled $|F M_F\rangle$ basis is

$$F_z |F M_F\rangle = M_F \hbar |F M_F\rangle. \tag{51}$$

Comparing Eqs. (50) and (51), we find that the allowed magnetic quantum numbers M_F are

$$M_F = m_s + m_I. \tag{52}$$

The allowed single-particle magnetic quantum numbers are $m_s = \pm 1/2$ and $m_I = \pm 1/2$, so the four allowed values of the total angular momentum magnetic quantum number M_F are 1, 0, 0, and -1. These eigenvalues are also evident by inspection of the diagonal elements of the F_z matrix in Eq. (49). A key point about these eigenvalues is that two of them are the same. Both the $|+-\rangle$ and $|-+\rangle$ states have the magnetic quantum number $M_F = 0$. This degeneracy of states is emphasized with the box in the F_z matrix in Eq. (49), showing that the matrix is block diagonal. The degeneracy of the $|+-\rangle$ and $|-+\rangle$ states implies an ambiguity as to the eigenstates corresponding to $M_F = 0$. This degeneracy is an important aspect that we exploit in a moment.

Now consider the matrix representation of the $\mathbf{F}^2$ operator, which is not so easy. The total angular momentum operator is

$$\begin{aligned} \mathbf{F}^2 = (\mathbf{S} + \mathbf{I})^2 &= \mathbf{S}^2 + \mathbf{I}^2 + \mathbf{S} \cdot \mathbf{I} + \mathbf{I} \cdot \mathbf{S} \\ &= \mathbf{S}^2 + \mathbf{I}^2 + 2\mathbf{S} \cdot \mathbf{I}, \end{aligned} \tag{53}$$

where again we have used the fact that the spin operators for the two particles commute with each other. Because the uncoupled states $|m_s m_I\rangle$ are eigenstates of $\mathbf{S}^2$ and $\mathbf{I}^2$, those operators are diagonal—in fact they are proportional to the identity in this subspace (Problem 6). We already know the matrix representing $\mathbf{S} \cdot \mathbf{I}$ from the hyperfine Hamiltonian, so using Eq. (38), we find the $\mathbf{F}^2$ operator in the $|m_s m_I\rangle$ basis:

$$\mathbf{F}^2 \doteq \hbar^2 \begin{pmatrix} 2 & 0 & 0 & 0 \\ 0 & \boxed{\begin{matrix} 1 & 1 \\ 1 & 1 \end{matrix}} & 0 \\ 0 & & & 0 \\ 0 & 0 & 0 & 2 \end{pmatrix} \begin{matrix} ++ \\ +- \\ -+ \\ -- \end{matrix} . \tag{54}$$

The $\mathbf{F}^2$ matrix is block diagonal, as was F_z, but it is *not* diagonal within the $|-+\rangle$, $|+-\rangle$ subspace of degenerate $M_F = 0$ states.

To find the eigenvalues and eigenvectors of the $\mathbf{F}^2$ operator, we diagonalize the matrix in Eq. (54). However, because the matrix is block-diagonal, we find the two eigenvalues $2\hbar^2$ for the $|++\rangle$ and $|--\rangle$ states by inspection. The eigenvalue equation for $\mathbf{F}^2$ in the coupled basis is

$$\mathbf{F}^2|FM_F\rangle = F(F+1)\hbar^2|FM_F\rangle, \tag{55}$$

so the eigenvalues $2\hbar^2$ imply a quantum number $F = 1$ for the states $|++\rangle$ and $|--\rangle$. The F_z eigenvalues M_F of these two states are obtained by inspection of the F_z matrix in Eq. (49) or from Eq. (52). These two eigenstates are thus

$$\begin{array}{c|c} coupled\ basis & uncoupled\ basis \\ |F = 1, M_F = 1\rangle = |++\rangle \\ |F = 1, M_F = -1\rangle = |--\rangle. \end{array} \tag{56}$$

To find the other two eigenvalues and eigenvectors of the $\mathbf{F}^2$ operator, we diagonalize the submatrix within the $|+-\rangle$ and $|-+\rangle$ states, as indicated by the box in Eq. (54). As you can show in Problem 10, the eigenvalues of the submatrix are $2\hbar^2$ and 0, which correspond to the values $F = 1$ and $F = 0$. The magnetic quantum numbers are both $M_F = 0$ for these two states, and the eigenstates are

$$\begin{array}{c|c} coupled\ basis & uncoupled\ basis \\ |F = 1, M_F = 0\rangle = \frac{1}{\sqrt{2}}[|+-\rangle + |-+\rangle] \\ |F = 0, M_F = 0\rangle = \frac{1}{\sqrt{2}}[|+-\rangle - |-+\rangle]. \end{array} \tag{57}$$

The diagonalization procedure is equivalent to a rotation in Hilbert space, so it will, in general, undiagonalize other matrices that are diagonal in the original basis. So you might expect that the diagonalization of $\mathbf{F}^2$ would undiagonalize the F_z matrix that we found to be diagonal in the $|m_s m_I\rangle$ basis. However, because the $|+-\rangle$ and $|-+\rangle$ states are degenerate with respect to F_z (i.e., they have the same $M_F = 0$ values), the F_z matrix is proportional to the identity matrix in the degenerate subspace of $|+-\rangle$ and $|-+\rangle$ states. The identity matrix is not altered by a rotation, so the ambiguity of eigenstates of F_z in the degenerate subspace has the benefit that the diagonalization of $\mathbf{F}^2$ does not undiagonalize F_z.

In summary, the four eigenstates $|FM_F\rangle$ of the coupled basis expressed in terms of the eigenstates $|m_s m_I\rangle$ of the uncoupled basis are

$$\begin{array}{c|c} coupled\ basis & uncoupled\ basis \\ |11\rangle = |++\rangle & \\ |10\rangle = \frac{1}{\sqrt{2}}[|+-\rangle + |-+\rangle] & \left.\right\} Triplet\ state \\ |1,-1\rangle = |--\rangle & \\ |00\rangle = \frac{1}{\sqrt{2}}[|+-\rangle - |-+\rangle] & \left.\right\} Singlet\ state \end{array}. \tag{58}$$

These states are typically referred to as the **triplet** $(F = 1)$ and **singlet** $(F = 0)$ states. These are *exactly the eigenstates* we found in Eqs. (40) and (42) when we diagonalized the hyperfine perturbation Hamiltonian in the $1s$ ground state.

Let's take a moment to reflect on what we have done. We started with two spin-1/2 particles and found that the total angular momentum of the combined system could be 0 or 1, (i.e., $F = s + I = 1$ and $F = s - I = 0$ were both allowed). For each allowed value of F, the allowed magnetic quantum numbers run from $-M_F$ to $+M_F$ in unit steps as is the case for all angular momenta, (i.e., $M_F = 1, 0, -1$ for the $F = 1$ case and $M_F = 0$ for the $F = 0$ case). We learned how to express the new coupled basis states $|FM_F\rangle$ in terms of the old uncoupled basis states $|m_s m_I\rangle$, as shown in Eq. (58). The expansion coefficients in Eq. (58) that connect the two bases are called **Clebsch-Gordan coefficients**. They are commonly tabulated as in Table 1.

Now we have two complete orthonormal bases to choose from—the coupled basis $|FM_F\rangle$ and the uncoupled basis $|m_s m_I\rangle$. The choice of which basis to use depends on which basis is best suited to the problem at hand, which typically depends on the Hamiltonian. For the hyperfine Hamiltonian, the coupled basis is the "good" basis because the coupled basis eigenstates are the energy eigenstates, which reflects the fact that the total angular momentum is conserved.

Now that we know that we could have chosen the coupled basis to solve the hyperfine problem much more easily, let's do that and make sure we get the same answer that we obtained from the uncoupled basis analysis. Choosing the coupled basis means writing the matrix representing the perturbation Hamiltonian using the $|FM_F\rangle$ states, rather than using the uncoupled $|m_s m_I\rangle$ states as we did in Section 4. To do this, we need to know how the $\mathbf{S}\cdot\mathbf{I}$ operator in the hyperfine Hamiltonian acts on the $|FM_F\rangle$ states. Using Eq. (53), we find that the operator $\mathbf{S}\cdot\mathbf{I}$ can be expressed in terms of other operators whose action on the $|FM_F\rangle$ basis is known:

$$\mathbf{S}\cdot\mathbf{I} = \tfrac{1}{2}\left(\mathbf{F}^2 - \mathbf{S}^2 - \mathbf{I}^2\right). \tag{59}$$

This leads to the hyperfine Hamiltonian

$$H'_{hf} = \frac{A}{\hbar^2}\mathbf{S}\cdot\mathbf{I}$$
$$= \frac{A}{2\hbar^2}\left(\mathbf{F}^2 - \mathbf{S}^2 - \mathbf{I}^2\right). \tag{60}$$

Table 1   Clebsch-Gordan Coefficients for System of Two Spin-1/2 Particles

$s = \tfrac{1}{2}$		F	1	1	1	0
	$I = \tfrac{1}{2}$	M_F	1	0	−1	0
m_s	m_I					
$\tfrac{1}{2}$	$\tfrac{1}{2}$		1	0	0	0
$\tfrac{1}{2}$	$-\tfrac{1}{2}$		0	$\tfrac{1}{\sqrt{2}}$	0	$\tfrac{1}{\sqrt{2}}$
$-\tfrac{1}{2}$	$\tfrac{1}{2}$		0	$\tfrac{1}{\sqrt{2}}$	0	$-\tfrac{1}{\sqrt{2}}$
$-\tfrac{1}{2}$	$-\tfrac{1}{2}$		0	0	1	0

The matrix representing $\mathbf{F}^2$ is diagonal because $|FM_F\rangle$ are eigenstates of $\mathbf{F}^2$. The matrices representing $\mathbf{S}^2$ and $\mathbf{I}^2$ are diagonal because the $|FM_F\rangle$ states all have the same quantum numbers $s = 1/2$ and $I = 1/2$. The result is that the matrix representing the hyperfine Hamiltonian in the coupled basis is (Problem 11)

$$H'_{hf} \doteq \frac{A}{4} \begin{pmatrix} 1 & 0 & 0 & 0 \\ 0 & 1 & 0 & 0 \\ 0 & 0 & 1 & 0 \\ 0 & 0 & 0 & -3 \end{pmatrix} \begin{matrix} 11 \\ 10 \\ 1,-1 \\ 00 \end{matrix}, \qquad (61)$$

where the rows (and columns) are labeled with the F, M_F quantum numbers.

As advertised, the hyperfine perturbation Hamiltonian is diagonal in the coupled basis. Degenerate perturbation theory calls for us to diagonalize this matrix in the degenerate $1s$ ground state, so we find the energy shifts by inspection of Eq. (61). The perturbation corrections are

$$E_{hf}^{(1)} = \begin{cases} +A/4; & F = 1 \\ -3A/4; & F = 0 \end{cases}, \qquad (62)$$

just as we found in Eqs. (40) and (42) by working in the uncoupled basis. We have solved the hyperfine perturbation problem in the coupled basis in a few lines instead of the several pages required for the uncoupled basis approach. That is the sense in which the coupled basis is the convenient basis for this problem. More important, the hyperfine eigenstates are the basis states of the coupled basis, so we call the coupled basis the "correct" basis.

We can also solve for the hyperfine energy corrections using an operator approach because the perturbation Hamiltonian is diagonal in the coupled basis. Degenerate perturbation theory is equivalent to nondegenerate perturbation theory when the matrix is already diagonal, so the first-order energy shifts are the expectations values of the perturbation:

$$\begin{aligned} E_{hf}^{(1)} &= \langle FM_F | H'_{hf} | FM_F \rangle \\ &= \frac{A}{2\hbar^2} \langle FM_F | \mathbf{F}^2 - \mathbf{S}^2 - \mathbf{I}^2 | FM_F \rangle. \end{aligned} \qquad (63)$$

The $|FM_F\rangle$ states are eigenstates of the three operators in Eq. (63), so the result is

$$\begin{aligned} E_{hf}^{(1)} &= \frac{A}{2\hbar^2} \big[F(F+1) - s(s+1) - I(I+1) \big] \hbar^2 \\ &= \frac{A}{2} \left[F(F+1) - \frac{3}{2} \right] \\ &= \begin{cases} +A/4; & F = 1 \\ -3A/4; & F = 0 \end{cases}, \end{aligned} \qquad (64)$$

which is the same result again.

6 ■ ADDITION OF GENERALIZED ANGULAR MOMENTA

To generalize from the example of adding the angular momenta of two spin-1/2 particles to the problem of adding any two generalized angular momenta, it is instructive to consider an alternative derivation of the coupled states $|FM_F\rangle$ that employs the angular momentum ladder operators. The state $|11\rangle = |++\rangle$ is an eigenstate in both the uncoupled and coupled bases, with the largest possible values of the magnetic quantum numbers m_s, m_I, and M_F. Such a state is called a **stretched state**. In this alternative method, we use the lowering operator F_- of the total angular momentum to generate other coupled basis states, and by comparing the action of F_- in the two bases, we learn how the coupled and uncoupled basis states are related to each other.

The action of the lowering operator F_- of the total angular momentum on the stretched state $|11\rangle = |++\rangle$ generates the state $|10\rangle$, with a multiplicative factor $\sqrt{2}\hbar$ according to Eq. (23). In the uncoupled basis, the lowering operator is $F_- = S_- + I_-$, so we can also calculate the result of the lowering operation in the uncoupled basis:

$$
\begin{array}{cc}
coupled\ basis & |\quad uncoupled\ basis \\
F_-|11\rangle = & F_-|++\rangle \\
F_-|11\rangle = & (S_- + I_-)|++\rangle \\
F_-|11\rangle = & S_-|++\rangle + I_-|++\rangle \\
\sqrt{2}\hbar|10\rangle = & \hbar\big[\,|+-\rangle + |-+\rangle\,\big].
\end{array}
\tag{65}
$$

This lowering operation produces the same state no matter which basis we work in, so we conclude that

$$
|10\rangle = \tfrac{1}{\sqrt{2}}\big[\,|+-\rangle + |-+\rangle\,\big]
\tag{66}
$$

just as we learned from the previous diagonalization procedures. Successive application of the lowering operator then allows us to construct the ladder of states from the initial stretched state $|11\rangle$ down to $|10\rangle$ and finally $|1,-1\rangle = |--\rangle$, as shown in Fig. 5. However, the ladder operator changes only the M_F quantum number, not the F quantum number, so we do not generate the $|00\rangle$ state with this procedure. Rather, we generate the $|00\rangle$ state by using the orthogonality condition to find a state that is orthogonal to the $|10\rangle$ state and comprises the same uncoupled states ($|+-\rangle$ and $|-+\rangle$) used in the $|10\rangle$ state. The general linear combination of $|+-\rangle$ and $|-+\rangle$ state is

$$
|00\rangle = a|+-\rangle + b|-+\rangle
\tag{67}
$$

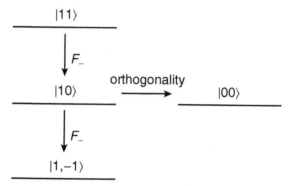

FIGURE 5 Generation of the coupled state manifold using the lowering operator and the orthogonality condition for the case of two spin-1/2 particles.

and the orthogonality condition is

$$0 = \langle 10|00 \rangle$$
$$= \tfrac{1}{\sqrt{2}}\big((\langle + - | + \langle - + |)(a| + - \rangle + b| - + \rangle\big) \tag{68}$$
$$= \tfrac{1}{\sqrt{2}}(a + b).$$

Hence, we conclude that $a = -b = 1/\sqrt{2}$ and

$$|00\rangle = \tfrac{1}{\sqrt{2}}\big(| + - \rangle - | - + \rangle\big) \tag{69}$$

as we found earlier.

This general procedure of using ladder operators and orthogonality generates all the states in any coupled basis, and also yields the proper Clebsch-Gordan coefficients. For the spin-1/2 case, the quantum numbers $M_F = \pm\tfrac{1}{2}$ never occur because the ladder starts with integer values of M_F and the lowering operator changes M_F by 1 each time. The orthogonality step preserves M_F but changes F.

Now let's generalize to the problem of adding any two angular momenta. Consider two angular momenta $\mathbf{J}_1$ and $\mathbf{J}_2$ coupled together to form a total angular momentum $\mathbf{J}$:

$$\mathbf{J} = \mathbf{J}_1 + \mathbf{J}_2. \tag{70}$$

The angular momenta $\mathbf{J}_1$ and $\mathbf{J}_2$ are characterized by the quantum numbers j_1, m_1 and j_2, m_2, respectively, and the total angular momentum $\mathbf{J}$ is characterized by the quantum numbers J, M. Specifying all the eigenvalues, we write the uncoupled and coupled bases as:

$$|j_1 j_2 m_1 m_2\rangle \quad \textit{uncoupled basis}$$
$$|j_1 j_2 JM\rangle \quad \textit{coupled basis.} \tag{71}$$

The uncoupled basis vectors are eigenstates of $\mathbf{J}_1^2$, $\mathbf{J}_2^2$, J_{1z}, and J_{2z}. The coupled basis vectors are eigenstates of $\mathbf{J}_1^2$, $\mathbf{J}_2^2$, $\mathbf{J}^2$, and J_z. In any given problem, the values of j_1 and j_2 are fixed, so we could suppress these labels. The convention we use is to suppress the j_1 and j_2 labels in the coupled states $|JM\rangle$, but not in the uncoupled states $|j_1 j_2 m_1 m_2\rangle$. This way, when we put in actual numbers (vs. algebraic symbols) we can immediately tell whether a state is in the coupled basis (two labels) or the uncoupled basis (four labels). Using this notation, the relation between the coupled and uncoupled bases for the system of two spin-1/2 particles is

$$\textit{coupled basis} \quad | \quad \textit{uncoupled basis}$$
$$|11\rangle = |\tfrac{1}{2}\tfrac{1}{2}\tfrac{1}{2}\tfrac{1}{2}\rangle$$
$$|10\rangle = \tfrac{1}{\sqrt{2}}\big(|\tfrac{1}{2}\tfrac{1}{2}\tfrac{1}{2}\tfrac{-1}{2}\rangle + |\tfrac{1}{2}\tfrac{1}{2}\tfrac{-1}{2}\tfrac{1}{2}\rangle\big) \tag{72}$$
$$|1,-1\rangle = |\tfrac{1}{2}\tfrac{1}{2}\tfrac{-1}{2}\tfrac{-1}{2}\rangle$$
$$|00\rangle = \tfrac{1}{\sqrt{2}}\big(|\tfrac{1}{2}\tfrac{1}{2}\tfrac{1}{2}\tfrac{-1}{2}\rangle - |\tfrac{1}{2}\tfrac{1}{2}\tfrac{-1}{2}\tfrac{1}{2}\rangle\big).$$

In terms of these generalized angular momentum labels, the spin-1/2 problem has $j_1 = 1/2$ and $j_2 = 1/2$ and the coupled J is equal to 0 or 1, which corresponds to the extreme values $j_1 + j_2$ and

$j_1 - j_2$. In the general case, the state generation procedure in Fig. 5 yields allowed values of J at all the integer steps in between these extreme values:

$$\boxed{J = j_1 + j_2, j_1 + j_2 - 1, j_1 + j_2 - 2, \dots |j_1 - j_2|}. \tag{73}$$

The absolute value is needed because we require $J \geq 0$. For example, if $j_1 = 3$ and $j_2 = 1$, then the allowed values of J are 4, 3, 2. For each allowed value of J, the allowed values of M are $-J$ to J in integer steps:

$$\boxed{M = -J, -J + 1, \dots, J - 1, J}, \tag{74}$$

which is what we expect for a generalized angular momentum. As a check, note that the total number of states is $(2j_1 + 1)(2j_2 + 1)$, whether one counts in the coupled or uncoupled bases, which must be the case (Problem 14). The state generation procedure in the general case is depicted in Fig. 6, and an example of the resultant spectrum of states is shown in Fig. 7 for the case $j_1 = 1$ and $j_2 = 1$. The stretched state $|J = j_1 + j_2, M = j_1 + j_2\rangle = |j_1 j_2, m_1 = j_1, m_2 = j_2\rangle$ is always an eigenstate of both bases, so the coupled state generation procedure can start there in all cases. In Fig. 7, the state $|22\rangle = |1111\rangle$ is the starting point for the generation procedure.

The general state generation procedure depicted in Fig. 6 works for any pair of j_1, j_2 values, and it tells us the Clebsch-Gordan coefficients we need to express the coupled basis states in terms of the coupled basis states, or vice versa. This procedure can be quite tedious for large angular momenta, as can the other method of diagonalizing the $\mathbf{J}^2$ and J_z matrices that we used in Section 5 for two spin-1/2 particles coupled together. Fortunately, the angular momentum addition problem has been solved by others and the resultant Clebsch-Gordan coefficients are conveniently tabulated. A general formula relating the coupled and the coupled states can be found by using the completeness relation. Because we don't mix j_1, j_2 manifolds, the completeness relation for the states in the uncoupled basis within a given j_1, j_2 manifold is

$$\sum_{m_1 = -j_1}^{j_1} \sum_{m_2 = -j_2}^{j_2} |j_1 j_2 m_1 m_2\rangle \langle j_1 j_2 m_1 m_2| = \mathbf{1}. \tag{75}$$

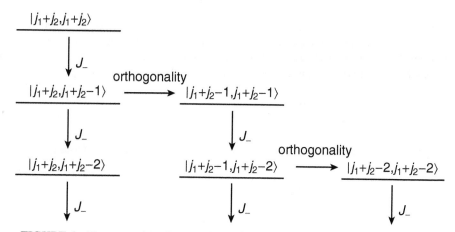

FIGURE 6   The generation of the coupled state manifold using the lowering operator and the orthogonality condition for the case of two generalized angular momenta j_1 and j_2.

$|22\rangle = |1111\rangle$

$|21\rangle = \frac{1}{\sqrt{2}}|1110\rangle + \frac{1}{\sqrt{2}}|1101\rangle$ $\qquad$ $|11\rangle = \frac{1}{\sqrt{2}}|1110\rangle - \frac{1}{\sqrt{2}}|1101\rangle$

$|20\rangle = \frac{1}{\sqrt{6}}|111-1\rangle + \sqrt{\frac{2}{3}}|1100\rangle + \frac{1}{\sqrt{6}}|11-11\rangle$ $\quad$ $|10\rangle = \frac{1}{\sqrt{2}}|111-1\rangle - \frac{1}{\sqrt{2}}|11-11\rangle$ $\quad$ $|00\rangle = \frac{1}{\sqrt{3}}|111-1\rangle - \frac{1}{\sqrt{3}}|1100\rangle + \frac{1}{\sqrt{3}}|11-11\rangle$

$|2-1\rangle = \frac{1}{\sqrt{2}}|110-1\rangle + \frac{1}{\sqrt{2}}|11-10\rangle$ $\qquad$ $|1-1\rangle = \frac{1}{\sqrt{2}}|110-1\rangle - \frac{1}{\sqrt{2}}|11-10\rangle$

$|2-2\rangle = |11-1-1\rangle$

FIGURE 7 The manifold of coupled angular momentum states for $j_1 = 1$, $j_2 = 1$, showing the coupled states $|JM\rangle$ expressed in terms of the uncoupled states $|j_1 j_2 m_1 m_2\rangle$.

Operate with this projection operator on a coupled state to get

$$|JM\rangle = \left\{ \sum_{m_1=-j_1}^{j_1} \sum_{m_2=-j_2}^{j_2} |j_1 j_2 m_1 m_2\rangle\langle j_1 j_2 m_1 m_2| \right\}|JM\rangle \tag{76}$$

$$= \sum_{m_1=-j_1}^{j_1} \sum_{m_2=-j_2}^{j_2} \left\{ \langle j_1 j_2 m_1 m_2|JM\rangle \right\}|j_1 j_2 m_1 m_2\rangle$$

with the result

$$\boxed{|JM\rangle = \sum_{m_1=-j_1}^{j_1} \sum_{m_2=-j_2}^{j_2} C_{m_1 m_2 M}^{j_1 j_2 J} |j_1 j_2 m_1 m_2\rangle}, \tag{77}$$

where the scalar products $\langle j_1 j_2 m_1 m_2|JM\rangle$ connecting the coupled and uncoupled bases are written as

$$C_{m_1 m_2 M}^{j_1 j_2 J} = \langle j_1 j_2 m_1 m_2|JM\rangle. \tag{78}$$

The coefficients $C_{m_1 m_2 M}^{j_1 j_2 J}$ are the Clebsch-Gordan coefficients we introduced in Section 5.

Clebsch-Gordan coefficients are tabulated in many books, although there are several different conventions on how to write the tables. A few examples of Clebsch-Gordan coefficients are shown in Tables 2–5. Columns represent coupled states expressed in terms of uncoupled states. For example, in the case of $j_1 = 1$, $j_2 = 1/2$, the coupled state $|\frac{3}{2}\frac{1}{2}\rangle$ can be read from the second column of Table 3:

$$|\tfrac{3}{2}\tfrac{1}{2}\rangle = \sqrt{\tfrac{1}{3}}|1\tfrac{1}{2}1, -\tfrac{1}{2}\rangle + \sqrt{\tfrac{2}{3}}|1\tfrac{1}{2}0\tfrac{1}{2}\rangle. \tag{79}$$

All the Clebsch-Gordan coefficients are real, so the inverse expansion uses the same coefficients:

$$|j_1 j_2 m_1 m_2\rangle = \sum_{J=|j_1-j_2|}^{j_1+j_2} |JM\rangle\langle JM|j_1 j_2 m_1 m_2\rangle \tag{80}$$

$$= \sum_{J=|j_1-j_2|}^{j_1+j_2} C_{m_1 m_2 M}^{j_1 j_2 J} |JM\rangle.$$

Note that there is no sum over M in Eq. (80) because $M = m_1 + m_2$ is the only allowed M state. Reading a row in the Clebsch-Gordan tables gives the inverse expansion of uncoupled states expressed in terms of coupled states. For example, in the case of $j_1=1$, $j_2=1/2$, the uncoupled state $\left|1\tfrac{1}{2}0\tfrac{1}{2}\right\rangle$ can be read from the third row of Table 3:

$$\left|1\tfrac{1}{2}0\tfrac{1}{2}\right\rangle = \sqrt{\tfrac{2}{3}}\left|\tfrac{3}{2}\tfrac{1}{2}\right\rangle - \sqrt{\tfrac{1}{3}}\left|\tfrac{1}{2}\tfrac{1}{2}\right\rangle. \tag{81}$$

Note the correspondence between the Clebsch-Gordan Table 5 for the case of $j_1=1$, $j_2=1$, and the manifold of states depicted in Fig. 7.

Note the large number of zeroes in the Clebsch-Gordan tables. These zeroes are important because angular overlap integrals of wave functions that are used to find transition probabilities can be expressed in terms of Clebsch-Gordan coefficients. The zeroes thus imply selection rules for transitions based upon the geometry of the states and the type of transition in question.

Table 2   Clebsch-Gordan Coefficients for $j_1 = \tfrac{1}{2}$ and $j_2 = \tfrac{1}{2}$

$j_1 = \tfrac{1}{2}$		j	1	1	1	0
	$j_2 = \tfrac{1}{2}$	m	1	0	-1	0
m_1	m_2					
$\tfrac{1}{2}$	$\tfrac{1}{2}$		1	0	0	0
$\tfrac{1}{2}$	$-\tfrac{1}{2}$		0	$\tfrac{1}{\sqrt{2}}$	0	$\tfrac{1}{\sqrt{2}}$
$-\tfrac{1}{2}$	$\tfrac{1}{2}$		0	$\tfrac{1}{\sqrt{2}}$	0	$-\tfrac{1}{\sqrt{2}}$
$-\tfrac{1}{2}$	$-\tfrac{1}{2}$		0	0	1	0

Table 3   Clebsch-Gordan Coefficients for $j_1 = 1$ and $j_2 = \tfrac{1}{2}$

$j_1 = 1$		j	$\tfrac{3}{2}$	$\tfrac{3}{2}$	$\tfrac{3}{2}$	$\tfrac{3}{2}$	$\tfrac{1}{2}$	$\tfrac{1}{2}$
	$j_2 = \tfrac{1}{2}$	m	$\tfrac{3}{2}$	$\tfrac{1}{2}$	$-\tfrac{1}{2}$	$-\tfrac{3}{2}$	$\tfrac{1}{2}$	$-\tfrac{1}{2}$
m_1	m_2							
1	$\tfrac{1}{2}$		1	0	0	0	0	0
1	$-\tfrac{1}{2}$		0	$\tfrac{1}{\sqrt{3}}$	0	0	$\sqrt{\tfrac{2}{3}}$	0
0	$\tfrac{1}{2}$		0	$\sqrt{\tfrac{2}{3}}$	0	0	$-\tfrac{1}{\sqrt{3}}$	0
0	$-\tfrac{1}{2}$		0	0	$\sqrt{\tfrac{2}{3}}$	0	0	$\tfrac{1}{\sqrt{3}}$
-1	$\tfrac{1}{2}$		0	0	$\tfrac{1}{\sqrt{3}}$	0	0	$-\sqrt{\tfrac{2}{3}}$
-1	$-\tfrac{1}{2}$		0	0	0	1	0	0

Table 4 **Clebsch-Gordan Coefficients for $j_1 = \frac{3}{2}$ and $j_2 = \frac{1}{2}$**

$j_1 = \frac{3}{2}$		j	2	2	2	2	2	1	1	1
	$j_2 = \frac{1}{2}$	m	2	1	0	−1	−2	1	0	−1
m_1	m_2									
$\frac{3}{2}$	$\frac{1}{2}$		1	0	0	0	0	0	0	0
$\frac{3}{2}$	$-\frac{1}{2}$		0	$\frac{1}{2}$	0	0	0	$\frac{\sqrt{3}}{2}$	0	0
$\frac{1}{2}$	$\frac{1}{2}$		0	$\frac{\sqrt{3}}{2}$	0	0	0	$-\frac{1}{2}$	0	0
$\frac{1}{2}$	$-\frac{1}{2}$		0	0	$\frac{1}{\sqrt{2}}$	0	0	0	$\frac{1}{\sqrt{2}}$	0
$-\frac{1}{2}$	$\frac{1}{2}$		0	0	$\frac{1}{\sqrt{2}}$	0	0	0	$-\frac{1}{\sqrt{2}}$	0
$-\frac{1}{2}$	$-\frac{1}{2}$		0	0	0	$\frac{\sqrt{3}}{2}$	0	0	0	$\frac{1}{2}$
$-\frac{3}{2}$	$\frac{1}{2}$		0	0	0	$\frac{1}{2}$	0	0	0	$-\frac{\sqrt{3}}{2}$
$-\frac{3}{2}$	$-\frac{1}{2}$		0	0	0	0	1	0	0	0

Table 5 **Clebsch-Gordan Coefficients for $j_1 = 1$ and $j_2 = 1$**

$j_1 = 1$		j	2	2	2	2	2	1	1	1	0
	$j_2 = 1$	m	2	1	0	−1	−2	1	0	−1	0
m_1	m_2										
1	1		1	0	0	0	0	0	0	0	0
1	0		0	$\frac{1}{\sqrt{2}}$	0	0	0	$\frac{1}{\sqrt{2}}$	0	0	0
1	−1		0	0	$\frac{1}{\sqrt{6}}$	0	0	0	$\frac{1}{\sqrt{2}}$	0	$\frac{1}{\sqrt{3}}$
0	1		0	$\frac{1}{\sqrt{2}}$	0	0	0	$-\frac{1}{\sqrt{2}}$	0	0	0
0	0		0	0	$\sqrt{\frac{2}{3}}$	0	0	0	0	0	$-\frac{1}{\sqrt{3}}$
0	−1		0	0	0	$\frac{1}{\sqrt{2}}$	0	0	0	$\frac{1}{\sqrt{2}}$	0
−1	1		0	0	$\frac{1}{\sqrt{6}}$	0	0	0	$-\frac{1}{\sqrt{2}}$	0	$\frac{1}{\sqrt{3}}$
−1	0		0	0	0	$\frac{1}{\sqrt{2}}$	0	0	0	$-\frac{1}{\sqrt{2}}$	0
−1	−1		0	0	0	0	1	0	0	0	0

7 ■ ANGULAR MOMENTUM IN ATOMS AND SPECTROSCOPIC NOTATION

An important application of angular momentum addition occurs in atoms where we must combine the orbital angular momentum and the spin angular momentum of the electrons (we neglect the spin angular momentum of the nucleus here). The total angular momentum of the electrons is typically denoted by $\mathbf{J}$:

$$\mathbf{J} = \mathbf{L} + \mathbf{S}. \tag{82}$$

For a single electron atom such as hydrogen, the spin is $s = 1/2$, so the allowed values of the total angular momentum j are

$$
\begin{aligned}
j &= \ell + s, ..., |\ell - s| \\
&= \begin{cases} \ell + \frac{1}{2}, \ell - \frac{1}{2}, & \ell \geq 1 \\ \frac{1}{2}, & \ell = 0 \end{cases}.
\end{aligned} \tag{83}
$$

The standard convention is to use lower-case letters (j, l, s) for the angular momenta of a single electron, and upper-case letters (J, L, S) for the angular momenta of the complete atom.

For atoms with more than one electron, we must add all the electron angular momenta together. Usually we add all the orbital angular momenta together to get the total orbital angular momentum L, add all the spin angular momenta to get the total spin S, and then couple L and S to get J. The results of this angular momentum coupling are denoted with **spectroscopic notation** to specify the atomic state (also called term notation or Russell-Saunders notation)

$$^{2S+1}L_J, \tag{84}$$

where S and J are numbers and L is a letter specifying the orbital angular momentum. The letters used for the orbital angular momentum states are

$$
\begin{array}{ccccccccc}
L = & 0 & 1 & 2 & 3 & 4 & 5 & 6 & 7 & ... \\
\text{letter} = & S & P & D & F & G & H & I & K & ...
\end{array} \tag{85}
$$

For example, the ground state of hydrogen has $L = 0$, $S = 1/2$, $J = 1/2$, and is denoted as $^2S_{1/2}$. This designation is the same for all the alkali atoms because they each have one electron outside a closed shell. The ground state of carbon has $L = 1$ and $S = 1$, which couple to form the $^3P_0$ state with $J = 0$. Other values of J are possible according to the rules we have developed, but they turn out to have higher energy because of internal perturbations.

SUMMARY

In this chapter, we have introduced the concept of adding or coupling angular momenta. We noted that all angular momenta, whether spin or orbital, obey the general eigenvalue equations

$$
\begin{aligned}
\mathbf{J}^2 |jm_j\rangle &= j(j+1)\hbar^2 |jm_j\rangle \\
J_z |jm_j\rangle &= m_j\hbar |jm_j\rangle.
\end{aligned} \tag{86}
$$

Hyperfine Structure and the Addition of Angular Momenta

We introduced the angular momentum ladder operators

$$J_+ = J_x + iJ_y$$
$$J_- = J_x - iJ_y$$
(87)

that raise and lower the magnetic quantum number according to the relation

$$J_\pm |jm_j\rangle = \hbar \left[j(j+1) - m_j(m_j \pm 1) \right]^{1/2} |j, m_j \pm 1\rangle.$$
(88)

We considered the general problem of coupling two angular momenta $\mathbf{J}_1$ and $\mathbf{J}_2$ together to form the total angular momentum

$$\mathbf{J} = \mathbf{J}_1 + \mathbf{J}_2.$$
(89)

We described a system of two angular momenta using either the uncoupled basis or the coupled basis

$$|j_1 j_2 m_1 m_2\rangle \quad \textit{uncoupled basis}$$
$$|JM\rangle \quad \textit{coupled basis.}$$
(90)

The allowed values of the coupled angular momentum quantum number are

$$J = j_1 + j_2, j_1 + j_2 - 1, j_1 + j_2 - 2, \dots |j_1 - j_2|$$
(91)

and the allowed coupled magnetic quantum numbers are

$$M = -J, -J + 1, \dots, J - 1, J.$$
(92)

We expressed the coupled basis vectors in terms of the uncoupled basis vectors using the expansion

$$|JM\rangle = \sum_{m_1=-j_1}^{j_1} \sum_{m_2=-j_2}^{j_2} C_{m_1 m_2 M}^{j_1 j_2 J} |j_1 j_2 m_1 m_2\rangle,$$
(93)

where the scalar products connecting the coupled and uncoupled bases are the Clebsch-Gordan coefficients

$$C_{m_1 m_2 M}^{j_1 j_2 J} = \langle j_1 j_2 m_1 m_2 | JM \rangle.$$
(94)

We studied the concept of angular momentum addition in the hyperfine structure of the ground state of hydrogen, which is governed by the Hamiltonian

$$H_{hf}' = \frac{A}{\hbar^2} \mathbf{S} \cdot \mathbf{I}$$
(95)

that couples together the electron spin $\mathbf{S}$ and the proton spin $\mathbf{I}$. The utility of the coupled basis was evidenced by the fact that the hyperfine Hamiltonian is not diagonal in the uncoupled basis, but it is diagonal in the coupled basis, where the coupled angular momentum is

$$\mathbf{F} = \mathbf{S} + \mathbf{I}.$$
(96)

Hyperfine Structure and the Addition of Angular Momenta

In this system of two spin-1/2 particles, the coupled basis in terms of the uncoupled basis is

$$\textit{coupled basis} \quad | \quad \textit{uncoupled basis}$$

$$\left.
\begin{aligned}
|11\rangle &= |\tfrac{1}{2}\tfrac{1}{2}\tfrac{1}{2}\tfrac{1}{2}\rangle = |++\rangle \\
|10\rangle &= \tfrac{1}{\sqrt{2}}\left(|\tfrac{1}{2}\tfrac{1}{2}\tfrac{1}{2}\tfrac{-1}{2}\rangle + |\tfrac{1}{2}\tfrac{1}{2}\tfrac{-1}{2}\tfrac{1}{2}\rangle\right) = \tfrac{1}{\sqrt{2}}\left(|+-\rangle + |-+\rangle\right) \\
|1,-1\rangle &= |\tfrac{1}{2}\tfrac{1}{2}\tfrac{-1}{2}\tfrac{-1}{2}\rangle = |--\rangle
\end{aligned}
\right\} \textit{Triplet} \tag{97}$$

$$\left.
|00\rangle = \tfrac{1}{\sqrt{2}}\left(|\tfrac{1}{2}\tfrac{1}{2}\tfrac{1}{2}\tfrac{-1}{2}\rangle - |\tfrac{1}{2}\tfrac{1}{2}\tfrac{-1}{2}\tfrac{1}{2}\rangle\right) = \tfrac{1}{\sqrt{2}}\left(|+-\rangle - |-+\rangle\right)
\right\} \textit{Singlet}.$$

In the hydrogen ground state, the hyperfine interaction causes the triplet levels to be displaced from the singlet level.

RESOURCES

Activities

This activity is available at

www.physics.oregonstate.edu/qmactivities

System of two spin-1/2 particles: Students review the spin eigenvalue equations, determine the possible states of a two-spin system, and find the matrix representations of operators in the two-spin system.

Further Reading

Pedagogical articles on the hyperfine interaction:

D. J. Griffiths, "Hyperfine splitting in the ground state of hydrogen," *Am. J. Phys.* **50**, 698–703 (1982).

G. W. Parker, "Spin current density and the hyperfine interaction in hydrogen," *Am. J. Phys.* **52**, 36–39 (1984).

Hyperfine Structure and the Addition of Angular Momenta: Problem Set

1 Verify the commutation relations in Eqs. (18),

$$[J_+, J_-] = 2\hbar J_z, \tag{18}$$

(19),

$$[\mathbf{J}^2, J_\pm] = 0, \tag{19}$$

and (20),

$$\begin{aligned}[J_z, J_+] &= +\hbar J_+ \\ [J_z, J_-] &= -\hbar J_-. \end{aligned} \tag{20}$$

2 Use the commutation relations in Eq. (20) to demonstrate that the angular momentum ladder operators act as advertised. Derive Eq. (23),

$$\boxed{J_\pm |jm_j\rangle = \hbar \left[j(j+1) - m_j(m_j \pm 1) \right]^{1/2} |j, m_j \pm 1\rangle}, \tag{23}$$

that characterizes the action of the ladder operators. (Hint: review the harmonic oscillator ladder operators.)

3 Show that the restriction that the angular momentum component J_z cannot be greater than the magnitude of $\mathbf{J}$ (i.e., the square root of $\mathbf{J}^2$) implies that the largest possible value of the magnetic quantum number is $m_j = j$.

4 Consider a generic spin-3/2 system.

a) Write down the eigenstates of this system and the eigenvalue equations for $\mathbf{S}^2$ and S_z.

b) Write down the matrices representing $\mathbf{S}^2$ and S_z by inspection.

c) Use Eq. (23) that characterizes the action of the ladder operators to generate the matrices representing S_x and S_y.

d) Find the eigenvalues of S_x.

5 Show that Eq. (31),

$$\begin{aligned} S_z |m_s m_I\rangle &= m_s \hbar |m_s m_I\rangle \\ I_z |m_s m_I\rangle &= m_I \hbar |m_s m_I\rangle, \end{aligned} \tag{31}$$

implies that the electron spin and proton spin operators commute with each other.

From Chapter 11 of *Quantum Mechanics: A Paradigms Approach*, First Edition. David H. McIntyre. Copyright © 2012 by Pearson Education, Inc. Published by Pearson Addison-Wesley. All rights reserved.

The companion websites for this text are http://physics.oregonstate.edu/portfolioswiki and http://physics.oregonstate.edu/qmactivities.

6 Use the eigenvalue equations (31) to derive the matrix representations in Eq. (32),

$$
S_z \doteq \frac{\hbar}{2}\begin{pmatrix} 1 & 0 & 0 & 0 \\ 0 & 1 & 0 & 0 \\ 0 & 0 & -1 & 0 \\ 0 & 0 & 0 & -1 \end{pmatrix}\begin{matrix} ++ \\ +- \\ -+ \\ -- \end{matrix}
$$

$$
I_z \doteq \frac{\hbar}{2}\begin{pmatrix} 1 & 0 & 0 & 0 \\ 0 & -1 & 0 & 0 \\ 0 & 0 & 1 & 0 \\ 0 & 0 & 0 & -1 \end{pmatrix}\begin{matrix} ++ \\ +- \\ -+ \\ -- \end{matrix} ,
$$

(32)

for the electron spin and proton spin component operators in the uncoupled basis. By similar means, find the matrix representations of $\mathbf{S}^2$ and $\mathbf{I}^2$ in the uncoupled basis and confirm that each is proportional to the identity matrix (see activity on system of two spin-1/2 particles).

7 Show that $\mathbf{S}\cdot\mathbf{I} = S_x I_x + S_y I_y + S_z I_z$ can be rewritten using the angular momentum ladder operators as $\mathbf{S}\cdot\mathbf{I} = \frac{1}{2}(S_+ I_- + S_- I_+) + S_z I_z$.

8 Calculate the action of the ladder operators S_+, S_-, I_+, I_- on each of the four uncoupled angular momentum states $|\pm\pm\rangle$ of the ground state of hydrogen. Use your results to calculate the matrix representing the hyperfine Hamiltonian $H'_{hf} = A\mathbf{S}\cdot\mathbf{I}/\hbar^2$ in the uncoupled basis.

9 Show that the electron and proton spin observables $\mathbf{S}^2$ and $\mathbf{I}^2$ commute with the hyperfine Hamiltonian $H'_{hf} = A\mathbf{S}\cdot\mathbf{I}/\hbar^2$ and that the component observables S_z and I_z do not.

10 Diagonalize the matrix representing $\mathbf{F}^2$ in Eq. (54),

$$
\mathbf{F}^2 \doteq \hbar^2\begin{pmatrix} 2 & 0 & 0 & 0 \\ 0 & \boxed{\begin{matrix}1 & 1\\1 & 1\end{matrix}} & 0 \\ 0 & & 0 \\ 0 & 0 & 0 & 2 \end{pmatrix}\begin{matrix} ++ \\ +- \\ -+ \\ -- \end{matrix} ,
$$

(54)

and confirm the eigenvalues and eigenstates quoted in the text.

11 Consider the ground state hyperfine system of the hydrogen atom. Calculate the matrices for $\mathbf{S}^2$, $\mathbf{I}^2$, and $\mathbf{F}^2$ in the coupled basis and show that the hyperfine Hamiltonian is diagonal in this basis.

12 Consider a system of two particles. Particle #1 has spin 1 $(s_1 = 1)$ and particle #2 has spin 1/2 $(s_2 = 1/2)$. The total spin of the system is $\mathbf{S} = \mathbf{S}_1 + \mathbf{S}_2$.

 a) List all the possible uncoupled basis states $|s_1 s_2 m_1 m_2\rangle$.

 b) Identify the stretched state $|s_1 s_2 s_1 s_2\rangle$.

 c) Starting with the stretched state, generate all the coupled basis states $|SM\rangle$ using the lowering operator and the orthogonality condition as outlined in Section 6 of the text.

 d) From the results in (c), construct the Clebsch-Gordan table for this system.

13 Use the scheme developed in Section 6 for generating coupled basis states to create the Clebsch-Gordan coefficients in Table 3.

14 Consider a system of two angular momenta j_1 and j_2. Demonstrate that the total number of states is $(2j_1 + 1)(2j_2 + 1)$ whether you count states in the coupled or the uncoupled basis.

15 Consider a system of two angular momenta with $j_1 = 1$ and $j_2 = \frac{1}{2}$.

    a) Write down all the possible states of this system in the uncoupled basis $|j_1 j_2 m_1 m_2\rangle$.

    b) What are the allowed values of the coupled angular momentum quantum numbers J and M for this system?

    c) Write down all the possible states of this system in the coupled basis $|JM\rangle$.

    d) Use the Clebsch-Gordan coefficients in Table 3 to express the coupled basis states $|JM\rangle$ in terms of the uncoupled basis states $|j_1 j_2 m_1 m_2\rangle$.

16 Deuterium is an isotope of hydrogen with one electron bound to a nucleus (the deuteron) comprising a proton and a neutron. The deuteron has spin $I = 1$ and has a gyromagnetic ratio $g_D = 0.857$, which is the only change needed to use Eq. (10),

$$A = \frac{2\mu_0}{3} g_e \mu_B g_p \mu_N |\psi_{1s}(0)|^2, \tag{10}$$

for the hyperfine interaction in deuterium. Determine the hyperfine structure of the ground state of deuterium (i.e., find the eigenvalues and eigenstates). Calculate the splitting of the ground state and produce a figure like Fig. 4 for deuterium.

17 A positronium atom is a hydrogen-like atom with a positron $(m = m_e, q = +e, \text{spin } 1/2)$ as a nucleus and a bound electron. The hyperfine structure in the ground state of positronium is described by a perturbation Hamiltonian $H' = A \mathbf{S}_1 \cdot \mathbf{S}_2 / \hbar^2$ where $\mathbf{S}_i$ are the spins of the electron and positron.

    a) What is the Bohr energy of the ground state of positronium (ignore hyperfine structure for now)?

    b) The electron and positron spins can be coupled to form the total spin $\mathbf{S}$ of the atom. Write down the spin states of the coupled and uncoupled bases and how they relate to each other.

    c) Express the hyperfine Hamiltonian in the ground state as a matrix in both the coupled and uncoupled spin bases.

    d) Determine the effect of the hyperfine perturbation interaction on the ground state of positronium. Draw an energy level diagram to illustrate your results.

18 Consider two electrons, each with spin angular momentum $s_i = 1/2$ and orbital angular momentum $\ell_i = 1$.

    a) What are the possible values of the quantum number L for the total orbital angular momentum $\mathbf{L} = \mathbf{L}_1 + \mathbf{L}_2$?

    b) What are the possible values of the quantum number S for the total spin angular momentum $\mathbf{S} = \mathbf{S}_1 + \mathbf{S}_2$?

    c) Using the results from (a) and (b), find the possible quantum numbers J for the total angular momentum $\mathbf{J} = \mathbf{L} + \mathbf{S}$.

    d) What are the possible values of the quantum number j_1 of the total angular momentum $\mathbf{J}_1 = \mathbf{L}_1 + \mathbf{S}_1$ of electron #1? Same question for electron #2.

    e) Using the results from (d), find the possible quantum numbers J for the total angular momentum $\mathbf{J} = \mathbf{J}_1 + \mathbf{J}_2$ and compare to the results in (c).

19 Express the angular momentum ladder operators in the position representation. Apply the raising operator to the spherical harmonic $Y_2^0(\theta, \phi)$ and verify that your result agrees with Eq. (23).

20 Consider a system of two particles. Particle #1 has spin 1 ($s_1 = 1$) and particle #2 has spin 1/2 ($s_2 = 1/2$). The system is in a state with total spin 1/2 and z–component $-\hbar/2$. If you measure the z–component of the spin of particle #1, what are the possible results, and what are the probabilities of the measurements? Same question for particle #2.

21 Consider a system comprising three electrons, each with spin angular momentum $s_i = 1/2$. Ignore the orbital angular momentum.

a) How many possible spin states are there in this system? Identify the states in the uncoupled basis.

b) Identify the stretched state of the system and use the lowering operator and the orthogonality condition as outlined in Section 6 of the text to generate all the coupled basis states. (Hint: use Gram-Schmidt orthogonalization.)

c) From the results in (b), construct a "Clebsch-Gordan table" for this system. Your answer is not unique.

Perturbation of Hydrogen

From Chapter 12 of *Quantum Mechanics: A Paradigms Approach*, First Edition. David H. McIntyre. Copyright © 2012 by Pearson Education, Inc. Published by Pearson Addison-Wesley. All rights reserved.

The companion websites for this text are http://physics.oregonstate.edu/portfolioswiki and http://physics. oregonstate.edu/qmactivities.

Perturbation of Hydrogen

Spectroscopy of the hydrogen atom has played a central role in the development of quantum mechanics itself and of perturbation theory in particular. Nobel Laureates Arthur Schawlow and Theodor Hänsch made important advances in hydrogen atom spectroscopy and noted that, "The spectrum of the hydrogen atom has proved to be the Rosetta stone of modern physics: once this pattern of lines had been deciphered much else could also be understood." The scientific process whereby advances in experimental precision of spectroscopic measurements have led to advances in theoretical understanding of the hydrogen atom has been repeated throughout the last century. State of the art techniques now permit the energy levels of the hydrogen atom to be measured with 15 digits of precision, providing one of the best testing grounds for quantum theory.

Recall the Stark effect—the perturbation of hydrogen energy levels by an external electric field. Also recall the hyperfine interaction—the perturbation of hydrogen energy levels by the magnetic interaction between the electron spin and the nuclear spin. In this chapter we study further magnetic perturbations—due to both external and internal magnetic fields. The internal fields give rise to the **fine structure** of the hydrogen energy levels and to the hyperfine structure. The external fields give rise to the **Zeeman effect**—the magnetic analog to the Stark effect. We also study internal perturbations due to relativistic effects, which are part of the fine structure. We treat all of these effects as small perturbations to the hydrogen energy levels. It is possible to treat some of the internal perturbations exactly using the relativistic Dirac equation, but that is beyond the scope of this text.

1 ■ HYDROGEN ENERGY LEVELS

Let's review what we know about the energy levels of hydrogen. The zeroth-order hydrogen atom Hamiltonian is a combination of kinetic and potential energy terms:

$$H_0 = \frac{p^2}{2m} - \frac{e^2}{4\pi\varepsilon_0 r}. \tag{1}$$

The zeroth-order energy eigenvalue equation is

$$H_0|n\ell m\rangle = E_n^{(0)}|n\ell m\rangle, \tag{2}$$

where the zeroth-order eigenstate wave functions are

$$|n\ell m\rangle \doteq R_{n\ell}(r)Y_\ell^m(\theta,\phi) \tag{3}$$

and the zeroth-order energy eigenvalues are

$$E_n^{(0)} = -\frac{1}{n^2} \frac{m}{2\hbar^2} \left(\frac{e^2}{4\pi\varepsilon_0} \right)^2.$$

(4)

We refer to these energy levels as the Bohr energies, even though Bohr found them using an incomplete quantum mechanical analysis. The Bohr energies are independent of the quantum numbers ℓ and m, which implies a degeneracy of n^2 for each n level. A diagram of the zeroth-order energy levels is shown in Fig. 1, where we have identified the separate ℓ states of each n level. One important result of this chapter is that some of the degeneracy of the n levels is lifted. In Eq. (2), we have suppressed the superscript on the zeroth-order eigenstates $|n\ell m\rangle$ but not the energies $E_n^{(0)}$ because we are focused on finding energy corrections and will not be concerned with eigenstate corrections, so all references to eigenstates in this chapter are to zeroth-order eigenstates.

The zeroth-order hydrogen energies are often expressed in terms of the Rydberg energy

$$Ryd = \frac{m}{2\hbar^2} \left(\frac{e^2}{4\pi\varepsilon_0} \right)^2 \cong 13.6 \text{ eV}.$$

(5)

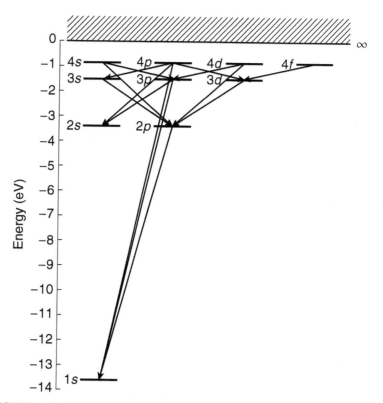

FIGURE 1 Energy level diagram of hydrogen showing the $n = 1$ through $n = 4$ states. Arrows indicate the allowed optical transitions between the levels shown.

It is convenient to express the Rydberg energy in terms of another characteristic energy multiplied by a dimensionless constant:

$$Ryd = \frac{1}{2}mc^2 \left(\frac{e^2}{4\pi\varepsilon_0\hbar c}\right)^2.$$

(6)

The characteristic energy is the electron rest mass energy $E_{rest} = mc^2$, and the dimensionless constant is the fine-structure constant

$$\alpha = \frac{e^2}{4\pi\varepsilon_0\hbar c}.$$

(7)

With these choices, the hydrogen energy levels take on the simple form:

$$\boxed{E_n^{(0)} = -\frac{1}{n^2}\frac{1}{2}\alpha^2 mc^2}.$$

(8)

Given all these different formulae, it may not be clear which numbers are most important. Most would agree that there are three numbers from these formulae that you should have ingrained into your memory as well as your own name. With these in your memory banks, you will be able to do quantum mechanical calculations when stranded on a desert island. They are: (1) the hydrogen ground state energy:

$$\boxed{E_{1s}^{(0)} = -13.6 \text{ eV}},$$

(9)

(2) the electron rest mass energy:

$$\boxed{mc^2 = 511 \text{ keV}},$$

(10)

and (3) the fine-structure constant:

$$\boxed{\alpha = \frac{1}{137}}.$$

(11)

Because these three constants are related by Eq. (8),

$$E_{1s}^{(0)} = -\frac{1}{2}\alpha^2 mc^2$$

$$-13.6 \text{ eV} \cong -\frac{1}{2}\frac{1}{(137)^2} 511 \text{ keV}$$

(12)

you need remember only two of them if you know the hydrogen energy level equation (8).

Our plan in this chapter is to discuss the real hydrogen atom by looking at various perturbations that shift the energy levels from the Bohr energies shown in Fig. 1. In order to provide a road map for our journey, we show these perturbation corrections in Fig. 2 for the first two states of hydrogen, ordered from left to right by decreasing magnitude of the correction. The first correction is the fine structure, which includes several terms arising from the electron spin and from relativity. The **Lamb shift** is a quantum electrodynamic effect that we discuss only qualitatively. The hyperfine structure is caused by the interaction of the electron and nuclear magnetic moments.

Perturbation of Hydrogen

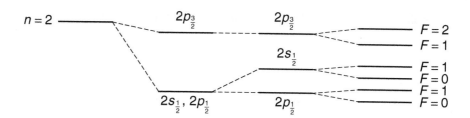

Bohr Energies   Fine Structure   Lamb Shift   Hyperfine Structure

FIGURE 2   Corrections to the $n = 1$ and $n = 2$ Bohr energy levels ordered by magnitude (large to small, left to right). The shifts are not drawn to scale and are increasingly magnified from left to right.

The fine-structure constant α sets the scale for these perturbations, as outlined in Table 1. The reason is that the fine-structure constant is a dimensionless measure of the strength of the electromagnetic interaction; it is also called the electromagnetic coupling constant. Because $\alpha \ll 1$, the perturbation approach to quantum electrodynamics is valid.

The fine-structure constant in hydrogen perturbations also sets the scale of the electron velocity. The total energy of the hydrogen atom is roughly equal parts kinetic and potential energies:

$$E \sim T \sim V. \tag{13}$$

Relating the Bohr energy to the kinetic term

$$\frac{1}{2}\alpha^2 mc^2 \sim \frac{1}{2}mv^2 \quad \Rightarrow \quad \alpha^2 \sim \frac{v^2}{c^2} \tag{14}$$

tells us that

$$\alpha \sim \frac{v}{c}. \tag{15}$$

Table 1   Hydrogen Energy Scales

Term	Scale
Bohr energy	$\alpha^2 mc^2$
Fine structure	$\alpha^4 mc^2$
Lamb shift	$\alpha^5 mc^2$
Hyperfine structure	$(m_e/m_p)\alpha^4 mc^2$

Hence, the electron has a speed roughly 1% of the speed of light $\left(\alpha = 1/137 \simeq 1\%\right)$. This velocity is large enough to make relativity important to the bound state energies, but it is small enough that the perturbative approach is valid.

2 ■ FINE STRUCTURE OF HYDROGEN

The fine structure of hydrogen has two primary contributions: (1) the relativistic correction caused by the electron velocity, and (2) the spin-orbit correction caused by the magnetic interaction between the electron spin magnetic moment and the magnetic field generated by the electron orbital angular momentum.

2.1 ■ Relativistic Correction

The relativistic energy of a particle includes kinetic energy and rest mass energy, but not potential energy:

$$E = \left(m^2c^4 + p^2c^2\right)^{1/2}. \tag{16}$$

We would like to expand E in terms of a small parameter. From our discussion above, we expect that small parameter to be the ratio v/c. In quantum mechanics, we use momentum instead of velocity, so the relevant small parameter is the ratio p/mc. We create a perturbative expansion of the relativistic energy by factoring out mc^2 from Eq. (16) to isolate the ratio p/mc

$$E = mc^2\sqrt{1 + \left(\frac{p}{mc}\right)^2}, \tag{17}$$

using the binomial expansion

$$E = mc^2\left[1 + \frac{1}{2}\left(\frac{p}{mc}\right)^2 - \frac{1}{8}\left(\frac{p}{mc}\right)^4 + ...\right], \tag{18}$$

and keeping the three leading terms:

$$E \cong mc^2 + \frac{p^2}{2m} - \frac{p^4}{8m^3c^2}. \tag{19}$$

The leading term in Eq. (19) is the rest energy of the electron, which we did not include in the zeroth-order Hamiltonian in Eq. (1). There is no need to include it now because it only shifts the zero level of energies. The second term in Eq. (19) is the classical expression for the kinetic energy that we used in the zeroth-order Hamiltonian. The third term is the new relativistic kinetic energy correction, and it becomes the Hamiltonian for the relativistic perturbation:

$$H'_{rel} = -\frac{p^4}{8m^3c^2}. \tag{20}$$

Note that this perturbation is negative, which means it increases the binding energy. This perturbation Hamiltonian is two orders of p/mc smaller than the zeroth-order Hamiltonian, so we expect the resultant energy correction to be smaller than the zeroth-order energy differences by two orders of the fine-structure constant α, as indicated in Table 1.

Now that we have the Hamiltonian, we apply perturbation theory to find the energy level corrections due to this relativistic term. We first ask whether we should use nondegenerate or degenerate perturbation theory. We know that the hydrogen energy levels are degenerate with respect to the quantum numbers ℓ and m, so we expect to require degenerate perturbation theory. However, the operator p^4 commutes with the operators $\mathbf{L}^2$ and L_z, so the perturbation Hamiltonian is diagonal within each degenerate subspace (Problem 1). Degenerate perturbation theory requires us to diagonalize the perturbation matrix within each degenerate subspace, so we simply identify the energy corrections from the diagonal elements. This perturbation has nothing to do with the spin, so it commutes with the spin operator. This means we can ignore the spin for now and use the states $|n\ell m\rangle$ for the unperturbed basis. (Note that we use m for mass and for the magnetic quantum number, but it is clear from the context which is which.)

The first-order relativistic energy correction is

$$E_{rel}^{(1)} = \langle H'_{rel} \rangle = \langle n\ell m | H'_{rel} | n\ell m \rangle$$

$$= -\frac{1}{8m^3c^2} \langle n\ell m | p^4 | n\ell m \rangle. \tag{21}$$

The matrix element of the operator p^4 requires integrals of fourth-order derivatives of the wave functions. There is an easier way. Use the zeroth-order Hamiltonian to express the operator p^2 in terms of other operators:

$$H_0 = \frac{p^2}{2m} - \frac{e^2}{4\pi\varepsilon_0 r}$$

$$p^2 = 2m\left(H_0 + \frac{e^2}{4\pi\varepsilon_0 r}\right). \tag{22}$$

The matrix elements we need are

$$\langle n\ell m | p^4 | n\ell m \rangle = \langle n\ell m | p^2 p^2 | n\ell m \rangle$$

$$= \langle n\ell m | 2m\left(H_0 + \frac{e^2}{4\pi\varepsilon_0 r}\right) 2m\left(H_0 + \frac{e^2}{4\pi\varepsilon_0 r}\right) | n\ell m \rangle. \tag{23}$$

The zeroth-order eigenvalue equation $H_0 | n\ell m \rangle = E_n^{(0)} | n\ell m \rangle$ tells us the action of the Hamiltonian H_0 on the eigenstates, so we get

$$\langle n\ell m | p^4 | n\ell m \rangle = 4m^2 \langle n\ell m | \left(E_n^{(0)} + \frac{e^2}{4\pi\varepsilon_0 r}\right)\left(E_n^{(0)} + \frac{e^2}{4\pi\varepsilon_0 r}\right) | n\ell m \rangle$$

$$= 4m^2\left(\left(E_n^{(0)}\right)^2 + 2E_n^{(0)}\frac{e^2}{4\pi\varepsilon_0}\left\langle \frac{1}{r}\right\rangle_{n\ell} + \left(\frac{e^2}{4\pi\varepsilon_0}\right)^2 \left\langle \frac{1}{r^2}\right\rangle_{n\ell}\right), \tag{24}$$

where we have used shorthand for the matrix elements (and have dropped the m label because the matrix elements do not depend on m):

$$\langle f(r) \rangle_{n\ell} = \langle n\ell m | f(r) | n\ell m \rangle. \tag{25}$$

The resultant relativistic energy correction is

$$\langle H'_{rel} \rangle = -\frac{1}{2mc^2} \left[\left(E_n^{(0)} \right)^2 + 2\frac{e^2}{4\pi\varepsilon_0} E_n^{(0)} \left\langle \frac{1}{r} \right\rangle_{n\ell} + \frac{e^4}{(4\pi\varepsilon_0)^2} \left\langle \frac{1}{r^2} \right\rangle_{n\ell} \right]. \tag{26}$$

Now we are left with two spatial integrals that are much simpler than the ones you would have obtained from the matrix elements of p^4 directly. These integrals are quite common because they tell us the expectation values of different powers of the radial position. The radial operator does not involve the angular variables, so the angular parts of the integrals are unity (the $R_{n\ell}(r)$ and $Y_\ell^m(\theta, \phi)$ wave functions are separately normalized) and the matrix elements reduce to radial integrals:

$$\left\langle \frac{1}{r} \right\rangle_{n\ell} = \int_0^\infty \frac{1}{r} R_{n\ell}^2(r) r^2 dr = \frac{1}{n^2 a_0}$$

$$\left\langle \frac{1}{r^2} \right\rangle_{n\ell} = \int_0^\infty \frac{1}{r^2} R_{n\ell}^2(r) r^2 dr = \frac{1}{\left(\ell + \frac{1}{2} \right) n^3 a_0^2}. \tag{27}$$

To make the three terms in Eq. (26) have the same form and to collect constants, use the hydrogen energy formula

$$E_n^{(0)} = -\frac{1}{n^2} \frac{e^2}{2(4\pi\varepsilon_0) a_0} = -\frac{1}{2n^2} \alpha^2 mc^2 \tag{28}$$

to rewrite $e^2/4\pi\varepsilon_0$

$$\frac{e^2}{4\pi\varepsilon_0} = a_0 \alpha^2 mc^2, \tag{29}$$

with the final result that

$$E_{rel}^{(1)} = -\frac{1}{2} \alpha^4 mc^2 \left[\frac{1}{n^3 \left(\ell + \frac{1}{2} \right)} - \frac{3}{4n^4} \right]. \tag{30}$$

As we expected, the relativistic correction is α^2 times smaller than the Bohr energy and is negative.

2.2 ■ Spin-Orbit Coupling

Spin-orbit coupling is the second part of the hydrogen fine structure. The *orbital* motion of the electron causes the electron to experience a magnetic field, which interacts with the *spin* magnetic moment of the electron, hence the name. This internal magnetic field effect is distinct from effects due to external magnetic fields—the Zeeman effect—that we study later in this chapter. It is also distinct from the magnetic field generated by the nuclear spin, which causes the hyperfine interaction. The origin of the internal orbital magnetic field can be understood in either of two ways. In one view, the electron moves in the electric field of the proton, which gives rise to a motional magnetic field. Or we can view the problem from the electron's point of view: the electron sees a proton orbiting it, which creates a magnetic field at the electron, with the same resultant interaction. Let's use this second viewpoint to calculate the effect classically and then extend it to quantum mechanics.

We treat the proton orbiting the electron as a current loop, as shown in Fig. 3, and use the Biot-Savart law to calculate the magnetic field from that loop of current. The magnetic field at the center of the loop is

$$B = \frac{\mu_0 I}{2r},$$

(31)

where the current I is that of the proton with charge $+e$ orbiting in a period $T = 2\pi r/v$, with v being the speed. The speed of the proton in the electron frame is the same as the speed of the electron in the proton frame, so we relate the field experienced by the electron to the electron angular momentum through its relation with the velocity:

$$L = mvr$$
$$v = \frac{L}{mr}.$$

(32)

The resulting magnetic field is

$$B = \frac{\mu_0}{2r} \frac{eL}{2\pi mr^2} = \frac{\mu_0 eL}{4\pi mr^3} = \frac{eL}{4\pi \varepsilon_0 mc^2 r^3}.$$

(33)

We make this into a vector equation because $\mathbf{B}$ and $\mathbf{L}$ point in the same direction:

$$\mathbf{B} = \frac{e}{4\pi \varepsilon_0 mc^2 r^3} \mathbf{L}.$$

(34)

The energy of interaction between a magnetic dipole and a magnetic field is

$$E = -\boldsymbol{\mu} \cdot \mathbf{B}.$$

(35)

The intrinsic (spin) magnetic moment of the electron is

$$\boldsymbol{\mu} = -\frac{e}{m} \mathbf{S},$$

(36)

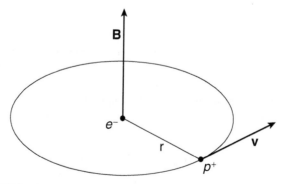

FIGURE 3 A proton rotating about an electron generates a magnetic field at the electron position.

using the electron gyromagnetic ratio $g_e = 2$. The resultant spin-orbit interaction energy is

$$E_{SO} = -\left(-\frac{e}{m}\mathbf{S}\right)\cdot\frac{e}{4\pi\varepsilon_0 mc^2 r^3}\mathbf{L}$$

$$= \frac{e^2}{4\pi\varepsilon_0 m^2 c^2 r^3}\mathbf{L}\cdot\mathbf{S}. \tag{37}$$

By substituting the quantum mechanical operators for spin and orbital angular momentum, we arrive at the Hamiltonian for the spin-orbit perturbation. However, the classical result in Eq. (37) is incorrect by a factor of $1/2$ due to Thomas precession—a relativistic effect due to the acceleration of the electron. We include this correction in our quantum mechanical Hamiltonian:

$$H'_{SO} = \frac{e^2}{8\pi\varepsilon_0 m^2 c^2 r^3}\mathbf{L}\cdot\mathbf{S}. \tag{38}$$

We are now in a position to use the addition of angular momentum tools. We are including spin in the hydrogen atom now, so we must incorporate spin into the eigenstates. Previously, we specified the hydrogen energy eigenstates as $|n\ell m\rangle$. We now specify the zeroth-order eigenstates as $|n\ell s m_\ell m_s\rangle$, where the subscript on the orbital magnetic quantum number m_ℓ distinguishes it from the spin magnetic quantum number m_s. The states $|n\ell s m_\ell m_s\rangle$ are still zeroth-order energy eigenstates because spin does not play a role in the zeroth-order Hamiltonian. The states $|n\ell s m_\ell m_s\rangle$ are the "uncoupled states", but you could also use the "coupled basis" $|n\ell s j m_j\rangle$, which is characterized by the total angular momentum $\mathbf{J} = \mathbf{L} + \mathbf{S}$. The coupled basis is preferred for the hyperfine interaction problem because the total angular momentum $\mathbf{F} = \mathbf{S} + \mathbf{I}$ is conserved, but the individual angular momenta $\mathbf{S}$ and $\mathbf{I}$ are not due to the interaction $\mathbf{S}\cdot\mathbf{I}$. Similarly, the $\mathbf{L}\cdot\mathbf{S}$ interaction in the spin-orbit perturbation Hamiltonian in Eq. (38) causes the individual angular momenta $\mathbf{L}$ and $\mathbf{S}$ to not be conserved and the total angular momentum $\mathbf{J} = \mathbf{L} + \mathbf{S}$ to be conserved. Hence, the spin-orbit Hamiltonian is not diagonal in the uncoupled $|n\ell s m_\ell m_s\rangle$basis, but it is diagonal in the coupled $|n\ell s j m_j\rangle$basis. Once again, the "smart" choice is the coupled basis because it makes the diagonalization procedure required by degenerate perturbation theory much easier—trivial, in fact.

As with the hyperfine interaction, we use the definition of the total angular momentum to find a convenient expression for the scalar product term $\mathbf{L}\cdot\mathbf{S}$ in the spin-orbit interaction in terms of coupled basis operators:

$$\mathbf{J} = \mathbf{L} + \mathbf{S}$$
$$\mathbf{J}^2 = \mathbf{L}^2 + \mathbf{S}^2 + 2\mathbf{L}\cdot\mathbf{S} \tag{39}$$
$$\mathbf{L}\cdot\mathbf{S} = \tfrac{1}{2}(\mathbf{J}^2 - \mathbf{L}^2 - \mathbf{S}^2).$$

The operators J^2, L^2, and S^2 are diagonal in the coupled basis, so the spin-orbit Hamiltonian is diagonal. If we had chosen the uncoupled basis, then we would have expressed the scalar product $\mathbf{L}\cdot\mathbf{S}$ using uncoupled basis operators:

$$\mathbf{L}\cdot\mathbf{S} = L_x S_x + L_y S_y + L_z S_z$$
$$= \tfrac{1}{2}(L_+ S_- + L_- S_+) + L_z S_z. \tag{40}$$

$\mathbf{L \cdot S}$ is not diagonal in the uncoupled basis because the angular momentum ladder operators connect adjacent states, just as we find for the $\mathbf{S \cdot I}$ matrix for the hyperfine structure calculation (Problem 2).

When the perturbing Hamiltonian is already diagonal within the degenerate subspace, then first-order nondegenerate and degenerate perturbation theory are equivalent. Hence, the energy correction due to spin-orbit coupling is obtained by finding the expectation values

$$E_{SO}^{(1)} = \langle H'_{SO} \rangle = \langle n\ell sjm_j | H'_{SO} | n\ell sjm_j \rangle, \tag{41}$$

which are the diagonal matrix elements of the perturbation Hamiltonian in the degenerate subspace in the coupled basis. Substituting the spin-orbit Hamiltonian from Eq. (38) yields

$$E_{SO}^{(1)} = \frac{e^2}{8\pi\varepsilon_0 m^2 c^2} \langle n\ell sjm_j | \frac{1}{r^3} \mathbf{L \cdot S} | n\ell sjm_j \rangle, \tag{42}$$

and using Eq. (39), we find

$$E_{SO}^{(1)} = \frac{e^2}{16\pi\varepsilon_0 m^2 c^2} \left\langle \frac{1}{r^3} \right\rangle_{n\ell} \langle \ell sjm_j | \mathbf{J}^2 - \mathbf{L}^2 - \mathbf{S}^2 | \ell sjm_j \rangle. \tag{43}$$

The angular momentum matrix element is

$$\langle \ell sjm_j | \mathbf{J}^2 - \mathbf{L}^2 - \mathbf{S}^2 | \ell sjm_j \rangle = \left[j(j+1) - \ell(\ell+1) - s(s+1) \right] \hbar^2, \tag{44}$$

and the radial matrix element is

$$\left\langle \frac{1}{r^3} \right\rangle_{n\ell} = \frac{1}{a_0^3 n^3 \ell \left(\ell + \frac{1}{2} \right)(\ell + 1)}. \tag{45}$$

Collecting constants, and writing the Bohr radius as $a_0 = \hbar/\alpha mc$, we find the spin-orbit energy correction

$$E_{SO}^{(1)} = \frac{1}{4} \alpha^4 mc^2 \frac{j(j+1) - \ell(\ell+1) - \frac{3}{4}}{n^3 \ell \left(\ell + \frac{1}{2} \right)(\ell + 1)}. \tag{46}$$

The spin-orbit shift is α^2 times smaller than the Bohr energy, as is the relativistic correction. For an s state, with $\ell = 0$, the expression in Eq. (46) is problematic because the denominator is zero, but the numerator is also zero because $j = 1/2$ is the only possibility for the total angular momentum quantum number when $\ell = 0$. This problem with the $\ell = 0$ case is not really a problem, because we do not expect any spin-orbit coupling for s states with no orbital angular momentum to create a magnetic field. Hence, the spin-orbit correction in Eq. (46) applies only to the cases $\ell \neq 0$.

The total fine-structure correction is the sum of the relativistic and spin-orbit corrections. If we ignore the problem with the $\ell = 0$ spin-orbit term for the moment and add together the results in Eqs. (30) and (46), we obtain (Problem 3):

$$E_{fs}^{(1)} = E_{rel}^{(1)} + E_{SO}^{(1)} = -\frac{1}{2} \alpha^4 mc^2 \frac{1}{n^3} \left[\frac{1}{j + \frac{1}{2}} - \frac{3}{4n} \right]. \tag{47}$$

This result depends on j, but not on ℓ, so the problem of the $\ell = 0$ singularity is gone (see below) and miraculously we can use Eq. (47) for all ℓ levels. The j dependence in the fine-structure correction lifts some of the degeneracy of the nonrelativistic $E_n^{(0)}$ levels in hydrogen, which are $2n^2$ degenerate when spin is included. The lifting of the degeneracy is depicted in Fig. 4 for the energy levels $n = 1, 2, 3$. States with the same quantum numbers n and j have the same fine-structure energy, even though they may have different values of the orbital angular momentum quantum number ℓ. This degeneracy is exact to all orders in the relativistic Dirac theory (but not in the real atom—see below).

The miraculous resolution of the $\ell = 0$ problem where the relativistic and spin-orbit terms add to give the total fine-structure correction, masks a subtle physical effect. By ignoring the restriction of the spin-orbit correction to $\ell \neq 0$ as we did, the sum of the spin-orbit and relativistic corrections just happens to include a new term for the $\ell = 0$ case. This new term is known as the **Darwin term**. The physical explanation of the Darwin term requires relativistic quantum mechanics in the form of the Dirac equation, which predicts that the electron wave function includes some components at relativistic energies that lead to high frequency oscillation of the electron motion. This trembling or jittering motion of the electron—**zitterbewegung** in German—smears out the electron, making it appear bigger than an ideal point particle. A larger electron is bound less strongly to a point nucleus if the electron-nucleus separation is less than the effective size of the trembling electron. The *zitterbewegung* effect is still much smaller than the Bohr radius a_0, so the Darwin term is limited to s-states because they are the only states with a finite probability of being near the origin.

The separate contributions of the spin-orbit, relativistic, and Darwin terms to the fine structure are shown in Fig. 5 for the $n = 2$ states. The ℓ-dependent spin-orbit interaction splits the degeneracy of the $n = 2$ levels, but the relativistic effect plus the Darwin term brings the two $j = 1/2$ levels, $2s_{1/2}$ and $2p_{1/2}$, back together. The sign difference between the spin-orbit corrections of the $2p_{1/2}$ and $2p_{3/2}$ states arises from the differing relative orientations of the spin and orbital angular momenta in these states, which is also evident later when we study the Zeeman effect.

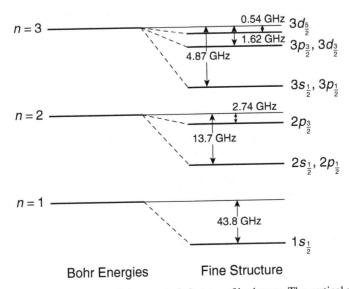

FIGURE 4 Fine structure of the $n = 1, 2, 3$ states of hydrogen. The vertical scale is different for each n level and the separation between n levels is not to scale.

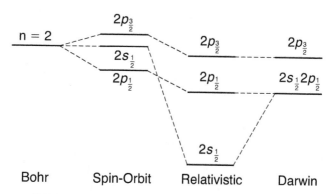

FIGURE 5 Hydrogen fine structure in the $n = 2$ level.

The degeneracy of j states in the Dirac model is finally lifted when we consider **quantum electrodynamics (QED)**. In QED, the electromagnetic field is quantized in a manner similar to an harmonic oscillator problem. This approach works because the electromagnetic field energy is the sum of squares $(\mathbf{E}^2 + \mathbf{B}^2)$ and the same concept of ladder operators is applicable. The ladder operators of the electromagnetic field correspond to the creation and annihilation of photons, with the state $|n\rangle$ representing n photons in one mode of the light field. The ground state $|0\rangle$ represents the vacuum state, where no photons are present. However, the ground state energy $\hbar\omega/2$ implies that there is some residual electromagnetic field in the vacuum, even when no photons are present. This residual field acts on the electron and causes it to move about and become smeared out—similar to the *zitterbewegung* of the Darwin term (the same effect but a different cause). The result of this perturbation is that s-states are bound less tightly and are shifted up slightly in energy, as shown in Fig. 2. This shift is known as the **Lamb shift**, named after Willis Lamb who discovered this effect in 1947. Lamb and his graduate student Robert Retherford measured the energy difference between the $2s_{1/2}$ and $2p_{1/2}$ states by inducing transitions between these two states using microwave equipment that had been developed during World War II. Soon after the experiment, Hans Bethe made a theoretical estimate of the effect, which laid the groundwork for the development of QED. Willis Lamb won the Nobel Prize in physics in 1955 for this groundbreaking work.

3 ■ ZEEMAN EFFECT

The **Zeeman effect** is the shift of atomic energy levels caused by an external applied magnetic field. The applied field couples to the magnetic moments in the atom associated with the orbital and spin angular momenta of the electron and the proton spin angular momentum. The Zeeman effect occurs in all atoms, but we limit this presentation to the hydrogen atom.

The energy of interaction between the applied magnetic field and the magnetic moments in the atom is

$$E = -\boldsymbol{\mu}\cdot\mathbf{B}. \tag{48}$$

The magnetic moments of the electron are proportional to the Bohr magneton

$$\mu_B = \frac{e\hbar}{2m_e} \cong h \times 1.4 \frac{\text{MHz}}{\text{Gauss}}. \tag{49}$$

The magnetic moment of the proton is approximately 1000 times smaller because of the large proton mass, so we neglect the proton contribution to the Zeeman effect.

3.1 ■ Zeeman Effect without Spin

Let's begin by considering a spin-independent Zeeman effect, where we ignore the spin of the electron. This effect is called the "normal Zeeman effect" in the literature, but that name is misleading because the spin and orbital magnetic moments contribute equally. Nevertheless, we use this unrealistic model because it is an easy calculation and it introduces us to the essential features of the Zeeman effect. Because we are ignoring the electron spin, we also ignore the fine structure and consider the model of the hydrogen atom that includes only the kinetic energy and the Coulomb interaction energy, with eigenstates $|n\ell m_\ell\rangle$ and Bohr energies $E_n^{(0)} = -Ryd/n^2$. We perturb the system by applying a magnetic field $\mathbf{B}$ aligned along the z-axis. The electron magnetic moment associated with the orbital motion

$$\boldsymbol{\mu}_L = -\frac{e}{2m_e}\mathbf{L} = -g_\ell\mu_B\frac{\mathbf{L}}{\hbar} \tag{50}$$

interacts with the applied field $\mathbf{B}$, giving an energy

$$E = -\boldsymbol{\mu}_L\cdot\mathbf{B}$$
$$= g_\ell\mu_B\frac{1}{\hbar}\mathbf{L}\cdot\mathbf{B}, \tag{51}$$

where $g_\ell = 1$ is the orbital gyromagnetic ratio (we keep the g_ℓ so we can distinguish orbital and spin contributions later). The resultant Zeeman perturbation Hamiltonian is

$$H_Z' = g_\ell\mu_B\frac{1}{\hbar}\mathbf{L}\cdot\mathbf{B}$$
$$= g_\ell\mu_B\frac{B}{\hbar}L_z. \tag{52}$$

The zeroth-order energy eigenstates $|n\ell m_\ell\rangle$ are degenerate, so we must use degenerate perturbation theory to find the energy corrections caused by the Zeeman perturbation in Eq. (52). However, the states $|n\ell m_\ell\rangle$ are eigenstates of L_z, so once again we have made the "smart" choice of basis. The matrix representing H_Z' is diagonal, so the first-order energy corrections are the diagonal elements of the perturbation Hamiltonian

$$E_Z^{(1)} = \langle H_Z'\rangle = \langle n\ell m_\ell|H_Z'|n\ell m_\ell\rangle$$
$$= g_\ell\mu_B\frac{B}{\hbar}\langle n\ell m_\ell|L_z|n\ell m_\ell\rangle. \tag{53}$$

Evaluating the matrix elements yields

$$\boxed{E_Z^{(1)} = g_\ell\mu_B B m_\ell}. \tag{54}$$

The normal Zeeman effect is proportional to the orbital gyromagnetic ratio g_ℓ, the Bohr magneton μ_B, the magnetic field strength B, and the magnetic quantum number m_ℓ. This general form is repeated when we study the Zeeman effect in more realistic models. The gyromagnetic ratio and the particular magnetic quantum number change as we include other magnetic moments in the model. A typical Zeeman energy level diagram without spin is shown in Fig. 6 for the $2p$ state of hydrogen, with the energy shifts proportional to m_ℓ and the applied field strength B. The $m_\ell = 1$ state has the orbital angular momentum aligned with the field, which means that the magnetic moment is anti-aligned, and the magnetic interaction energy is therefore positive. The degeneracy present in the zeroth-order state is lifted by the perturbation.

The Zeeman energy structure displayed in Fig. 6 provides a better understanding of a Stern-Gerlach experiment. The experiment measures spin magnetic moments, but the Stern-Gerlach effect applies equally well to the measurement of magnetic moments arising from orbital angular momentum as in the normal Zeeman effect. In a Stern-Gerlach device, the external magnetic field varies spatially, which implies a spatially varying Zeeman energy perturbation. A spatial dependence of the energy (strictly speaking a potential energy, which is the case here) gives rise to a force

$$
\begin{aligned}
F_z &= -\frac{\partial}{\partial z} E_z^{(1)} \\
&= -\frac{\partial E_z^{(1)}}{\partial B} \frac{\partial B}{\partial z} \\
&= -g_\ell \mu_B m_\ell \frac{\partial B}{\partial z}.
\end{aligned}
\tag{55}
$$

Each value of the magnetic quantum number m_ℓ leads to a different value of the force and hence to a different deflection of the beam in a Stern-Gerlach device. For example, a p state has three m_ℓ values $(1, 0, -1)$ corresponding to the three energy levels in the Zeeman structure of Fig. 6, and results in three beams exiting a Stern-Gerlach analyzer, as depicted in Fig. 7. The effective magnetic moment of the atom is given by the slope $-\partial E_z^{(1)}/\partial B$ of the Zeeman energy plot, which is $-g_\ell \mu_B m_\ell$ for the Zeeman effect without spin.

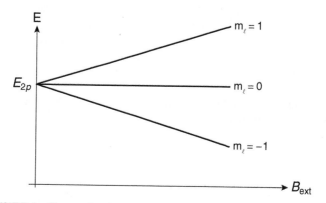

FIGURE 6 Zeeman level structure of the hydrogen $2p$ state, ignoring spin.

Perturbation of Hydrogen

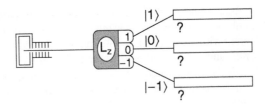

FIGURE 7 Stern-Gerlach measurement of the orbital angular momentum component L_z.

3.2 ■ Zeeman Effect with Spin

A more realistic model of the atom includes the electron spin. In this case, the Zeeman effect is referred to as the "anomalous Zeeman effect" in the literature because it was discovered experimentally before spin was known and it did not agree with the expected "normal" Zeeman effect predictions. In the Zeeman effect with spin, we include the interaction of the spin magnetic moment with the external applied field, in addition to the interaction of the orbital magnetic moment with the applied field as we did in the previous section. Thus, the total atomic magnetic moment is

$$\boldsymbol{\mu} = \boldsymbol{\mu}_S + \boldsymbol{\mu}_L = -g_e \frac{e}{2m_e}\mathbf{S} - g_\ell \frac{e}{2m_e}\mathbf{L} = -g_e\mu_B \frac{\mathbf{S}}{\hbar} - g_\ell\mu_B \frac{\mathbf{L}}{\hbar}, \tag{56}$$

where the spin gyromagnetic ratio g_e is approximately 2 (with its own correction of order α^2). The interaction Hamiltonian is

$$H'_z = -\boldsymbol{\mu}\cdot\mathbf{B} = \frac{\mu_B}{\hbar}\left(g_\ell\mathbf{L} + g_e\mathbf{S}\right)\cdot\mathbf{B}$$

$$= \frac{\mu_B B}{\hbar}\left(g_\ell L_z + g_e S_z\right). \tag{57}$$

In this more realistic model of the atom, we must include the fine structure that we calculated in Section 2. The relative roles of the fine structure and the Zeeman effect are determined by the magnitudes of the energy corrections caused by each effect. The magnitude of the fine-structure corrections are displayed in Fig. 4 for a few states. The magnitude of the Zeeman corrections scale with the magnitude of the applied field, as illustrated in Fig. 6. The Zeeman effect applied to the fine-structure states of Fig. 4 lifts some of the degeneracy and splits levels into Zeeman structures like Fig. 6. For small enough magnetic fields, the Zeeman corrections are much smaller than the fine-structure splittings, in which case we treat the fine structure as part of the zeroth-order Hamiltonian and treat the Zeeman effect as a small perturbation. For large magnetic fields, we include the Zeeman effect in the zeroth-order Hamiltonian, and treat the fine structure as a small perturbation. For magnetic fields where the fine structure and Zeeman corrections are comparable, we must treat both effects as one perturbation.

3.2.1 ■ Weak magnetic field

Let's start with the weak magnetic field case, and treat the fine structure as part of the zeroth-order Hamiltonian. In this case, the zeroth-order states are the coupled basis states $\left|n\ell s j m_j\right\rangle$ in which the fine structure is diagonal, and the zeroth-order energies are the Bohr energies $E_n^{(0)}$ plus the fine-structure shifts in Eq. (47). Our task is to find the effect of the Zeeman perturbation in Eq. (57) on these zeroth-order energies.

Inspection of the Zeeman interaction Hamiltonian in Eq. (57) shows that it is diagonal in the uncoupled basis $|n\ell s m_\ell m_s\rangle$, but it is not diagonal in the coupled basis $|n\ell s j m_j\rangle$. Unfortunately, we must use the coupled basis because that is the basis we used to diagonalize the zeroth-order Hamiltonian, which now includes the fine structure. We no longer have the freedom to search for a "good" basis where the perturbation is diagonal. There doesn't appear to be a straightforward way to find a general expression for the Zeeman energy shifts in this case. Of course, we can solve the problem by brute force by finding the matrix representations in the coupled basis of the non-diagonal L_z and S_z matrices that comprise the Zeeman Hamiltonian, and then diagonalizing the perturbation Hamiltonian in a degenerate subspace, which is given by a specific n and j in this case. It turns out that there is a way to solve this problem in general, but it requires some advanced concepts from angular momentum theory that we do not have yet. So, to motivate why these advanced concepts work, let's do one problem by brute force and then quote without proof the angular momentum concepts we need to derive a general result.

The angular momentum operators L_z and S_z are both diagonal in the uncoupled basis $|n\ell s m_\ell m_s\rangle$, and we know that the uncoupled and coupled bases are connected through the Clebsch-Gordan coefficients. Hence, it is straightforward (but tedious) using the Clebsch-Gordan expansion

$$|j m_j\rangle = \sum_{m_\ell m_s} |\ell s m_\ell m_s\rangle\langle \ell s m_\ell m_s|j m_j\rangle \qquad (58)$$

to find the matrix representations of L_z and S_z in the coupled basis. We'll calculate one matrix element to demonstrate the method and leave the others for you to do (Problem 6 and activity on Zeeman perturbation matrices in the coupled basis).

Consider the hydrogen $2p$ states with $n = 2$, $\ell = 1$, and $s = 1/2$. The allowed values of the coupled basis quantum number j ($\mathbf{J} = \mathbf{L} + \mathbf{S}$) are $j = 3/2$ and $j = 1/2$. Clebsch-Gordan coefficients tell us that two particular coupled states are

$$\left|\tfrac{3}{2}\tfrac{1}{2}\right\rangle = \tfrac{1}{\sqrt{3}}\left|1\tfrac{1}{2}1\tfrac{-1}{2}\right\rangle + \sqrt{\tfrac{2}{3}}\left|1\tfrac{1}{2}0\tfrac{1}{2}\right\rangle$$

$$\left|\tfrac{1}{2}\tfrac{1}{2}\right\rangle = \sqrt{\tfrac{2}{3}}\left|1\tfrac{1}{2}1\tfrac{-1}{2}\right\rangle - \tfrac{1}{\sqrt{3}}\left|1\tfrac{1}{2}0\tfrac{1}{2}\right\rangle. \qquad (59)$$

Using these expansions, we calculate the matrix element of L_z in the coupled basis in terms of uncoupled-basis matrix elements:

$$\left\langle\tfrac{1}{2}\tfrac{1}{2}\right|L_z\left|\tfrac{3}{2}\tfrac{1}{2}\right\rangle = \left(\sqrt{\tfrac{2}{3}}\left\langle 1\tfrac{1}{2}1\tfrac{-1}{2}\right| - \tfrac{1}{\sqrt{3}}\left\langle 1\tfrac{1}{2}0\tfrac{1}{2}\right|\right)L_z\left(\tfrac{1}{\sqrt{3}}\left|1\tfrac{1}{2}1\tfrac{-1}{2}\right\rangle + \sqrt{\tfrac{2}{3}}\left|1\tfrac{1}{2}0\tfrac{1}{2}\right\rangle\right). \qquad (60)$$

The uncoupled-basis matrix elements are diagonal, leaving

$$\left\langle\tfrac{1}{2}\tfrac{1}{2}\right|L_z\left|\tfrac{3}{2}\tfrac{1}{2}\right\rangle = \tfrac{\sqrt{2}}{3}\left\langle 1\tfrac{1}{2}1\tfrac{-1}{2}\right|L_z\left|1\tfrac{1}{2}1\tfrac{-1}{2}\right\rangle - \tfrac{\sqrt{2}}{3}\left\langle 1\tfrac{1}{2}0\tfrac{1}{2}\right|L_z\left|1\tfrac{1}{2}0\tfrac{1}{2}\right\rangle. \qquad (61)$$

The diagonal uncoupled-basis matrix elements are $m_\ell \hbar$, yielding the result

$$\left\langle\tfrac{1}{2}\tfrac{1}{2}\right|L_z\left|\tfrac{3}{2}\tfrac{1}{2}\right\rangle = \tfrac{\sqrt{2}}{3}(1\hbar) - \tfrac{\sqrt{2}}{3}(0\hbar)$$

$$= \tfrac{\sqrt{2}}{3}\hbar. \qquad (62)$$

Repeating this calculation for all possible values of j, m_j in the hydrogen $2p$ level, we find the complete L_z and S_z matrices in the coupled basis (Problem 6):

$$
L_z \doteq \hbar
\begin{pmatrix}
1 & 0 & 0 & 0 & 0 & 0 \\
0 & \frac{1}{3} & 0 & 0 & \frac{\sqrt{2}}{3} & 0 \\
0 & 0 & \frac{1}{3} & 0 & 0 & \frac{\sqrt{2}}{3} \\
0 & 0 & 0 & -1 & 0 & 0 \\
0 & \frac{\sqrt{2}}{3} & 0 & 0 & \frac{2}{3} & 0 \\
0 & 0 & \frac{\sqrt{2}}{3} & 0 & 0 & \frac{2}{3}
\end{pmatrix}
\begin{matrix}
\frac{3}{2},\frac{3}{2} \\
\frac{3}{2},\frac{1}{2} \\
\frac{3}{2},\frac{-1}{2} \\
\frac{3}{2},\frac{-3}{2} \\
\frac{1}{2},\frac{1}{2} \\
\frac{1}{2},\frac{-1}{2}
\end{matrix}
\tag{63}
$$

$$
S_z \doteq \hbar
\begin{pmatrix}
\frac{1}{2} & 0 & 0 & 0 & 0 & 0 \\
0 & \frac{1}{6} & 0 & 0 & \frac{-\sqrt{2}}{3} & 0 \\
0 & 0 & \frac{-1}{6} & 0 & 0 & \frac{-\sqrt{2}}{3} \\
0 & 0 & 0 & \frac{-1}{2} & 0 & 0 \\
0 & \frac{-\sqrt{2}}{3} & 0 & 0 & \frac{-1}{6} & 0 \\
0 & 0 & \frac{-\sqrt{2}}{3} & 0 & 0 & \frac{1}{6}
\end{pmatrix}
\begin{matrix}
\frac{3}{2},\frac{3}{2} \\
\frac{3}{2},\frac{1}{2} \\
\frac{3}{2},\frac{-1}{2} \\
\frac{3}{2},\frac{-3}{2} \\
\frac{1}{2},\frac{1}{2} \\
\frac{1}{2},\frac{-1}{2}
\end{matrix}
,
\tag{64}
$$

where we have labeled the rows and columns with the j, m_j quantum numbers and boxed subspaces as discussed below. Degenerate perturbation theory requires us to construct the perturbation Hamiltonian Eq. (57) using these matrices and then diagonalize the resultant. However, we need do that only within each degenerate subspace. The fine structure lifts the degeneracy of the $j = 3/2$ and $j = 1/2$ states, so we treat these subspaces separately. Inspection of the L_z and S_z matrices in Eqs. (63) and (64) shows that the only off-diagonal matrix elements in L_z and S_z are between states with different values of j, which have different fine-structure shifts. L_z and S_z are each diagonal within the separate $j = 3/2$ and $j = 1/2$ subspaces boxed in Eqs. (63) and (64) and we can neglect the off-diagonal elements in applying degenerate perturbation theory. We got lucky! We did not have the freedom to choose a basis to make the perturbation diagonal, but in the basis of fine-structure eigenstates, the Zeeman perturbation is already diagonal within each degenerate subspace. For the $j = 3/2$ subspace, the Zeeman Hamiltonian is represented by the matrix

$$
H_Z' \doteq \mu_B B
\begin{pmatrix}
2 & 0 & 0 & 0 \\
0 & \frac{2}{3} & 0 & 0 \\
0 & 0 & \frac{-2}{3} & 0 \\
0 & 0 & 0 & -2
\end{pmatrix}
\begin{matrix}
\frac{3}{2},\frac{3}{2} \\
\frac{3}{2},\frac{1}{2} \\
\frac{3}{2},\frac{-1}{2} \\
\frac{3}{2},\frac{-3}{2}
\end{matrix}
,
\tag{65}
$$

where we have substituted the gyromagnetic ratios: $g_\ell = 1$, $g_e = 2$. From the matrix in Eq. (65), we find the Zeeman energy shifts by inspection to be $2\mu_B B$, $2\mu_B B/3$, $-2\mu_B B/3$, $-2\mu_B B$. For the $j = 1/2$ subspace, the Zeeman Hamiltonian must also include the $2s_{1/2}$ states in addition to the $2p_{1/2}$ states (Problem 7).

To find a general expression for the Zeeman energy shift rather than solving each case by matrix construction, we invoke a result from advanced angular momentum theory. To motivate this new idea, consider the total angular momentum component operator $J_z = L_z + S_z$. For the hydrogen $2p$ state, the matrix representing J_z is

$$J_z \doteq \hbar \begin{pmatrix} \frac{3}{2} & 0 & 0 & 0 & 0 & 0 \\ 0 & \frac{1}{2} & 0 & 0 & 0 & 0 \\ 0 & 0 & \frac{-1}{2} & 0 & 0 & 0 \\ 0 & 0 & 0 & \frac{-3}{2} & 0 & 0 \\ 0 & 0 & 0 & 0 & \frac{1}{2} & 0 \\ 0 & 0 & 0 & 0 & 0 & \frac{-1}{2} \end{pmatrix} \begin{matrix} \frac{3}{2},\frac{3}{2} \\ \frac{3}{2},\frac{1}{2} \\ \frac{3}{2},\frac{-1}{2} \\ \frac{3}{2},\frac{-3}{2} \\ \frac{1}{2},\frac{1}{2} \\ \frac{1}{2},\frac{-1}{2} \end{matrix} . \qquad (66)$$

Compare this J_z matrix to the L_z and S_z matrices in Eqs. (63) and (64), concentrating on the separate $j = 3/2$ and $j = 1/2$ boxed subspaces and ignoring the off-diagonal elements in L_z and S_z. The submatrices for L_z and S_z within a given j subspace are proportional to the J_z submatrix in that same subspace, with proportionality factors that are j-dependent. For L_z, the proportionality factors are $2/3$ for the $j = 3/2$ case and $4/3$ for the $j = 1/2$ case. For S_z, the proportionality factors are $1/3$ for the $j = 3/2$ case and $-1/3$ for the $j = 1/2$ case. These relations between the matrices in the coupled basis that represent L_z and S_z and the matrix that represents the total angular momentum J_z are specific examples of the **Wigner-Eckhart theorem**, which is a fundamental part of the theory of angular momentum.

The specific formula we need from the Wigner-Eckhart theorem relates the matrix element of any general vector component V_z to the matrix element of the total angular momentum component J_z:

$$\left\langle jm_j \left| V_z \right| jm_j' \right\rangle = \frac{\left\langle jm_j \left| \mathbf{V} \cdot \mathbf{J} \right| jm_j \right\rangle}{\hbar^2 j(j+1)} \left\langle jm_j \left| J_z \right| jm_j' \right\rangle. \qquad (67)$$

For the Zeeman calculation, $\mathbf{L}$ or $\mathbf{S}$ play the role of the vector $\mathbf{V}$. Equation (67) is called the **projection theorem** because of the role of the projection $\mathbf{V} \cdot \mathbf{J}$ in determining the constant of proportionality between the matrix elements of V_z and J_z. Note that the matrix element of the projection $\mathbf{V} \cdot \mathbf{J}$ is a diagonal element, but the V_z and J_z matrix elements are general matrix elements between different m_j states within a given j subspace.

To use the projection theorem, we need to know the diagonal matrix elements $\left\langle jm_j \left| \mathbf{V} \cdot \mathbf{J} \right| jm_j \right\rangle$, which depend on the vector $\mathbf{V}$ we are using. For the orbital angular momentum $\mathbf{L}$, the required projection is obtained from the relation

$$\mathbf{J} = \mathbf{L} + \mathbf{S} \qquad (68)$$

by rearranging and squaring:

$$\begin{aligned} \mathbf{S} &= \mathbf{J} - \mathbf{L} \\ \mathbf{S}^2 &= \mathbf{J}^2 + \mathbf{L}^2 - 2\mathbf{L} \cdot \mathbf{J} \\ \mathbf{L} \cdot \mathbf{J} &= \tfrac{1}{2}\left(\mathbf{J}^2 + \mathbf{L}^2 - \mathbf{S}^2\right). \end{aligned} \qquad (69)$$

Similarly, for the spin angular momentum:

$$\mathbf{S} \cdot \mathbf{J} = \tfrac{1}{2}\big(\mathbf{J}^2 + \mathbf{S}^2 - \mathbf{L}^2\big). \tag{70}$$

Hence, the diagonal matrix elements required in the projection theorem are

$$\langle jm_j|\mathbf{S}\cdot\mathbf{J}|jm_j\rangle = \frac{\hbar^2}{2}\big[j(j+1) + s(s+1) - \ell(\ell+1)\big]$$

$$\langle jm_j|\mathbf{L}\cdot\mathbf{J}|jm_j\rangle = \frac{\hbar^2}{2}\big[j(j+1) + \ell(\ell+1) - s(s+1)\big]. \tag{71}$$

Using these coefficients in the projection theorem yields the L_z and S_z matrix elements in the coupled basis within a given j subspace

$$\langle jm_j|S_z|jm_j'\rangle = \frac{j(j+1) + s(s+1) - \ell(\ell+1)}{2j(j+1)}\langle jm_j|J_z|jm_j'\rangle$$

$$\langle jm_j|L_z|jm_j'\rangle = \frac{j(j+1) + \ell(\ell+1) - s(s+1)}{2j(j+1)}\langle jm_j|J_z|jm_j'\rangle. \tag{72}$$

Thus, the projection theorem has allowed us to find the matrix representations, within a specific subspace, of operators that are not diagonal in the coupled basis. Because J_z is diagonal in the coupled basis, Eq. (72) tells us that L_z and S_z are also diagonal within a given j subspace, as we saw in Eqs. (63) and (64). For the hydrogen $2p$ example, the proportionality constants in Eq. (72) are exactly those we found by inspection above.

We put all these results together to find the first-order Zeeman energy correction:

$$\begin{aligned} E_Z^{(1)} &= \langle H_Z' \rangle = \langle n\ell sjm_j|H_Z'|n\ell sjm_j\rangle \\[2mm] &= \langle n\ell sjm_j|\frac{\mu_B B}{\hbar}\big(g_\ell L_z + g_e S_z\big)|n\ell sjm_j\rangle \\[2mm] &= \frac{\mu_B B}{\hbar}\Big(g_\ell\langle n\ell sjm_j|L_z|n\ell sjm_j\rangle + g_e\langle n\ell sjm_j|S_z|n\ell sjm_j\rangle\Big) \\[2mm] &= \frac{\mu_B B}{\hbar}\left(g_\ell\frac{j(j+1)+\ell(\ell+1)-s(s+1)}{2j(j+1)} + g_e\frac{j(j+1)+s(s+1)-\ell(\ell+1)}{2j(j+1)}\right)\langle n\ell sjm_j|J_z|n\ell sjm_j\rangle \\[2mm] &= \frac{\mu_B B}{\hbar}\left(g_\ell\frac{j(j+1)+\ell(\ell+1)-s(s+1)}{2j(j+1)} + g_e\frac{j(j+1)+s(s+1)-\ell(\ell+1)}{2j(j+1)}\right)m_j\hbar. \end{aligned} \tag{73}$$

This result can be written in the standard Zeeman form

$$E_Z^{(1)} = g_j\mu_B B m_j \tag{74}$$

if we define a new gyromagnetic ratio g_j:

$$g_j = g_\ell \frac{j(j+1) + \ell(\ell+1) - s(s+1)}{2j(j+1)} + g_e \frac{j(j+1) + s(s+1) - \ell(\ell+1)}{2j(j+1)}, \tag{75}$$

which we refer to as the **Landé g factor**. This gyromagnetic ratio accounts for the relative contributions of the magnetic moments due to the spin and orbital angular momenta caused by their differing magnitudes (gyromagnetic ratios: $g_\ell = 1$, $g_e = 2$) and differing alignments (projection theorem). Substituting the gyromagnetic ratios into Eq. (75), we obtain the Landé g factor

$$g_j = 1 + \frac{j(j+1) + s(s+1) - \ell(\ell+1)}{2j(j+1)}. \tag{76}$$

For the hydrogen 2p example, the Landé factors are $g_{3/2} = 4/3$ and $g_{1/2} = 2/3$. For the $2s_{1/2}$ state, the Landé g factor is 2, i.e. $g_j = g_e$ because the only magnetic moment comes from the electron spin in that state. For hydrogen, with only one electron, $s = 1/2$, so $j = \ell \pm 1/2$, and we can write the Landé g factor in general as

$$g_j = 1 \pm \frac{1}{2\ell + 1}. \tag{77}$$

We thus get a Zeeman energy correction that is dependent on j and ℓ:

$$E_Z^{(1)} = \mu_B B m_j \left(1 \pm \frac{1}{2\ell + 1} \right), \tag{78}$$

with the $\pm$ sign for $j = \ell \pm 1/2$. Figure 8 shows the weak-field Zeeman level splittings in the $2p$ levels of hydrogen.

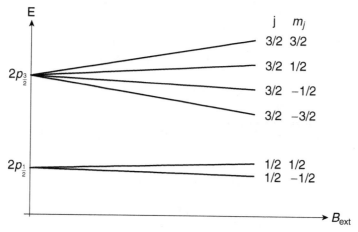

FIGURE 8 Weak-field Zeeman structure of the hydrogen $2p$ fine-structure levels labeled with the quantum numbers of the coupled basis states.

3.2.2 ■ Strong magnetic field

Now consider the case where the magnetic field is strong enough that the Zeeman shifts are much larger than the fine-structure shifts. The perturbation assumption regarding the Zeeman effect is no longer valid and it is more appropriate to include the Zeeman Hamiltonian

$$H'_Z = \frac{\mu_B B}{\hbar}(g_\ell L_z + g_e S_z) \tag{79}$$

in zeroth-order and treat the fine structure as a perturbation. In that case, the uncoupled basis $|n\ell s m_\ell m_s\rangle$ is the preferred basis because the Zeeman Hamiltonian is diagonal in that basis. With this new choice, the zeroth-order energies are the Bohr energies plus the the Zeeman corrections:

$$E_n^{(0)} = -\frac{Ryd}{n^2} + \langle n\ell s m_\ell m_s|H'_Z|n\ell s m_\ell m_s\rangle. \tag{80}$$

The additional Zeeman energies are the expectation values

$$\begin{aligned}\Delta E_{Zeeman} &= \langle n\ell s m_\ell m_s|H'_Z|n\ell s m_\ell m_s\rangle \\ &= \langle n\ell s m_\ell m_s|\frac{\mu_B B}{\hbar}(g_\ell L_z + g_e S_z)|n\ell s m_\ell m_s\rangle \\ &= \frac{\mu_B B}{\hbar}(g_\ell m_\ell \hbar + g_e m_s \hbar).\end{aligned} \tag{81}$$

Substituting the values $g_\ell = 1$ and $g_e = 2$ yields

$$\Delta E_{Zeeman} = \mu_B B(m_\ell + 2m_s) \tag{82}$$

for the strong-field Zeeman effect. These zeroth-order energies for the $2p$ state as a function of magnetic field are shown as dashed lines in Fig. 9, keeping in mind that these are valid only at high fields. The Zeeman effect lifts most of the degeneracy of the Bohr energies.

Now we treat the fine structure as a perturbation to the zeroth-order states that include the Zeeman interaction. Because we are using the uncoupled basis, we have to revisit our calculations of the fine-structure corrections. The relativistic Hamiltonian is diagonal in both the uncoupled and coupled bases, but the spin-orbit Hamiltonian is diagonal only in the coupled basis. However, the off-diagonal matrix elements of the spin-orbit Hamiltonian do not couple any of the states that are degenerate with respect to the Zeeman Hamiltonian (Problem 8). Hence we can use nondegenerate perturbation theory to find the first-order fine-structure corrections. In the uncoupled basis, the spin-orbit energy corrections are the expectation values

$$\begin{aligned}E_{SO}^{(1)} &= \langle H'_{SO}\rangle = \langle n\ell s m_\ell m_s|H'_{SO}|n\ell s m_\ell m_s\rangle \\ &= \frac{e^2}{8\pi\varepsilon_0 m^2 c^2}\langle n\ell s m_\ell m_s|\frac{1}{r^3}\mathbf{L}\cdot\mathbf{S}|n\ell s m_\ell m_s\rangle \\ &= \frac{e^2}{8\pi\varepsilon_0 m^2 c^2}\left\langle\frac{1}{r^3}\right\rangle_{n\ell}\langle \ell s m_\ell m_s|\tfrac{1}{2}(L_+ S_- + L_- S_+) + L_z S_z|\ell s m_\ell m_s\rangle.\end{aligned} \tag{83}$$

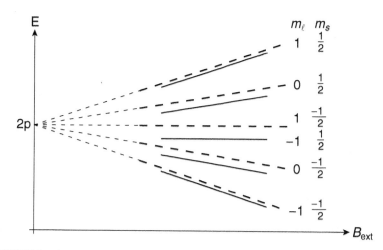

FIGURE 9   Strong-field Zeeman structure of the $2p$ states of hydrogen. Solid lines show the fine-structure corrections to the Zeeman levels (dashed lines). The quantum numbers indicate the uncoupled basis states.

Because the ladder operators connect adjacent states, they produce no diagonal matrix elements and Eq. (83) reduces to

$$E_{SO}^{(1)} = \frac{e^2}{8\pi\varepsilon_0 m^2 c^2} \left\langle \frac{1}{r^3} \right\rangle_{n\ell} \left\langle \ell s m_\ell m_s \big| L_z S_z \big| \ell s m_\ell m_s \right\rangle$$

$$= \frac{e^2}{8\pi\varepsilon_0 m^2 c^2} \left\langle \frac{1}{r^3} \right\rangle_{n\ell} m_\ell m_s \hbar^2. \tag{84}$$

Using Eq. (45) for the radial matrix element, we obtain

$$E_{SO}^{(1)} = \frac{1}{2}\alpha^4 mc^2 \frac{m_\ell m_s}{n^3 \ell \left(\ell+\frac{1}{2}\right)(\ell+1)}. \tag{85}$$

Adding together the relativistic [Eq. (30)] and spin-orbit corrections yields the fine-structure shifts

$$E_{fs}^{(1)} = \frac{1}{2}\alpha^4 mc^2 \left[\frac{3}{4n^3} - \frac{\ell(\ell+1) - m_\ell m_s}{n^3 \ell \left(\ell+\frac{1}{2}\right)(\ell+1)} \right], \tag{86}$$

which are shown in Fig. 9 for the $2p$ states.

3.2.3 ■ Intermediate magnetic field

In the intermediate magnetic field regime where the Zeeman corrections and the fine-structure corrections are comparable, we have to treat both effects as perturbations to the zeroth-order Bohr energy levels. We then have to diagonalize the perturbation Hamiltonian $H' = H'_{fs} + H'_Z$ in each degenerate $E_n^{(0)}$ energy subspace. In the uncoupled basis $\big|n\ell s m_\ell m_s\big\rangle$, H'_Z is diagonal but H'_{fs} is not diagonal, while in the coupled basis $\big|n\ell s j m_j\big\rangle$, H'_{fs} is diagonal but H'_Z is not diagonal. Hence, there is no obvious preferred basis; we have to do some work to diagonalize the perturbation Hamiltonian matrix in either case. For example, in the $n = 2$ subspace the matrix representing the perturbation Hamiltonian in the coupled basis is [we have left out the $2s$ states here—they do not couple to the $2p$ states so they can be diagonalized separately (Problem 9)]

$$H' \doteq \begin{pmatrix} -a+2b & 0 & 0 & 0 & 0 & 0 \\ 0 & -a+\frac{2}{3}b & 0 & 0 & \frac{-\sqrt{2}}{3}b & 0 \\ 0 & 0 & -a-\frac{2}{3}b & 0 & 0 & \frac{-\sqrt{2}}{3}b \\ 0 & 0 & 0 & -a-2b & 0 & 0 \\ 0 & \frac{-\sqrt{2}}{3}b & 0 & 0 & -5a+\frac{1}{3}b & 0 \\ 0 & 0 & \frac{-\sqrt{2}}{3}b & 0 & 0 & -5a-\frac{1}{3}b \end{pmatrix} \begin{matrix} \frac{3}{2},\frac{3}{2} \\ \frac{3}{2},\frac{1}{2} \\ \frac{3}{2},\frac{-1}{2} \\ \frac{3}{2},\frac{-3}{2} \\ \frac{1}{2},\frac{1}{2} \\ \frac{1}{2},\frac{-1}{2} \end{matrix}, \qquad (87)$$

where we have defined

$$a = \tfrac{1}{128}\alpha^4 mc^2$$
$$b = \mu_B B. \qquad (88)$$

The off-diagonal terms in Eq. (87) come from the off-diagonal matrix elements of the L_z and S_z matrices in Eqs. (63) and (64). We were able to ignore those terms in the weak-field Zeeman calculation because they represented coupling between *different* zeroth-order degenerate subspaces. In the intermediate field case, these terms represent coupling between states within the *same* degenerate subspace, so they must be included in the degenerate perturbation theory calculation. Diagonalization of the matrix in Eq. (87) yields the energy shifts shown in Fig. 10 (Problem 9).

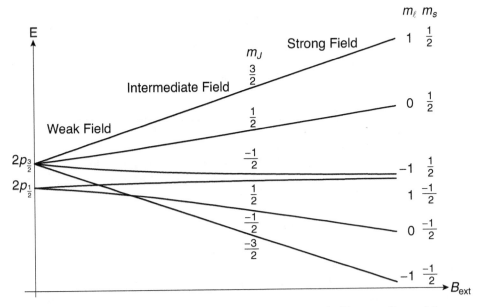

FIGURE 10 Perturbation of the hydrogen $2p$ states caused by the Zeeman effect and the fine structure as a function of the applied magnetic field.

Note the linear-to-quadratic-to-linear behavior of some of the energy shifts as the applied field goes from weak to intermediate to strong. For the weak field case, the coupled basis is the "good" basis with states defined by the quantum numbers j and m_j as in Fig. 8, while for the strong field, the uncoupled basis is the "good" basis, with states defined by the quantum numbers m_ℓ and m_s as in Fig. 9. The results of the intermediate-field calculation are valid at all fields and give the previous results in the appropriate limits (Problem 9).

3.3 ■ Zeeman Perturbation of the 1s Hyperfine Structure

Let's study the Zeeman effect in the ground state of hydrogen. The only energy level structure in the hydrogen ground state is the hyperfine structure. The fine-structure effects and the QED Lamb shift do not lift any of the degeneracy in the ground state—they only shift the level, as shown in Fig. 2. Hence we include the fine structure and Lamb shifts as part of the zeroth-order energy and treat the Zeeman effect and the hyperfine interaction as the two relevant perturbations for this problem.

The energy eigenvalues and eigenstates of the hyperfine perturbation in the $1s_{1/2}$ ground state of hydrogen. We find that the hyperfine Hamiltonian

$$H'_{hf} = \frac{A}{\hbar^2}\mathbf{S}\cdot\mathbf{I} \tag{89}$$

is diagonal in the coupled basis of $|FM_F\rangle$ states. For the $1s_{1/2}$ state of hydrogen, the orbital angular momentum is zero and the Zeeman Hamiltonian of Eq. (57) reduces to

$$H'_Z = \frac{2\mu_B B}{\hbar}S_z, \tag{90}$$

where we have set $g_e = 2$.

The solution of this problem is analogous to the anomalous Zeeman effect where we had two perturbations: the fine structure and the Zeeman effect. In this problem, the hyperfine interaction takes the place of the fine-structure interactions, and we also consider three regimes of magnetic field strength corresponding to the relative magnitudes of the Zeeman and hyperfine shifts. For weak fields, we (1) include the hyperfine structure in the zeroth-order Hamiltonian, (2) use the coupled states $|FM_F\rangle$ as the "good" basis because the hyperfine Hamiltonian is diagonal in that basis, and (3) treat the Zeeman effect as a perturbation. For strong fields, we (1) include the Zeeman effect in the zeroth-order Hamiltonian, (2) use the uncoupled states $|sIm_s m_I\rangle$ as the "good" basis because the Zeeman Hamiltonian is diagonal in that basis, and (3) treat the hyperfine interaction as a perturbation. In intermediate fields, we treat both the hyperfine interaction and the Zeeman effect as perturbations and diagonalize the full perturbation Hamiltonian in whichever basis we like because neither is preferred. We'll do the intermediate case and leave the weak and strong cases for homework (Problem 12).

In the coupled basis, the hyperfine interaction is diagonal:

$$H'_{hfs} \doteq \frac{A}{4}\begin{pmatrix} 1 & 0 & 0 & 0 \\ 0 & 1 & 0 & 0 \\ 0 & 0 & 1 & 0 \\ 0 & 0 & 0 & -3 \end{pmatrix}\begin{matrix} 11 \\ 10 \\ 1,-1 \\ 00 \end{matrix}, \tag{91}$$

where A is the hyperfine splitting between the degenerate $F = 1$ triplet states and the $F = 0$ singlet state and the matrix rows are labeled with the coupled basis quantum numbers F and M_F. In this same basis, the Zeeman Hamiltonian is (Problem 12)

$$H'_Z \doteq \mu_B B \begin{pmatrix} 1 & 0 & 0 & 0 \\ 0 & 0 & 0 & 1 \\ 0 & 0 & -1 & 0 \\ 0 & 1 & 0 & 0 \end{pmatrix} \begin{matrix} 11 \\ 10 \\ 1,-1 \\ 00 \end{matrix}. \tag{92}$$

Diagonalization of the sum of these two matrices yields the energies plotted in Fig. 11 (Problem 13). In weak fields, the Zeeman shift is linear in the field and proportional to the coupled basis magnetic quantum number M_F, analogous to the weak field result in Eq. (78) and in Fig. 8. In strong fields, the Zeeman shift is linear in the field and proportional to the uncoupled basis magnetic quantum number m_s, analogous to the strong field result in Eq. (82) and in Fig. 9. In intermediate fields, neither basis is a "good" basis and some of the energies exhibit quadratic dependence on the field strength, analogous to Fig. 10.

The deflection of an atom in a Stern-Gerlach device is proportional to the slope $-\partial E_z^{(1)}/\partial B$ of the Zeeman energy plot [Eq. (55)]. In the linear case of Fig. 6, this results in three beams output from the Stern-Gerlach analyzer, as shown in Fig. 7. The Zeeman structure of the ground state of hydrogen displayed in Fig. 11 tells us that the slope and therefore the number of output beams depends on the magnitude of the magnetic field. Hence, the effective magnetic moment of the atom as measured by a Stern-Gerlach analyzer depends on the strength of the magnetic field. The hydrogen ground state atom produces three beams from a Stern-Gerlach analyzer in weak fields, two beams in strong fields, and four beams in intermediate fields (Problem 16). I. I. Rabi used this concept to study nuclear magnetic moments, for which he was awarded the Nobel Prize in physics in 1944.

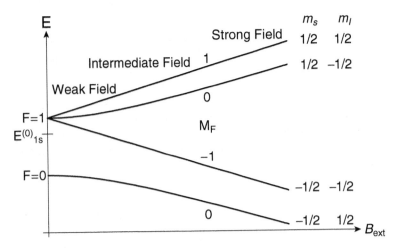

FIGURE 11   The Zeeman structure of the hydrogen ground state hyperfine levels.

SUMMARY

The Bohr energy levels of hydrogen are perturbed by the fine-structure effects, which include the relativistic correction and the spin-orbit interaction. These effects partially lift the degeneracy of the n levels, splitting each into its possible j states. The fine-structure energy corrections are α^2 smaller than the Bohr energies, where $\alpha \cong 1/137$ is the fine-structure constant.

An applied magnetic field causes Zeeman splitting of each degenerate fine-structure or hyperfine-structure level into the states labeled with the magnetic quantum number m. For weak or strong fields, the Zeeman corrections are linear in the applied magnetic field, with the splitting given by the general expression

$$E_Z^{(1)} = g\mu_B Bm, \qquad (93)$$

where the appropriate g-factor and the magnetic quantum number m depend on which level is being split. For intermediate fields, the Zeeman perturbation and the fine structure and/or hyperfine structure must be simultaneously diagonalized, leading to energy corrections that are quadratic in the applied magnetic field.

RESOURCES

Activities

This activity is available at

www.physics.oregonstate.edu/qmactivities

Zeeman perturbation matrices in the coupled basis: Students write down angular momentum matrices in the uncoupled basis by inspection, and use Clebsch-Gordan coefficients to calculate angular momentum matrices in the coupled basis.

Further Reading

The history of hydrogen atom spectroscopy and advances afforded by laser techniques are detailed in
T. W. Hänsch, A. L. Schawlow, and G. W. Series, "The spectrum of atomic hydrogen,"
Scientific American 94–110 (March 1979).
Arthur L. Schawlow, Nobel lecture.
http://nobelprize.org/nobel_prizes/physics/laureates/1981/schawlow-lecture.html
Theodor W. Hänsch, Nobel Lecture.
http://nobelprize.org/nobel_prizes/physics/laureates/2005/hansch-lecture.html
T. W. Hänsch, "Nobel Lecture: Passion for Precision," *Rev. Mod. Phys.* **78**, 1297 (2006).

Rabi's technique for studying nuclear magnetic moments:
G. Breit and I. I. Rabi, "Measurement of Nuclear Spin," *Phys. Rev.* **38**, 2082 (1931).
G. H. Fuller, "Nuclear Spins and Moments," *J. Phys. Chem. Ref. Data* **5**, 835 (1976).

Perturbation of Hydrogen: Problem Set

1 Show that the operator p^4 commutes with the operators L^2 and L_z, so that the relativistic perturbation Hamiltonian is diagonal within each degenerate subspace.

2 Find the matrix representation of $\mathbf{L} \cdot \mathbf{S}$ in the coupled basis and in the uncoupled basis for the $n = 2$ state of hydrogen.

3 Derive the fine-structure result in Eq. (47),

$$E_{fs}^{(1)} = E_{rel}^{(1)} + E_{SO}^{(1)} = -\frac{1}{2}\alpha^4 mc^2 \frac{1}{n^3}\left[\frac{1}{j+\frac{1}{2}} - \frac{3}{4n}\right], \tag{47}$$

to demonstrate the miraculous resolution of the $\ell = 0$ problem.

4 Explain in words why the Zeeman interaction Hamiltonian in Eq. (57),

$$H_z' = -\boldsymbol{\mu} \cdot \mathbf{B} = \frac{\mu_B}{\hbar}\left(g_\ell \mathbf{L} + g_e \mathbf{S}\right) \cdot \mathbf{B}$$

$$= \frac{\mu_B B}{\hbar}\left(g_\ell L_z + g_e S_z\right), \tag{57}$$

is diagonal in the uncoupled basis $|n\ell s m_\ell m_s\rangle$ but not diagonal in the coupled basis $|n\ell s j m_j\rangle$.

5 Find the matrix representations of L_z and S_z in the uncoupled basis $|n\ell s m_\ell m_s\rangle$ for the $2p$ states of hydrogen.

6 Use the Clebsch-Gordan expansion method demonstrated in Section 3.2 to calculate the matrix representations of L_z and S_z in the coupled basis $|n\ell s j m_j\rangle$ for the $2p$ states of hydrogen.

7 Find the matrix representation of the Zeeman Hamiltonian in the coupled basis $|n\ell s j m_j\rangle$ for the $n = 2, j = 1/2$ subspace. Make sure to include the $2s_{1/2}$ states in addition to the $2p_{1/2}$. Find the weak-field Zeeman energy shifts and plot them as a function of the magnetic field.

8 Consider the strong-field Zeeman effect perturbation calculation, where we found it best to work in the uncoupled basis. Show that the off-diagonal matrix elements of the spin-orbit Hamiltonian do not couple any of the states that are degenerate with respect to the Zeeman Hamiltonian.

9 Diagonalize the intermediate-field perturbation matrix for the $2p$ states in Eq. (87),

$$H' \doteq \begin{pmatrix} -a+2b & 0 & 0 & 0 & 0 & 0 \\ 0 & -a+\frac{2}{3}b & 0 & 0 & \frac{-\sqrt{2}}{3}b & 0 \\ 0 & 0 & -a-\frac{2}{3}b & 0 & 0 & \frac{-\sqrt{2}}{3}b \\ 0 & 0 & 0 & -a-2b & 0 & 0 \\ 0 & \frac{-\sqrt{2}}{3}b & 0 & 0 & -5a+\frac{1}{3}b & 0 \\ 0 & 0 & \frac{-\sqrt{2}}{3}b & 0 & 0 & -5a-\frac{1}{3}b \end{pmatrix} \begin{matrix} \frac{3}{2},\frac{3}{2} \\ \frac{3}{2},\frac{1}{2} \\ \frac{3}{2},\frac{-1}{2} \\ \frac{3}{2},\frac{-3}{2} \\ \frac{1}{2},\frac{1}{2} \\ \frac{1}{2},\frac{-1}{2} \end{matrix}, \tag{87}$$

From Chapter 12 of *Quantum Mechanics: A Paradigms Approach*, First Edition. David H. McIntyre. Copyright © 2012 by Pearson Education, Inc. Published by Pearson Addison-Wesley. All rights reserved.

The companion websites for this text are http://physics.oregonstate.edu/portfolioswiki and http://physics.oregonstate.edu/qmactivities.

and produce the plot in Fig. 10. Show that the energy shifts approach the weak- and strong-field results in the appropriate limits. Calculate the energy shifts of the $2s$ levels and add them to the plot.

10 Find the matrix representation of the perturbation Hamiltonian $H' = H'_{fs} + H'_Z$ in the uncoupled basis for the $2p$ states of hydrogen. Diagonalize the perturbation Hamiltonian and produce the plot in Fig. 10.

11 Rearrange the rows and columns of the intermediate-field perturbation matrix for the $2p$ states in Eq. (87) in order to make it appear block diagonal. Explain how the block diagonal nature of the matrix is manifested in Fig. 10.

12 Calculate the perturbed energies of the hydrogen $1s$ ground state caused by the Zeeman effect and the hyperfine interaction in (a) the weak field limit, and (b) the strong field limit. Estimate the magnitude of the applied magnetic field that separates these two limits.

13 Diagonalize the intermediate-field perturbation Hamiltonian representing the Zeeman effect and the hyperfine interaction in the hydrogen $1s$ ground state and produce the energy diagram in Fig. 11, with energy and magnetic field scales added.

14 Calculate the size of the following energy terms and spin orbit and relativistic corrections for the hydrogen atom (for (a)-(d), tabulate your results and give answers in three forms: theoretical in terms of $\alpha^n mc^2$, numerical in eV or meV, and in GHz).

  a) The energy difference between the $n = 1$ and $n = 2$ states BEFORE any perturbations were considered.

  b) The correction to the $n = 1$ and $n = 2$ states due to spin-orbit coupling. Note that the formula we derived in class is problematic for $\ell = 0$. Show that if you set $j = \ell + \frac{1}{2}$ and then use $j = \frac{1}{2}$, the problem goes away. (This is the Darwin term we talked about, but go ahead and call it spin-orbit here.)

  c) The correction to the $n = 1$ and $n = 2$ states due to the relativistic term.

  d) The total correction to these states, (i.e., the fine-structure correction).

  e) What wavelength resolution must your detector have to be able to resolve the two lines in the $n = 2$ to $n = 1$ transition? Be careful here. When you include the correction, you will find that it is very small compared to the unperturbed value. Be sensible about how to include the effects.

  f) Is it important to use the reduced mass of the electron in your calculations or is it OK to use the free mass?

15 Deuterium is an isotope of hydrogen with one electron bound to a nucleus (the deuteron) comprising a proton and a neutron. The deuteron has spin $I = 1$ and has a gyromagnetic ratio $g_D = 0.857$, which is the only change needed to use the following equation for the hyperfine interaction in deuterium.

$$A = \frac{2\mu_0}{3} g_e \mu_B g_p \mu_N |\psi_{1s}(0)|^2.$$

Perturbation of Hydrogen: Problem Set

a) Find the hyperfine structure of the ground state of deuterium. Calculate the splitting of the ground state (in MHz) and produce a figure like the following

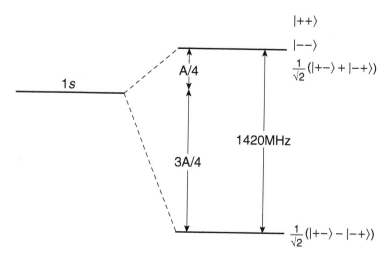

Hyperfine structure of the ground state of hydrogen.

b) Solve for the Zeeman splitting of the ground state of deuterium in intermediate fields and produce a figure like Fig. 11.

16 Calculate the effective magnetic moment of the hydrogen atom in its ground state and confirm that the hydrogen ground state atom produces three beams from a Stern-Gerlach analyzer in weak fields, two beams in strong fields, and four beams in intermediate fields.

Identical Particles

From Chapter 13 of *Quantum Mechanics: A Paradigms Approach*, First Edition. David H. McIntyre. Copyright © 2012 by Pearson Education, Inc. Published by Pearson Addison-Wesley. All rights reserved.

The companion websites for this text are http://physics.oregonstate.edu/portfolioswiki and http://physics.oregonstate.edu/qmactivities.

Identical Particles

To study systems like multielectron atoms, we need to properly account for the fact that all fundamental particles like electrons and protons are **identical**. In classical physics, particles are not identical—we can always find a way to uniquely identify a particular particle. Even if we make two classical particles "the same" to the utmost level of precision, we can still find a way to identify the two particles without affecting their classical motion. For example, billiard balls behave identically, but can be identified by their numbers. In quantum mechanics, there is no way to identify two different electrons—they are **indistinguishable**. Two hydrogen atoms are identical no matter where they are in the universe. Researchers rely on this fact when they compare their experimental results on the spectra of hydrogen atoms in different laboratories. To account for the indistinguishability of fundamental particles, we introduce a new postulate in quantum mechanics, which leads to the Pauli exclusion principle that is responsible for the periodic table and all of chemistry. We apply this new postulate to the helium atom to learn how the indistinguishability of the two electrons in the atom affects the energies and the allowed states.

1 ■ TWO SPIN-1/2 PARTICLES

To start our discussion of identical particles, let's review the system of two spin-1/2 particles. We can describe the system using either of two bases:

$$
\begin{aligned}
|++\rangle, \; |+-\rangle, \; |-+\rangle, \; |--\rangle \quad & \textit{uncoupled basis} \quad |s_1 s_2 m_1 m_2\rangle \\
|11\rangle, \; |10\rangle, \; |1,-1\rangle, \; |00\rangle \quad & \textit{coupled basis} \quad\;\; |S M_S\rangle.
\end{aligned}
\tag{1}
$$

The coupled basis is preferred when the two particles or systems interact, such as in the hyperfine interaction or the spin-orbit interaction, because the Hamiltonian is diagonal in that basis. In general, our choice of basis depends on the problem at hand, but that choice is one we make based solely on convenience in finding the energy eigenvalues. If we choose the other basis, we still find the correct eigenvalues—it just takes a little more work. However, if the two particles are *identical*, then that *freedom of choice of basis is no longer available*. Let's see why.

Consider the ket $|+-\rangle$ in the uncoupled basis that represents a quantum state in which particle 1 has spin up and particle 2 has spin down. If the two particles in question are a proton and an electron, then this representation is clear and unambiguous. However, if the two particles are electrons, then this representation is more problematic. How can we possibly know that the particle that we measure to have spin up is electron 1 and not electron 2? *We cannot.* In quantum mechanics there is no way to distinguish the two particles, and we cannot tell which particle has spin up and which has spin down.

Or as Dr. Seuss said, we cannot know "*Whether this one was that one . . . or that one was this one Or which one was what one . . . or what one was who.*" There is no experiment we can perform on the system of two electrons that would distinguish the state $|+-\rangle$ from the state $|-+\rangle$. This leads us to conclude that the uncoupled basis is inappropriate for representing this system of two identical spin-1/2 particles. So how do we mathematically represent the state with one particle having spin up and one particle having spin down?

The best way would be to start over and abandon the attempt at labeling the quantum numbers of individual particles and instead specify how many particles have particular sets of quantum numbers. This approach is the basis of more advanced treatments, but is too much of a change for us to make at this stage. So we adapt our labeling scheme to this new problem. A reasonable guess for representing the state with one particle having spin up and one particle having spin down would be to use a superposition of the two states $|+-\rangle$ and $|-+\rangle$ in a way that does not favor one over the other. From the addition of angular momenta, we know that such superpositions already exist in the coupled basis representation:

$$|10\rangle = \tfrac{1}{\sqrt{2}}[|+-\rangle + |-+\rangle]$$
$$|00\rangle = \tfrac{1}{\sqrt{2}}[|+-\rangle - |-+\rangle]. \tag{2}$$

These two states differ only by the minus sign coefficient. Let's see what the importance of that minus sign is, and in doing so, learn why the coupled basis is appropriate for describing systems of identical particles.

Imagine that, unbeknownst to us, someone *exchanged* the two identical particles in the system, so that what we originally thought was particle 1 is now particle 2 and vice versa. The two states in Eq. (2) would then become

$$\tfrac{1}{\sqrt{2}}[|+-\rangle + |-+\rangle] \xrightarrow{exchange} \tfrac{1}{\sqrt{2}}[|-+\rangle + |+-\rangle] = \tfrac{1}{\sqrt{2}}[|+-\rangle + |-+\rangle]$$
$$\tfrac{1}{\sqrt{2}}[|+-\rangle - |-+\rangle] \xrightarrow{exchange} \tfrac{1}{\sqrt{2}}[|-+\rangle - |+-\rangle] = -\tfrac{1}{\sqrt{2}}[|+-\rangle - |-+\rangle]. \tag{3}$$

The first state is unchanged and the second state acquires a minus sign, which is an overall phase shift of 180°. An overall phase shift causes no measurable change (Problem 1.3), so the physical states are unchanged by this exchange operation. We denote the exchange operation by the **exchange operator** P_{12}, whose action on uncoupled basis states is

$$P_{12}|s_1 s_2 m_1 m_2\rangle = |s_2 s_1 m_2 m_1\rangle. \tag{4}$$

In terms of the coupled basis representation, the action of the exchange operator P_{12} on the two states in Eq. (2) is

$$P_{12}|10\rangle = +|10\rangle$$
$$P_{12}|00\rangle = -|00\rangle. \tag{5}$$

These results tell us that the coupled basis states $|10\rangle$ and $|00\rangle$ are eigenstates of the exchange operator with eigenvalues $+1$ and -1, respectively. We call these states *symmetric* $(|10\rangle)$ and *antisymmetric* $(|00\rangle)$ states, by which we mean that they are symmetric and antisymmetric with respect to the exchange of the two particles, as opposed to symmetric and antisymmetric with respect to space or something else. Note that the other two coupled basis states $|11\rangle$ and $|1,-1\rangle$ are both symmetric with respect to exchange, (i.e., have eigenvalues of $+1$):

$$P_{12}|11\rangle = P_{12}|++\rangle = |++\rangle = +|11\rangle$$
$$P_{12}|1,-1\rangle = P_{12}|--\rangle = |--\rangle = +|1,-1\rangle. \tag{6}$$

Now consider a measurement upon an eigenstate of the exchange operator, which we denote by $|\psi_\pm\rangle$, where the $\pm$ indicates the eigenvalue. The probability of recording some final result is

$$\mathcal{P}_{\psi_\pm \to \psi_f} = \left|\langle\psi_f|\psi_\pm\rangle\right|^2. \tag{7}$$

If we exchange the two particles before the measurement, then the probability is

$$\mathcal{P}_{P_{12}\psi_\pm \to \psi_f} = \left|\langle\psi_f|\{P_{12}|\psi_\pm\rangle\}\rangle\right|^2 = \left|\langle\psi_f|P_{12}|\psi_\pm\rangle\right|^2$$
$$= \left|\langle\psi_f|(\pm 1)|\psi_\pm\rangle\right|^2 = \left|\langle\psi_f|\psi_\pm\rangle\right|^2 \tag{8}$$
$$= \mathcal{P}_{\psi_\pm \to \psi_f}.$$

Hence, the calculated probability for a measurement made upon a state $|\psi_\pm\rangle$ is not changed if the particles are exchanged. This agrees with our statement above that experiments cannot distinguish between systems with the identical particles exchanged. Thus the coupled basis superpositions are promising representations of the physical system of identical particles.

At this point, both coupled states $|10\rangle$ and $|00\rangle$ plausibly represent the physical state of a system of two identical spin-1/2 particles with one particle having spin up and one having spin down. However, we know from angular momentum addition that these two states have an important difference. The state $|10\rangle$ has total spin angular momentum $S = 1$, while the state $|00\rangle$ has total spin angular momentum $S = 0$. Thus, they are clearly not describing the same system. So how do we know which of these two states to use to describe our system of two electrons with one having spin up and the other having spin down?

Nature chooses for us. You probably already know about the **Pauli exclusion principle** that forbids having two electrons in the same quantum state. The Pauli exclusion principle is a specific example of a broader quantum mechanical principle that we call the **symmetrization postulate**.

The symmetrization postulate stipulates that a system of identical particles is required to have a quantum state vector that is either symmetric or antisymmetric with respect to exchange of any pair of particles. Nature has sorted particles into two classes depending on whether they obey the symmetric or antisymmetric version of this principle. Particles that are required to have symmetric states are called **bosons** and particles that are required to have antisymmetric states are called **fermions**. Furthermore, this symmetry property is correlated with the spin angular momentum of the particles comprising the system. Bosons are particles with integer spin (0, 1, 2, ...) and are required to have symmetric quantum states. Fermions are particles with half-integer spin (1/2, 3/2, 5/2, ...) and are required to have antisymmetric quantum states. This connection between the spins of particles and their exchange symmetry can be proved using relativistic quantum mechanics, so we take it as a postulate. It has been confirmed in many experiments. Because the exchange symmetry determines the statistical behavior of these particles, this concept is often called the **spin-statistics theorem**.

Electrons have spin 1/2, so they are fermions, as are protons and neutrons. Photons and mesons are examples of bosons. Composite particles, like atoms, are fermions or bosons, depending on the total spin of the system. For example, hydrogen has one electron and one proton—two spin-1/2 fermions—so it has integer total spin (1 or 0) and is a boson. Deuterium has one electron and a nucleus (the deuteron) comprising one proton and one neutron, so it has half-integer spin and is a fermion. Thus, different isotopes of the same atom can behave differently when one considers the collective behavior of atoms. For example, samples of liquid ^{3}He (fermion) and liquid ^{4}He (boson) behave quite differently at very low temperatures.

To summarize, the symmetrization postulate tells us that the quantum state vector of a system of two (or more) identical particles must be either symmetric or antisymmetric with respect to exchange of the two (or any two) particles. All particles are divided into either fermions or bosons:

Bosons (integer spin: 0, 1, 2, ...) must have symmetric states.

Fermions (half-integer spin: 1/2, 3/2, 5/2, ...) must have antisymmetric states.

For the system of two identical spin-1/2 particles we discussed above, you would then conclude that the two particles must be in the antisymmetric state $|00\rangle$, and the symmetric states $|11\rangle$, $|10\rangle$, and $|1, -1\rangle$ are not allowed. However, we cannot yet reach that conclusion because the symmetrization postulate applies to the complete state vector, and we have not yet included the spatial part of the state vector.

We assume that we can separate the spin and spatial aspects of the state vectors. This is not always possible, but it works for all the systems we study. The complete quantum state vector then has the form

$$|\psi\rangle = |\psi_{spatial}\rangle|\psi_{spin}\rangle. \tag{9}$$

The symmetrization postulate must be applied to this complete quantum state. For *bosons*, the complete state vector must be *symmetric* under exchange of particles. Thus, the spatial part must be symmetric if the spin part is symmetric, or the spatial part must be antisymmetric if the spin part is antisymmetric:

$$\begin{aligned}
\left|\psi_{boson}^{SS}\right\rangle &= \left|\psi_{spatial}^{S}\right\rangle\left|\psi_{spin}^{S}\right\rangle \\
\left|\psi_{boson}^{AA}\right\rangle &= \left|\psi_{spatial}^{A}\right\rangle\left|\psi_{spin}^{A}\right\rangle.
\end{aligned} \tag{10}$$

The two parts *must* have the same exchange symmetry, or else the full eigenstate would not be symmetric. For *fermions*, the complete state vector must be *antisymmetric* under exchange. Thus, the spatial part must be symmetric if the spin part is antisymmetric, or the spatial part must be antisymmetric if the spin part is symmetric:

$$\begin{aligned}
\left|\psi_{fermion}^{SA}\right\rangle &= \left|\psi_{spatial}^{S}\right\rangle\left|\psi_{spin}^{A}\right\rangle \\
\left|\psi_{fermion}^{AS}\right\rangle &= \left|\psi_{spatial}^{A}\right\rangle\left|\psi_{spin}^{S}\right\rangle.
\end{aligned} \tag{11}$$

The two parts *cannot* have the same exchange symmetry, or else the full eigenstate would not be antisymmetric. In Eqs. (10) and (11) we use superscripts to denote the exchange symmetry of the state vectors.

2 ■ TWO IDENTICAL PARTICLES IN ONE DIMENSION

We take the example of a system of two identical particles bound within a one-dimensional potential energy well to study the application of the symmetrization postulate to the complete state vector. Limiting the discussion to one dimension is sufficient to illustrate the most important ramifications of the symmetrization principle. Let's first look at the spatial part of the state vector. The Hamiltonian for a single particle in one dimension is

$$H_{single} = \frac{p^2}{2m} + V(x). \tag{12}$$

Assume we know the wave function solutions to the energy eigenvalue equation:

$$H_{single}\varphi_n(x) = E_n\varphi_n(x). \tag{13}$$

The Hamiltonian for two particles in this potential energy well is

$$H = \frac{p_1^2}{2m} + V(x_1) + \frac{p_2^2}{2m} + V(x_2), \tag{14}$$

where x_1 labels the position of particle 1 along the x-axis, and p_1 is the momentum of particle 1; x_2 and p_2 are the equivalent for particle 2. We assume for the moment that the two particles do not interact with each other and that the Hamiltonian has no spin dependence. The two-particle energy eigenvalue equation is

$$H\psi(x_1,x_2) = E\psi(x_1,x_2). \tag{15}$$

The wave function $\psi(x_1,x_2)$ of the system is a function of the two coordinates x_1 and x_2 locating the two particles. This **two-particle wave function** is a new concept, so a few comments about it are in order.

The complex square of the two-particle wave function yields the probability density

$$\mathcal{P}(x_1,x_2) = \left|\psi(x_1,x_2)\right|^2, \tag{16}$$

but because we have two particles, we must be clear what this density means. We interpret the probability density as a **two-particle probability density**, and so

$$\left|\psi(x_1,x_2)\right|^2 dx_1\, dx_2 \tag{17}$$

is the probability of finding particle 1 at position x_1 within a volume dx_1 *and* finding particle 2 at position x_2 within a volume dx_2. ("Volume" in this case is a length, but in a three-dimensional problem, it would be a true volume.) We normalize the system wave function by integrating the two-particle probability density over both coordinates:

$$\iint \left|\psi(x_1,x_2)\right|^2 dx_1\, dx_2 = 1, \tag{18}$$

which means that the probability of finding both particles within the whole volume available to the system is unity.

In this noninteracting example, the two-particle Hamiltonian is the sum of two single-particle Hamiltonians, so the product function $\varphi_{n_a}(x_1)\varphi_{n_b}(x_2)$ describing the system with particle 1 in energy state n_a and particle 2 in energy state n_b satisfies the energy eigenvalue equation (15) with energy $E_{n_a} + E_{n_b}$. That would be the end of the story if the two particles were *distinguishable* (like an electron and a proton, for example), but for *indistinguishable* or *identical* particles we must find spatial eigenstates that are either symmetric or antisymmetric with respect to exchange of the two particles. As we did with the spin state vectors for the spin-1/2 states in the last section, we form the symmetric or antisymmetric superpositions

$$\left|\psi_{space}^S\right\rangle \doteq \psi_{n_a n_b}^S(x_1, x_2) = N_S\left[\varphi_{n_a}(x_1)\varphi_{n_b}(x_2) + \varphi_{n_a}(x_2)\varphi_{n_b}(x_1)\right]$$

$$\left|\psi_{space}^A\right\rangle \doteq \psi_{n_a n_b}^A(x_1, x_2) = N_A\left[\varphi_{n_a}(x_1)\varphi_{n_b}(x_2) - \varphi_{n_a}(x_2)\varphi_{n_b}(x_1)\right], \tag{19}$$

where $N_{S,A}$ are the normalization constants. The wave function $\psi_{n_a n_b}^S(x_1, x_2)$ is symmetric with respect to exchange of the two particles, and the wave function $\psi_{n_a n_b}^A(x_1, x_2)$ is antisymmetric. Each of these solutions has the two-particle energy

$$E_{n_a n_b} = E_{n_a} + E_{n_b}. \tag{20}$$

2.1 ■ Two-Particle Ground State

The ground state of this system has both particles in the single-particle ground state, so $n_a = 1$ and $n_b = 1$ and the energy of the state is $E_{11} = 2E_1$. The symmetric two-particle ground-state wave function is

$$\psi_{11}^S(x_1, x_2) = \varphi_1(x_1)\varphi_1(x_2). \tag{21}$$

However, the antisymmetric two-particle wave function is identically equal to zero:

$$\psi_{11}^A(x_1, x_2) = N_A\left[\varphi_1(x_1)\varphi_1(x_2) - \varphi_1(x_2)\varphi_1(x_1)\right] = 0, \tag{22}$$

so there is no possibility of having an antisymmetric spatial wave function in the ground state, regardless of whether the system comprises bosons or fermions.

To properly apply the symmetrization postulate to the complete state vector of this system, we must include the spin in the state vector. Let's assume that the system is either composed of two spin-0 bosons, or two spin-1/2 fermions. For two spin-0 bosons, the total spin must be zero and the only possible system spin state is $|SM\rangle = |00\rangle$, which is equal to the uncoupled basis state $|s_1 s_2 m_1 m_2\rangle = |0000\rangle$. This spin state is symmetric under exchange of the two particles (Problem 2). The complete state vector for bosons must be symmetric, so the spatial wave function must always be symmetric in this spin-0 example. Hence, the ground state of the two spin-0 bosons in a one-dimensional system is

$$\left|\psi_{11}^{SS}\right\rangle \doteq \psi_{11}^S(x_1, x_2)|00\rangle = \varphi_1(x_1)\varphi_1(x_2)|00\rangle. \tag{23}$$

The notation in Eq. (23) is a mixture of wave function language and abstract ket notation, but it makes the space-spin distinction clear.

For two spin-1/2 fermions, the total spin is 0 or 1, with the coupled basis states

$$\left.\begin{aligned}|11\rangle &= |++\rangle \\ |10\rangle &= \tfrac{1}{\sqrt{2}}[|+-\rangle + |-+\rangle] \\ |1,-1\rangle &= |--\rangle\end{aligned}\right\} \textit{Symmetric Triplet states} \tag{24}$$

$$|00\rangle = \tfrac{1}{\sqrt{2}}[|+-\rangle - |-+\rangle]\} \textit{ Antisymmetric Singlet state}$$

being the eigenstates of the exchange operator we need to construct the complete state vectors. For the ground state, the symmetric spin triplet states are excluded because the required antisymmetric spatial state is identically zero [Eq. (22)]. The ground state of two spin-1/2 fermions is therefore

$$|\psi_{11}^{SA}\rangle \doteq \psi_{11}^S(x_1,x_2)|00\rangle = \varphi_1(x_1)\varphi_1(x_2)|00\rangle. \tag{25}$$

This result exposes a problem with our notation. The spin state $|00\rangle$ in Eq. (23) is *not* the same as the spin state $|00\rangle$ in Eq. (25). For two spin-0 bosons, the state $|00\rangle$ is really $|s_1 = 0, s_2 = 0, S = 0, M = 0\rangle$ and is symmetric under particle exchange, whereas for two spin-1/2 fermions, the state $|00\rangle$ is $|s_1 = \tfrac{1}{2}, s_2 = \tfrac{1}{2}, S = 0, M = 0\rangle$ and is antisymmetric under particle exchange. We will continue with the notation $|SM\rangle$ for coupled basis states, but note this limitation.

2.2 ■ Two-Particle Excited State

The first excited state of the two-particle system has one particle in the single-particle ground state and one particle in the first single-particle excited state, so $n_a = 1$, $n_b = 2$ and the energy of the state is $E_{12} = E_1 + E_2$. In this case, both the symmetric and antisymmetric spatial wave functions in Eq. (19) are nonzero.

For the spin-0 boson case, the spatial wave function must be symmetric because there is only a symmetric spin state, so the state vector is

$$|\psi_{12}^{SS}\rangle \doteq \psi_{12}^S(x_1,x_2)|00\rangle = \tfrac{1}{\sqrt{2}}[\varphi_1(x_1)\varphi_2(x_2) + \varphi_2(x_1)\varphi_1(x_2)]|00\rangle. \tag{26}$$

For the spin-1/2 fermion case, the total state vector must be antisymmetric, so the symmetric spatial wave function must combine with the antisymmetric singlet spin state

$$|\psi_{12}^{SA}\rangle \doteq \psi_{12}^S(x_1,x_2)|00\rangle = \tfrac{1}{\sqrt{2}}[\varphi_1(x_1)\varphi_2(x_2) + \varphi_1(x_2)\varphi_2(x_1)]|00\rangle, \tag{27}$$

and the antisymmetric spatial wave function must combine with the symmetric triplet spin states

$$|\psi_{12}^{AS}\rangle \doteq \psi_{12}^A(x_1,x_2)|1M\rangle = \tfrac{1}{\sqrt{2}}[\varphi_1(x_1)\varphi_2(x_2) - \varphi_1(x_2)\varphi_2(x_1)]|1M\rangle, \tag{28}$$

with $M = 1, 0, -1$. The first excited state of the fermion system is four-fold degenerate, while the boson state is nondegenerate.

If the two particles were distinguishable, then the first excited state would be two-fold degenerate (assuming no spin), with states $\psi_{12}(x_1,x_2) = \varphi_1(x_1)\varphi_2(x_2)$ and $\psi_{21}(x_1,x_2) = \varphi_2(x_1)\varphi_1(x_2)$. A schematic of the ground and first excited states for all three cases is shown in Fig. 1. For the spin-1/2 fermions in Fig. 1(c), we use arrows to indicate the spin combinations. The states $|11\rangle$ and $|1,-1\rangle$ have the two spins aligned, in which case the notation is clear. However, the states $|10\rangle$ and $|00\rangle$ are different superpositions of spin up and down states, so the notation is somewhat unclear. You must remember that $|10\rangle = \tfrac{1}{\sqrt{2}}(|+-\rangle + |-+\rangle)$ and $|00\rangle = \tfrac{1}{\sqrt{2}}(|+-\rangle - |-+\rangle)$.

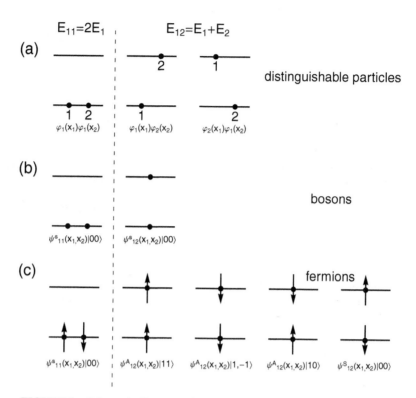

FIGURE 1   Schematic diagrams of ground and first excited states of two particles in a one-dimensional well for (a) distinguishable particles, (b) identical spin-0 bosons, and (c) identical spin-1/2 fermions.

2.3 ■ Visualization of States

To visualize the spatial aspect of these states, assume the two particles are bound in an infinite square potential energy well. The one-particle energy eigenstate wave functions for the infinite square well are

$$|n\rangle \doteq \varphi_n(x) = \sqrt{\frac{2}{L}} \sin\left(\frac{n\pi x}{L}\right). \tag{29}$$

The spatial wave function for the ground state is the same [Eq. (21)] for all three cases of distinguishable particles, identical bosons, and identical fermions. The two-particle probability density for the ground state is thus

$$
\begin{aligned}
\mathcal{P}(x_1, x_2) &= |\psi(x_1, x_2)|^2 \\
&= |\varphi_1(x_1)\varphi_1(x_2)|^2 \\
&= \frac{4}{L^2} \sin^2\left(\frac{\pi x_1}{L}\right) \sin^2\left(\frac{\pi x_2}{L}\right),
\end{aligned}
\tag{30}
$$

as shown in Fig. 2. The system probability density is two-dimensional because there are two particles, each with a one-dimensional probability density.

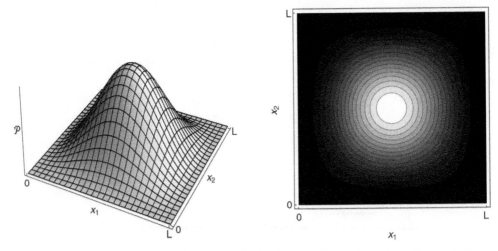

FIGURE 2 Two-particle spatial probability density for the ground state of a system of two particles in an infinite square well, displayed using height (left) or grayscale with contours (right). This probability density is the same for distinguishable particles, identical bosons, and identical fermions.

For the first excited state of the system with one particle in the single-particle ground state and one particle in the first single-particle excited state, the wave function does depend on the type of particle, as shown in Fig. 1. For the distinguishable particle case, there are two possible states, shown in Fig. 3(a) and (b). For the spin-0 boson case, there is only one possible state, which is the symmetric wave function $\psi_{12}^{S}(x_1,x_2)$ given in Eq. (26) with the probability density shown in Fig. 3(c). For the case of two spin-1/2 fermions, the excited state can either be in the symmetric [Fig. 3(c)] or antisymmetric [Fig. 3(d)] spatial wave function, depending on the spin state as given in Eqs. (27) and (28), respectively. For bosons and fermions, the *probability density* is symmetric with respect to particle exchange, which is evident in the symmetry about the diagonal line $x_1 = x_2$ in Figs. 3(c) and (d). The *wave function* $\psi_{12}^{A}(x_1,x_2)$ that underlies the probability density in Fig. 3(d), is antisy-metric about the line $x_1 = x_2$, but its square—the *probability density*—is symmetric. The probability density of the asymmetric spatial state $\psi_{12}^{A}(x_1,x_2)$ is identically zero along the line $x_1 = x_2$:

$$\psi_{12}^{A}(x_1,x_1) = \tfrac{1}{\sqrt{2}}\big[\varphi_1(x_1)\varphi_2(x_1) - \varphi_1(x_1)\varphi_2(x_1)\big] = 0, \tag{31}$$

illustrating that two fermions in a symmetric spin state cannot be in the same location. This is the Pauli exclusion principle that two electrons with the same spin orientation ($|11\rangle = |++\rangle$ or $|1,-1\rangle = |--\rangle$ states) cannot be in the same spatial state. The symmetrization postulate tells us that this also applies to two electrons with opposite spin but combined in a symmetric manner ($|10\rangle$ state). The spatial probability density shown in Fig. 3(d) illustrates the idea that fermions in a symmetric spin state appear to "repel" each other. In contrast, two fermions with opposite spins combined in an anti-symmetric manner ($|00\rangle$ state) to make a spin-singlet state have a symmetric spatial wave function and the probability density shown in Fig. 3(c), the same as two bosons. In this case, the probability density is peaked along the line $x_1 = x_2$, illustrating that two bosons or two spin-singlet fermions have a tendency to "attract" each other.

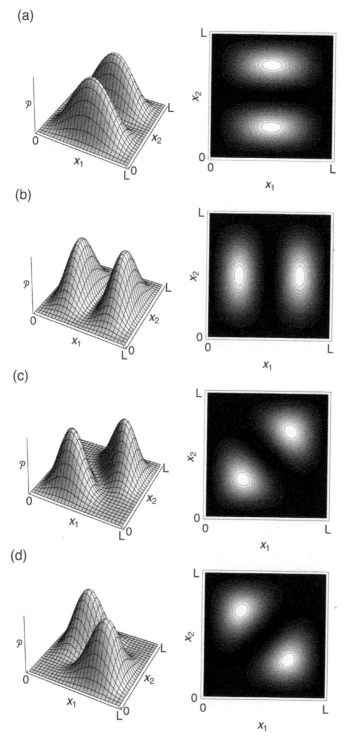

FIGURE 3 Two particle probability densities for the first excited state of a system of two particles in an infinite square well. (a, b) Distinguishable particles, (c) Symmetric spatial state for spin-0 bosons or spin-singlet fermions, (d) Antisymmetric spatial state for spin-triplet fermions.

Identical Particles

2.4 ■ Exchange Interaction

This apparent spatial attraction between bosons and spin-singlet fermions and repulsion between spin-triplet fermions does not reflect any potential energy of interaction between the two particles—we have assumed that the particles *do not interact* in this simple model. Rather, this *apparent interaction* is a consequence of the symmetrization requirement imposed on the wave functions. This effect is called the **exchange force** or the **exchange interaction**. One way to quantify the exchange interaction and demonstrate the difference between particles in symmetric and antisymmetric spatial states is to calculate the expectation value of the square of the separation between the two particles

$$
\begin{aligned}
\left\langle (x_1 - x_2)^2 \right\rangle &= \left\langle x_1^2 - 2x_1 x_2 + x_2^2 \right\rangle \\
&= \left\langle x_1^2 \right\rangle + \left\langle x_2^2 \right\rangle - 2\left\langle x_1 x_2 \right\rangle.
\end{aligned}
\tag{32}
$$

We'll leave the bulk of this calculation to you, but let's demonstrate how to calculate one of these two-particle expectation values.

Consider the expectation value $\left\langle x_1^2 \right\rangle$ in the fermionic state $\left| \psi_{12}^{AS} \right\rangle = \left| \psi_{12}^A \right\rangle |1M\rangle$, where $\left| \psi_{12}^A \right\rangle \doteq \psi_{12}^A(x_1, x_2)$ is the spatial part. Using Dirac bra-ket notation to begin, we have

$$
\begin{aligned}
\left\langle x_1^2 \right\rangle &= \left\langle \psi_{12}^{AS} \left| x_1^2 \right| \psi_{12}^{AS} \right\rangle \\
&= \left\langle \psi_{12}^A \right| \left\langle 1M \left| x_1^2 \right| \psi_{12}^A \right\rangle |1M\rangle.
\end{aligned}
\tag{33}
$$

We separate the space and spin parts of the matrix element and recall that the position x_1 does not act on the spin states, so

$$
\left\langle x_1^2 \right\rangle = \left\langle \psi_{12}^A \left| x_1^2 \right| \psi_{12}^A \right\rangle \langle 1M | 1M \rangle.
\tag{34}
$$

The spin state projection is unity: $\langle 1M | 1M \rangle = 1$. Let's keep the spatial matrix element in Dirac notation by using the notation $|n\rangle_1 \doteq \varphi_n(x_1)$, such that $|1\rangle_1 \doteq \varphi_1(x_1)$ and $|1\rangle_2 \doteq \varphi_1(x_2)$. The Dirac ket representation of the two-particle spatial state [Eq. (28)] in terms of the single-particle spatial states $\left[\left| \psi_{12}^A \right\rangle = \frac{1}{\sqrt{2}} \left(|1\rangle_1 |2\rangle_2 - |2\rangle_1 |1\rangle_2 \right) \right]$ yields

$$
\begin{aligned}
\left\langle x_1^2 \right\rangle &= \tfrac{1}{\sqrt{2}} \left({}_1\langle 1|{}_2\langle 2| - {}_2\langle 1|{}_1\langle 2| \right) (x_1^2) \tfrac{1}{\sqrt{2}} \left(|1\rangle_1 |2\rangle_2 - |1\rangle_2 |2\rangle_1 \right) \\
&= \tfrac{1}{2} \Big\{ \left({}_1\langle 1| x_1^2 |1\rangle_1 \right) \left({}_2\langle 2|2\rangle_2 \right) - \left({}_1\langle 1| x_1^2 |2\rangle_1 \right) \left({}_2\langle 2|1\rangle_2 \right) \\
&\quad - \left({}_1\langle 2| x_1^2 |1\rangle_1 \right) \left({}_2\langle 1|2\rangle_2 \right) + \left({}_1\langle 2| x_1^2 |2\rangle_1 \right) \left({}_2\langle 1|1\rangle_2 \right) \Big\},
\end{aligned}
\tag{35}
$$

where we have isolated the separate matrix elements and projections for particles 1 and particle 2. Invoking the orthonormality of the single-particle eigenstates yields

$$
\left\langle x_1^2 \right\rangle = \tfrac{1}{2} \left({}_1\langle 1| x_1^2 |1\rangle_1 + {}_1\langle 2| x_1^2 |2\rangle_1 \right).
\tag{36}
$$

Thus we are left with calculating two single-particle expectation values. The subscript label indicating the particle number is irrelevant for that calculation, leaving

$$
\left\langle x_1^2 \right\rangle = \tfrac{1}{2} \left(\langle 1| x^2 |1\rangle + \langle 2| x^2 |2\rangle \right).
\tag{37}
$$

To calculate the single-particle expectation values for the particle in the infinite square well, we must use an integral in the position representation:

$$\langle n | x^2 | n \rangle = \int_0^L \varphi_n^*(x)\, x^2\, \varphi_n(x)\, dx. \tag{38}$$

Following this example, you can calculate the expectation value of the interparticle spacing in Eq. (32). The difference between the results for different spatial states resides in the cross-term $\langle x_1 x_2 \rangle$. The final result for the state with one particle in the $n = 1$ state and one particle in the $n = 2$ state of the infinite square well is (Problem 6)

$$\sqrt{\langle (x_1 - x_2)^2 \rangle_S} = 0.20L$$
$$\sqrt{\langle (x_1 - x_2)^2 \rangle_D} = 0.32L \tag{39}$$
$$\sqrt{\langle (x_1 - x_2)^2 \rangle_A} = 0.41L$$

for the three cases of distinguishable particles (D), identical particles in symmetric spatial states (S) (bosons or spin-singlet fermions), and identical particles in antisymmetric spatial states (A) (spin-triplet fermions). These results indicate that particles in symmetric spatial states (typically bosons) are closer to each other, and particles in antisymmetric spatial states (typically fermions) are farther apart from each other, compared to the distinguishable particle case.

The relation between the symmetry/antisymmetry of the spatial wave function and the interparticle spacing is also evident if we measure the particle separation probability density $\mathcal{P}(x_1 - x_2)$. This *one-dimensional* probability density is measured by recording the positions of each particle and finding the interparticle separation $(x_1 - x_2)$. To calculate this one-dimensional probability density, we integrate the two-particle probability density $\mathcal{P}(x_1, x_2)$ parallel to the $x_1 = x_2$ line (i.e., project the two-particle probability densities of Fig. 3 onto the diagonal line $x_2 = L - x_1$). The result of this calculation for the state with one particle in the $n = 1$ state and one particle in the $n = 2$ state of the infinite square well is shown in Fig. 4 (Problem 8). The distribution for symmetric spatial states is peaked at the origin, indicating that these identical particles are more likely than distinguishable particles to be found close to each other. The distribution for antisymmetric spatial states is zero at the origin (i.e., $x_1 = x_2$), indicating that the two identical particles cannot be found at the same location.

2.5 ■ Consequences of the Symmetrization Postulate

We have seen the effect of the symmetrization postulate on a two-particle system (an effective interaction that leads to changes in the interparticle spacing). The consequences of the symmetrization postulate for a many-particle system are much more radical, and are much different for systems of bosons and fermions. For example, in a three-particle system, the ground states are different because only two spin-1/2 fermions can be in the single-particle ground state, as illustrated in Figs. 5(a) and (b). For systems of N particles, the boson ground state has *all* N particles in the single-particle ground state and system energy NE_1 [Fig. 5(c)], while the spin-1/2 fermion ground state has energy levels occupied up to the $N/2$ single-particle state and system energy $\gg NE_1$ [Fig. 5(d)]. The proper study of these types of systems requires statistical mechanics and thermodynamics. The states depicted in Fig. 5 require temperatures near absolute zero so that the thermal energy is much less than the energy spacings.

For a system of bosons, if the requisite low temperature is reached and the density of the particles is high enough, then the ground state of the system exhibits a wealth of interesting quantum mechanical

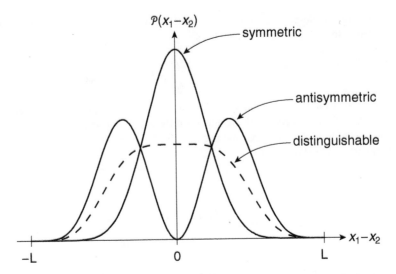

FIGURE 4 Probability density of interparticle separation for the first excited state
($n_a = 1, n_b = 2$) of a system of two particles in the infinite square well for the cases of
distinguishable particles (dashed line), identical particles in symmetric spatial states
(peaked at zero) and identical particles in antisymmetric spatial states (minimum at zero).

effects. When the inter-particle spacing is comparable to the de Broglie wavelength of the particles, then the system of bosons begins to behave as a single macroscopic quantum object. As the critical value of low temperature and high density is reached, the quantum mechanical attraction of the bosons arising from the symmetrization postulate takes over and the system "collapses" into the ground state. This dramatic event is a phase transition in the state of the matter and is called **Bose-Einstein condensation**. Liquid helium exhibits this phase transition at 2.18 K. The specific heat and the thermal conductivity increase discontinuously to signal the onset of the Bose-Einstein condensation. The viscosity of liquid helium drops dramatically and the system behaves as a **superfluid**, easily flowing through small capillaries and even up and out of its container. Liquid helium is a strongly interact-

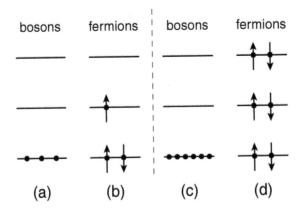

FIGURE 5 Ground states of multiple particle systems in a one-dimensional potential
for a three-particle system of (a) bosons or (b) spin-1/2 fermions, and a six-particle system
of (c) bosons or (d) spin-1/2 fermions.

458

ing system, so the theory of its low temperature quantum behavior is quite complicated. Dilute atomic gases provide a better testing ground for the study of the basic quantum mechanics of Bose-Einstein condensation. Recent experiments have cooled atoms to temperatures below 1 μK and achieved Bose-Einstein condensation. The atoms are close enough to have overlapping de Broglie wavelengths, but far enough apart that the atomic interactions are small. Moreover, the strength of the interactions can be adjusted through magnetic field changes, and the quantum effects can be studied as a function of the strength of the interaction. This new field has spawned a wealth of interesting effects and garnered the Nobel Prize in Physics in 2001.

For fermions, the behavior of a multiparticle system is dominated by the particles near the highest occupied state. The fermions at the low energy levels are "buried" in the sea of fermions and have nowhere to go, because the Pauli exclusion principle forbids them from making transitions to states that are already occupied. Only particles near the top of the distribution see nearby unoccupied levels to which they might make transitions. For example, in atoms, the electrons near the top are the valence electrons that determine the spectroscopy and chemistry of the atom. For electrons in solids, the energy at the top of the distribution of fermions is called the **Fermi energy** and plays a vital role in the behavior of the solid.

3 ■ INTERACTING PARTICLES

The apparent spatial "attraction" or "repulsion" of identical particles evident in Eq. (39) and Fig. 4 has a profound effect when we consider a real interaction between the two particles. The different spatial correlations of the particles lead to different energy shifts for the different spatial symmetry states. Consider two particles in a one-dimensional potential energy well, with an interaction potential energy between the two particles. We assume that this new term is small enough that we can treat it with perturbation theory. Assume that this interaction potential energy depends only on the particle separation:

$$H' = V_{int}(x_1 - x_2).$$

(40)

We use perturbation theory to find the first-order energy corrections

$$E^{(1)} = \left\langle \psi^{(0)} \middle| H' \middle| \psi^{(0)} \right\rangle$$

(41)

using the states from the last section as the zeroth-order states. We assume that the interaction is spin independent, so the spin does not affect this perturbation calculation. That is, in the matrix element

$$
\begin{aligned}
\left\langle \psi^{(0)} \middle| H' \middle| \psi^{(0)} \right\rangle &= \left\langle \psi_{spatial} \middle| \left\langle \psi_{spin} \middle| H' \middle| \psi_{spatial} \right\rangle \middle| \psi_{spin} \right\rangle \\
&= \left\langle \psi_{spatial} \middle| H' \middle| \psi_{spatial} \right\rangle \left\langle \psi_{spin} \middle| \psi_{spin} \right\rangle \\
&= \left\langle \psi_{spatial} \middle| H' \middle| \psi_{spatial} \right\rangle,
\end{aligned}
$$

(42)

the spatial and spin states separate and only the spatial states enter into the perturbation calculation. The only role of the spin is to determine the allowed spatial states through the symmetrization postulate.

For a system of two identical spin-0 bosons, the zeroth-order ground state is

$$\left| \psi_{11}^{SS} \right\rangle \doteq \psi_{11}^{S}(x_1, x_2) |00\rangle = \varphi_1(x_1)\varphi_1(x_2)|00\rangle,$$

(43)

so the first-order perturbation is

$$E_{11}^{(1)} = \langle \psi_{11}^S | H' | \psi_{11}^S \rangle \langle 00 | 00 \rangle$$
$$= \langle \psi_{11}^S | V_{int}(x_1 - x_2) | \psi_{11}^S \rangle$$
$$= \int_{-\infty}^{\infty} \int_{-\infty}^{\infty} \varphi_1^*(x_1)\varphi_1^*(x_2) V_{int}(x_1 - x_2)\varphi_1(x_1)\varphi_1(x_2)\,dx_1\,dx_2$$
$$= \int_{-\infty}^{\infty} \int_{-\infty}^{\infty} |\varphi_1(x_1)|^2 V_{int}(x_1 - x_2)|\varphi_1(x_2)|^2 dx_1\,dx_2. \tag{44}$$

It is convenient to define the general form of this matrix element as the **direct integral**

$$J_{nm} = \int_{-\infty}^{\infty} \int_{-\infty}^{\infty} |\varphi_n(x_1)|^2 V_{int}(x_1 - x_2)|\varphi_m(x_2)|^2 dx_1\,dx_2. \tag{45}$$

The direct integral is the interaction energy between the two probability densities $P_n(x_1) = |\varphi_n(x_1)|^2$ and $P_m(x_2) = |\varphi_m(x_2)|^2$ that represent the two particles. With this definition, the perturbed ground-state energy for a system of two spin-0 bosons is

$$E_{11} = 2E_1^{(0)} + J_{11}. \tag{46}$$

For a system of two identical spin-1/2 fermions, the zeroth-order ground state is

$$|\psi_{11}^{SA}\rangle \doteq \psi_{11}^S(x_1, x_2)|00\rangle = \varphi_1(x_1)\varphi_1(x_2)|00\rangle \tag{47}$$

and the first-order perturbation is

$$E_{11}^{(1)} = \langle \psi_{11}^S | H' | \psi_{11}^S \rangle \langle 00 | 00 \rangle$$
$$= \langle \psi_{11}^S | V_{int}(x_1 - x_2) | \psi_{11}^S \rangle \tag{48}$$
$$= J_{11},$$

which is the same as the boson case. The interaction is spin independent, and the ground-state spatial wave function is the same for bosons and fermions.

For the first excited state of the two-particle system, the identical spin-0 bosons must have a symmetric wave function [Eq. (26)], so the state vector is

$$|\psi_{12}^{SS}\rangle \doteq \psi_{12}^S(x_1, x_2|00) = \tfrac{1}{\sqrt{2}}[\varphi_1(x_1)\varphi_2(x_2) + \varphi_1(x_2)\varphi_2(x_1)]|00\rangle \tag{49}$$

and the first-order perturbation is

$$E_{12}^{(1)} = \langle \psi_{12}^S | H' | \psi_{12}^S \rangle \langle 00 | 00 \rangle$$
$$= \langle \psi_{12}^S | V_{int}(x_1 - x_2) | \psi_{12}^S \rangle$$
$$= \tfrac{1}{2} \int_{-\infty}^{\infty} \int_{-\infty}^{\infty} [\varphi_1^*(x_1)\varphi_2^*(x_2) + \varphi_1^*(x_2)\varphi_2^*(x_1)] V_{int}(x_1 - x_2)$$
$$[\varphi_1(x_1)\varphi_2(x_2) + \varphi_1(x_2)\varphi_2(x_1)]\,dx_1\,dx_2. \tag{50}$$

Identical Particles

This gives four terms, but they are equal in pairs if we swap the integration dummy variables x_1 and x_2, yielding (Problem 10)

$$E_{12}^{(1)} = \int_{-\infty}^{\infty} \int_{-\infty}^{\infty} |\varphi_1(x_1)|^2 V_{int}(x_1 - x_2) |\varphi_2(x_2)|^2 dx_1\, dx_2$$
$$+ \int_{-\infty}^{\infty} \int_{-\infty}^{\infty} \varphi_1^*(x_1)\varphi_2^*(x_2) V_{int}(x_1 - x_2) \varphi_1(x_2)\varphi_2(x_1) dx_1\, dx_2. \tag{51}$$

The first term in Eq. (51) is the direct integral J_{12} defined in Eq. (45). The second term is a new term, which we call the **exchange integral** and define, in general, as

$$K_{nm} = \int_{-\infty}^{\infty} \int_{-\infty}^{\infty} \varphi_n^*(x_1)\varphi_m^*(x_2) V_{int}(x_1 - x_2) \varphi_n(x_2)\varphi_m(x_1) dx_1\, dx_2. \tag{52}$$

With this definition, the energy of the first excited state of the system of two identical spin-0 bosons is

$$E_{12} = E_1^{(0)} + E_2^{(0)} + J_{12} + K_{12}. \tag{53}$$

The exchange integral has no classical explanation. It is a manifestation of the symmetrization requirement. It is not caused by spin, but it is intimately related to spin because of the role of spin in the symmetrization postulate.

For two identical spin-1/2 fermions, the excited state spatial wave function can be either symmetric or antisymmetric depending on the spin state. For the antisymmetric singlet spin state, the spatial wave function must be symmetric

$$|\psi_{12}^{SA}\rangle \doteq \psi_{12}^S(x_1,x_2)|00\rangle = \tfrac{1}{\sqrt{2}}\left[\varphi_1(x_1)\varphi_2(x_2) + \varphi_1(x_2)\varphi_2(x_1)\right]|00\rangle. \tag{54}$$

The first-order energy shift is

$$E_{12}^{(1)} = \langle \psi_{12}^S | H' | \psi_{12}^S \rangle \langle 00|00\rangle$$
$$= \langle \psi_{12}^S | V_{int}(x_1 - x_2) | \psi_{12}^S \rangle \tag{55}$$
$$= J_{12} + K_{12}.$$

This is the same shift as the boson excited state because the spatial wave function is the same and the spin does not affect the expectation value.

For the symmetric triplet spin state, the spatial wave function is antisymmetric

$$|\psi_{12}^{AS}\rangle \doteq \psi_{12}^A(x_1,x_2)|1M\rangle = \tfrac{1}{\sqrt{2}}\left[\varphi_1(x_1)\varphi_2(x_2) - \varphi_2(x_1)\varphi_1(x_2)\right]|1M\rangle. \tag{56}$$

The resultant first-order energy correction

$$E_{12}^{(1)} = \langle \psi_{12}^A | H' | \psi_{12}^A \rangle \langle 1M|1M\rangle$$
$$= \langle \psi_{12}^A | V_{int}(x_1 - x_2) | \psi_{12}^A \rangle \tag{57}$$
$$= J_{12} - K_{12}$$

has a negative exchange integral contribution because of the minus sign in the asymmetric spatial wave function (Problem 12). We combine the results in Eqs. (55) and (57) to express the energy of the first excited state of the two spin-1/2 fermion system as

$$E_{12} = E_1^{(0)} + E_2^{(0)} + J_{12} \pm K_{12}, \tag{58}$$

where the $+(-)$ sign refers to the symmetric (antisymmetric) spatial state and the respective singlet (triplet) state.

The energies of the ground and excited states are shown in Fig. 6, where we assume that the direct and exchange integrals J and K are positive, which is typical for the Coulomb interaction between identical charged particles. The direct integral raises all energy states because of the positive repulsive interaction expected classically for charged particles of the same sign. The exchange integral reflects the additional repulsive interaction caused by the spatial correlation or anticorrelation of the particles arising from the symmetrization postulate. For bosons and spin-singlet fermions, the spatial "attraction" that arises from the symmetrization postulate [Fig. 3(c)] increases the positive repulsive interaction energy because they are closer together in space. For spin-triplet fermions, the spatial "repulsion" that arises from the symmetrization postulate [Fig. 3(d)] decreases the interaction energy. The degeneracy of the excited state in the fermion case is partially lifted by the exchange

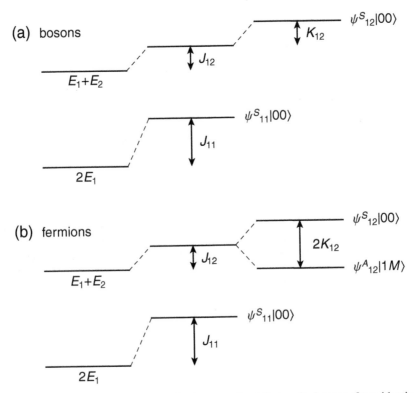

FIGURE 6 Energies and state vectors for the ground and first excited states of two identical (a) spin-0 bosons or (b) spin-1/2 fermions in a one-dimensional potential energy well.

integral term. The resultant energies depend on the spin of the system even though spin is not part of the interaction Hamiltonian. The spin plays its role by determining which spatial states are allowed.

4 ■ EXAMPLE: THE HELIUM ATOM

The symmetrization postulate and the resultant Pauli exclusion principle are key elements in understanding atomic structure and the periodic table. The ramifications of the symmetrization postulate are first evident in the case of the helium atom with two electrons. The helium Hamiltonian is similar to hydrogen but with added potential energy terms due to the second electron interacting with the doubly charged nucleus and the two electrons interacting with each other. The helium Hamiltonian is

$$H = \left(\frac{p_1^2}{2m} - \frac{2e^2}{4\pi\varepsilon_0 r_1} \right) + \left(\frac{p_2^2}{2m} - \frac{2e^2}{4\pi\varepsilon_0 r_2} \right) + \frac{e^2}{4\pi\varepsilon_0 r_{12}}, \tag{59}$$

where r_{12} is the separation of the two electrons, as shown in Fig. 7. The Coulomb repulsion term between the two electrons is clearly of the same order of magnitude as the Coulomb terms representing the interaction of each electron with the nucleus, but we treat it as a perturbation so that we can write the Hamiltonian as a zeroth-order term whose solutions we know, plus a perturbation:

$$H = H_0 + H'$$

$$H' = \frac{e^2}{4\pi\varepsilon_0 r_{12}}. \tag{60}$$

The zeroth-order Hamiltonian is the sum of two hydrogen atom Hamiltonians, each with a nuclear charge $Z = 2$. The eigenstates and eigenenergies of a hydrogenic atom with nuclear charge Z are obtained from the hydrogen atom solutions by the substitution $e^2 \rightarrow Ze^2$, which scales the energies by a factor Z^2 and the size of the radial wave function by $1/Z$. For example, the ground-state wave function of a hydrogenic atom with nucleus $+Ze$ is

$$\psi_{100}(r, \theta, \phi) = \sqrt{\frac{Z^3}{\pi a_0^3}} e^{-Zr/a_0}, \tag{61}$$

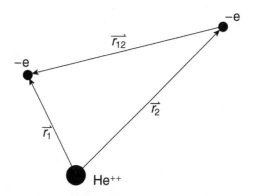

FIGURE 7   Helium atom coordinates.

where $a_0 = 4\pi\varepsilon_0 \hbar^2/me^2$ is the Bohr radius. The zeroth-order energy of the helium atom with one electron in state n_a and one electron in state n_b is the sum of the hydrogenic energies:

$$
\begin{aligned}
E^{(0)}_{n_a n_b} &= -Z^2 \, Ryd \left(\frac{1}{n_a^2} + \frac{1}{n_b^2} \right) \\
&= -4 \, Ryd \left(\frac{1}{n_a^2} + \frac{1}{n_b^2} \right).
\end{aligned}
\tag{62}
$$

Though we don't expect this perturbation approach to yield very precise results, it is a useful first attempt and illustrates many of the important new aspects that arise from the symmetrization postulate.

As we did in the previous section, we separate the spin and spatial aspects of the state vectors because spin and position are not coupled. The complete eigenstates have the form

$$
|\psi\rangle = |\psi_{spatial}\rangle |\psi_{spin}\rangle
\tag{63}
$$

and must be antisymmetric under exchange of the two fermions. Thus the spatial part must be symmetric if the spin part is antisymmetric, or the spatial part must be antisymmetric if the spin part is symmetric.

The spatial part of the state vector represents the state with one particle in the hydrogenic state $n_a \ell_a m_a$ and one particle in the state $n_b \ell_b m_b$. The properly symmetrized spatial wave functions are

$$
\begin{aligned}
\psi^S_{n_a \ell_a m_a, n_b \ell_b m_b}(\mathbf{r}_1, \mathbf{r}_2) &= \tfrac{1}{\sqrt{2}} \left[\psi_{n_a \ell_a m_a}(\mathbf{r}_1) \psi_{n_b \ell_b m_b}(\mathbf{r}_2) + \psi_{n_a \ell_a m_a}(\mathbf{r}_2) \psi_{n_b \ell_b m_b}(\mathbf{r}_1) \right] \\
\psi^A_{n_a \ell_a m_a, n_b \ell_b m_b}(\mathbf{r}_1, \mathbf{r}_2) &= \tfrac{1}{\sqrt{2}} \left[\psi_{n_a \ell_a m_a}(\mathbf{r}_1) \psi_{n_b \ell_b m_b}(\mathbf{r}_2) - \psi_{n_a \ell_a m_a}(\mathbf{r}_2) \psi_{n_b \ell_b m_b}(\mathbf{r}_1) \right].
\end{aligned}
\tag{64}
$$

The spin part of the state vector is obtained by properly symmetrizing the spin states of two spin-1/2 fermions, which yields the eigenstates $|SM\rangle$ of the total spin with $S = 0$ or 1. The four states are

$$
\left.
\begin{aligned}
|11\rangle &= |++\rangle \\
|10\rangle &= \tfrac{1}{\sqrt{2}} [|+-\rangle + |-+\rangle] \\
|1,-1\rangle &= |--\rangle
\end{aligned}
\right\} \; Triplet \; state
\tag{65}
$$

$$
|00\rangle = \tfrac{1}{\sqrt{2}} [|+-\rangle - |-+\rangle] \,\} \; Singlet \; state.
$$

The complete antisymmetric quantum state vector of the helium atom is obtained by combining the antisymmetric singlet state with symmetric spatial wave function or by combining the symmetric triplet state with antisymmetric spatial wave function. Thus, the only possible states are:

$$
\begin{aligned}
\left| \psi^{SA}_{n_a \ell_a m_a, n_b \ell_b m_b} \right\rangle &= \left| \psi^S_{n_a \ell_a m_a, n_b \ell_b m_b} \right\rangle |00\rangle \\
\left| \psi^{AS}_{n_a \ell_a m_a, n_b \ell_b m_b} \right\rangle &= \left| \psi^A_{n_a \ell_a m_a, n_b \ell_b m_b} \right\rangle |1M\rangle.
\end{aligned}
\tag{66}
$$

The other combinations are not possible states for this system.

4.1 ■ Helium Ground State

The ground state of helium has both electrons in hydrogenic ground states, so the antisymmetric spatial state is identically zero [Eq. (22)] and only the symmetric spatial state is allowed. To ensure that the total state vector is antisymmetric, Eq. (66) tells us that the spin part of the ground state must be the antisymmetric singlet state $|00\rangle$. The triplet state $|1M\rangle$ is not permitted in the helium ground state. Thus the ground state of helium is

$$\left|\psi_{ground}\right\rangle = \left|\psi_{1s,1s}^{SA}\right\rangle = \left|\psi_{1s,1s}^{S}\right\rangle|00\rangle, \tag{67}$$

with a zeroth-order energy determined by the sum of two hydrogenic ground-state energies:

$$E_{1s,1s}^{(0)} = -4\ Ryd\left(\frac{1}{1^2} + \frac{1}{1^2}\right) = -8\ Ryd = -108.8\ \text{eV}. \tag{68}$$

The zeroth-order helium energy states are shown in Fig. 8, obtained using Eq. (62).

An aside about energy levels is in order here. In hydrogen, the ground-state energy is -13.6 eV, where zero energy corresponds to the electron and proton infinitely far apart and at rest. We refer to this zero energy level as the **ionization level**. For the calculation we have just done for the helium ground state, the zero of energy corresponds to both electrons removed to infinity, and so is referred to as the **double ionization level**. However, it is more common in the literature to quote atomic energy

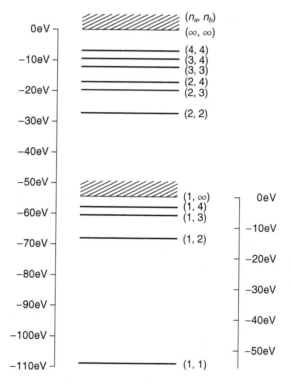

FIGURE 8   Helium atom energies in zeroth order, where hydrogenic Bohr energies are assumed. The energy scale on the left is referenced to the double ionization level and the energy scale on the right is referenced to the single ionization level, which is at -54.4 eV with respect to the double ionization level.

levels with respect to the **single ionization level** corresponding to one electron removed from the atom. If we remove one electron from helium, we are left with a hydrogenic ion with an energy

$$E_{1s,\infty}^{(0)} = -4\,Ryd\left(\frac{1}{1^2} - \frac{1}{\infty^2}\right) = -4\,Ryd = -54.4\,\text{eV}, \tag{69}$$

which is half of the energy in Eq. (68). To quote energies referenced to the single ionization level, we must subtract this energy (as shown in Fig. 8), in which case we get a helium ground-state energy of -54.4 eV.

The experimental value for the helium ground-state energy is -25 eV (referenced to the single ionization level), which is quite different from our zeroth-order estimate. This is not unexpected, as we said above that the electron-electron interaction, which is neglected in zeroth-order, is the same order of magnitude as the electron-nucleus interactions that are responsible for the binding. Even though they are the same order, our approach is to treat the electron-electron repulsion as a perturbation and find the perturbed energies of this system. The helium ground state is nondegenerate, so we find the shift caused by the perturbation by finding the expectation value of the perturbation in the zeroth-order state:

$$
\begin{aligned}
E_{1s,1s}^{(1)} &= \left\langle \psi_{1s,1s}^{SA}\middle| H'\middle|\psi_{1s,1s}^{SA}\right\rangle \\
&= \left\langle \psi_{1s,1s}^{S}\middle|\left\langle 00\middle|\frac{e^2}{4\pi\varepsilon_0 r_{12}}\middle|\psi_{1s,1s}^{S}\right\rangle\middle|00\right\rangle \\
&= \left\langle \psi_{1s,1s}^{S}\middle|\frac{e^2}{4\pi\varepsilon_0 r_{12}}\middle|\psi_{1s,1s}^{S}\right\rangle\left\langle 00\middle|00\right\rangle \\
&= \iint \psi_{100}^{*}(\mathbf{r}_1)\psi_{100}^{*}(\mathbf{r}_2)\frac{e^2}{4\pi\varepsilon_0|\mathbf{r}_1 - \mathbf{r}_2|}\psi_{100}(\mathbf{r}_2)\psi_{100}(\mathbf{r}_1)d^3\mathbf{r}_1\,d^3\mathbf{r}_2.
\end{aligned}
\tag{70}
$$

This integral is the direct integral we defined in the one-dimensional example in Eq. (45). In this three-dimensional Coulomb interaction problem, we define the direct integral as

$$J_{n\ell,n'\ell'} = \iint |\psi_{n\ell m}(\mathbf{r}_1)|^2\frac{e^2}{4\pi\varepsilon_0|\mathbf{r}_1 - \mathbf{r}_2|}|\psi_{n'\ell'm'}(\mathbf{r}_2)|^2\,d^3\mathbf{r}_1\,d^3\mathbf{r}_2. \tag{71}$$

These integrals are independent of m, but not ℓ, which is why we drop the m subscript on the energies. To calculate the direct integrals, it is useful to use the spherical harmonic addition theorem

$$\frac{1}{|\mathbf{r}_1 - \mathbf{r}_2|} = \sum_{\ell=0}^{\infty}\sum_{m=-\ell}^{\ell}\frac{4\pi}{2\ell + 1}\frac{r_<^\ell}{r_>^{\ell+1}}Y_{\ell m}^{*}(\theta_1,\phi_1)Y_{\ell m}(\theta_2,\phi_2), \tag{72}$$

where $r_>$ stands for the larger of the two distances r_1 and r_2, and $r_<$ the smaller.

The ground-state direct integral in Eq. (70) can be done and the result is (Problem 14):

$$E_{1s,1s}^{(1)} = \frac{5}{8}\frac{Ze^2}{4\pi\varepsilon_0 a_0} = \frac{5}{4}\frac{e^2}{4\pi\varepsilon_0 a_0} = \frac{10}{4}Ryd = 34\,\text{eV}. \tag{73}$$

The shift is positive because the electrons repel each other, yielding a positive Coulomb potential energy. The new estimate of the ground-state energy (relative to the single ionization level) is

$$E_{1s,1s} \cong E_{1s,1s}^{(0)} + E_{1s,1s}^{(1)} = -54.4\,\text{eV} + 34\,\text{eV} = -20.4\,\text{eV}, \tag{74}$$

which is now much closer to the experimental value of -25 eV. To make a better estimate, we would have to account for the shielding of the nuclear charge by the presence of the second electron.

4.2 ■Helium Excited States

Now let's turn our attention to the excited states of helium. The zeroth-order energy level diagram in Fig. 8 makes it clear that all states with both electrons excited have a zeroth-order energy above the single ionization level $E_{1s,\infty}^{(0)}$. For example, the doubly excited state $n_a = 2$, $n_b = 2$ has an energy

$$E_{2,2}^{(0)} = -4 \; Ryd \left(\frac{1}{2^2} + \frac{1}{2^2} \right) = -2 \; Ryd = -27.2 \text{ eV}, \tag{75}$$

which is 27.2 eV above the single ionization level. Such doubly excited states are not stable. They decay to a lower energy state with one electron in the hydrogenic ground state and the second electron traveling to infinity with the excess energy. This decay is very likely and so the lifetime of the doubly excited states is very short. The likelihood of this process leads to its name: **auto-ionization**. For this reason, it is common to limit the discussion of excited atomic states (in this helium example as well as other atomic systems) to those where only one electron is excited and the others remain in the atomic ground state.

Because the excited electron is in a different spatial state than the remaining ground-state electron, both the symmetric and antisymmetric spatial states are allowed. We also expect additional degeneracy because the hydrogen excited states are degenerate with respect to the angular momentum quantum numbers ℓ and m.

The first excited state of helium has $n_a = 1$, $n_b = 2$. The two possible states are:

$$\begin{aligned}
\left| \psi_{1s,2\ell}^{SA} \right\rangle &= \left| \psi_{1s,2\ell}^{S} \right\rangle |00\rangle \doteq \tfrac{1}{\sqrt{2}} \left[\psi_{100}(\mathbf{r}_1)\psi_{2\ell m}(\mathbf{r}_2) + \psi_{100}(\mathbf{r}_2)\psi_{2\ell m}(\mathbf{r}_1) \right] |00\rangle \\
\left| \psi_{1s,2\ell}^{AS} \right\rangle &= \left| \psi_{1s,2\ell}^{A} \right\rangle |1M\rangle \doteq \tfrac{1}{\sqrt{2}} \left[\psi_{100}(\mathbf{r}_1)\psi_{2\ell m}(\mathbf{r}_2) - \psi_{100}(\mathbf{r}_2)\psi_{2\ell m}(\mathbf{r}_1) \right] |1M\rangle.
\end{aligned} \tag{76}$$

In both the symmetric and antisymmetric spatial cases, there are four possible states corresponding to the single $2s$ ($\ell = 0$, $m = 0$) and the three $2p$ ($\ell = 1$, $m = 0, \pm 1$) states. When we combine these states with the single spin singlet state and the three spin triplet states, we find that there are 16 possible states overall. All these states are degenerate in the unperturbed system with Hamiltonian H_0.

The unperturbed energy of these states is the hydrogenic energy shown in Fig. 8. We apply degenerate perturbation theory to find the effect of the electron-electron repulsion term H' on these 16 degenerate states. The perturbation Hamiltonian is diagonal, so the energy corrections are the diagonal elements

$$E_{1s,2\ell}^{(1)} = \left\langle \psi_{1s,2\ell}^{SA} \left| H' \right| \psi_{1s,2\ell}^{SA} \right\rangle \tag{77}$$

for the symmetric spatial state, and

$$E_{1s,2\ell}^{(1)} = \left\langle \psi_{1s,2\ell}^{AS} \left| H' \right| \psi_{1s,2\ell}^{AS} \right\rangle \tag{78}$$

for the antisymmetric spatial state. In both cases, the spin states are unaffected by the perturbation [see Eq. (70)] so we are left with a spatial integral:

$$\begin{aligned}
E_{1s,2\ell}^{(1)} = \iint &\tfrac{1}{\sqrt{2}} \left[\psi_{100}^*(\mathbf{r}_1)\psi_{2\ell m}^*(\mathbf{r}_2) \pm \psi_{100}(\mathbf{r}_2)\psi_{2\ell m}(\mathbf{r}_1) \right] \frac{e^2}{4\pi\varepsilon_0 |\mathbf{r}_1 - \mathbf{r}_2|} \\
&\tfrac{1}{\sqrt{2}} \left[\psi_{100}^*(\mathbf{r}_1)\psi_{2\ell m}^*(\mathbf{r}_2) \pm \psi_{100}(\mathbf{r}_2)\psi_{2\ell m}(\mathbf{r}_1) \right] d^3\mathbf{r}_1 \, d^3\mathbf{r}_2,
\end{aligned} \tag{79}$$

where the $\pm$ distinguishes the two states in Eq. (76). This gives four terms, but they are equal in pairs if we swap the integration dummies $\mathbf{r}_1$ and $\mathbf{r}_2$. Hence, we cancel the factor of $1/2$ and get two terms:

$$
\begin{aligned}
E_{1s,2\ell}^{(1)} = &\iint \left|\psi_{100}(\mathbf{r}_1)\right|^2 \frac{e^2}{4\pi\varepsilon_0 \left|\mathbf{r}_1 - \mathbf{r}_2\right|} \left|\psi_{2\ell m}(\mathbf{r}_2)\right|^2 d^3\mathbf{r}_1\, d^3\mathbf{r}_2 \\
&\pm \iint \psi_{100}^*(\mathbf{r}_1)\psi_{2\ell m}^*(\mathbf{r}_2) \frac{e^2}{4\pi\varepsilon_0 \left|\mathbf{r}_1 - \mathbf{r}_2\right|} \psi_{100}(\mathbf{r}_2)\psi_{2\ell m}(\mathbf{r}_1) d^3\mathbf{r}_1\, d^3\mathbf{r}_2.
\end{aligned}
\tag{80}
$$

The first term is the direct integral and the second term is the exchange integral, which in general is

$$
K_{n\ell,n'\ell'} = \iint \psi_{n\ell m}^*(\mathbf{r}_1)\psi_{n'\ell'm'}^*(\mathbf{r}_2) \frac{e^2}{4\pi\varepsilon_0 \left|\mathbf{r}_1 - \mathbf{r}_2\right|} \psi_{n\ell m}(\mathbf{r}_2)\psi_{n'\ell'm'}(\mathbf{r}_1) d^3\mathbf{r}_1\, d^3\mathbf{r}_2.
\tag{81}
$$

So we write the energy perturbation as

$$
E_{1s,2\ell}^{(1)} = J_{1s,2\ell} \pm K_{1s,2\ell},
\tag{82}
$$

where the $+(-)$ sign refers to the symmetric (antisymmetric) spatial state and the respective singlet (triplet) state. The direct integral is also called the Coulomb interaction energy because it is the electrostatic interaction potential energy of the two electrons: one in the $1s$ state and the other in the $2s$ or $2p$ state.

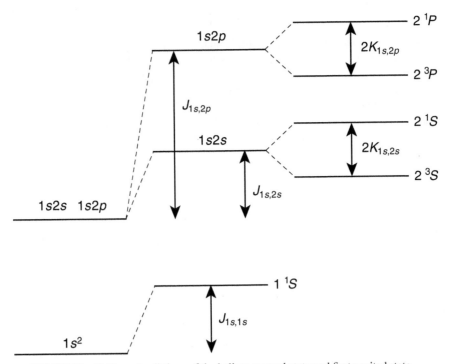

FIGURE 9 Shifts and splittings of the helium ground state and first excited state caused by the direct and exchange interactions.

Both the direct and exchange integrals in helium are positive, so the singlet states are higher in energy than the corresponding triplet states, as shown in Fig. 9. The energy levels are labeled with a modified spectroscopic notation $n\ ^{2S+1}L$, with n being the state of the excited electron. The J label is suppressed because it has no bearing on the energy at this order of approximation. We understand the singlet-triplet ordering of the energy levels by noting that in the singlet state, the spin state is antisymmetric and the spatial state is symmetric, implying that the two electrons get closer to each other and therefore increase the repulsive Coulomb potential energy. In the triplet state, the spin state is symmetric, the spatial state is antisymmetric, and the two electrons are farther apart, thus lowering the Coulomb potential energy.

This ordering of the energy levels, with the singlet state above the triplet state, is evident throughout the excited states of helium. Another important feature of the singlet and triplet states is that optical transitions between these states are forbidden. The electromagnetic light field does not couple to the spin, so the selection rules for optical transitions require there to be no change in the spin quantum number between two states. Hence, transitions between the singlet and triplet states of helium are forbidden, and it was originally believed that there were two types of helium: parahelium ($S = 0$) and orthohelium ($S = 1$). Thus, energy diagrams of helium often show the singlet and triplet levels separately, as in Fig. 10. We now know that transitions between parahelium and orthohelium do occur, with small probability, due to higher-order effects. Note that the 2^3S state of orthohelium is the lowest state on the triplet side. Due to the spin selection rule, it is metastable against decay to the ground state 1^1S. The lifetime of this metastable state is 8000 seconds, which is generally much longer than the time it takes a helium atom to travel through an experimental system, so the state effectively has an infinite lifetime in laboratory experiments.

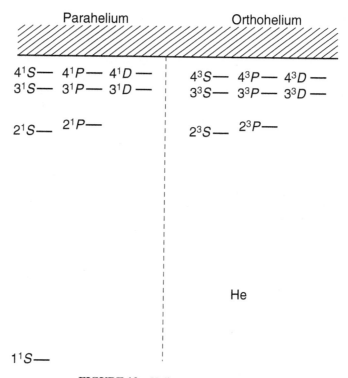

FIGURE 10   Helium energy spectrum.

5 ■ THE PERIODIC TABLE

The helium atom illustrates the importance of the symmetrization postulate in determining the spectrum of energy levels of a multielectron atom. Let's now qualitatively explain how the symmetrization postulate, in the guise of the Pauli exclusion principle, determines the structure of the periodic table as the atomic number Z increases. To a zeroth approximation, the states of multielectron atoms are the hydrogenic states labeled with n, ℓ, and m. However, we must also include spin, so there are four quantum numbers n, ℓ, m_ℓ and m_s labeling each electron (the fifth number $s = 1/2$ is the same for all electrons so we suppress it). The zeroth-order hydrogen energy states E_n depend only on the quantum number n and are n^2 degenerate with respect to ℓ and m_ℓ. The additional m_s degree of freedom doubles the degeneracy, so that each hydrogenic energy level is $2n^2$ degenerate. We refer to each n energy level as a **shell** and to each $n\ell$ orbital as a **subshell**. Each subshell has $2(2\ell + 1)$ possible states.

If electron were bosons, any number could occupy the hydrogenic ground state $n = 1$, similar to Fig. 5(c), and chemistry would be boring. But because electrons are fermions, only one electron can occupy each state specified by the four quantum numbers n, ℓ, m_ℓ, and m_s. Hence, as the atomic number Z increases through the periodic table, we expect that each additional electron occupies the lowest available hydrogenic energy state, filling each subshell with $2(2\ell + 1)$ electrons and each shell with $2n^2$ electrons, analogous to Fig. 5(d). The resulting electronic configurations are denoted by listing the subshells with the number of electrons in each subshell as a superscript, (e.g., $1s^2$). We thus expect the periodic table to reflect the pyramidal structure shown in Table 1. But that would mean that the seven rows of the periodic table would have 280 atoms, whereas we know there are just over 100 atoms. The periodic table does have a pyramidal structure, but not one that reflects the numbers in Table 1. Why not?

The primary reason is that the nuclear charge is shielded by inner shell electrons in a way that lifts the ℓ degeneracy we expect from the simple hydrogen case, giving rise to energy levels specified by the n and ℓ quantum numbers. For a given n, higher values of ℓ correspond to orbits farther from the nucleus because the increased angular momentum leads to a larger centrifugal barrier. Hence, the electrons in high angular momentum orbitals are shielded from the nuclear attraction by the electrons in lower orbits and are bound less tightly. This screening effect explains why electrons fill the hydrogenic orbitals in the sequence $1s$, $2s$, $2p$, $3s$, etc. However, the screening effect is so large that it exceeds the hydrogenic $n \to n + 1$ level separation in some cases, which disturbs the expected shell filling structure of Table 1. A schematic of the ordering of the energy levels of multielectron atoms is shown

Table 1 Electronic Configurations in a Periodic Table Based Upon Purely Hydrogenic Energy Levels

Shell (n)	Subshell Configuration	Degeneracy ($2n^2$)
1	$1s^2$	2
2	$2s^2\, 2p^6$	8
3	$3s^2\, 3p^6\, 3d^{10}$	18
4	$4s^2\, 4p^6\, 4d^{10}\, 4f^{14}$	32
5	$5s^2\, 5p^6\, 5d^{10}\, 5f^{14}\, 5g^{18}$	50
6	$6s^2\, 6p^6\, 6d^{10}\, 6f^{14}\, 6g^{18}\, 6h^{22}$	72
7	$7s^2\, 7p^6\, 7d^{10}\, 7f^{14}\, 7g^{18}\, 7h^{22}\, 7i^{26}$	98

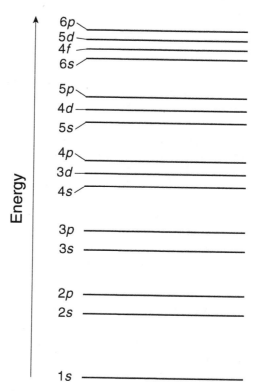

FIGURE 11 Approximate ordering of the energies of subshells after accounting for the shielding of the nuclear charge. The energies are not to scale.

in Fig. 11. The screening effect results in four major differences from the unshielded hydrogenic model: (1) the ℓ degeneracy is lifted, (2) the nd levels are shifted up to lie above the $(n+1)s$ levels, (3) the nf levels are shifted up to lie above the $(n+2)s$ levels, and (4) the np levels are the highest levels within their "group" of levels. Hence the energy filling proceeds in the manner shown in Table 2, with the number of atoms per row shown at right.

Table 2   Electronic Configurations in the Periodic Table

Row	Subshell Configuration				Number of Atoms
1	$1s^2$				2
2	$2s^2$			$2p^6$	8
3	$3s^2$			$3p^6$	8
4	$4s^2$		$3d^{10}$	$4p^6$	18
5	$5s^2$		$4d^{10}$	$5p^6$	18
6	$6s^2$	$4f^{14}$	$5d^{10}$	$6p^6$	32
7	$7s^2$	$5f^{14}$	$6d^{10}$	$7p^6$	32

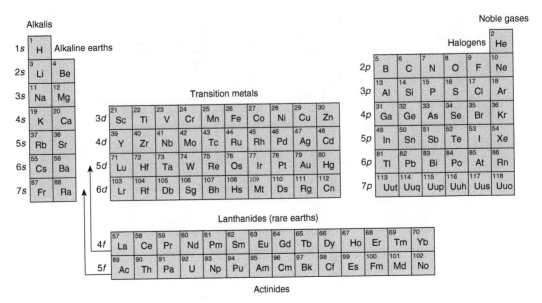

FIGURE 12 Periodic table of the elements.

The full periodic table is shown in Fig. 12 and reflects the pyramidal structure of Table 2 rather than Table 1. Electrons fill up the $1s$ subshell in the first row and the $2s$ and $2p$ subshells in the second row, as shown in Table 3. So far, this follows the purely hydrogenic case. But the

Table 3   Electronic Configurations of Some Elements

1	H	$1s^2$	25	Mn	$[Ar]\,4s^2\,3d^5$
2	He	$1s^2$	28	Ni	$[Ar]\,4s^2\,3d^8$
3	Li	$[He]\,2s^1$	29	Cu	$[Ar]\,4s^1\,3d^{10}$
4	Be	$[He]\,2s^2$	30	Zn	$[Ar]\,4s^2\,3d^{10}$
5	B	$[He]\,2s^2\,2p^1$	36	Kr	$[Ar]\,4s^2\,3d^{10}\,4p^6$
6	C	$[He]\,2s^2\,2p^2$	37	Rb	$[Kr]\,5s^1$
7	N	$[He]\,2s^2\,2p^3$	46	Pd	$[Kr]\,4d^{10}$
8	O	$[He]\,2s^2\,2p^4$	54	Xe	$[Kr]\,5s^2\,4d^{10}\,5p^6$
9	F	$[He]\,2s^2\,2p^5$	55	Cs	$[Xe]\,6s^1$
10	Ne	$[He]\,2s^2\,2p^6$	57	La	$[Xe]\,6s^2\,5d^1$
11	Na	$[Ne]\,3s^1$	58	Ce	$[Xe]\,6s^2\,4f^1\,5d^1$
18	Ar	$[Ne]\,3s^2\,3p^6$	59	Pr	$[Xe]\,6s^2\,4f^3$
19	K	$[Ar]\,4s^1$	86	Rn	$[Xe]\,6s^2\,4f^{14}\,5d^{10}\,6p^6$
21	Sc	$[Ar]\,4s^2\,3d^1$	87	Fr	$[Rn]\,7s^1$
23	V	$[Ar]\,4s^2\,3d^3$	92	U	$[Rn]\,7s^2\,5f^3\,6d^1$
24	Cr	$[Ar]\,4s^1\,3d^5$	94	Pt	$[Rn]\,7s^2\,5f^6$

screening effect pushes the $3d$ energy level up near the $4s$ energy level, so the third row has only the $3s$ and $3p$ subshells. The $3d$ states are not filled until the fourth row of the periodic table. The $4s$ states are filled first for potassium and calcium, then the $3d$ states are filled for scandium through zinc, and finally the $4p$ states are filled for gallium through krypton. The $4s$ and $3d$ levels are so close that there are some anomalies in the transition metals in the fourth row, as indicated in Table 3. Chromium and copper each have only one $4s$ electron and one more $3d$ electron than you might expect. The fifth row fills in the order $5s$, $4d$, and $5p$, analogous to the fourth row because the f subshells are pushed up two groups. The fifth row transition metals also exhibit anomalies in the $5s$ and $4d$ ordering, with palladium being the most extreme in having no $5s$ electrons. The sixth and seventh rows both include f subshells and also have anomalous filling among the $s, f,$ and d subshells.

6 ■ EXAMPLE: THE HYDROGEN MOLECULE

Now let's take a look at another two-electron system that will introduce us to some molecular physics and prepare us for the periodic systems. Consider the hydrogen molecule with two nuclei (protons), each with a bound electron, with the two atoms bound to each other to make a four-particle system, as shown in Fig. 13. We label the electrons 1 and 2 and the protons A and B. The Hamiltonian for the molecule includes hydrogen Hamiltonians for each electron-proton pair; additional Coulomb potential energy terms for the electron-electron, proton-proton, and electron-other-proton pairs; and kinetic energy for the nuclei:

$$H = H_{atom,1A} + H_{atom,2B} + V_{ee} + V_{pp} + V_{ep} + T_N, \tag{83}$$

where

$$
\begin{aligned}
H_{atom,1A} &= \left(\frac{p_1^2}{2m} - \frac{e^2}{4\pi\varepsilon_0 r_{1A}} \right) \\[2mm]
H_{atom,2B} &= \left(\frac{p_2^2}{2m} - \frac{e^2}{4\pi\varepsilon_0 r_{2B}} \right) \\[2mm]
V_{ee} &= \frac{e^2}{4\pi\varepsilon_0 r_{12}} \\[2mm]
V_{pp} &= \frac{e^2}{4\pi\varepsilon_0 R_{AB}} \\[2mm]
V_{ep} &= -\frac{e^2}{4\pi\varepsilon_0 r_{1B}} - \frac{e^2}{4\pi\varepsilon_0 r_{2A}} \\[2mm]
T_{nuc} &= \frac{p_A^2}{2M_A} + \frac{p_B^2}{2M_B}.
\end{aligned}
\tag{84}
$$

We treat this two-electron system as we did the helium atom in the sense that we put the electrons into the lowest energy states of the one-electron system and then account for the required symmetrization of the two identical electrons. So we must first discuss the one-electron molecule.

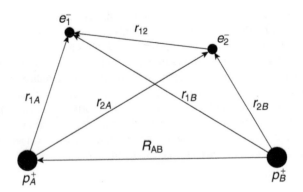

FIGURE 13 Hydrogen molecule.

6.1 ■ The Hydrogen Molecular Ion H_2^+

The hydrogen molecular ion H_2^+ has one electron and has a Hamiltonian

$$H_{ion} = \frac{p_1^2}{2m} - \frac{e^2}{4\pi\varepsilon_0 r_{1A}} - \frac{e^2}{4\pi\varepsilon_0 r_{1B}} + \frac{e^2}{4\pi\varepsilon_0 R_{AB}} + \frac{p_A^2}{2M_A} + \frac{p_B^2}{2M_B}. \tag{85}$$

We do not need the subscript labeling the electron as #1, but we keep it to connect with the H_2 case. To construct approximate energy eigenstates, we use the method of **linear combination of atomic orbitals** (LCAO), which assumes that we can use the atomic energy eigenstates as basis functions. If the two protons are far apart, then we expect that in the ground state of the ion, the electron is attached to one proton and is in the hydrogen atomic ground state. The electronic wave function in this case is

$$|\psi_{separated}\rangle \doteq \psi_{1s}(\mathbf{r}_{1A}), \tag{86}$$

assuming the electron is on proton A. However, the ion Hamiltonian in Eq. (85) is spatially symmetric about the center of the molecule located at the midpoint of the internuclear separation R_{AB} and the eigenstates should reflect this spatial symmetry. Hence we construct two possible ground states of the ion that are symmetric and antisymmetric spatially:

$$\begin{aligned}|\psi_{1s}^g\rangle_1 &\doteq \tfrac{1}{\sqrt{2}}[\psi_{1s}(\mathbf{r}_{1A}) + \psi_{1s}(\mathbf{r}_{1B})] \\ |\psi_{1s}^u\rangle_1 &\doteq \tfrac{1}{\sqrt{2}}[\psi_{1s}(\mathbf{r}_{1A}) - \psi_{1s}(\mathbf{r}_{1B})].\end{aligned} \tag{87}$$

These states are even (g) and odd (u), respectively, under reflection about the midpoint of R_{AB}, and are labeled as *gerade* and *ungerade* states (German for even and odd). We use this labeling notation to distinguish the *spatial* symmetry (g, u) from the *exchange* symmetry (S, A) that we'll need for the H_2 two-electron molecule.

To estimate the ground-state energy of the ion, we calculate the expectation value of the energy $\langle E\rangle = \langle H_{ion}\rangle$ using the wave functions in Eq. (87). We ignore the motion of the nuclei by assuming that the internuclear separation R_{AB} is fixed. In calculating the energy expectation value, we integrate over the electron position, but the result is still dependent on the choice for the fixed value of R_{AB}. This dependence is evident in the results shown in Fig. 14. For both the *gerade* and *ungerade* states, the energy at large internuclear separation is simply the hydrogen energy -13.6 eV expected

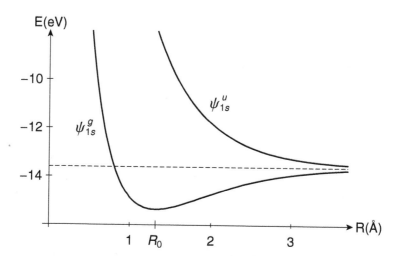

FIGURE 14 Energies of the bonding and antibonding orbitals of the hydrogen molecular ion, as a function of the internuclear separation.

for the system of one ground state atom and one distant proton. At very small internuclear separation $(R_{AB} \ll a_0)$, the energy of both states becomes positive and very large due to the strong proton-proton Coulomb repulsion. For intermediate internuclear separation, the *gerade* and *ungerade* states have different energies. The minimum in the *gerade* state energy indicates an attraction that leads to a stable molecule with an internuclear separation given by the bond length R_0. The energy of the *ungerade* state has no minimum and is repulsive at all distances, implying that a system in this state will dissociate into a bound hydrogen atom and an isolated proton. Hence, we refer to the *gerade* state as a **bonding orbital** and the *ungerade* state as an **antibonding orbital**. Note that the energy of the bonding orbital shown in Fig. 14 is the potential energy function to find the motion of the nuclei in a diatomic molecule. This approximate method of treating the electron motion first and then the nuclear motion is the **Born-Oppenheimer approximation**. It relies on the assumption that the nuclear motion is much slower than the electron motion because of the large mass difference.

To gain a qualitative understanding of the differences between the *gerade* and *ungerade* states, consider a one-dimensional view of the wave functions and probability densities of the two states. Along the line of the internuclear separation, the *gerade* and *ungerade* states are

$$|\psi_{1s}^{g}\rangle \doteq \frac{1}{\sqrt{2}}\left[\psi_{1s}\left(r + \frac{R_{AB}}{2}\right) + \psi_{1s}\left(r - \frac{R_{AB}}{2}\right)\right]$$

$$|\psi_{1s}^{u}\rangle \doteq \frac{1}{\sqrt{2}}\left[\psi_{1s}\left(r + \frac{R_{AB}}{2}\right) - \psi_{1s}\left(r - \frac{R_{AB}}{2}\right)\right]. \tag{88}$$

Substituting the hydrogen atomic ground-state wave function $\psi_{1s}(r) = e^{-r/a_0}/\sqrt{\pi a_0^3}$ into Eq. (88) yields the plots shown in Fig. 15. For the *gerade* state, the wave functions add [Fig. 15(a)] and the resulting electron probability density [Fig. 15(b)] is large between the two protons. This excess negative charge increases the attractive Coulomb interaction of the electron and protons enough to overcome the proton-proton Coulomb repulsion and permit a stable bound molecule. In contrast, the wave functions of the *ungerade* state subtract [Fig. 15(c)] and produce a

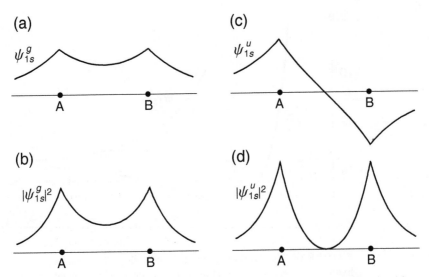

FIGURE 15 Hydrogen molecular ion wave functions (a, c) and probability densities (b, d) for *gerade* (a, b) and *ungerade* (c, d) states.

zero point in the electron density [Fig. 15(d)] between the two protons. This deficiency of negative charge between the protons causes the proton-proton Coulomb repulsion to dominate and leads to the antibonding behavior of the *ungerade* state.

6.2 ■ The Hydrogen Molecule H_2

We now return to the hydrogen molecule with two electrons. In the atomic case, our first guess for the ground state of the two-electron helium atom was to put both electrons in the $1s$ ground hydrogenic atomic state (with $Z = 2$) in a symmetric spatial state and to form an antisymmetric spin-singlet state to satisfy the symmetrization postulate. By analogy, our first guess for the ground state of the two-electron hydrogen molecule puts each electron in the $\left| \psi_{1s}^g \right\rangle$ ground hydrogen molecular ion state to make a spatial state that is symmetric with respect to exchange and puts the two electrons in an anti-symmetric spin-singlet state to satisfy the symmetrization postulate:

$$\left| \psi_{1s,1s}^{SA} \right\rangle = \left| \psi_{1s}^g \right\rangle_1 \left| \psi_{1s}^g \right\rangle_2 \left| 00 \right\rangle \doteq \tfrac{1}{2} \left[\psi_{1s}(\mathbf{r}_{1A}) + \psi_{1s}(\mathbf{r}_{1B}) \right] \left[\psi_{1s}(\mathbf{r}_{2A}) + \psi_{1s}(\mathbf{r}_{2B}) \right] \left| 00 \right\rangle. \quad (89)$$

Just as we found for helium, there is no possible way to make a spatial state that is antisymmetric with respect to electron exchange when both electrons are in the $\left| \psi_{1s}^g \right\rangle$ one-electron ground state, so $\left| \psi_{1s,1s}^{SA} \right\rangle$ is the only possible state in the ground state of the molecule. We conclude that the ground state of the hydrogen molecule is a spin singlet state.

We can gain more insight into the molecular ground state by looking at the state $\left| \psi_{1s,1s}^{SA} \right\rangle$ more closely. If we expand Eq. (89), we obtain

$$\left| \psi_{1s,1s}^{SA} \right\rangle \doteq \tfrac{1}{2} \big[\psi_{1s}(\mathbf{r}_{1A})\psi_{1s}(\mathbf{r}_{2A}) + \psi_{1s}(\mathbf{r}_{1B})\psi_{1s}(\mathbf{r}_{2B})$$
$$+ \psi_{1s}(\mathbf{r}_{1A})\psi_{1s}(\mathbf{r}_{2B}) + \psi_{1s}(\mathbf{r}_{2A})\psi_{1s}(\mathbf{r}_{1B}) \big] \left| 00 \right\rangle. \quad (90)$$

Identical Particles

We can divide this into two terms, labeled "covalent" and "ionic"

$$\left|\psi_{cov}^{S}\right\rangle \doteq \tfrac{1}{2}\left[\psi_{1s}\left(\mathbf{r}_{1A}\right)\psi_{1s}\left(\mathbf{r}_{2B}\right) + \psi_{1s}\left(\mathbf{r}_{2A}\right)\psi_{1s}\left(\mathbf{r}_{1B}\right)\right]$$
$$\left|\psi_{ion}^{S}\right\rangle \doteq \tfrac{1}{2}\left[\psi_{1s}\left(\mathbf{r}_{1A}\right)\psi_{1s}\left(\mathbf{r}_{2A}\right) + \psi_{1s}\left(\mathbf{r}_{1B}\right)\psi_{1s}\left(\mathbf{r}_{2B}\right)\right],$$

(91)

so that

$$\left|\psi_{1s,1s}^{SA}\right\rangle = \left(\left|\psi_{cov}^{S}\right\rangle + \left|\psi_{ion}^{S}\right\rangle\right)|00\rangle.$$

(92)

The state $\left|\psi_{cov}^{S}\right\rangle$ corresponds to the situation with one electron associated with each nucleus, whereas the state $\left|\psi_{ion}^{S}\right\rangle$ corresponds to the situation with both electrons associated with one nucleus. When the nuclei are well separated, $\left|\psi_{cov}^{S}\right\rangle$ corresponds to two isolated hydrogen atoms and $\left|\psi_{ion}^{S}\right\rangle$ corresponds to a proton and a negative hydrogen ion, which has an energy larger than the two isolated hydrogen atoms. Hence, we expect that $\left|\psi_{cov}^{S}\right\rangle$ would be a better guess for the ground state of the molecule. The state $\left|\psi_{cov}^{S}\right\rangle$ represents **covalent bonding** and the state $\left|\psi_{ion}^{S}\right\rangle$ represents **ionic bonding**.

For the covalent bond, we can also form an antisymmetric state

$$\left|\psi_{cov}^{A}\right\rangle \doteq \tfrac{1}{2}\left[\psi_{1s}\left(\mathbf{r}_{1A}\right)\psi_{1s}\left(\mathbf{r}_{2B}\right) - \psi_{1s}\left(\mathbf{r}_{2A}\right)\psi_{1s}\left(\mathbf{r}_{1B}\right)\right],$$

(93)

which must be associated with the symmetric spin-triplet state:

$$\left|\psi_{cov}^{AS}\right\rangle = \left|\psi_{cov}^{A}\right\rangle|1M\rangle.$$

(94)

If we use the two states $\left|\psi_{cov}^{SA}\right\rangle = \left|\psi_{cov}^{S}\right\rangle|00\rangle$ and $\left|\psi_{cov}^{AS}\right\rangle = \left|\psi_{cov}^{A}\right\rangle|1M\rangle$ to find the energy expectation values, then we are using the **valence bond method**. The results of this calculation for the case with both electrons in the $1s$ atomic states are shown in Fig. 16. The results are qualitatively similar to

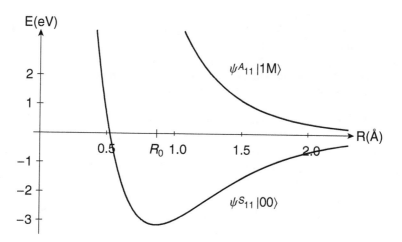

FIGURE 16 Energies of the bonding and antibonding orbitals of the hydrogen molecule obtained with the valence bond method, with the zero of energy referenced to the dissociation limit.

Fig. 14 in that there is a bonding orbital and antibonding orbital. This is to be expected because the state $\left|\psi_{cov}^{S}\right\rangle$ is a *gerade* state and the state $\left|\psi_{cov}^{A}\right\rangle$ is an *ungerade* state. But now for the H_2 molecule, these states are also linked to the exchange symmetry and hence the spin. Following the argument for the hydrogen ion, we conclude that the symmetric spatial state (singlet spin state) has a lower energy than the antisymmetric spatial state (triplet spin state) because of the increased electron-proton Coulomb attraction in the *gerade* state. Note that this ordering of the singlet and triplet states is opposite the case for the excited states of helium. In that case, the increased overlap of the electrons in the symmetric spatial state led to an increased Coulomb repulsion of the two electrons and a higher energy for the spin singlet state.

SUMMARY

For a proper quantum mechanical description of multiple-particle systems, we must account for the indistinguishability of fundamental particles. The symmetrization postulate requires that the quantum state vector of a system of identical particles be either symmetric or antisymmetric with respect to exchange of any pair of identical particles within the system. Nature dictates that integer spin particles—bosons—have symmetric states, while half-integer spin particles—fermions—have antisymmetric states. The symmetrization postulate applies to the complete quantum state vector, including both the spin and space parts of the system. As a consequence of the symmetrization postulate, some states are not allowed. The best known manifestation of this is the Pauli exclusion principle, which limits the number of electrons in given atomic levels and leads to the structure of the periodic table.

RESOURCES

Further Reading

The work on Bose-Einstein Condensation that was awarded the 2001 Nobel Prize in Physics is described at:

nobelprize.org/nobel_prizes/physics/laureates/2001/

Further details on molecular energy calculations are presented in

B. H. Bransden and C. J. Joachain, *Physics of Atoms and Molecules*, 2nd ed., Harlow, England:Prentice Hall, 2003.

Dr. Seuss's take on indistinguishability can be found in

Dr. Seuss, *The Sneetches and Other Stories*, New York: Random House, 1961.

Identical Particles: Problem Set

1 Show that the eigenvalues of the exchange operator P_{12} are ± 1.

2 For a system of two identical spin-0 bosons, the total spin must be zero and the only possible system spin state is $|SM\rangle = |00\rangle$. Express this state in the uncoupled basis and show that it is symmetric with respect to exchange of the two particles.

3 Consider a system of two identical spin-1 particles. Find the spin states for this system that are symmetric or antisymmetric with respect to exchange of the two particles.

4 Specify the exchange symmetry of the following wave functions:

$$\psi_a(x_1, x_2) = \frac{1}{(x_1 + x_2)}$$

$$\psi_b(x_1, x_2) = \frac{a(x_1 - x_2)}{(x_1 - x_2)^2 + b}$$

$$\psi_c(x_1, x_2) = \frac{a(x_1 - 3x_2)}{(x_1 + x_2)^2 + b}$$

$$\psi_d(x_1, x_2, x_3) = \frac{x_1 x_2 x_3}{x_1^2 + x_2^2 + x_3^2 + b}.$$

5 Use your favorite software tool to plot the two-particle probability density for two non-interacting particles in a one-dimensional harmonic oscillator potential for the case where one of the particles is in the single-particle ground state and the other is in the single-particle first excited state. Do this for (a) distinguishable particles (of the same mass), (b) identical spin-0 bosons, and (c) identical spin-1/2 fermions in a spin triplet state. In each case, write the system wave function and discuss the important features of your plots.

6 Consider two noninteracting particles of mass m in an infinite square well. For the case with one particle in the single-particle state $|n\rangle$ and the other in the state $|k\rangle (n \neq k)$, calculate the expectation value of the squared interparticle spacing $\langle (x_1 - x_2)^2 \rangle$, assuming (a) the particles are distinguishable, (b) the particles are identical spin-0 bosons, and (c) the particles are identical spin-1/2 fermions in a spin triplet state. Use bra-ket the notation as far as you can, but you will have to do some integrals. Verify the results in Eq. (39),

$$\sqrt{\langle (x_1 - x_2)^2 \rangle_S} = 0.20L$$

$$\sqrt{\langle (x_1 - x_2)^2 \rangle_D} = 0.32L \qquad (39)$$

$$\sqrt{\langle (x_1 - x_2)^2 \rangle_A} = 0.41L.$$

7 Consider two noninteracting particles of mass m in the harmonic oscillator potential well. For the case with one particle in the single-particle state $|n\rangle$ and the other in state $|k\rangle$ $(n \neq k)$, calculate the expectation value of the squared interparticle spacing $\langle (x_1 - x_2)^2 \rangle$, assuming

From Chapter 13 of *Quantum Mechanics: A Paradigms Approach*, First Edition. David H. McIntyre. Copyright © 2012 by Pearson Education, Inc. Published by Pearson Addison-Wesley. All rights reserved.

The companion websites for this text are http://physics.oregonstate.edu/portfolioswiki and http://physics.oregonstate.edu/qmactivities.

(a) the particles are distinguishable, (b) the particles are identical spin-0 bosons, and (c) the particles are identical spin-1/2 fermions in a spin triplet state. Use bra-ket notation as far as you can, but you will have to do some integrals.

8 Calculate the one-dimensional particle separation probability density $\mathcal{P}(x_1 - x_2)$ for a system of two identical particles in an infinite square well with one particle in the single-particle ground state $|1\rangle \doteq \varphi_1(x)$ and the other in the state $|2\rangle \doteq \varphi_2(x)$. Do this for the three cases of (a) distinguishable particles (of the same mass), (b) identical particles in a symmetric spatial state, and (c) identical particles in an antisymmetric spatial state. Reproduce Fig. 4.

9 Calculate the one-particle probability density $\mathcal{P}(x_1)$ by integrating the two-particle probability density $\mathcal{P}(x_1, x_2)$ over the position x_2 of particle 2 (i.e., projecting the two-particle probability density onto the x_1 axis). Do this for the three cases of (a) distinguishable particles (of the same mass), (b) identical particles in a symmetric spatial state, and (c) identical particles in an anti-symmetric spatial state. Demonstrate that measuring the position of one particle independent of the location of the other particle is the same for all three cases.

10 Show that Eq. (51),

$$E_{12}^{(1)} = \int_{-\infty}^{\infty} \int_{-\infty}^{\infty} |\varphi_1(x_1)|^2 V_{int}(x_1 - x_2) |\varphi_2(x_2)|^2 dx_1\, dx_2$$
$$+ \int_{-\infty}^{\infty} \int_{-\infty}^{\infty} \varphi_1^*(x_1)\varphi_2^*(x_2) V_{int}(x_1 - x_2)\varphi_1(x_2)\varphi_2(x_1) dx_1\, dx_2,$$

(51)

follows from Eq. (50),

$$\begin{aligned} E_{12}^{(1)} &= \langle \psi_{12}^S | H' | \psi_{12}^S \rangle \langle 00|00\rangle \\ &= \langle \psi_{12}^S | V_{int}(x_1 - x_2) | \psi_{12}^S \rangle \\ &= \tfrac{1}{2} \int_{-\infty}^{\infty} \int_{-\infty}^{\infty} [\varphi_1^*(x_1)\varphi_2^*(x_2) + \varphi_1^*(x_2)\varphi_2^*(x_1)] V_{int}(x_1 - x_2) \\ &\qquad\qquad [\varphi_1(x_1)\varphi_2(x_2) + \varphi_1(x_2)\varphi_2(x_1)] dx_1\, dx_2. \end{aligned}$$

(50)

11 Consider two indistinguishable, uncharged spin-1/2 fermions in the one-dimensional harmonic oscillator potential $V(x) = \tfrac{1}{2} m\omega^2 x^2$. The two particles interact with each other through a perturbing potential $H' = \tfrac{1}{2}\alpha(x_1 - x_2)^2$, where the positive constant α is considered small ($\alpha \ll m\omega^2$).

a) For the unperturbed two-particle system, find the energy eigenvalues and eigenstates of the ground state and the first excited state (you need not determine the spatial wave functions, bra-ket notation is sufficient). Specify and discuss the degeneracy of each level.

b) Discuss qualitatively how the energies in (a) are perturbed by the interaction of the particles. Draw an energy level diagram showing the unperturbed and perturbed energy levels.

12 Show that the sign of the exchange contribution K_{12} is negative for the spin-triplet state in the first excited state of a system of two identical spin-1/2 particles [see Eq. (57)],

$$\begin{aligned} E_{12}^{(1)} &= \langle \psi_{12}^A | H' | \psi_{12}^A \rangle \langle 1M|1M\rangle \\ &= \langle \psi_{12}^A | V_{int}(x_1 - x_2) | \psi_{12}^A \rangle \\ &= J_{12} - K_{12}. \end{aligned}$$

(57)

13 Consider the first excited state of helium where one electron is in the $n = 1$ hydrogenic state and the other electron is in the $n = 2$ hydrogenic state.

  a) Using term or spectroscopic notation, list all the allowed states of this system.

  b) How many total states are there?

  c) What is the energy of this level, ignoring the interactions of the electrons with each other?

  d) Describe qualitatively the shifts of this energy level that result from considering the interactions of the electrons with each other.

14 Find the first-order perturbed energy of the helium ground state by calculating the direct integral J in Eq. (70),

$$
\begin{aligned}
E^{(1)}_{1s,1s} &= \left\langle \psi^{SA}_{1s,1s} \middle| H' \middle| \psi^{SA}_{1s,1s} \right\rangle \\
&= \left\langle \psi^{S}_{1s,1s} \middle| \langle 00 \middle| \frac{e^2}{4\pi\varepsilon_0 r_{12}} \middle| \psi^{S}_{1s,1s} \right\rangle |00\rangle \\
&= \left\langle \psi^{S}_{1s,1s} \middle| \frac{e^2}{4\pi\varepsilon_0 r_{12}} \middle| \psi^{S}_{1s,1s} \right\rangle \langle 00|00\rangle \\
&= \iint \psi^{*}_{100}(\mathbf{r}_1)\psi^{*}_{100}(\mathbf{r}_2) \frac{e^2}{4\pi\varepsilon_0 |\mathbf{r}_1 - \mathbf{r}_2|} \psi_{100}(\mathbf{r}_2)\psi_{100}(\mathbf{r}_1) d^3\mathbf{r}_1\, d^3\mathbf{r}_2,
\end{aligned}
\tag{70}
$$

Find the numerical value of your result (in eV) and confirm Eq. (73),

$$
E^{(1)}_{1s,1s} = \frac{5}{8}\frac{Ze^2}{4\pi\varepsilon_0 a_0} = \frac{5}{4}\frac{e^2}{4\pi\varepsilon_0 a_0} = \frac{10}{4} Ryd = 34 \text{ eV}.
\tag{73}
$$

15 Find the first-order perturbed energies of the helium excited states $1s\,2s$ and $1s\,2p$ by calculating the direct and exchange integrals J, K in Eqs. (71),

$$
J_{n\ell,n'\ell'} = \iint |\psi_{n\ell m}(\mathbf{r}_1)|^2 \frac{e^2}{4\pi\varepsilon_0 |\mathbf{r}_1 - \mathbf{r}_2|} |\psi_{n'\ell'm'}(\mathbf{r}_2)|^2\, d^3\mathbf{r}_1\, d^3\mathbf{r}_2,
\tag{71}
$$

and (81),

$$
K_{n\ell,n'\ell'} = \iint \psi^{*}_{n\ell m}(\mathbf{r}_1)\psi^{*}_{n'\ell'm'}(\mathbf{r}_2) \frac{e^2}{4\pi\varepsilon_0 |\mathbf{r}_1 - \mathbf{r}_2|} \psi_{n\ell m}(\mathbf{r}_2)\psi_{n'\ell'm'}(\mathbf{r}_1)\, d^3\mathbf{r}_1\, d^3\mathbf{r}_2,
\tag{81}
$$

Find the numerical values of your results (in eV) and make a diagram similar to Fig. 9.

16 Show that the state of the hydrogen molecule that is antisymmetric with respect to electron exchange when both electrons are in the $\left|\psi^{g}_{1s}\right\rangle$ state is identically zero.

17 Consider two indistinguishable, noninteracting spin-1/2 fermions in a one-dimensional infinite square well potential of length L.

  a) What is the ground-state energy of the two-particle system?

  b) What is the ground-state wave function?

  c) What is the first excited state energy of the two-particle system?

  d) What are the wave functions of the first excited state?

  e) What is the degeneracy of the first excited state?

  f) Discuss qualitatively how the excited-state energies change if we consider the particles to be interacting through the Coulomb potential.

Time-Dependent Perturbation Theory

Consider *time-independent* perturbation theory and that changes in the Hamiltonian lead to changes in the energy eigenstates of a system. When the Hamiltonian is not time dependent, the perturbed energy levels are still stationary states of the system. Now we turn to the problem of understanding how a system responds to changes in the Hamiltonian that are a function of time. We will find that the new perturbed energy states are no longer stationary states and that changes or **transitions** between states can occur. Consider that we solve the time-dependent case exactly for a sinusoidal perturbation of the two-level spin system. Spin flips or transitions between spin up and down states occur when the frequency of the time dependence is close to the Bohr frequency characterizing the energy splitting of the two states. This resonance condition is also an important idea in this chapter.

The transitions between energy states that arise from a time-dependent Hamiltonian play a major role in experimental studies of quantum mechanical systems. You have probably encountered many references to spectroscopic experiments that provide evidence of the energies of quantum systems. These spectroscopic experiments rely on the interaction between the oscillating electromagnetic fields of laser beams and atoms or molecules that respond to these time-dependent fields. The examples in this chapter will help us better understand these light-matter interactions.

1 ■ TRANSITION PROBABILITY

The typical experiment that we wish to model with time-dependent perturbation theory is the following: we start with a system in a particular initial quantum state $|i\rangle$, we turn on a perturbing Hamiltonian $H'(t)$ at time $t = 0$, and then we measure the probability that the system is in a new final quantum state $|f\rangle$ at a later time. For example, a hydrogen atom in its ground state $|1s\rangle$ is perturbed by an incident laser beam, and we wish to know the probability of the atom making a transition to the $|3p\rangle$ excited state. The Hamiltonian is assumed to be H_0 before the perturbation, and as in time-independent perturbation theory, we assume that we know the solutions to the unperturbed energy eigenvalue equation:

$$H_0|n\rangle = E_n|n\rangle. \tag{1}$$

In the hydrogen example, H_0 is the hydrogen atom Hamiltonian and E_n and $|n\rangle$ (shorthand for $|n\ell m\rangle$) are the eigenenergies and eigenstates.

The companion websites for this text are http://physics.oregonstate.edu/portfolioswiki and http://physics.oregonstate.edu/qmactivities.

Time-Dependent Perturbation Theory

The Schrödinger equation that governs the time evolution of a quantum system is

$$H|\psi\rangle = i\hbar \frac{d}{dt}|\psi\rangle. \tag{2}$$

The full Hamiltonian

$$H = H_0 + H'(t) \tag{3}$$

is now time dependent, so we cannot follow the standard recipe for determining the time evolution of the quantum state vector. In principle, we have to rediagonalize the Hamiltonian and find the new energy eigenstates, and then do that each time the Hamiltonian changes. Because the Hamiltonian is continuously changing, that is nearly impossible to do.

Rather, we take an approach that is similar to that taken in time-independent perturbation theory: we assume the perturbation is small enough that the zeroth-order energy eigenstates are a good approximation for starting the solution. But now we are more interested in solving the Schrödinger equation than in solving the energy eigenvalue equation. We are not so interested in how the perturbation changes the energies of the states; rather, we want to find how the perturbation changes the time evolution of the system. We use the original energy basis for expanding general states of the system, even though these states may not be energy eigenstates of the perturbed system.

Using the zeroth-order energy basis, the initial state of the system, before the perturbation is turned on, is

$$|\psi(t=0)\rangle = \sum_n c_n |n\rangle. \tag{4}$$

We know from the Schrödinger recipe that the time evolution of this initial state without any perturbation would be

$$|\psi_{H'=0}(t)\rangle = \sum_n c_n e^{-iE_n t/\hbar}|n\rangle, \tag{5}$$

where each term acquires a time-dependent phase evolution factor dependent on the energy of that term. The application of the perturbation $H'(t)$ gives rise to new energy eigenstates and hence new time evolution phase factors. However, if the perturbation is small, then we expect that the new solution will be close to the zeroth-order solution of Eq. (5). Hence, we assume that we can modify the zeroth-order solution by including another factor that reflects the additional time dependence caused by the perturbation. We do this by allowing the expansion coefficients to be time dependent:

$$|\psi_{H'\neq 0}(t)\rangle = \sum_n c_n(t) e^{-iE_n t/\hbar}|n\rangle. \tag{6}$$

Now our task is to determine how the coefficients $c_n(t)$ depend on time, with the obvious restriction that they equal their original values $c_n(0)$ at $t=0$. Substituting Eq. (6) for the time evolved state into the Schrödinger equation (2), we find

$$\left(H_0 + H'(t)\right)|\psi(t)\rangle = i\hbar \frac{d}{dt}|\psi(t)\rangle$$

$$\left(H_0 + H'(t)\right)\sum_n c_n(t) e^{-iE_n t/\hbar}|n\rangle = i\hbar \frac{d}{dt}\sum_n c_n(t) e^{-iE_n t/\hbar}|n\rangle, \tag{7}$$

Time-Dependent Perturbation Theory

and using the zeroth-order energy eigenvalue equation (1) to cancel some terms yields

$$\sum_n \left[E_n c_n(t) e^{-iE_nt/\hbar}|n\rangle + H'(t)c_n(t)e^{-iE_nt/\hbar}|n\rangle \right] = i\hbar \sum_n \left[\frac{dc_n(t)}{dt}e^{-iE_nt/\hbar}|n\rangle - i\frac{E_n}{\hbar}c_n(t)e^{-iE_nt/\hbar}|n\rangle \right]$$

$$\sum_n H'(t)c_n(t)e^{-iE_nt/\hbar}|n\rangle = i\hbar \sum_n \frac{dc_n(t)}{dt}e^{-iE_nt/\hbar}|n\rangle. \tag{8}$$

To simplify this differential equation, we isolate one coefficient in the sum on the right side by projecting the whole equation onto a particular energy state, say $|k\rangle$, and use orthogonality to find

$$\langle k| \sum_n H'(t)c_n(t)e^{-iE_nt/\hbar}|n\rangle = \langle k|i\hbar \sum_n \frac{dc_n(t)}{dt}e^{-iE_nt/\hbar}|n\rangle$$

$$\sum_n c_n(t)e^{-iE_nt/\hbar}\langle k|H'(t)|n\rangle = i\hbar\frac{dc_k(t)}{dt}e^{-iE_kt/\hbar}. \tag{9}$$

Rearranging terms yields a differential equation

$$i\hbar\frac{dc_k(t)}{dt} = \sum_n c_n(t)e^{i(E_k-E_n)t/\hbar}\langle k|H'(t)|n\rangle \tag{10}$$

for each coefficient c_k of the expansion. This result is still exact, but it gives us a set of coupled differential equations that is difficult to solve. We seek a perturbative solution by using an iterative approach. We expand the coefficient c_n in a perturbation series

$$c_n = c_n^{(0)} + c_n^{(1)} + c_n^{(2)} + ..., \tag{11}$$

where the superscript denotes the order of the perturbation. The right side of Eq. (10) already has one order of the perturbation in $H'(t)$, so when we equate the two sides of the equation to the same order of the perturbation, we end up with the order of c_n on the right side being one less than the order on the left side (Problem 1). The zeroth-order term of Eq. (10) is

$$i\hbar\frac{dc_k^{(0)}(t)}{dt} = 0. \tag{12}$$

This says that the coefficients c_n have no time dependence when there is no perturbation, which is consistent with Eq. (5) where all the Schrödinger evolution time dependence is already specified. The first-order term of Eq. (10) is

$$i\hbar\frac{dc_k^{(1)}(t)}{dt} = \sum_n c_n^{(0)}(t)e^{i(E_k-E_n)t/\hbar}\langle k|H'(t)|n\rangle. \tag{13}$$

We can continue in this manner to all orders if we wish, but we will not go beyond the first-order solution. To collapse the sum on the right side of Eq. (13), we make the assumption mentioned above that the system starts in one particular eigenstate $|i\rangle$ of the zeroth-order Hamiltonian, that is $|\psi(0)\rangle = |i\rangle$. Thus the initial coefficients obey:

$$c_n(0) = \delta_{ni}. \tag{14}$$

In zeroth-order there is no time dependence, according to Eq. (12), so we obtain

$$c_n^{(0)}(t) = \delta_{ni}. \tag{15}$$

Substituting Eq. (15) into Eq. (13) collapses the sum to just one term and yields the first-order differential equation for the coefficient $c_k(t)$:

$$i\hbar \frac{dc_k^{(1)}(t)}{dt} = e^{i(E_k - E_n)t/\hbar} \langle k|H'(t)|i\rangle. \tag{16}$$

We solve Eq. (16) by integrating directly to give

$$\boxed{c_k(t) = \frac{1}{i\hbar} \int_0^t \langle k|H'(t')|i\rangle e^{i(E_k - E_i)t'/\hbar} dt'.} \tag{17}$$

We have dropped the superscript on $c_k(t)$ because $c_k^{(0)}(t) = 0$ for $k \neq i$ and we will not solve for higher-order terms, so Eq. (17) gives us the complete coefficient to our desired order. Equation (17) tells us how the expansion coefficient $c_k(t)$ for the energy eigenstate $|k\rangle$ evolves with time subject to the perturbation $H'(t)$, given that the system started in the state $|i\rangle$. Equation (17) has the familiar form of a Fourier transform, so we interpret the result as the Fourier coefficient (in frequency space) of the perturbation $H'(t)$ at the Bohr frequency

$$\omega_{ki} = \frac{E_k - E_i}{\hbar}. \tag{18}$$

If the perturbation $H'(t)$ has an appreciable component at the Bohr frequency ω_{ki} associated with the energy difference between the initial state $|i\rangle$ and some other state $|k\rangle$, then the probability of the system making a transition from the initial state $|i\rangle$ to the state $|k\rangle$ is large.

To find the probability that the system is measured to be in a particular final state $|f\rangle$ at a later time, we project the time-evolved state Eq. (6) onto the final state

$$\mathcal{P}_{i\to f}(t) = |\langle f|\psi(t)\rangle|^2$$

$$= \left| \langle f| \sum_n c_n(t) e^{-iE_n t/\hbar} |n\rangle \right|^2 \tag{19}$$

$$= |c_f(t)|^2$$

and substitute Eq. (17) to obtain

$$\boxed{\mathcal{P}_{i\to f}(t) = \frac{1}{\hbar^2} \left| \int_0^t \langle f|H'(t')|i\rangle e^{i(E_f - E_i)t'/\hbar} dt' \right|^2.} \tag{20}$$

Of course, to actually do the integral and find the probability, we need to know the form of the perturbation $H'(t)$.

486

Example 1: Constant perturbation The simplest example of a time-dependent perturbation is one that is turned on at $t = 0$ and then turned off at a later time, but that is constant during the time it is on. The integral in Eq. (17) to find the coefficient $c_f(t)$ of the final state is straightforward:

$$
\begin{aligned}
c_f(t) &= \frac{1}{i\hbar}\langle f|H'|i\rangle \int_0^t e^{i\omega_{fi}t'}dt' \\
&= \frac{1}{i\hbar}\langle f|H'|i\rangle \frac{e^{i\omega_{fi}t}-1}{i\omega_{fi}} \\
&= \frac{1}{i\hbar}\langle f|H'|i\rangle e^{i\omega_{fi}t/2}\frac{e^{i\omega_{fi}t/2}-e^{-i\omega_{fi}t/2}}{i\omega_{fi}} \\
&= \frac{2}{i\hbar}\langle f|H'|i\rangle e^{i\omega_{fi}t/2}\frac{\sin\left(\omega_{fi}t/2\right)}{\omega_{fi}}.
\end{aligned}
\tag{21}
$$

The probability that the system is measured in the final state $|f\rangle$ is

$$
\mathcal{P}_{i\to f}(t) = \left|c_f(t)\right|^2 = \frac{4|\langle f|H'|i\rangle|^2}{\hbar^2\omega_{fi}^2}\sin^2\left(\omega_{fi}t/2\right).
\tag{22}
$$

This agrees with the Rabi formula for the probability of a spin flip caused by a small perturbing constant magnetic field. Equation (22) tells us that to make the transition from the state $|i\rangle$ to the state $|f\rangle$, there are two essential requirements: (1) the matrix element $\langle f|H'|i\rangle$ that determines whether the perturbation connects the two levels must be nonzero, and (2) to get appreciable probability, there must be frequency components in the time-dependent Hamiltonian that include the Bohr frequency ω_{fi} for the transition. The first requirement is related to the selection rules that we discuss more fully in Section 4. The second requirement is the resonance condition inherent in the Fourier integral of Eq. (17). Even though the perturbation $H'(t)$ in this example is constant during its application, there is a frequency component at the Bohr frequency ω_{fi} arising from the off-on-off time dependence.

Example 2: Gaussian perturbation Now let's add some more interesting time dependence by assuming that a perturbation is turned on and then turned off with a Gaussian time dependence as shown in Fig. 1. The form of the perturbation is

$$
H'(t) = V_0 e^{-t^2/\tau^2},
\tag{23}
$$

where τ is the characteristic time constant of the perturbation. This perturbation is peaked at $t = 0$ and becomes minimal a few time constants away from that. It differs mathematically from the situation we had above where the perturbation started at $t = 0$. We accommodate this change by shifting the starting time of the integral in Eq. (17). The major contribution to the integral comes from times that are a few time constants before and after the peak at $t = 0$, but mathematically it

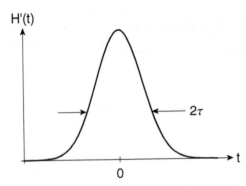

FIGURE 1 Gaussian time dependence of perturbation.

is simpler to integrate between $\pm\infty$. The coefficient $c_f(\infty)$ after the perturbation has been applied is therefore

$$c_f(\infty) = \frac{1}{i\hbar} \int_{-\infty}^{\infty} \langle f|H'(t')|i\rangle e^{i(E_f - E_i)t'/\hbar} \, dt'$$

$$= \frac{1}{i\hbar} \int_{-\infty}^{\infty} \langle f|V_0|i\rangle e^{-t'^2/\tau^2} e^{i\omega_{fi}t'} \, dt'. \tag{24}$$

The $\sin(\omega_{fi}t')$ part of the complex exponential $e^{i\omega_{fi}t'}$ is odd with respect to $t' = 0$, so that part of the integral is zero, giving

$$c_f(\infty) = \frac{1}{i\hbar} \langle f|V_0|i\rangle \int_{-\infty}^{\infty} e^{-t'^2/\tau^2} \cos(\omega_{fi}t') \, dt'$$

$$= \frac{1}{i\hbar} \langle f|V_0|i\rangle \sqrt{\pi}\tau e^{-\omega_{fi}^2\tau^2/4}. \tag{25}$$

The probability that after the perturbation the system is measured in the final state $|f\rangle$ is

$$\mathcal{P}_{i \to f} = |c_f(\infty)|^2 = \frac{\pi\tau^2}{\hbar^2} |\langle f|V_0|i\rangle|^2 e^{-\omega_{fi}^2\tau^2/2}. \tag{26}$$

This result tells us that to have appreciable probability for the transition from the state $|i\rangle$ to the state $|f\rangle$, the time constant τ must be of order $1/\omega_{fi}$, so that there are frequency components in the time-dependent Hamiltonian that include the Bohr frequency ω_{fi} for the transition.

An important lesson from this example concerns a perturbation that is turned on and off very slowly (i.e., the time constant is very long compared with other times relevant to the system). As the time constant τ becomes large enough that the product $\omega_{fi}\tau$ approaches infinity, the probability $\mathcal{P}_{i \to f}$ in Eq. (26) approaches zero, meaning that the system does not change states. This is an example of the adiabatic theorem in quantum mechanics.

2 ■ HARMONIC PERTURBATION

The previous examples have illustrated the importance of frequency components that match the Bohr frequency of the transition. Frequency components in the time dependence of the Hamiltonian that are far from the Bohr frequency of a particular transition do not produce appreciable probability for that transition. Hence, the most efficient way to make a transition is to impose a sinusoidal perturbation *at the transition frequency*. The study of such resonant interactions is the most important example of time-dependent perturbation theory.

At $t = 0$ we turn on a time-dependent perturbation Hamiltonian that has separate space and time parts:

$$H'(t) = 2V(\vec{r})\cos\omega t$$
$$= V(\vec{r})(e^{i\omega t} + e^{-i\omega t}). \tag{27}$$

There are different conventions for including the factor of 2 in Eq. (27) or not; without it, one needs a factor of 1/2 for each complex exponential. Substituting this harmonic perturbation into Eq. (17) yields the probability amplitude for making a transition from an initial state $|i\rangle$ to a final state $|f\rangle$:

$$
\begin{aligned}
c_f(t) &= \frac{1}{i\hbar}\int_0^t \langle f|V(\vec{r})(e^{i\omega t'} + e^{-i\omega t'})|i\rangle e^{i(E_f - E_i)t'/\hbar}\,dt' \\
&= \frac{1}{i\hbar}\langle f|V|i\rangle \int_0^t \left[e^{i(\omega_{fi} + \omega)t'} + e^{i(\omega_{fi} - \omega)t'} \right]dt' \\
&= \frac{1}{i\hbar}\langle f|V|i\rangle \left[\frac{e^{i(\omega_{fi} + \omega)t} - 1}{i(\omega_{fi} + \omega)} + \frac{e^{i(\omega_{fi} - \omega)t} - 1}{i(\omega_{fi} - \omega)} \right] \\
&= \frac{1}{i\hbar}\langle f|V|i\rangle \left[e^{i(\omega_{fi} + \omega)t/2}\frac{\sin\frac{\omega_{fi} + \omega}{2}t}{\frac{\omega_{fi} + \omega}{2}} + e^{i(\omega_{fi} - \omega)t/2}\frac{\sin\frac{\omega_{fi} - \omega}{2}t}{\frac{\omega_{fi} - \omega}{2}} \right].
\end{aligned}
\tag{28}
$$

To find the probability, we square this amplitude, which leads to cross terms and a complicated expression. This is what we have to do if the two terms inside the square brackets are of comparable size, which happens if the frequency is far from a resonance. However, if the resonance condition is satisfied or nearly satisfied, then one of the two terms inside the square brackets dominates because the denominator approaches zero. Which term dominates depends on the sign of the energy difference $E_f - E_i = \hbar\omega_{fi}$.

1) If the initial state is lower in energy than the final state, then the energy difference $E_f - E_i = \hbar\omega_{fi}$ is positive and the second term in Eq. (28) is large for an excitation frequency that matches the Bohr frequency: $\omega = \omega_{fi}$. In this case, the dominant probability amplitude is for the transition from a lower state to an upper state, which we call **absorption** [see Fig. 2(a)]. The system absorbs energy from the external perturbation.

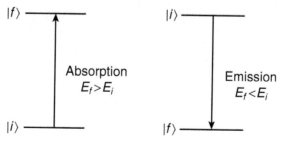

FIGURE 2   (a) Absorption and (b) emission processes.

2) If the initial state is higher than the final state, then the energy difference $E_f - E_i = \hbar\omega_{fi}$ is negative and the first term in Eq. (28) is large for an excitation frequency that matches the Bohr frequency: $\omega = -\omega_{fi}$. In this case, the dominant probability amplitude is for the transition from an upper state to a lower state, which we call **emission** [Fig. 2(b)]. The system emits energy to the external perturbation. This emission is caused by the applied field, so it is referred to as **stimulated emission**.

Only one of these two terms plays a role in any particular experiment, so we needn't worry about both together. For now, we consider the absorption case only (we just need to change the sign preceding ω if we change to the emission case). The probability of measuring the system in the final state is

$$\mathcal{P}_{i \to f}(t) = \frac{|V_{fi}|^2}{\hbar^2} \frac{\sin^2 \frac{\omega_{fi}-\omega}{2}t}{\left(\frac{\omega_{fi}-\omega}{2}\right)^2},\tag{29}$$

where we have adopted a shorthand notation for the matrix element of the perturbation:

$$V_{fi} = \langle f|V|i\rangle.\tag{30}$$

It is useful to look at this result both as a function of time and as a function of frequency. As a function of time, there is an oscillatory dependence as shown in Fig. 3, with a period of $2\pi/(\omega_{fi} - \omega)$. We see similar results for the Rabi oscillations in the spin case, with a slightly different oscillation or flopping frequency. The perturbation result in Eq. (29) is equal to the Rabi flopping probability for the case of small perturbations. In practice, this oscillating probability is hard to observe, which is related to the finite lifetime of excited states that we address in Section 5.

As a function of frequency, the transition probability is shown in Fig. 4 and displays the expected resonance behavior, with a peak in the probability at $\omega = \omega_{fi}$. The peak of the probability in Fig. 4 grows as t^2, so it could become greater than one, which would violate our perturbation approximation. The resonance curve in Fig. 4 has a finite width, which implies that the resonance condition $\omega = \omega_{fi}$ is not an exact requirement. Rather, there is a spread of frequencies $\Delta\omega$ that cause appreciable transition probability. The frequency width of the probability plot in Fig. 4 is approximately $\Delta\omega = 4\pi/t$, where the time t is the duration of the interaction. If we call this duration Δt, then we have

$$\Delta\omega\Delta t \approx \frac{4\pi}{\Delta t}\Delta t = 4\pi,\tag{31}$$

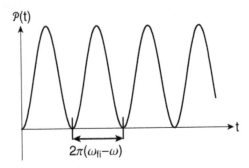

FIGURE 3 Oscillations of the transition probability as a function of time.

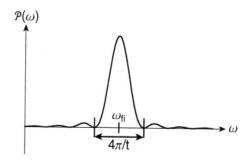

FIGURE 4 Probability of excitation as a function of frequency.

which is the Fourier frequency-time uncertainty relation. We can convert this to a Fourier energy-time uncertainty relation by using $\Delta E = \hbar \Delta \omega$ to obtain

$$\begin{aligned} \Delta E \Delta t &\approx \hbar \Delta \omega \Delta t = \hbar 4\pi \\ &\approx \hbar . \end{aligned} \tag{32}$$

The neglect of the factor of 4π is consistent with the level of this approximation. This uncertainty relation tells us that the longer we observe a system, the better we can measure the energy.

The resonance peak in Fig. 4 resembles a Dirac delta function in the limit that the frequency width $\Delta \omega = 4\pi/t \to 0$, which implies $t \to \infty$. Mathematically, the *sinc* function in Eq. (29) becomes a Dirac delta function in this limit:

$$\lim_{t \to \infty} \frac{\sin^2 \frac{\omega_{fi} - \omega}{2} t}{\left(\frac{\omega_{fi} - \omega}{2} \right)^2} = 2\pi t \delta(\omega_{fi} - \omega). \tag{33}$$

If we assume this long time limit in Eq. (29), we obtain the probability

$$\mathcal{P}_{i \to f}(t \to \infty) = \frac{2\pi t}{\hbar^2} |V_{fi}|^2 \delta(\omega_{fi} - \omega). \tag{34}$$

This form makes it evident that the probability increases linearly with time. This behavior is more common than the oscillating probability of Fig. 3. The linear time dependence seems reasonable because we expect that the more we perturb a system, the more likely it is to undergo a change. The linear time dependence in Eq. (34) allows us to define a **transition rate** as the probability per unit time, which we obtain by differentiating the probability:

$$R_{i \to f} = \frac{d}{dt} \mathcal{P}_{i \to f}(t), \tag{35}$$

with the result:

$$\boxed{R_{i \to f} = \frac{2\pi}{\hbar^2} |V_{fi}|^2 \delta(\omega_{fi} - \omega)} . \tag{36}$$

The delta function in Eq. (36) is called the energy conserving delta function—it requires that the quantum of energy causing the transition (e.g., the photon of a laser beam) match the energy difference between the two states. In many practical applications, there is a spread of final energy states rather than a discrete quantum state. For example, in a solid, the band structure of the electronic energy levels represents a continuous range of allowed states. In those cases, the relevant transition rate is a sum over the rates to all accessible states. We assume that these rates are incoherent so that we can add the rates (i.e., probabilities) rather than the amplitudes. We assume that the spread in energies is larger than the width of the *sinc* function that we turned into a delta function but small enough that the rates to all states are the same. Let $g(E)$ be the density of states per unit energy, such that $g(E)dE$ is the number of energy levels between E and $E + dE$. Then the total rate is given by the integral over all the rates:

$$R_{i \to f} = \int_{E_f - \varepsilon}^{E_f + \varepsilon} \frac{2\pi}{\hbar^2} |V_{fi}|^2 \delta(\omega_{fi} - \omega) g(E) dE$$

$$= \frac{2\pi}{\hbar^2} |V_{fi}|^2 \int_{E_f - \varepsilon}^{E_f + \varepsilon} \delta(\omega_{fi} - \omega) g(E) \hbar \, d\omega. \tag{37}$$

The range over which we integrate in Eq. (37) is not important because of the Dirac delta function. The resultant transition rate is

$$\boxed{R_{i \to f} = \frac{2\pi}{\hbar} |V_{fi}|^2 g(E_f)}. \tag{38}$$

This result is referred to as **Fermi's golden rule**. It is much more practical than Eq. (36) because the nonphysical delta function is gone. Fermi's golden rule is general enough that it applies to many types of interactions. In the next section we'll study one particular application.

3 ■ ELECTRIC DIPOLE INTERACTION

One of the most important applications of time-dependent perturbation theory is to the interaction between an atom and an electromagnetic field. Studying this problem tells us how lasers and atoms interact, and it also leads to an understanding of the finite lifetime of excited quantum states. The interaction Hamiltonian between an atom and an applied electromagnetic field is the same as we use for the Stark effect, except that the electric field is now time dependent. We neglect the interaction of the atom with the magnetic component of the electromagnetic field because it is smaller by a factor of the fine structure constant α.

The electric dipole Hamiltonian is

$$H' = -\mathbf{d} \cdot \mathbf{E}. \tag{39}$$

The electric field is

$$\mathbf{E}(t) = 2\mathcal{E}_0 \hat{\varepsilon} \cos\omega t$$

$$= \hat{\varepsilon}\left(\mathcal{E}_0 e^{i\omega t} + \mathcal{E}_0 e^{-i\omega t}\right), \tag{40}$$

with the same form of the time dependence as in the generic harmonic perturbation example in the previous section. The polarization of the electric field is specified by the unit vector $\hat{\varepsilon}$. We ignore the spatial variation of the field because the size of the atom (~ 0.1 nm) is much smaller than the wavelength of visible light (~ 500 nm), which is the most common case. This means that at any given instant, the whole atom sees the same electric field. This assumption is the **electric dipole approximation**. We use the previous harmonic perturbation calculation and identify the perturbation in Eq. (27) as:

$$V = -\mathbf{d} \cdot \hat{\varepsilon}\mathcal{E}_0. \tag{41}$$

The atom's electric dipole moment is

$$\mathbf{d} = -e\mathbf{r}, \tag{42}$$

resulting in the perturbation

$$V = e\mathcal{E}_0\hat{\varepsilon}\cdot\mathbf{r}. \tag{43}$$

Application of Fermi's golden rule in the form of Eq. (36) yields the transition rate:

$$R_{i\to f} = \frac{2\pi}{\hbar^2}\left|\langle f|e\mathcal{E}_0\hat{\varepsilon}\cdot\mathbf{r}|i\rangle\right|^2 \delta(\omega_{fi} - \omega). \tag{44}$$

Only the **r** term in the matrix element depends on the atomic states, so we simplify the rate to

$$R_{i\to f} = \frac{2\pi e^2 \mathcal{E}_0^2}{\hbar^2}\left|\hat{\varepsilon}\cdot\langle f|\mathbf{r}|i\rangle\right|^2 \delta(\omega_{fi} - \omega). \tag{45}$$

The delta function in Eq. (45) is not physical, so we must see how to apply this transition rate expression to a real situation. The two most common situations are depicted in Fig. 5: (a) the perturbing field is not a single frequency and is not coherent, in which case we sum over transition rates caused by the spread of frequencies; or (b) the quantum energy states are continuous, in which case we sum over transition rates to a spread of energy states, as we did in the last section. The first case is necessary when a broadband light source excites a discrete atomic transition. The second case is necessary when using a monochromatic laser to excite a system to a spread of excited states, or even to a single excited state that is broadened by its finite lifetime. We start with the first case because it allows us to study the interaction between blackbody radiation and atoms, which Einstein used to model the broadening of atomic states. Once we know how the atomic states are broadened, we'll use that knowledge to study the second case of single frequency excitation.

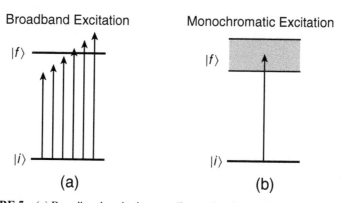

FIGURE 5 (a) Broadband excitation to a discrete level, and (b) monochromatic excitation to a broadened level.

3.1 ■ Einstein Model: Broadband Excitation

The Einstein model assumes a gas of two-level atoms in thermal equilibrium with blackbody radiation at temperature T. The atoms are considered to have discrete energy levels and the blackbody radiation is modeled as a broadband incoherent electromagnetic field. The goal is to reduce Eq. (45) to a simple form for the transition rate involving the atom properties and the field properties.

The electromagnetic field of the blackbody radiation has an energy density per unit volume given by

$$u = \frac{\varepsilon_0}{2}\mathcal{E}^2 + \frac{1}{2\mu_0}B^2. \tag{46}$$

The energy density in the electric and magnetic fields is the same. Substituting Eq. (40) into Eq. (46) gives

$$u = \varepsilon_0 \mathcal{E}^2 = 4\varepsilon_0 \mathcal{E}_0^2 \cos^2(\omega t). \tag{47}$$

The time-average over one cycle gives a factor of 1/2, resulting in

$$u_{rms} = 2\varepsilon_0 \mathcal{E}_0^2. \tag{48}$$

For broadband radiation, the energy density in the electromagnetic field is

$$u_{rms} = \rho(\omega)d\omega, \tag{49}$$

where $\rho(\omega)$ is the field energy per unit volume per unit angular frequency interval. Combining Eqs. (48) and (49) gives

$$\mathcal{E}_0^2 = \frac{\rho(\omega)}{2\varepsilon_0}d\omega, \tag{50}$$

which we substitute into Eq. (45) to obtain the transition rate. We integrate over all the transition rates due to each frequency component because the blackbody light is incoherent, which gives

$$\begin{aligned}
R_{i \to f} &= \frac{\pi e^2}{\varepsilon_0 \hbar^2}|\hat{\varepsilon}\cdot\langle f|\mathbf{r}|i\rangle|^2 \int_0^\infty \rho(\omega)\,\delta(\omega_{fi} - \omega)\,d\omega \\
&= \frac{\pi e^2}{\varepsilon_0 \hbar^2}\rho(\omega_{fi})|\hat{\varepsilon}\cdot\langle f|\mathbf{r}|i\rangle|^2.
\end{aligned} \tag{51}$$

Inside the black box containing the blackbody radiation and the atoms, the radiation is isotropic and the polarization vector is random, so we average Eq. (51) over all possible directions of the polarization vector $\hat{\varepsilon}$. To do this average, let θ be the angle between $\hat{\varepsilon}$ and $\mathbf{r}$. The three-dimensional spatial average of $|\hat{\varepsilon}\cdot\hat{\mathbf{r}}|^2$ is

$$\begin{aligned}
\langle|\hat{\varepsilon}\cdot\hat{\mathbf{r}}|^2\rangle &= \frac{1}{4\pi}\int|\hat{\varepsilon}\cdot\hat{\mathbf{r}}|^2 d\Omega \\
&= \frac{1}{4\pi}\int_0^{2\pi}\int_0^\pi \cos^2\theta \sin\theta\,d\theta\,d\phi \\
&= \frac{1}{4\pi}2\pi\left[-\frac{1}{3}\cos^3\theta\right]_0^\pi \\
&= \frac{1}{3}.
\end{aligned} \tag{52}$$

Thus we get for the transition rate:

$$R_{i \to f} = \frac{\pi e^2}{3\varepsilon_0 \hbar^2} \rho(\omega_{fi}) |\langle f|\mathbf{r}|i\rangle|^2. \tag{53}$$

Einstein grouped the atomic factors into the now-famous **Einstein B coefficient**

$$\boxed{B_{if} = \frac{\pi e^2}{3\varepsilon_0 \hbar^2} |\langle f|\mathbf{r}|i\rangle|^2} \tag{54}$$

and wrote the transition rate as

$$R_{i \to f} = B_{if} \rho(\omega_{fi}). \tag{55}$$

The Einstein B coefficient is the same if we swap initial and final states, as is the electromagnetic energy density $\rho(\omega_{fi})$ evaluated at the transition frequency, so the rates of emission and absorption are the same.

In the Einstein model, a collection of atoms is in thermal equilibrium with blackbody radiation at a temperature T. The atoms are treated as having two states $|1\rangle$ and $|2\rangle$ with energies E_1 and E_2, respectively. The radiation induces transitions from $|1\rangle$ to $|2\rangle$—absorption, and from $|2\rangle$ to $|1\rangle$—stimulated emission, as depicted in Fig. 6. Because the absorption and stimulated emission rates are the same, the populations of the two levels would be the same if there were no other processes. But the Boltzmann thermal distribution law tells us that the populations of levels decrease as the energy level increases. Einstein argued that there must be a third process—**spontaneous emission**—connecting the two levels in order for thermal equilibrium to be maintained. This is called the principle of **detailed balance**. Spontaneous emission occurs spontaneously, independent of the applied field, and therefore it causes the excited state $|2\rangle$ to decay to the ground state $|1\rangle$ even when no field is present. Because of this spontaneous decay, the excited state $|2\rangle$ has a *finite lifetime*, in contradiction to our previous declaration that all energy eigenstates are stationary states. The transition rate for spontaneous emission was defined by Einstein as A_{21} and is called the **Einstein A coefficient**. The spontaneous emission rate is *independent* of the applied field. The stimulated emission rate *depends* on the applied field according to Eq. (55).

Let's now calculate the Einstein A coefficient of spontaneous emission. Assume that there are N_1 atoms in the lower state $|1\rangle$ and N_2 atoms in the upper state $|2\rangle$. The transition rates we have discussed so far are the rates for single atoms, so the rates for a collection or ensemble of atoms are obtained by multiplying the single atom rates by the population of the initial state. For example, the number of atoms per second that absorb photons and change from state $|1\rangle$ to state $|2\rangle$ is the transition rate for

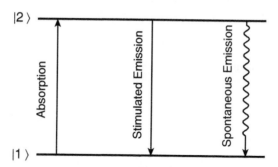

FIGURE 6   Einstein model of absorption and emission of photons.

a single atom $B_{12}\rho(\omega_{21})$ times the number of atoms N_1 in state $|1\rangle$: $N_1 B_{12}\rho(\omega_{21})$. This absorption process decreases the number of atoms in state $|1\rangle$, while the two emission processes increase the number. The sum of the three rates yields the **rate equation** for state $|1\rangle$:

$$\frac{dN_1}{dt} = -N_1 B_{12}\rho(\omega_{21}) + N_2 B_{21}\rho(\omega_{21}) + N_2 A_{21}. \tag{56}$$

The rate equation for state $|2\rangle$ is similarly

$$\frac{dN_2}{dt} = +N_1 B_{12}\rho(\omega_{21}) - N_2 B_{21}\rho(\omega_{21}) - N_2 A_{21}. \tag{57}$$

Note that $dN_1/dt = -dN_2/dt$ because there are only two levels in this model system and all atoms leaving one state end up in the other state.

In steady state, the number of atoms in either state is constant (but not equal to each other), with as many atoms making upward transitions as downward transitions. Hence, the change dN_1/dt equals zero and we can solve Eq. (56) for the radiation energy density:

$$\rho(\omega_{21}) = \frac{A_{21}}{B_{12}} \frac{1}{(N_1/N_2)(B_{12}/B_{21}) - 1}. \tag{58}$$

The blackbody energy density is determined by the Planck blackbody radiation formula:

$$\rho(\omega) = \frac{\hbar}{\pi^2 c^3} \frac{\omega^3}{e^{\hbar\omega/k_B T} - 1}, \tag{59}$$

which comes from the Boltzmann probability of occupation of the modes of the radiation field. In thermal equilibrium, elementary statistical mechanics tells us that the number of atoms in an energy level E is proportional to the Boltzmann factor $\exp(-E/k_B T)$, where k_B is Boltzmann's constant. Hence, the ratio of level populations is:

$$\frac{N_1}{N_2} = \frac{e^{-E_1/k_B T}}{e^{-E_2/k_B T}} = e^{(E_2-E_1)/k_B T} = e^{\hbar\omega_{21}/k_B T}. \tag{60}$$

Combining Eqs. (58), (59), and (60) leads to two conditions:

$$B_{21} = B_{12}, \tag{61}$$

which we already knew from Eq. (54), and

$$A_{21} = \frac{\hbar\omega_{21}^3}{\pi^2 c^3} B_{21}, \tag{62}$$

which relates the Einstein A and B coefficients. Using Eq. (54) for the Einstein B coefficient leads us to the spontaneous emission rate:

$$\boxed{A_{21} = \frac{e^2 \omega_{21}^3}{3\pi\varepsilon_0 \hbar c^3} |\langle 2|\mathbf{r}|1\rangle|^2}. \tag{63}$$

The decay of a state caused by spontaneous emission implies that excited states are not stationary states, as we have assumed all along about quantum energy eigenstates. Rather, excited states have an inherent finite lifetime due to spontaneous emission. If we have a system of atoms in the excited state, with no electromagnetic fields present, then the rate equation for the upper level is

$$\frac{dN_2}{dt} = -N_2 A_{21}. \tag{64}$$

Solving this differential equation yields the time dependence of the upper level population

$$N_2(t) = N_2(0)e^{-A_{21}t} = N_2(0)e^{-t/\tau}. \tag{65}$$

The upper level population decays exponentially, as shown in Fig. 7, with a lifetime τ given by the inverse of the Einstein A coefficient

$$\boxed{\tau = \frac{1}{A_{21}}}. \tag{66}$$

This inherent finite lifetime of the excited state means that there is a fundamental limit to the time we have to observe the system in this state. Therefore, the energy-time uncertainty relation in Eq. (32) implies that the finite lifetime of the excited state places a *fundamental limit on how well we can measure the energy*. Hence, the energy of an excited state is uncertain or broadened. The uncertainty in our measurement of the energy difference between the ground and the excited state is

$$\Delta E = \frac{\hbar}{\Delta t} = \frac{\hbar}{\tau} = \hbar A_{21}. \tag{67}$$

No matter how precise our measurement apparatus is, we cannot overcome this limitation. The energy uncertainty in Eq. (67) is the spread in energy of a state that was depicted in Fig. 5(b), which we address in the next section.

Though we now have a way to calculate the spontaneous emission rate, we have not discovered the mechanism that is responsible for the decay of excited states in the absence of a perturbing radiation field. The approach that we have taken here to atom-light interactions is known as the semiclassical method because we have treated the atoms quantum mechanically, but we have treated the light as a classical field. To properly explain spontaneous emission, we must use quantum electrodynamics (QED). Quantum electrodynamics treats the light quantum mechanically as a harmonic oscillator, with the state $|n\rangle$ representing a light field with n photons. The ground state $|0\rangle$ has no photons (i.e., no field excitations), but has an energy $\hbar\omega/2$, just as the ground state of the harmonic oscillator does. This vacuum state energy represents residual energy in the electromagnetic field, which "stimulates"

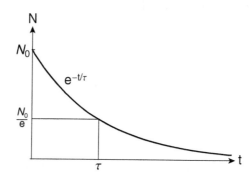

FIGURE 7 Exponential time decay of the population of an excited atomic state.

the emission of photons from excited atoms. Hence, spontaneous emission can be considered to be emission that is stimulated by the vacuum. Recent experiments have made this interpretation clear by showing that the spontaneous emission rate can be changed by altering the vacuum, which is possible if you put an atom in a specially sized box, a cavity, that alters the allowed radiation modes at the frequency of interest. The quantum mechanical interaction of atoms and quantized light fields is known as **cavity QED**.

3.2 ■ Laser Excitation

We now address the problem of a monochromatic laser exciting an atom with an upper level that is not sharply defined, as depicted in Fig. 5(b). We assume that the spread in energy of the upper atomic level is caused by spontaneous emission, though collisions or other environmental factors are also possible causes. Fermi's golden rule in Eq. (38) tells us that the transition rate depends on the density of energy states. We found the spread of the final energy state in Eq. (67) for the case of spontaneous emission. The functional form of the density of energy states $g(E)$, or equivalently the frequency density, is determined by the Fourier transform of the emitted electromagnetic field. For the exponential time dependence of a spontaneously decaying upper state, this Fourier transform yields a Lorentzian function (Problem 5). For a transition between states $|1\rangle$ and $|2\rangle$ with a spontaneous decay rate A_{21} from state $|2\rangle$, the Lorentzian density of states for the upper state is

$$g(E) = \frac{\hbar A_{21}/2\pi}{\left(E - \hbar\omega_{21}\right)^2 + \left(\dfrac{\hbar A_{21}}{2}\right)^2}. \tag{68}$$

The density of states is normalized to unity, $\int_0^\infty g(E)\,dE = 1$, because there is only one state at the upper level; it is just spread out by its finite lifetime. Substituting the density of states into Fermi's golden rule in Eq. (38) yields the transition rate

$$\begin{aligned}
R_{1\to 2} &= \frac{2\pi}{\hbar}\left|V_{21}\right|^2 g(E_f)\\[2mm]
&= \frac{2\pi e^2 E_0^2}{\hbar}\left|\hat{\varepsilon}\cdot\langle 2|\mathbf{r}|1\rangle\right|^2 \frac{\hbar A_{21}/2\pi}{\left(E - \hbar\omega_{21}\right)^2 + \left(\dfrac{\hbar A_{21}}{2}\right)^2}.
\end{aligned} \tag{69}$$

Using the frequency Lorentzian $\left(f(\omega)\,d\omega = g(E)\,dE\right)$

$$f(\omega) = \frac{A_{21}/2\pi}{\left(\omega - \omega_{21}\right)^2 + \left(\dfrac{A_{21}}{2}\right)^2}, \tag{70}$$

we express the transition rate as

$$R_{1\to 2} = \frac{2\pi e^2 \mathcal{E}_0^2}{\hbar^2}\left|\hat{\varepsilon}\cdot\langle 2|\mathbf{r}|1\rangle\right|^2 f(\omega) \tag{71}$$

In terms of the Einstein B coefficient, the transition rate is

$$R_{1\rightarrow 2} = 6\varepsilon_0 \mathcal{E}_0^2 B_{21} f(\omega). \tag{72}$$

If we excite the transition with a monochromatic laser with intensity $I = 2c\varepsilon_0\mathcal{E}_0^2$, the transition rate is

$$R_{1\rightarrow 2} = 3\frac{I}{c}B_{12} f(\omega). \tag{73}$$

This excitation probability rate has the Lorentzian frequency dependence shown in Fig. 8, with a full width at half maximum (FWHM) of A_{21}. Once again, we see the resonance behavior of the interaction, such that the laser must be tuned within this frequency window in order to have appreciable probability of inducing excitation of the atom.

Another useful way to quantify the excitation of an atom by a laser is with a quantity known as the **cross section**. To understand why an area is useful in this regard, consider characterizing the efficiency of the interaction as the ratio of *what you get out* to *what you put in*:

$$\text{efficiency} = \frac{\text{output}}{\text{input}}. \tag{74}$$

In this case, you put in light and get out excited atoms.

We usually characterize the input laser light in terms of the intensity I, measured in Watts per square meter. However, to simplify matters, let's quantify the light in terms of the number of photons per unit area per unit time. Each photon in the laser beam has an energy $\hbar\omega$, so the number of photons per unit area per unit time is the intensity divided by the energy per photon:

$$\frac{\#\ \text{photons}}{\text{area} \cdot \text{time}} = \frac{I}{\hbar\omega}. \tag{75}$$

We quantify the output of excited atoms by the transition rate R, which is a probability (i.e., number) per unit time. Thus the efficiency we have defined becomes:

$$\text{efficiency} = \frac{\text{output}}{\text{input}}$$
$$= \frac{R_{1\rightarrow 2}}{\dfrac{I}{\hbar\omega}} = \frac{\#\ \text{per unit time}}{\#\ \text{per unit time per unit area}}. \tag{76}$$

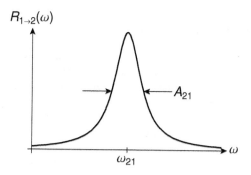

FIGURE 8 Lorentzian frequency dependence of the excitation probability.

By dimensional analysis, the efficiency we have defined is really an effective area for excitation. This effective area is what we call the cross section σ. To calculate the cross section, we assume that the laser is on resonance ($\omega = \omega_{21}$) in order to provide the maximum efficiency:

$$\begin{aligned}\sigma &= \frac{R_{1\to2}}{I/\hbar\omega} = \frac{3(I/c)B_{12}f(\omega_{21})}{I/\hbar\omega_{21}} \\ &= \frac{3(I/c)B_{12}(2/\pi A_{21})}{I/\hbar\omega_{21}} \\ &= \frac{6\hbar\omega_{21}}{\pi c}\frac{B_{12}}{A_{21}}.\end{aligned}\tag{77}$$

From Eq. (62) relating the Einstein rate coefficients, we know the ratio of B_{12} to A_{21}. This allows us to calculate the cross section for on-resonance excitation:

$$\begin{aligned}\sigma &= \frac{6\hbar\omega_{21}}{\pi c}\frac{B_{12}}{A_{21}} = \frac{6\hbar\omega_{21}}{\pi c}\frac{\pi^2 c^3}{\hbar\omega_{21}^3} \\ &= 6\pi\frac{c^2}{\omega_{21}^2} = 6\pi\frac{1}{k_{21}^2} = 6\pi\frac{1}{(2\pi/\lambda_{21})^2},\end{aligned}\tag{78}$$

resulting in

$$\boxed{\sigma = 3\frac{\lambda_{21}^2}{2\pi}}.\tag{79}$$

This result is amazingly simple. It says that the atom is effectively the size of the wavelength of light ($\sim 100 - 1000\,\text{nm}$) when considering its interaction with resonant light! The physical size of the atom (the Bohr radius $\sim 0.1\,\text{nm}$) is irrelevant in this case, although it would be more appropriate if we were considering collisions between two atoms. For atom-light interactions, the atom acts as an efficient antenna, despite its small size.

4 ■ SELECTION RULES

The Einstein A and B coefficients depend upon the matrix element $\langle f|\hat{\varepsilon}\cdot\mathbf{r}|i\rangle$ from the electric dipole interaction between the two states. If this matrix element is zero for some reason, then there is no probability that the transition between the states will occur. There are some general guidelines as to when such matrix elements are expected to be zero, and we call these **selection rules**. Transitions for which the matrix element is zero are therefore not allowed and are called **forbidden transitions**. However, recall that we are working within the electric dipole approximation, which means that we have neglected magnetic dipole, electric quadrupole, and higher multipole interactions. It may happen that a transition is forbidden within the electric dipole approximation but is allowed by a higher-order multipole interaction. The higher-order interactions typically have transition rates that are reduced by an extra order of the fine structure constant α.

The selection rules derive from general properties of the electric dipole matrix elements, not from the details of a specific atom or molecule. To see this, first separate the radial and angular parts of the matrix element:

$$\langle f|\hat{\varepsilon}\cdot\mathbf{r}|i\rangle = \hat{\varepsilon}\cdot\langle f|r\hat{\mathbf{r}}|i\rangle$$

$$= \int_0^\infty r^2\,dr \int d\Omega\, R^*_{n_f\ell_f}(r)\, Y^{m_f*}_{\ell_f}(\theta,\phi)\,\hat{\varepsilon}\cdot\hat{\mathbf{r}}\, r\, R_{n_i\ell_i}(r)\, Y^{m_i}_{\ell_i}(\theta,\phi)$$

$$= \left(\int_0^\infty R^*_{n_f\ell_f}(r)\, R_{n_i\ell_i}(r)\, r^3\,dr\right)\left(\int Y^{m_f*}_{\ell_f}(\theta,\phi)\,\hat{\varepsilon}\cdot\hat{\mathbf{r}}\, Y^{m_i}_{\ell_i}(\theta,\phi)\,d\Omega\right). \tag{80}$$

The radial integral *does* depend critically on the details of a specific atom or molecule and is not typically zero. The angular integral, however, depends on the spherical harmonics, which are independent of the details of the central potential. The dot product term in Eq. (80) is expressed in terms of the angles θ and ϕ between the electric field polarization vector $\hat{\varepsilon}$ and the electron position unit vector $\hat{\mathbf{r}}$

$$\hat{\varepsilon}\cdot\hat{\mathbf{r}} = \varepsilon_x \sin\theta\cos\phi + \varepsilon_y\sin\theta\sin\phi + \varepsilon_z\cos\theta. \tag{81}$$

It is useful to express the trigonometric functions in Eq. (81) in terms of the spherical harmonics:

$$\hat{\varepsilon}\cdot\hat{\mathbf{r}} = \sqrt{\frac{4\pi}{3}}\left(\varepsilon_z Y^0_1(\theta,\phi) + \frac{-\varepsilon_x+i\varepsilon_y}{\sqrt{2}}Y^1_1(\theta,\phi) + \frac{\varepsilon_x+i\varepsilon_y}{\sqrt{2}}Y^{-1}_1(\theta,\phi)\right). \tag{82}$$

Thus, the dot product $\hat{\varepsilon}\cdot\hat{\mathbf{r}}$ is proportional to spherical harmonics of order 1. This key point derives from making the electric dipole approximation. Higher-order multipole matrix elements involve higher-order spherical harmonics and hence yield different selection rules.

Using Eq. (82), we find that the angular integral of the electric dipole matrix element in Eq. (80) becomes three integrals, each of which is an integral of the product of three spherical harmonics:

$$\int Y^{m_f*}_{\ell_f}(\theta,\phi)Y^m_1(\theta,\phi)Y^{m_i}_{\ell_i}(\theta,\phi)d\Omega, \tag{83}$$

where one spherical harmonic is limited to order 1 by the electric dipole approximation and the index m varies over 1, 0, −1 according to the three terms in Eq. (82). You would expect that such an integral over three spherical harmonic functions would be difficult to do. However, we now make use of the Clebsch-Gordan coefficients on the addition of angular momenta. A coupled angular momentum state can be expressed in terms of uncoupled states using the Clebsch-Gordan coefficients. For orbital angular momentum this means that one spherical harmonic can be decomposed into products of pairs of other spherical harmonics. Given this knowledge of Clebsch-Gordan coefficients, we find the angular integral:

$$\int Y^{m_f*}_{\ell_f}(\theta,\phi)Y^m_1(\theta,\phi)Y^{m_i}_{\ell_i}(\theta,\phi)d\Omega = \left[\frac{3(2\ell_i+1)}{4\pi(2\ell_f+1)}\right]^{\frac{1}{2}}\langle\ell_i 1 m_i m|\ell_f m_f\rangle\langle\ell_i 1 0 0|\ell_f 0\rangle. \tag{84}$$

The Clebsch-Gordan coefficient $\langle\ell_i 1 m_i m|\ell_f m_f\rangle$ is the key to understanding the selection rules. Only certain values of the coupled angular momentum quantum numbers are allowed for a given set of uncoupled angular momentum quantum numbers, and that many entries in the tables of the Clebsch-Gordan coefficients are zero. The Clebsch-Gordan coefficient $\langle \ell_i 1 m_i m | \ell_f m_f \rangle$ characterizes the addition of the uncoupled angular momenta $j_1 = \ell_i$ and $j_2 = 1$ to form the coupled angular momentum $j = \ell_f$. The rules of adding angular momenta limit the values of the coupled angular momentum ℓ_f to:

$$\ell_f = \ell_i + 1, \ell_i, \ell_i - 1. \tag{85}$$

The magnetic quantum numbers are also limited by the Clebsch-Gordan coefficient $\langle \ell_i 1 m_i m | \ell_f m_f \rangle$ to:

$$\begin{aligned} m_i + m &= m_f \\ m &= m_f - m_i. \end{aligned} \tag{86}$$

A further restriction on the matrix elements comes from a consideration of parity. The integrand in Eq. (84) must be even with respect to spatial symmetry inversion for the integral to be nonzero. The spherical harmonics have parity given by $(-1)^\ell$, that is

$$Y_l^m(\theta, \phi) = (-1)^\ell Y_l^m(\pi - \theta, \phi + \pi). \tag{87}$$

For the three cases allowed by Eq. (85), the integrand with $\ell_f = \ell_i$ has odd parity $(2\ell_i + 1)$, while the integrand with $\ell_f = \ell_i \pm 1$ has even parity $(2\ell_i \text{ or } 2\ell_i + 2)$. We conclude that the angular integral with $\ell_f = \ell_i$ is identically zero, and find another rule:

$$\ell_f \neq \ell_i. \tag{88}$$

We say that $\ell_f = \ell_i$ is not allowed by parity. Combining the rules in Eqs. (85), (86), and (88), we find the selection rules for *electric dipole transitions*:

$$\boxed{\begin{aligned} \Delta\ell &= \pm 1 \\ \Delta m &= 0, \pm 1 \end{aligned}} . \tag{89}$$

These selection rules arise solely from the angular integral in Eq. (80) and they reflect the conservation of angular momentum of the system of atom and photon. The photon has an angular momentum or spin of 1. When the atom absorbs or emits a photon, the final atomic state must reflect the change in angular momentum of the electromagnetic field.

Application of the $\Delta\ell = \pm 1$ selection rule to the hydrogen atom limits the possible spontaneous emission transitions to those shown in Fig. 9. For example, within the $n = 2$ level, the $2p$ state can decay to the $1s$ state, and does so with a 1.6 ns lifetime (Problem 7). However, the $2s$ state cannot decay to the ground state because $\Delta\ell = 0$ is not allowed. The Lamb shift does displace the $2s_{1/2}$ state slightly above the $2p_{1/2}$ state to which it can decay, but the transition rate is very small due to the cube of the Bohr frequency in Eq. (63). Hence, the $2s_{1/2}$ state has a very long decay lifetime of 1/7 sec, which is caused by a two-photon decay mechanism to the ground state.

Application of the $\Delta m = 0, \pm 1$ selection rule to the hydrogen $2p \rightarrow 1s$ transition yields the allowed transitions shown in Fig. 10, for the case of emission. In the $\Delta m = +1$ transition, the atom gains one unit of angular momentum projection along the z-axis, so the emitted photon must have one unit of angular momentum projection in the negative z-direction. Such a photon is called

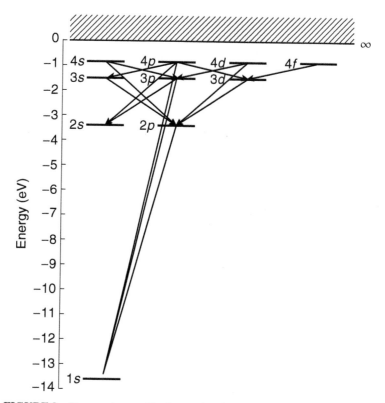

FIGURE 9   Decay scheme of hydrogen for allowed electric dipole transitions.

a σ^- polarized photon or a photon with negative **helicity**. The $\Delta m = -1$ transition produces a σ^+ photon with positive helicity. The σ^+ and σ^- photons have a polarization vector that rotates around the z-axis and are also called circularly polarized states. The $\Delta m = 0$ transition produces a photon that has linear polarization along the z-axis, which is referred to as a π polarized photon. For the case of absorption, the Δm values in Fig. 10 change sign, but the σ^+ and σ^- labels remain unchanged (Problem 13).

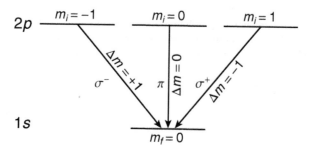

FIGURE 10   Hydrogen $2p \rightarrow 1s$ transition.

SUMMARY

In *time-dependent* perturbation theory, we focus on finding the probability that an applied perturbation causes a transition between energy levels of the unperturbed Hamiltonian. In contrast, in *time-independent* perturbation theory, we focus on finding the changes in energy levels caused by the perturbing Hamiltonian (assumed static).

The probability amplitude for a transition from the initial state $|i\rangle$ to the final state $|f\rangle$ subject to the time-dependent perturbation $H'(t)$ is

$$c_f(t) = \frac{1}{i\hbar}\int_0^t \langle f|H'(t')|i\rangle e^{i(E_f - E_i)t'/\hbar}\, dt'. \tag{90}$$

The probability of the transition is

$$\mathcal{P}_{i\to f}(t) = \frac{1}{\hbar^2}\left|\int_0^t \langle f|H'(t')|i\rangle e^{i(E_f - E_i)t'/\hbar}\, dt'\right|^2. \tag{91}$$

For harmonic perturbation at frequency ω, the transition probability for long times grows linearly with time and we define the transition rate

$$R_{i\to f} = \frac{2\pi}{\hbar^2}\left|V_{fi}\right|^2 \delta(\omega_{fi} - \omega). \tag{92}$$

For an electric dipole interaction, the transition rate is

$$R_{i\to f} = B_{if}\rho(\omega_{fi}) \tag{93}$$

if the excitation source is broadband where $\rho(\omega_{fi})$ is the energy density and B_{if} is the Einstein B coefficient

$$B_{if} = \frac{\pi e^2}{3\varepsilon_0 \hbar^2}|\langle f|\mathbf{r}|i\rangle|^2. \tag{94}$$

If the transition is excited with a monochromatic source with intensity $I = 2c\varepsilon_0\mathcal{E}_0^2$, the transition rate is

$$R_{1\to 2} = 3\frac{I}{c}B_{12}f(\omega), \tag{95}$$

where $f(\omega)$ is the frequency response function of the atom.

An excited state in an atom has a finite lifetime due to spontaneous emission. The lifetime is the inverse of the Einstein A coefficient

$$A_{21} = \frac{e^2\omega_{21}^3}{3\pi\varepsilon_0 \hbar c^3}|\langle 2|\mathbf{r}|1\rangle|^2. \tag{96}$$

Electric dipole transitions have the selection rules

$$\begin{aligned}\Delta\ell &= \pm 1 \\ \Delta m &= 0, \pm 1.\end{aligned} \tag{97}$$

RESOURCES

Further Reading

More details on atom-light interactions can be found in:

A. Corney, *Atomic and Laser Spectroscopy*, Oxford: Clarendon Press, 1977.

C. J. Foot, *Atomic Physics*, Oxford: Oxford University Press, 2005.

M. Fox, *Quantum Optics*, Oxford: Oxford University Press, 2006.

R. Loudon, *Quantum Theory of Light*, Oxford: Oxford University Press, 2000.

Time-Dependent Perturbation Theory: Problem Set

1 Use the perturbation series expansion of the coefficient c_n given by Eq. (11),

$$c_n = c_n^{(0)} + c_n^{(1)} + c_n^{(2)} + ...,\qquad(11)$$

in the differential equation (10),

$$i\hbar\frac{dc_k(t)}{dt} = \sum_n c_n(t)e^{i(E_k-E_n)t/\hbar}\langle k|H'(t)|n\rangle,\qquad(10)$$

and verify the zeroth-order and first-order equations (12),

$$i\hbar\frac{dc_k^{(0)}(t)}{dt} = 0,\qquad(12)$$

and (13),

$$i\hbar\frac{dc_k^{(1)}(t)}{dt} = \sum_n c_n^{(0)}(t)e^{i(E_k-E_n)t/\hbar}\langle k|H'(t)|n\rangle,\qquad(13)$$

You may wish to use the λ notation to keep track of orders.

2 A particle of mass m is initially in the ground state (E_1) of an infinite square well of width L. Starting at time $t = 0$, the system is subject to the perturbation

$$H'(t) = V_0 x^2 e^{-t/\tau},$$

where V_0 and τ are constants. Find the probability that the energy after time T is measured to be E_2. Calculate the probability in the limit $T \to \infty$.

3 A particle of mass m is initially in the ground state (E_1) of an infinite square well of width L. Starting at time $t = 0$, the system is subject to the perturbation

$$H'(t) = V_0 x e^{-\alpha t^2},$$

where V_0 and α are constants.

a) Find the probability that the energy is measured to be E_2 in the limit $t \to \infty$.

b) Find the probability that the energy is measured to be E_3 in the limit $t \to \infty$.

4 A particle of mass m is initially in the ground state (E_1) of an infinite square well of width L. From $t = 0$ to $t = T$, the potential is perturbed so that it becomes

$$V(x) = \begin{cases} V_0, & 0 < x < L/2 \\ 0, & L/2 < x < L \\ \infty, & \text{elsewhere,} \end{cases}$$

where $V_0 \ll E_1$. Find the probability that the energy after time T is measured to be E_2.

5 Spontaneous emission causes the population of an atom to decay with the form $e^{-t/\tau}$. The radiated electromagnetic power exhibits this same time dependence, but the field has the form $e^{-t/2\tau}$ because the power is proportional to the field squared. Calculate the Fourier transform of the emitted field and take its complex square to find the frequency spectrum of the radiated power in spontaneous emission. Convert this frequency spectrum to an energy spectrum and normalize it to unity to verify the energy density of states in Eq. (68),

$$g(E) = \frac{\hbar A_{21}/2\pi}{\left(E - \hbar\omega_{21}\right)^2 + \left(\dfrac{\hbar A_{21}}{2}\right)^2}. \tag{68}$$

6 A hydrogen atom in its ground state is subject to an applied electric field

$$\mathbf{E} = \mathcal{E}_0(\hat{\mathbf{x}} + \hat{\mathbf{y}} + \hat{\mathbf{z}})e^{-t/\tau}.$$

Find the probabilities that after a long time the atom is found be in each of the four $n = 2$ states.

7 Calculate the lifetime (in seconds) of each of the four $n = 2$ states of hydrogen $(\lvert n\ell m\rangle)$. The lifetime is the inverse of the spontaneous emission rate (Einstein A coefficient).

8 A particle in a square well potential (with walls at $x = 0$ and $x = L$; that is, $V(x) = 0$ for $0 < x < L$; $V(x) = \infty$ otherwise) starts out in the ground state

$$\lvert\psi(t = 0)\rangle = \lvert 1\rangle,$$

where $\lvert n\rangle$ are the normalized eigenstates of the unperturbed Hamiltonian. Starting at $t = 0$, a time-dependent perturbation is applied given by

$$H'(x,t) = V_0 \sin\frac{\pi x}{L}e^{-\gamma t}.$$

a) Calculate the probability for the particle to make a transition to an excited state $\lvert n\rangle (n \neq 1)$ after a long time. Define "long time."

b) Are there any selection rules for this transition? If so, what are they?

9 A particle in the harmonic oscillator potential $V(x) = \frac{1}{2}m\omega^2 x^2$ starts out in the ground state

$$\lvert\psi(t = 0)\rangle = \lvert 0\rangle,$$

Time-Dependent Perturbation Theory: Problem Set

where $|n\rangle$ are the normalized eigenstates of the Hamiltonian. Starting at $t = 0$, a time-dependent perturbation is applied given by

$$H'(x,t) = Ax^3 e^{-\gamma t}.$$

a) Calculate the probability for the particle to make a transition to an excited state $|n\rangle (n \neq 0)$ after a long time. Define "long time."

b) Are there any selection rules for this transition? If so, what are they?

10 Consider two possible types of electric dipole transitions: a $p \rightarrow s$ transition and a $p \rightarrow d$ transition. In each case, choose one *allowed* set of m quantum numbers and explicitly perform the angular integral in Eq. (84),

$$\int Y_{\ell_f}^{m_f *}(\theta,\phi) Y_1^m (\theta,\phi) Y_{\ell_i}^{m_i} (\theta,\phi) d\Omega = \left[\frac{3(2\ell_i + 1)}{4\pi(2\ell_f + 1)} \right]^{\frac{1}{2}} \langle \ell_i 1 m_i m | \ell_f m_f \rangle \langle \ell_i 100 | \ell_f 0 \rangle, \quad (84)$$

then use the Clebsch-Gordan table below to confirm your result.

Clebsch-Gordan Coefficients for $j_1 = 1$ and $j_2 = 1$

$j_1 = 1$		j	2	2	2	2	2	1	1	1	0
	$j_2 = 1$	m	2	1	0	−1	−2	1	0	−1	0
m_1	m_2										
1	1		1	0	0	0	0	0	0	0	0
1	0		0	$\frac{1}{\sqrt{2}}$	0	0	0	$\frac{1}{\sqrt{2}}$	0	0	0
1	−1		0	0	$\frac{1}{\sqrt{6}}$	0	0	0	$\frac{1}{\sqrt{2}}$	0	$\frac{1}{\sqrt{3}}$
0	1		0	$\frac{1}{\sqrt{2}}$	0	0	0	$-\frac{1}{\sqrt{2}}$	0	0	0
0	0		0	0	$\sqrt{\frac{2}{3}}$	0	0	0	0	0	$-\frac{1}{\sqrt{3}}$
0	−1		0	0	0	$\frac{1}{\sqrt{2}}$	0	0	0	$\frac{1}{\sqrt{2}}$	0
−1	1		0	0	$\frac{1}{\sqrt{6}}$	0	0	0	$-\frac{1}{\sqrt{2}}$	0	$\frac{1}{\sqrt{3}}$
−1	0		0	0	0	$\frac{1}{\sqrt{2}}$	0	0	0	$-\frac{1}{\sqrt{2}}$	0
−1	−1		0	0	0	0	1	0	0	0	0

11 Use the result in Eq. (84) and the above Clebsch-Gordan table to identify each possible electric dipole transition from an initial p state. Identify the particular Clebsch-Gordan coefficient in the above table that represents the parity rule $\ell_f \neq \ell_i$.

12 A hydrogen atom starts in the state $n = 4, l = 3, m_\ell = 3$, where we ignore the spin. What possible states will the atom go through as it decays to the ground state? What are the polarizations of the photons that are emitted?

13 Draw a transition diagram like Fig. 10, but for absorption from $1s \to 2p$ rather than emission. Explain why the Δm values change sign but the σ^+ and σ^- labels remain unchanged.

14 A particle of mass m and charge q is confined in a one-dimensional harmonic oscillator potential of natural frequency ω.

a) What are the selection rules governing spontaneous emission from excited states?

b) Which states can decay directly to the ground state?

c) Find the spontaneous emission rate from the first excited state to the ground state.

d) Calculate the lifetime of the first excited state for an electron bound in a potential with $\omega = 10^{15}$ rad/s.

Periodic Systems

In this chapter, we explore the energy eigenvalues and eigenstates of a periodic series of potential energy wells, as shown in Fig. 1, with the purpose of creating a rudimentary model of a solid. In this model, a single well represents an atom, and the chain of wells represents a molecule or a solid. Recall the energy eigenstates of the finite square well potential, which is a single element of the periodic series shown in Fig. 1(a). There are a finite number of bound eigenstates and a continuum of unbound eigenstates. The shape of the well changes only the details of the shape of the wave functions and shifts the eigenvalues slightly. The hydrogen atom is another example, schematically depicted as an element of the series in Fig. 1(b). It also has bound states (but an infinite number) and continuum states. It is a three-dimensional problem, rather than the one-dimensional problem we will consider here. The similarities outweigh the differences, and the basic features of the band structure of a solid appear when we string several such "one-dimensional atoms" together to model a solid.

Our model uses an approximate approach that emphasizes the interaction between neighboring atoms. We will find out how the eigenstates of the periodic potential (or molecule or solid) can be constructed from the eigenstates of the single elements of the periodic potential (or atoms). We will also learn that the eigenstates of a solid are characterized by a wavelength, and that the energies of those eigenstates form bands centered near the atomic energy eigenvalues. The approximation presented here is a powerful method that is widely used in solid state physics and chemistry, where it goes under the name of tight-binding or **LCAO** (Linear Combination of Atomic Orbitals). The LCAO approach is intuitive, starting from the easily understood atomic orbitals, and building molecular orbitals by considering how the atoms interact.

It is also possible to find the energy eigenvalues and eigenstates by directly solving the energy eigenvalue equation, and we will discuss this approach at the end of the chapter. The problem presented here is a *single-particle problem* whose solution is the possible states of a *single* electron subject to the periodic potential, so we do not concern ourselves with the identical-particle aspects. Despite this gross oversimplification, the results are surprisingly robust if we simply assume that subsequent electrons would occupy these same states, subject to the Pauli exclusion principle. This **independent electron approximation** is sufficient to explain the presence of energy gaps in the energy-level structure of real solids, and to provide a basis for understanding the concept of the density of levels and the rudiments of electron transport.

Our goal is to gain a basic understanding of an **energy band diagram** and **density of states plot** of a solid, such as depicted in Fig. 2 for the semiconductor Si. The plot on the left is simply an energy spectrum—a plot of the allowed energies of an electron. The difference between this plot and the energy spectrum for atomic hydrogen, say, is that the horizontal axis represents a new

The companion websites for this text are http://physics.oregonstate.edu/portfolioswiki and http://physics.oregonstate.edu/qmactivities.

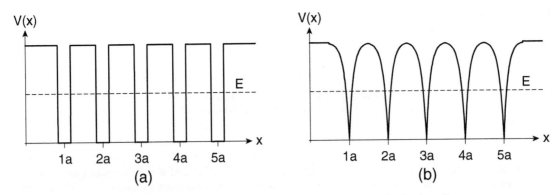

FIGURE 1   Chain of periodic wells: (a) square wells, (b) Coulomb wells.

momentum variable associated with the eigenstate that arises because of the periodic nature of the potential. The graph on the right of Fig. 2 is a density of states plot. It represents the relative number of allowed states (per unit energy) at each energy, regardless of the momentum variable. Such plots help us determine whether materials are metallic or insulating, and tell us something about the optical and electronic transport properties of the solid. We begin by tackling a one-dimensional periodic potential, which will lead us to a simple version of one panel of the band structure plot in Fig. 2.

Silicon Band Structure and Density of States

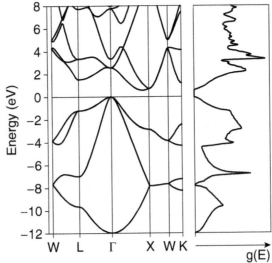

FIGURE 2   Band structure and density of states of Si.

1 ■ THE ENERGY EIGENVALUES AND EIGENSTATES OF A PERIODIC CHAIN OF WELLS

Our goal in this section is to use the LCAO method to find approximate solutions to the energy eigenvalue equation for a chain of periodic wells. We'll study the one-dimensional chain of square wells shown in Fig. 1(a) as our model system. We'll solve this problem exactly later in the chapter, but the approximate LCAO method is sufficient to illustrate most of the important features of a periodic system and is also more revealing. To get started, we'll study a chain with two square wells, and then we'll solve the N-well problem.

In the LCAO method, we regard each individual well as an "atom." We assume that we have already solved the energy eigenvalue equation for one isolated well and so we know the energy eigenvalues and the eigenstates, which we refer to as the "atomic" energies and states. For example, we can solve the energy eigenvalue equation of the finite square well. The eigenstates for two different square wells are shown in Fig. 3. In our discussions, we won't need more than the lowest two states in the well, so we'll label them as ground (g) and excited (e) states to simplify the notation. We will use kets $|g\rangle$ and $|e\rangle$ or wave functions $\varphi^g(x) = \langle x|g\rangle$ or $\varphi^e(x) = \langle x|e\rangle$ as appropriate.

1.1 ■ A Two-Well Chain

The simplest system with more than one well is the "chain" of two wells, depicted in Fig. 4. We'll make the problem even simpler and assume that each individual well has just one possible bound state, as in Fig. 3(a). Our goal is to solve the energy eigenvalue equation

$$H|\psi\rangle = E|\psi\rangle, \tag{1}$$

where the Hamiltonian H includes the usual kinetic energy of the single electron and the potential energy depicted in Fig. 4. The two wells (atoms) are separated by a distance a (the interatomic spacing). The ket $|\psi\rangle$ represents an eigenstate of the two-well Hamiltonian, and E is the corresponding energy. We refer to $|\psi\rangle$ as a "molecular" eigenstate.

The central idea of the LCAO or "interacting atoms" approach is to represent the system state vector $|\psi\rangle$ in the basis of the "atomic" states that are the solutions to the energy eigenvalue problem for a single isolated well. In the simplified case that we are considering, the only two atomic states in

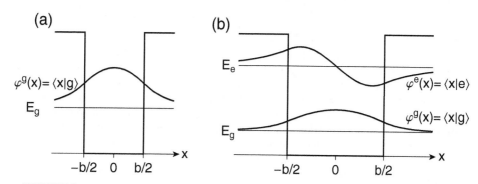

FIGURE 3 Finite square well and bound energy eigenstates for cases with (a) one energy level, and (b) two energy levels. These eigenstates are the basis for the eigenstates of the full periodic Hamilitonian.

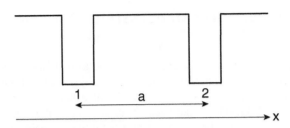

FIGURE 4   Two square wells with separation a.

the system are the ground states of the two wells, centered on wells 1 and 2. We could label them as $|1, g\rangle$ and $|2, g\rangle$, but we immediately simplify the notation to $|1\rangle$ and $|2\rangle$ because there is only one state per well. The wave functions representing these states are identical [as in Fig. 3(a)] except that they are displaced by a from each other:

$$
\begin{aligned}
|1\rangle &\doteq \varphi^g(x - 1a) \\
|2\rangle &\doteq \varphi^g(x - 2a).
\end{aligned}
\tag{2}
$$

The LCAO method assumes that the molecular state is a linear combination of the known atomic states:

$$
|\psi\rangle = c_1|1\rangle + c_2|2\rangle.
\tag{3}
$$

The beauty of the LCAO method is that we use the already known atomic wave functions as the preferred basis, so we solve the energy eigenvalue equation with the matrix approach rather than the differential equation approach used to find the atomic states. This is clearly an approximation because we expect the spatial wave functions to be altered by the new potential configuration, but the results are quite good in many cases.

For the two-atom chain, there are only two atomic states, so the matrix representing the Hamiltonian of the system is a 2×2 matrix. This matrix has the form

$$
H \doteq \begin{pmatrix} \alpha & \beta \\ \beta & \alpha \end{pmatrix}.
\tag{4}
$$

The matrix elements of the Hamiltonian are

$$
\begin{aligned}
\alpha &= H_{11} = H_{22} = \langle 1|H|1\rangle = \langle 2|H|2\rangle \\
\beta &= H_{12} = H_{21} = \langle 1|H|2\rangle = \langle 2|H|1\rangle.
\end{aligned}
\tag{5}
$$

The two diagonal terms are equal and the two off-diagonal terms are equal because of the symmetry of the two-well chain. The parameters α and β are straightforward to calculate given the atomic states and will depend on the well depth and the spacing. We can proceed with this problem without actually calculating α and β—the important features of the band structure will be perfectly clear without knowing their values. However, as a physicist, you ought to be very interested in knowing how to calculate them and in knowing what they mean. We'll pursue these calculations in Section 8 and as homework problems. It turns out that the diagonal matrix elements α are approximately equal to the energy of the atomic state. The off-diagonal matrix elements β are related to the probability for an electron to move between the wells, and so are referred to as "hopping" matrix elements.

We have now reduced the two-well problem to a two-dimensional Hilbert space comprising the ground atomic states, and we proceed to find the molecular eigenstates and eigenenergies by

Periodic Systems

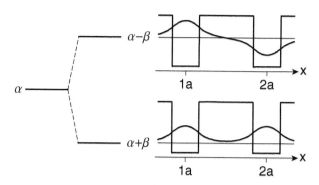

FIGURE 5 Two atomic states combine to form two molecular states. The bonding state is symmetric and the antibonding state is antisymmetric if $\beta < 0$.

diagonalizing the Hamiltonian in Eq. (4). You have already diagonalized many 2×2 matrices, so we'll skip the details. The energy eigenvalues are

$$E_+ = \alpha + \beta$$
$$E_- = \alpha - \beta \tag{6}$$

and the energy eigenstates are

$$|\psi_+\rangle = \tfrac{1}{\sqrt{2}}|1\rangle + \tfrac{1}{\sqrt{2}}|2\rangle \quad \text{for } E_+ = \alpha + \beta$$
$$|\psi_-\rangle = \tfrac{1}{\sqrt{2}}|1\rangle - \tfrac{1}{\sqrt{2}}|2\rangle \quad \text{for } E_- = \alpha - \beta. \tag{7}$$

There are two molecular states, one a symmetric and equal superposition of the two atomic states, and the other an equal and antisymmetric combination. The energies of the two molecular states are displaced from the energy α, by an energy β, and the sign of β determines which state has the higher energy. For the two square-well chain, $\beta < 0$ and the lower-energy state (called the bonding orbital) is the symmetric combination, and the higher-energy state (called the antibonding orbital) is antisymmetric. Figure 5 depicts the level scheme and the wave functions for this two-well system. This solution is reminiscent of degenerate perturbation theory in that the coupling β between the two states lifts the degeneracy of the atomic states.

1.2 ■ *N*-Well Chain

Now consider a system with N one-dimensional wells as depicted in Fig. 1. As N increases beyond 2, the molecule contains more and more atoms, and eventually there will be enough to think of it as a solid. In this language, a solid is just a giant molecule, and we'll continue to refer to the eigenstate of the periodic system as the "molecular state" (as distinct from the "atomic state" of the isolated well). Let's continue to assume that each isolated well has only one bound atomic state, so for the N-atom chain, there are N atomic states, which we label with their location as $|n\rangle$. The molecular state is the linear combination of atomic states

$$|\psi\rangle = \sum_{n=1}^{N} c_n |n\rangle, \tag{8}$$

and the matrix representing the Hamiltonian of the system is an $N\times N$ matrix. We now make one additional assumption. We assume that the "hopping" matrix elements β are zero unless the two wells are adjacent. This **nearest-neighbor approximation** is easily relaxed, but doing so gives little new physical insight and increases the algebraic complexity. With this new assumption, the matrix representing the Hamiltonian is an extension of the two-well Hamiltonian [Eq. (4)] with the β terms adjacent to the main diagonal:

$$H \doteq \begin{pmatrix} \alpha & \beta & 0 & 0 & \cdots \\ \beta & \alpha & \beta & 0 & \cdots \\ 0 & \beta & \alpha & \beta & \cdots \\ 0 & 0 & \beta & \alpha & \cdots \\ \vdots & \vdots & \vdots & \vdots & \ddots \end{pmatrix}. \tag{9}$$

The nonzero matrix elements are

$$\begin{aligned} \alpha &= H_{nn} = \langle n|H|n\rangle \\ \beta &= H_{n,n\pm1} = \langle n|H|n\pm1\rangle. \end{aligned} \tag{10}$$

For small values of N, the Hamiltonian in Eq. (9) can be diagonalized either analytically or using a computer to find the energy eigenvalues and eigenstates just as we did for the $N = 2$ case in the last section. We'll leave that approach to the homework problems. For large N, we use a different solution technique that gets at the heart of the problem. Using the matrix in Eq. (9), we express the energy eigenvalue equation $H|\psi\rangle = E|\psi\rangle$ as

$$\begin{pmatrix} \alpha & \beta & 0 & 0 & \cdots \\ \beta & \alpha & \beta & 0 & \cdots \\ 0 & \beta & \alpha & \beta & \cdots \\ 0 & 0 & \beta & \alpha & \cdots \\ \vdots & \vdots & \vdots & \vdots & \ddots \end{pmatrix} \begin{pmatrix} c_1 \\ c_2 \\ c_3 \\ c_4 \\ \vdots \end{pmatrix} = E \begin{pmatrix} c_1 \\ c_2 \\ c_3 \\ c_4 \\ \vdots \end{pmatrix}. \tag{11}$$

This leads to the equations

$$\begin{aligned} \alpha c_1 + \beta c_2 &= Ec_1 \\ \beta c_1 + \alpha c_2 + \beta c_3 &= Ec_2 \\ \beta c_2 + \alpha c_3 + \beta c_4 &= Ec_3 \\ \beta c_3 + \alpha c_4 + \beta c_5 &= Ec_4. \\ \vdots \end{aligned} \tag{12}$$

The first equation and the last equation (not shown) are different, but all the other equations have the identical form

$$\beta c_{p-1} + \alpha c_p + \beta c_{p+1} = Ec_p. \tag{13}$$

For now, we focus on solving this equation and ignore the different endpoint equations that we'll come back to in the next section.

The mathematical form of Eq. (13) is identical to the equation of motion of a collection of mechanical oscillators, each coupled to its two nearest neighbors, as in a beaded string. We use the technique of **normal mode solutions** to solve Eq. (13) for the coefficients c_p and the energy E. The normal-mode approach assumes wavelike solutions of the form

$$c_p = Ae^{ipka}. \tag{14}$$

In Eq. (14), p is an integer from 1 to N that labels the atomic state, and each molecular eigenstate corresponds to a different set of N coefficients $(c_1, c_2, \dots c_N)$. The parameter a is the separation of the finite wells as shown in Fig. 1. The values of k and A are unknown for the moment; we have yet to determine them.

Substitute Eq. (14) into Eq. (13) to get

$$\beta Ae^{i(p-1)ka} + (\alpha - E)Ae^{ipka} + \beta Ae^{i(p+1)ka} = 0, \tag{15}$$

and factor out e^{ipka} to obtain

$$\beta e^{-ika} + (\alpha - E) + \beta e^{+ika} = 0. \tag{16}$$

Now solve for the eigenstate energy E, making use of the Euler relation, to find the **dispersion relation**

$$E = \alpha + 2\beta\cos(ka). \tag{17}$$

The dispersion relation is plotted in Fig. 6 for k a continuous variable, which is the case when there are very many atoms, as we will discuss later.

Notice that we assumed a form for the coefficients c_p in Eq. (14) and ended up solving for the energy! Before we return to the coefficients (which amounts to pinning down the values of A and k), we will take some time to discuss the dispersion relation, which contains a great deal of information. First, notice that the energy eigenvalue of the molecular state is determined by k, so k labels the molecular eigenstate. We'll find out in Section 2 what values k may have. The energy E is periodic in k with period $2\pi/a$, so clearly there is some redundancy in the information. Second, the values of E are bounded above and below, as indicated by the limits $\alpha - 2\beta$ and $\alpha + 2\beta$ in Fig. 6. The fact that there is a **band of allowed energies** is one of the most important characteristics of a solid that is replicated by our model. The progression from one atomic energy to two molecular energies to a band of energies for the one-well, two-well and $N \rightarrow \infty$ well cases,

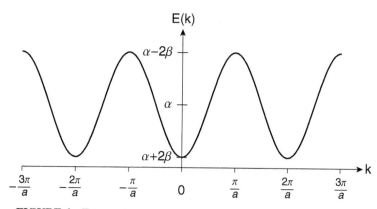

FIGURE 6   Energy eigenvalues as a function of wave vector, k, for an infinite chain of wells, with $\beta < 0$.

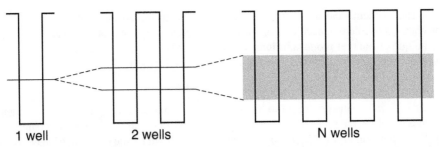

FIGURE 7 The development of a band of energies from a discrete atomic energy as the number of wells increases.

respectively, is shown in Fig. 7. Third, the **band width** is 4β, which indicates that the stronger the interaction between neighboring states, the wider the resulting band. Recall that β is the matrix element of the Hamiltonian evaluated between neighboring states and is therefore an indication of the interaction strength. In real solids with the same crystal structure, those with smaller lattice parameters have wider bands because atomic wave functions can overlap more efficiently.

It is now time to look more closely at k. Is it continuous or discrete, and what values does it take? What does k represent? Once we know k, we have complete knowledge of E from Eq. (17), and almost complete knowledge of the c_p [we still need A in Eq. (14)] and, hence, of the state vector from Eqs. (8) and (14).

2 ■ BOUNDARY CONDITIONS AND THE ALLOWED VALUES OF k

We introduced the quantity k in Eq. (14) $c_p = Ae^{ipka}$ as an undetermined constant in the coefficient of the atomic states $|p\rangle$ that contribute to the molecular state $|\psi\rangle$. k serves to label the molecular eigenstate under consideration. In fact, if we had anticipated the need for such a label, we might have written c_p^k, with the interpretation that c_p^k is the contribution of the pth atomic state to the kth molecular eigenstate. Because k appears in the exponential function in combination with the real-space length a, it must have dimensions of inverse length. We often refer to the set of k values as "**k space**," a **reciprocal space** to the real space that we are used to. We must apply real-space boundary conditions to determine which values k may assume. For solids containing a huge number of atoms $\left(10^{22} \text{ cm}^{-3}\right)$, it is best to use **periodic boundary conditions**, as illustrated in Fig. 8. One can think of bending the linear

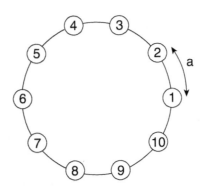

FIGURE 8 Periodic boundary conditions for a 10-well chain.

chain of atoms into a ring, so that the 1st atom and the Nth atom are now neighbors. The next atom after the Nth is the $(N + 1)^{th}$, which is the same as the 1st. The physical consequence of this procedure is to remove the effect of the boundaries, (i.e., the surface of the solid). This effectively makes the first and last equations of the set in Eq. (12) identical to all the other equations and justifies the neglect of the endpoint equations in the last section.

The periodic boundary condition amounts to writing

$$c_{n=1} = c_{n=N+1},\tag{18}$$

which, using Eq. (14), is equivalent to

$$e^{iNka} = 1.\tag{19}$$

This condition is satisfied for

$$Nka = q2\pi \Rightarrow k_q = \frac{q}{N}\frac{2\pi}{a},\tag{20}$$

where q is yet another integer. It is important that the integer q is *not* the label of the atomic states. It defines the allowed values of k, which labels the *molecular* states. There are N physically distinct molecular states that result from the N different k values corresponding to $q = 1, 2, ... N$. We get the *same* set of N molecular states for the set of q values $q = N + 1, N + 2, ... 2N$ or for the set $q = -N/2, -N/2 + 1, ... N/2$, or indeed for any N consecutive integers. Now we write the dispersion relation as

$$E_{k_q} = \alpha + 2\beta \cos(k_q a),\tag{21}$$

which is plotted in Fig. 9 for $N = 20$ and $\beta < 0$, for k corresponding to the set of integers $q = -N/2, -N/2 + 1, ... N/2$. We'll see in Section 6 that values of k outside this range yield exactly the same wave functions and energies, and hence give no new information.

The allowed values of k are separated by

$$\Delta k = k_q - k_{q-1} = \frac{2\pi}{Na}.\tag{22}$$

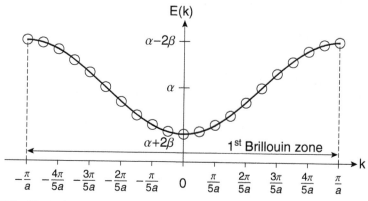

FIGURE 9 Dispersion relation for a chain of 20 wells. Circles represent k values that give distinct eigenstates.

The quantity Na, the product of the number of atoms and the interatomic spacing, is the (real-space) length of the solid, which we can call L. L usually has macroscopic dimensions (μm, mm, or cm) compared with the Å to nm scale for a. Because

$$\Delta k = \frac{2\pi}{L} \ll \frac{2\pi}{a}, \tag{23}$$

the k spacing is very much smaller than the range of k values, k may be considered a continuous quantity for most practical purposes in a macroscopic solid, and we can consider the dispersion relation a continuous function

$$\boxed{E(k) = \alpha + 2\beta\cos(ka)}. \tag{24}$$

3 ■ THE BRILLOUIN ZONES

Any set of N consecutive integers could be used to designate the N distinct k values in Eq. (20). The set of N integers that gives k values closest to zero defines the **first Brillouin zone** in k-space. This set is $q = -N/2, \dots N/2$, which means that the first Brillouin zone extends from $-\pi/a$ to $+\pi/a$ in k space, and it is this set that is shown in Fig. 9. Including the state $q = 0$, it would seem there are $N + 1$ states, but because of the periodicity, the state at $k = -\pi/a$ is the same as the one at $k = +\pi/a$, so there are exactly N distinct states for the N-atom chain. The width of the zone is $2\pi/a$, which illustrates a fundamental relationship between real space and reciprocal space—if the interatomic spacings are large (small) in real space, then the corresponding Brillouin zones are small (large) in k space.

One can also define the set of N integers that give k values larger than any in the first Brillouin zone, but otherwise closest to zero. This set is $q = N/2, \dots N$ and $-N/2, \dots -N$ and the corresponding k values form the second Brillouin zone. The second Brillouin zone is the same size as the first, but it is not contiguous. A similar procedure defines higher-order zones. A slightly modified process defines Brillouin zones in two and three dimensions, where again, higher-order zones have the same area or volume as the first zone, but are not contiguous regions of k space.

We have not yet specified what k actually represents, and this will become clearer in Section 6. The quantity $\hbar k$ has the dimensions of momentum, and it is often called the **crystal momentum** or quasimomentum, so called because it defines the wavelength of the *envelope* of the molecular wave function. In this respect,

$$k_{conventional} = \sqrt{2m(E - V)/\hbar^2}, \tag{25}$$

which defines the (local) wavelength of the electron wave function.

Next, we should use the allowed values of k to find the sets of coefficients that determine the specific contributions of each atomic orbital to each molecular orbital, and draw real-space representations of the molecular orbitals. Before we do this, let's make a short digression to describe how the LCAO approach described above that yielded the dispersion relation [Eq. (21) or (24)] for a single atomic state per well plays out if we choose well parameters that allow two or more atomic states per well.

4 ■ MULTIPLE BANDS FROM MULTIPLE ATOMIC LEVELS

Real solids have multiple bands of energies, not just one. The dispersion relation Eq. (21) resulted when we considered the interaction between the single levels in neighboring atoms in the periodic system (these might be considered analogous to the $1s$ ground state of a hydrogen atom). To model the effects of higher-energy atomic states, we must include them in the basis set. The basis would include the ground state $|g\rangle$ and the first excited state $|e\rangle$ for example, if we used two atomic levels per atom, for a total of $2 \times N$ atomic states in the basis. We would designate them $|n, g\rangle$ and $|n, e\rangle$. The integer n labels the atom or individual well, while the second designator labels the state within that well. The result would be the formation of additional energy bands with dispersion relations resembling the one we calculated in the previous section. In the nearest-neighbor approximation, the simplest case would be represented by the Hamiltonian matrix H_A in Fig. 10 below, where there is no interaction between the ground state of one well and the excited state of the adjacent well. In that case, there are two bands formed with dispersion relations *exactly* like Eq. (24), but with different band centers $(\alpha_g$ and $\alpha_e)$ and bandwidths $(\beta_g$ and $\beta_e)$ for each band.

Figure 11 shows the allowed energies for a periodic system with two atomic levels per atom at energies $\alpha_g = 2$ and $\alpha_e = 10$, and β-values of $\beta_g = -1$ and $\beta_e = +2$ in the same energy units. This choice makes the upper band twice as wide as the lower, and puts the maximum energy of that band at $k = 0$. The allowed k values are the same as before, $k_q = 2\pi q / Na$, but now there are *two* possible energy eigenvalues for each value of k_q, $E_q^{(g)}$ and $E_q^{(e)}$, with the upper index labeling the band. In this example, the β-values are smaller than the spacing between the atomic states $(\alpha_e - \alpha_g)$, the bands remain separate from one another, and the resulting band structure is a series of branches of $E(k)$ curves defining bands of allowed energies, separated by gaps of forbidden energies. This model qualitatively explains the band gaps we observe in real solids that are so important in semiconductors, for example. Band gaps are discussed further in Section 12.

When we discuss the energy band structure of real materials, we often label bands by the atomic states from which they are primarily derived. In Fig. 11, we might refer to the lower band as "the ground state band" and the upper as the "excited state band" to acknowledge that the lower (upper) band eigenstates are linear combinations of the ground (excited) atomic states. In real solids, we speak of the "1s band," the "3d band," and so forth. In the next section, we discuss the composition of the molecular states in more detail.

If there is a significant interaction (β_{ge}) between the ground state of one atom with the excited state of its neighbor, the Hamiltonian H_B in Fig 10 is appropriate. The dispersion relation calculation is a nice extension of the example presented here (Problem 4). The two bands each contain mixtures of both atomic states, rather than being derived exclusively from one or the other atomic state.

There are several software packages that find the energy eigenvalues and eigenstates of one-dimensional periodic potentials (see Resources). It is very instructive to use these to examine the energy spectrum and see the bands, and investigate the effect of changing the number of wells, their shape, and their separation. Such packages usually plot wave functions and the associated probability densities, too, and this is the topic of the next section.

$$
H_A \doteq
\begin{array}{c}
\langle 1g| \ \langle 2g| \ \langle 1e| \ \langle 2e| \\
\begin{pmatrix}
\alpha_g & \beta_g & 0 & 0 \\
\beta_g & \alpha_g & 0 & 0 \\
0 & 0 & \alpha_e & \beta_e \\
0 & 0 & \beta_e & \alpha_e
\end{pmatrix}
\begin{array}{l}
|1g\rangle \\
|2g\rangle \\
|1e\rangle \\
|2e\rangle
\end{array}
\end{array}
\qquad
H_B \doteq
\begin{pmatrix}
\alpha_g & \beta_g & 0 & \beta_{ge} \\
\beta_g & \alpha_g & \beta_{ge} & 0 \\
0 & \beta_{ge} & \alpha_e & \beta_e \\
\beta_{ge} & 0 & \beta_e & \alpha_e
\end{pmatrix}
$$

FIGURE 10 Hamiltonian matrices in the nearest-neighbor approximation for a periodic chain of two wells with two states per well. H_A describes a situation where the states are well separated in energy and there is no interaction between the upper state of one well and the lower state of the adjacent well. H_B relaxes that assumption.

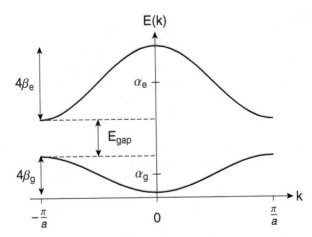

FIGURE 11   Dispersion relation showing two energy bands derived from two atomic states per well. In this example, the parameters are such that the bands do not overlap, and there is an energy gap where no states are allowed for any value of k.

Figure 11 begins to be reminiscent of the real band structure calculation that we began with in Fig. 2. In Fig. 11, if we label the point $k = 0$ as Γ and $k = \pi/a$ as X, we begin to see the similarity to the corresponding panel in Fig. 2. In Fig. 2, Γ, X, W, and K are simply labels of different k values (but in three-dimensional reciprocal space rather than one-dimensional), and the corresponding values of E are plotted for these directions in reciprocal space. There are several bands, some of them overlapping, and some of them with the simple shape that we have found in our rudimentary model. Nowadays, real band structure calculations are performed with powerful computers and with more sophisticated methods than the LCAO method discussed here, but the LCAO method allows us to understand and interpret such pictures rather well.

5 ■ BLOCH'S THEOREM AND THE MOLECULAR STATES

Having calculated the energy eigenvalues via the dispersion relation Eq. (24), we now calculate the molecular eigenstates from Eqs. (8) and (14). We return to the simple example of one atomic state per well, where the kth molecular state is represented as a superposition of all the atomic states $|n\rangle$:

$$|\psi_k\rangle = \sum_{n=1}^{N} A e^{inka} |n\rangle. \tag{26}$$

We have almost all the information we need. We know the atomic states $|n\rangle$ and the allowed values of k. We don't yet know the value of A, nor have we tested that the proposed molecular state has all the properties expected of an eigenstate of a periodic potential.

The constant A is easy to find. We built into the assumption (14) that every atomic state makes an equal contribution (in magnitude) to the molecular state. Why? Well, every atom is identical (assuming periodic boundary conditions), so how could the magnitude of any one atomic state's contribution be different than that of any other? The atomic state coefficients, then, must differ only by a phase factor, and that phase factor is already reflected in the exponential in Eq. (14). We require that the molecular state be normalized, and because the atomic basis states are orthogonal (approximately), the normalization condition is

$$\langle \psi_k | \psi_k \rangle = \sum_{n=1}^{N} |c_n|^2 = \sum_{n=1}^{N} |A|^2 = 1. \tag{27}$$

It is clear from Eq. (27) that the appropriate constant is $A = 1/\sqrt{N}$, so that

$$|\psi_k\rangle = \sum_{n=1}^{N} \frac{1}{\sqrt{N}} e^{inka} |n\rangle. \tag{28}$$

Now at last we have all the information we need to construct the eigenstate, and we will proceed to draw some pictures of the molecular wave functions; they are in Section 6, to which you can skip immediately if you like. However, we need to check that the eigenstate has all the properties we expect. (It does, of course, otherwise we wouldn't have gone to all this trouble!)

The structure of the solid or molecule is periodic, so the electron probability density, a measurable quantity, must also be periodic. In Dirac notation, this condition is

$$|\langle x | \psi_k \rangle|^2 = |\langle x + ma | \psi_k \rangle|^2, \tag{29}$$

where m is an integer. In wave function notation, (i.e., the position representation), this condition is

$$|\psi_k(x)|^2 = |\psi_k(x + ma)|^2. \tag{30}$$

You might be tempted to think that the wave function itself should be periodic, too, but that is too stringent a requirement and has no basis in measurement. But if the wave function satisfies the condition

$$\boxed{\psi_k(x + ma) = e^{imka} \psi_k(x)}, \tag{31}$$

it is easy to see that Eq. (30) is satisfied. The condition in Eq. (31) is one expression of **Bloch's theorem** in one dimension. Bloch's theorem stems from the translational symmetry of the periodic system of potential energy wells. Bloch's theorem can be generalized to two and three dimensions and it is a critical part of understanding any periodic system. For our purposes, the one-dimensional form will suffice. Now we must ask if the molecular eigenstates of the periodic potential that we have constructed from atomic eigenstates of the individual wells obey Bloch's theorem. If they do, then we have been successful, and Eq. (26) represents the molecular eigenstates. We perform the test with the wave function representation of Eq. (26):

$$\psi_k(x) = \frac{1}{\sqrt{N}} \sum_{n=1}^{N} e^{inka} \varphi_n(x), \tag{32}$$

where

$$\varphi_n(x) = \langle x | n \rangle. \tag{33}$$

All the atomic wave functions have the same shape, but they are displaced from one another by an integer number of well spacings. This statement is represented mathematically by the equation

$$\varphi_n(x + ma) = \varphi_{n-m}(x). \tag{34}$$

Equation (34) says that if we take the atomic wave function belonging to the nth well and translate it backwards by m lattice spacings (that's the left-hand side), it must look the same as the atomic wave function corresponding to the $(n–m)^{\text{th}}$ well (that's the right-hand side), which of course is exactly true.

With this in mind, start with the left-hand side of Bloch's theorem and use Eq. (32) with $x -> x + ma$:

$$
\begin{aligned}
\psi_k(x + ma) &= \frac{1}{\sqrt{N}} \sum_{n=1}^{N} e^{inka}\varphi_n(x + ma) \\
&= \frac{1}{\sqrt{N}} \sum_{n=1}^{N} e^{inka}\varphi_{n-m}(x) \quad \text{[from Eq. 34]} \\
&= \frac{1}{\sqrt{N}} \sum_{n=1-m}^{N-m} e^{i(n+m)ka}\varphi_n(x) \quad (n \rightarrow n + m) \\
&= \frac{1}{\sqrt{N}} \sum_{n=1}^{N} e^{i(n+m)ka}\varphi_n(x) \quad \text{(can start the count anywhere)}.
\end{aligned}
\tag{35}
$$

The last step is possible because, with periodic boundary conditions, we are summing over atomic sites around an N-member ring ($c_0 = c_N$, $c_1 = c_{N+1}$, etc.). It doesn't matter where we start the sum as long as we include N consecutive terms. The result is [using Eq. (32) again]

$$
\psi_k(x + ma) = e^{imka}\frac{1}{\sqrt{N}} \sum_{n=1}^{N} e^{inka}\varphi_n(x) = e^{imka}\psi_k(x),
\tag{36}
$$

which clearly satisfies Bloch's theorem [Eq. (31)] and guarantees that the probability density is periodic, as it must be. In the next section, we'll draw some pictures to appreciate the patterns in the molecular wave functions.

6 ■ MOLECULAR WAVE FUNCTIONS—A GALLERY

We can draw the molecular wave functions of Eq. (32) if we know the atomic wave functions. For a chain of finite square wells, the atomic wave functions are the eigenstates of the finite well. The wave functions shown in Fig. 12 are drawn using a schematic representation of the ground state of a finite square well. We assume for now that $\beta < 0$; we'll show it later. We continue to use the periodic boundary conditions we introduced in Section 2. The molecular wave function corresponding to the lowest energy state has $k = 0$ and is

$$
\psi_0(x) = \frac{1}{\sqrt{N}} \sum_{n=1}^{N} e^{i0a}\varphi_n(x) = \frac{1}{\sqrt{N}}\left[\varphi_1(x) + \varphi_2(x) + \varphi_3(x) + \varphi_4(x) + ...\right].
\tag{37}
$$

This is a simple in-phase addition of each of the basis functions, which happens to be real if the basis functions are real. The plot is shown in Fig. 12(a). Notice that there are no nodes in this lowest energy wave function, and in this regard, it is "s-like."

The molecular wave function corresponding to the highest energy state has $k = \pi/a$ (or $-\pi/a$):

$$
\psi_{\pi/a}(x) = \frac{1}{\sqrt{N}} \sum_{n=1}^{N} e^{in\pi}\varphi_n(x) = \frac{1}{\sqrt{N}}\left[\varphi_1(x) - \varphi_2(x) + \varphi_3(x) - \varphi_4(x) + ...\right].
\tag{38}
$$

This antiphase addition of the basis functions, shown in Fig. 12(c), also has only a real component. Notice that the envelope (dashed line) of the molecular wave function has a wavelength equal to $2\pi/k = 2a$, or twice the interatomic spacing. This is the smallest possible wavelength that could have physical meaning. In contrast, the "wavelength" of the $k = 0$ state in Fig. 12(a) is infinite.

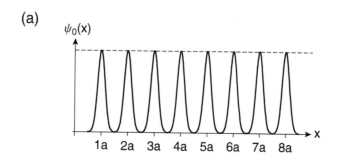

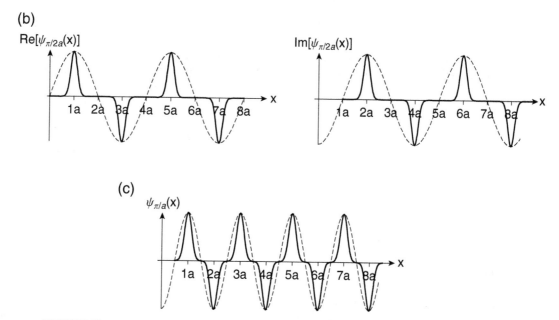

FIGURE 12 Wave functions of a system of periodic wells corresponding to the states (a) $k = 0$, (b) $k = \pi/2a$, and (c) $k = \pi/a$. The envelopes of the wave functions have wavelength $\lambda = 2\pi/k$.

For every other value of k, the system wave function is complex, with both a real and an imaginary part. One more example will suffice, and further examples for different values of k within the first Brillouin zone are in the homework problems. For $k = \pi/2a$, the molecular wave function is

$$\psi_{\pi/2a}(x) = \frac{1}{\sqrt{N}} \sum_{n=1}^{N} e^{in\pi/2} \varphi_n(x)$$

$$= \frac{1}{\sqrt{N}}\left[\varphi_1(x) + i\varphi_2(x) - \varphi_3(x) - i\varphi_4(x) + \varphi_5(x) + i\varphi_6(x)...\right] \qquad (39)$$

$$= \frac{1}{\sqrt{N}}\left[\varphi_1(x) - \varphi_3(x) + \varphi_5(x)...\right] + \frac{i}{\sqrt{N}}\left[\varphi_2(x) - \varphi_4(x) + \varphi_6(x)...\right].$$

Notice that the patterns of the real and imaginary parts are the same, and both have a wavelength corresponding to $2\pi/k = 4a$ as evident in Fig. 12(b). As a further homework problem, explore the wave functions obtained when you choose two values of k that differ by $2\pi/a$ (i.e., values of k in two different Brillouin zones).

Because k determines the wavelength of the envelope of the molecular wave function, we often call it the **wave vector** of the state. In one dimension, k is a "vector with one component," so it's not obviously distinguishable from a scalar, but in two (three) dimensions, k has two (three) components. In higher dimensions, the molecular wave function is

$$|\psi\rangle_{\mathbf{k}} = \frac{1}{\sqrt{N}} \sum_{\mathbf{R}} e^{i\mathbf{k}\cdot\mathbf{R}} |\mathbf{R}\rangle, \tag{40}$$

and $\mathbf{R}$ is the vector that locates the atom or well in real space, and also labels the atomic state associated with the atom. In one dimension, the equivalent label is na.

We have now solved the problem we set out to solve, namely finding the energies and wave functions of the allowed states of the periodic potential. The eigenfunctions of the periodic system can be written as linear combinations of the eigenfunctions of the individual wells making up the periodic chain. The different linear combinations are labeled by an index k that describes the modulation of the envelope of the wave function in terms of a wavelength $\lambda = 2\pi/k$. k is restricted to discrete values, but these values can be so closely spaced for large N that k can be considered a continuous variable. Unique molecular wave functions result from those k values that lie within the first Brillouin zone. The energy of the eigenstate labeled k is given by the dispersion relation in Eq. (21) or (24). The energies are bounded, and are so closely spaced as to form a band. If there are multiple states in a single well, there are multiple energy bands in the periodic well, and the bands may be separated by a relatively large energy gap, depending on the strength of the coupling between the states of adjacent wells. The molecular eigenstates in a band are often primarily derived from one of the atomic eigenstates.

7 ■ THE DENSITY OF STATES

Some properties of a solid do not depend on the value of the wave vector k of a particular state but rather on the number of states in a particular energy range, a quantity that we refer to as the **density of states**. The density of states $g(E)$ is easily visualized in the case where the allowed states are discrete, as shown in Fig. 13(a). Here, the dispersion relation $E(k)$ (see Fig. 9) is rotated 90° to make E the horizontal axis. To find the density of states from the dispersion plot, slice the energy axis into equal intervals, count the number of states (dots) in each energy interval, and plot the result as a histogram, as shown in Fig. 13(b). The solid line in Fig. 13(b) shows the functional form of the density of states in the limit that k becomes a continuous variable.

In one dimension, the number of states per unit energy is calculated rather easily from the density of states in k space, which we can call $g_k(k)$. If there are N wells in the periodic potential, and one state per well, then there are N molecular states, whose corresponding k values are evenly spaced between $-\pi/a$ and π/a [Eq. (20)]. The state density in k space is

$$g_k(k) = \frac{N}{2\pi/a} = \frac{L}{2\pi}, \tag{41}$$

where $L = Na$ is the length (one-dimensional volume) of the chain of wells. It makes no difference whether we count states according to their energy label or their k label, so it must be true that

$$g(E)dE = 2g_k(k)dk. \tag{42}$$

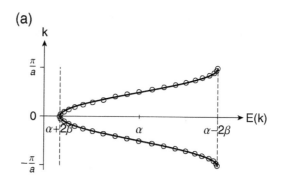

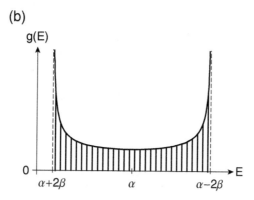

FIGURE 13 (a) The dispersion relation $E(k)$ rotated 90° to make E the horizontal axis. The dots represent the allowed states for small N; the solid line represents the continuous case. (b) The density of states $g(E)$ as a function of energy. The histogram corresponds to the small N case; the solid line represents the continuous case.

The factor of 2 accounts for the fact that for every state in an interval dk there is another state of the same energy at the opposite value of k. It follows that the density of states (in one dimension) is

$$g(E) = 2g_k(k)\frac{dk}{dE} = \frac{L}{\pi}\frac{dk}{dE}.$$ (43)

In the example considered here, the dispersion relation gives

$$\frac{dE}{dk} = 2\beta a \sin(ka),$$ (44)

resulting in

$$g(E) = \frac{L}{2\pi\beta a \sin(ka)},$$ (45)

which is plotted in Fig. 13(b). The density of states is proportional to the one-dimensional volume L, and it is often preferable to work with the volume-independent quantity $g(E)/L$. Strictly, because $g(E)$ is a function of E rather than k, we should express k in Eq. (45) in terms of E via Eq. (17), but the expression becomes cumbersome and is not particularly enlightening.

Notice that the density of states diverges at the Brillouin zone boundary. This is a quirk of the one-dimensional geometry, but it does not cause any unphysical results. For example, if we calculate the total energy of all the states, we arrive at a finite result (Problem 6):

$$E_{TOT} = \int_{E_{min}}^{E_{max}} E g(E) \, dE = N\alpha. \tag{46}$$

In Fig. 2, the real density of states for Si is plotted alongside the band structure. There are no infinities, but there are some sharply peaked features that correspond to local band minima or maxima.

8 ■ CALCULATION OF THE MODEL PARAMETERS

The parameters α and β were introduced in Eq. (5) as the matrix elements of the Hamiltonian in a periodic potential and they later appeared in the dispersion relation $E(k)$ as the band center (α) and the band width (4β). However, at that time, we did not calculate their values in terms of the atomic well parameters—the width, height, and separation. In this section, we do this calculation for the case where the individual wells are square wells.

To evaluate α and β, we must find matrix elements of the Hamiltonian H of the *full* periodic system in the basis of the eigenstates of the Hamiltonian H_0 of an *isolated* well. Both H and H_0 contain the same kinetic energy operator

$$T = \frac{p^2}{2m}, \tag{47}$$

but the potential energy term in H represents the full periodic potential [Fig. 14(a)], while the potential energy in H_0 represents a single well [Fig. 14(b)]. The parameter α is the diagonal element of the Hamiltonian matrix

$$\alpha = \langle n|H|n \rangle. \tag{48}$$

We rewrite this as

$$\alpha = \langle n|H_0 + V'|n \rangle, \tag{49}$$

where V' is the difference [Fig. 14(c)] between the full periodic potential and the potential energy of a single well. That is, V' is the periodic potential with one well missing—the one corresponding to H_0.

Let's suppose there is a single eigenstate in the isolated well with energy E_g. Then

$$H_0|n \rangle = E_g|n \rangle \tag{50}$$

and

$$\alpha = \langle n|H_0|n \rangle + \langle n|V'|n \rangle = E_g + \langle n|V'|n \rangle. \tag{51}$$

This calculation shows that α is equal to the energy of the isolated well eigenstate *plus* a term that is the matrix element of V' in the basis of the atomic states:

$$\langle n|V'|n \rangle = \int_{-\infty}^{\infty} \varphi_n^*(x) V'(x) \varphi_n(x) \, dx. \tag{52}$$

This matrix element is very small because it is the integral of a potential energy that is zero (i.e., *missing a well*) exactly where the wave function $\varphi_n(x)$ is nonzero! Where $V'(x)$ is nonzero, the wave function is very small. Figure 15 shows in graphical form what Eq. (52) says in symbolic form. For example, for an electron bound in a well that is $V_0 = 1$ eV deep and $b = 0.35$ nm wide, the single bound energy is 0.6 eV and the difference between α and E_g is -3.6 meV for a well spacing of $a = 3b$.

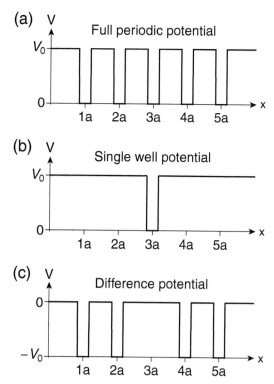

FIGURE 14   (a) The full periodic potential energy; (b) the atomic potential energy of an
isolated well located at the position of atom 2; (c) V', the potential energy difference between
(a) and (b).

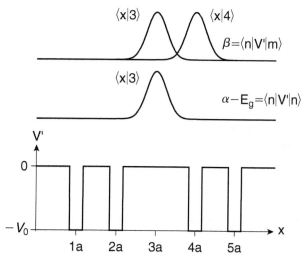

FIGURE 15   Schematic representation of the terms in Eqs. (52) and (53). The wave function
widths are exaggerated to show the overlap.

The evaluation of β is similar, except that n and m correspond to adjacent wells:

$$\beta = \langle n|H|m\rangle = \langle n|H_0 + V'|n \pm 1\rangle. \tag{53}$$

We assume that the atomic states on adjacent atoms are nearly orthogonal because the wave function overlap is small, so the matrix element $\langle n|H_0|n \pm 1\rangle$ is neglected and we find

$$\begin{aligned}\beta &= \langle n|V'|n \pm 1\rangle \\ &= \int_{-\infty}^{\infty} \varphi_n^*(x)V'(x)\varphi_{n\pm 1}(x)dx.\end{aligned} \tag{54}$$

This matrix element of $V'(x)$ is much larger than the one in Eq. (52) because where $V'(x)$ is nonzero, one of the atomic wave functions is large, and only one is very small. For the same parameters given above, β is -32 meV. This square-well example is the simplest integral to calculate analytically and you should do this for practice. Find the form of $\varphi_n(x)$, and perform the calculation. A simple Mathematica or Maple program will allow you to generalize to more bands by using deeper wells with more states.

8.1 ■LCAO Summary

- The LCAO approach to finding the molecular wave functions $\psi_k(x)$ and corresponding energies of a one-dimensional periodic potential of period a is to begin with the (atomic) wave functions $\varphi_n(x)$ of a single element of the potential. If there is one atomic state per well, there are N atomic states in the basis and there are N molecular wave functions, each a different superposition of the N atomic states:

$$\psi_k(x) = \frac{1}{\sqrt{N}}\sum_{n=1}^{N} e^{inka}\varphi_n(x),$$

where k labels the molecular state.

- There are N values of k ranging from $-\pi/a$ to π/a in steps of $2\pi/Na$, where N is the number of atoms/elements. This set of k values forms the first Brillouin zone.

- k has dimensions of inverse length and is called the wave vector. The associated wavelength, $\lambda = 2\pi/k$, is the wavelength of the envelope of the molecular wave function.

- The periodicity of the potential introduces translational symmetry into the problem. The result is that the molecular wave function obeys Bloch's theorem $\psi_k(x + ma) = e^{imka}\psi(x)$, which guarantees that the electron probability distribution is periodic, but does not require that the wave function itself is periodic.

- The dispersion relation gives the energy of a molecular state k. In the nearest-neighbor approximation, and when there is only one state per well,

$$E_{k_q} = \alpha + 2\beta\cos(k_q a).$$

These energies are effectively continuous if N is large.

- The parameters α and β, matrix elements of the Hamiltonian, are

$$\alpha = \langle n|H|n\rangle$$
$$\beta = \langle n|H|n \pm 1\rangle.$$

- α is the band center and is approximately equal to the atomic state energy. β measures the strength of the interaction between adjacent wells and 4β is the width of the band. Negative β puts the energy minimum at $k = 0$ and the maxima at the Brillouin zone boundaries, and vice versa for positive β.

9 ■ THE KRONIG-PENNEY MODEL

The final piece of the picture is to connect the LCAO approximation to the analytical, exact solution, which is possible for the simple case of a periodic chain of square wells. This example usually goes under the name of the **Kronig-Penney model**.

The LCAO approximation lets us see the progression from the atomic wave functions and the energy spectrum of isolated atoms to the band structure of a solid as the number of atoms becomes larger and the interaction between the atoms becomes stronger. The Kronig-Penney model, on the other hand, simply solves the eigenvalue equation for the exact periodic potential. It is a more "correct" approach, but lacks the intuitive connections to the atomic system. Moreover, in a real solid, the exact periodic potential is unknown, but the electronic energy levels and wave functions of atoms are not too difficult to calculate, so the LCAO model can be a good starting point. Figure 16 presents the LCAO dispersion relation, Eq. (24), and the exact dispersion relation that we are about to find [Eq. (61)], on the same plot. We see that the LCAO is a good approximation for the energies in the periodic system, especially when the coupling between states in adjacent wells is not too large.

Several excellent texts treat the Kronig-Penney example in great detail, and it is a good example to practice solving the energy eigenvalue equation. Here, we'll present a very broad overview, and concentrate on the energy spectrum rather than the eigenstates. The periodic potential V is sketched in Fig. 17 and all the relevant lengths and energies are defined. The width of the well is b, the well spacing is a, and the well depth is V_0. The bottom of the well is located at the zero of energy.

The eigenvalue equation is best solved in wave function notation (position representation), just as it is for the single finite well. The energy eigenvalue equation is the differential equation

$$H\psi(x) = E\psi(x)$$
$$-\frac{\hbar^2}{2m}\frac{d^2}{dx^2}\psi(x) + V(x)\psi(x) = E\psi(x). \tag{55}$$

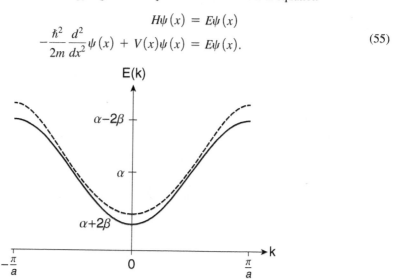

FIGURE 16   The dispersion relations for an N-well periodic system as calculated by the LCAO model (solid) and by the Kronig-Penney model (dashed).

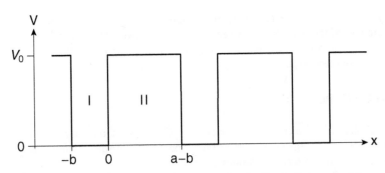

FIGURE 17 Periodic potential parameters for the Kronig-Penney model.

E is the eigenvalue corresponding to the eigenfunction $\psi(x)$. The solution that follows is valid for all values of $E > 0$, but in the end, we'll be interested in the bound states, $E < V_0$.

We need look only at a single element of the periodic potential, namely that for which $-b < x < a-b$, because Bloch's theorem, Eq. (31), assures us that once we have found the solution $\psi_k(x)$ in one element, then we can find the solution $\psi_k(x + ma)$ for any other element. The solutions to the energy eigenvalue equation in regions I and II are:

$$\psi_I(x) = Ae^{iqx} + Be^{-iqx}; \quad q = \frac{\sqrt{2mE}}{\hbar}$$

$$\psi_{II}(x) = Ce^{i\kappa x} + De^{-i\kappa x}; \quad \kappa = \frac{\sqrt{2m(E - V_0)}}{\hbar}, \tag{56}$$

where A, B, C, and D are constants.

The wave function and its derivative must be continuous, and in particular at $x = 0$, the boundary between regions I and II:

$$\psi_I(0) = \psi_{II}(0) \Rightarrow A + B = C + D$$

$$\psi_I'(0) = \psi_{II}'(0) \Rightarrow q[A - B] = \kappa[C - D]. \tag{57}$$

The wave function and its derivative at the edges of the well (one lattice spacing apart) are connected by Bloch's theorem:

$$e^{ika}\psi_I(-b) = \psi_{II}(-b + a) \Rightarrow Ae^{-iqb} + Be^{iqb} = e^{-ika}\left[Ce^{-i\kappa(a-b)} + De^{i\kappa(a-b)}\right]$$

$$e^{ika}\psi_I'(-b) = \psi_{II}'(-b + a) \Rightarrow q\left[Ae^{-iqb} - Be^{iqb}\right] = \kappa e^{-ika}\left[Ce^{-i\kappa(a-b)} - De^{i\kappa(a-b)}\right]. \tag{58}$$

Equations (57) and (58) are written succinctly in matrix form:

$$\begin{pmatrix} 1 & 1 & -1 & -1 \\ e^{-iqb} & e^{iqb} & -e^{-ika}e^{-i\kappa(a-b)} & -e^{-ika}e^{i\kappa(a-b)} \\ q & -q & -\kappa & \kappa \\ qe^{-iqb} & -qe^{iqb} & -\kappa e^{-ika}e^{-i\kappa(a-b)} & \kappa e^{-ika}e^{i\kappa(a-b)} \end{pmatrix} \begin{pmatrix} A \\ B \\ C \\ D \end{pmatrix} = 0. \tag{59}$$

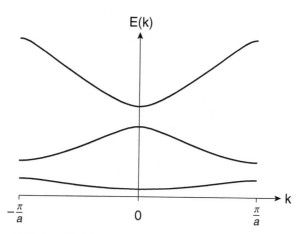

FIGURE 18   Energy spectrum for the Kronig-Penney model of a periodic system.

There are nontrivial solutions to the set of Eqs. (59) only if the determinant of the 4×4 matrix is zero. It is an uncomplicated but rather long process to show that the solution to the secular equation is

$$\cos(qb)\cos(\kappa(a-b)) - \frac{q^2 + \kappa^2}{2q\kappa}\sin(qb)\sin(\kappa(a-b)) = \cos(ka). \qquad (60)$$

Equation (60) is valid for any E, but if $E < V_0$, then κ is imaginary, and it is common to recast it explicitly in terms of real quantities:

$$\cos(qb)\cosh(|\kappa|(a-b)) - \frac{q^2 - \kappa^2}{2q\kappa}\sin(qb)\sinh(|\kappa|(a-b)) = \cos(ka). \qquad (61)$$

The quantities q and κ contain the energy E, so if we pick a value for k, we can invert Eq. (61) to find $E(k)$. This task is best assigned to a computer! Figure 18 shows a graph of the allowed energies for one particular choice of well parameters, and you can see the gaps in the energy spectrum, just as we found previously, when we employed the LCAO approach. In Fig. 16, the lowest band is plotted together with the LCAO-derived band, to show the good agreement when the bands are not too broad.

   This example illustrates that it is possible to solve the eigenvalue equation for the one-dimensional periodic chain of potential energy wells without resorting to approximate methods like LCAO. In more complicated cases in many dimensions with many electrons, exact methods are impossible for practical purposes and approximate methods are needed. This example gives a means to assess the degree of success of the approximation method in a simple case. The main features are similar in both methods, but the exact shapes of the dispersion relations differ in their details.

10 ■ PRACTICAL APPLICATIONS: METALS, INSULATORS, AND SEMICONDUCTORS

The purpose of much of the work in this chapter was to produce a rudimentary model of a solid or molecule. Remember though, that the problem that we have solved is for a single electron in a periodic potential, while real molecules and solids have very large numbers of electrons! For example, take the case of just two wells—this might be a model of a diatomic molecule, say H_2. However, we have really modeled H_2^+, the hydrogen molecule ion, and neglected the effect that the other electron would have had on the energy spectrum. Without resorting to much detail, a reasonable approximation is to assume that the states of the two-electron system would be about the same as the simple one-electron system, and that the ground state of the two-electron system would have both electrons occupying the ground state of the one-electron system, but with opposite spin, so as not to violate the Pauli exclusion principle. If there are many electrons, we would say that the ground state of the system is the configuration where electrons occupy the lowest-possible-energy one-electron states, subject to the Pauli exclusion principle, [i.e., two electrons with opposite spin per state]. This simple assumption leads to a qualitative explanation of the occurrence of metals and insulators. It must be abandoned, though, to explain many interesting and important phenomena, like magnetism and superconductivity, where the effects of electron correlation are too important to be neglected.

Figure 19 schematically depicts two bands in a one-dimensional 20-atom "solid". Circles represent allowed states and the circles are filled if electrons occupy the state. Take sodium as an example, where, in Fig. 19(a), the lower band might represent the $3s$ band, while the upper might represent the $3p$ band. Because there are 20 $3s$ valence electrons and each state accommodates 2 electrons, only the lowest 10 states in the $3s$ band are filled, and the band is half-full. (Don't worry about the slight difference in filling that results for the cases of even and odd numbers of wells—it's not important in a large solid.) A half-filled band is the hallmark of a **metal**, as we discuss below. Figure 19(b) might represent a "solid" of 20 He atoms, where we would need to accommodate 40 electrons in the $1s$ band, and all states in the lower band are filled. A filled band is characteristic of an **insulator**. The simple model correctly predicts that solid Na (along with any alkali metal) is metallic and solid He (or any solidified noble gas) is an insulator. This might seem like a trivial conclusion that we could have reached much more simply just by considering the valence shell of the individual atom, but real systems are far more complex.

An example of the complexity is given by solid hydrogen, which you might expect to be metallic similar to the (effectively) one-electron solids Na, K, etc. Normal solid hydrogen is insulating, because there is a structural distortion of the lattice that causes the $1s$ band to split in the middle, and the H electrons completely fill the lower band. Another important case where our model is too simplistic is that of the group IV elements, typified by silicon and represented in Fig. 19(c). A simple "valence shell" argument would predict that solid Si consists of filled $1s$, $2s$, $2p$ and $3s$ bands, and a one-third filled $3p$ band, and hence is metallic. Wrong! If you worked out the α and β parameters for the Si $3s$ and $3p$ states (in three dimensions of course), and included all these states in the calculation,

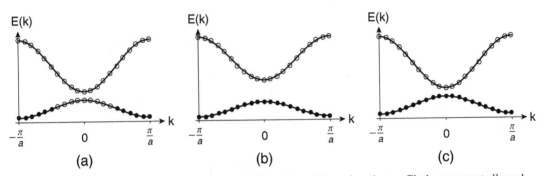

FIGURE 19 Schematic band diagrams: (a) metal, (b) insulator, (c) semiconductor. Circles represent allowed states; they are filled if the state is occupied by an electron.

you would discover that, in fact, the $3s$ and $3p$ atomic states of all the atoms combine to form two distinct hybrid bands separated by a small energy gap of about 1 eV. The lower band is completely occupied by the Si electrons (we call it the **valence band**). The upper band is empty (we call it the **conduction band**). In Fig. 2, the highest energy of the valence band is (arbitrarily) labeled zero. So Si is an insulator at very low temperatures where electrons fill the states strictly in energy order. At room temperature, the thermal energy of about 0.025 eV is sufficient to deplete the valence band of a small number of electrons and populate the conduction band. In that case, Si has two partially filled bands, so it is "metallic" (i.e., conducting), but very weakly so, because there are so few current carriers compared to a metal. Si is therefore a **semiconductor**.

Why is it that a partially filled band is considered the signature of a metal and a filled band that of an insulator? To answer, we have to think about how to represent the motion of an electron in a solid under the influence of an electric field. The eigenstates of energy $E(k)$ that we have derived have the property that an electron in such a state has an equal probability of being found on any atom in the crystal (see Fig. 12). For consideration of the effects of electric fields on electrons, it is useful to take a more "particle-like" point of view and represent the electron by a wave packet or superposition of eigenstates that concentrates the probability of finding the electron in a more restricted region of space. The Heisenberg uncertainty principle is important here: in "localizing" the electron in a wave packet of extent Δx, we are conceding an uncertainty in the momentum $\Delta p = h/\Delta x$. This uncertainty is expressed by the range of k values of the Bloch states used to construct the wave packet.

The motion of an electron's wave packet is characterized by a *group velocity*. This is the velocity of the group of superimposed waves (i.e., the velocity of the envelope of a pattern of interfering waves). The crests and troughs of individual waves travel at the *phase velocity*, which is not necessarily the same as the group velocity. For waves with a dispersion relation $\omega(k)$, the phase velocity is ω/k while the group velocity is $d\omega/dk$. These are the same only if the dispersion relation is linear in k, as is the case, for example, for long-wavelength sound waves in a solid.

For an electron in a Bloch state $|\psi_k\rangle$, the electron velocity is the expectation value of p/m (momentum/mass), that is,

$$v_e = \frac{1}{m}\langle \psi_k|p|\psi_k\rangle = \frac{1}{m}\int_{-\infty}^{\infty}\psi_k^*(x)\left(-i\hbar\frac{d}{dx}\right)\psi_k(x)dx \qquad (62)$$

in one dimension. If the electron energy dispersion relation is $E(k)$, then the electron's (group) velocity is (because $E = \hbar\omega$)

$$v_g = \frac{1}{\hbar}\frac{dE(k)}{dk}. \qquad (63)$$

We will not carry this out, but it is possible to show that v_e and v_g are the same if $|\psi_k\rangle$ are Bloch states.

Now consider what happens when an electric field $\mathbf{E} = \mathcal{E}\hat{\mathbf{x}}$ is applied to the solid, for example, by attaching electrical leads to opposite ends of the crystal and connecting them to a battery. The electrons experience a force $\mathbf{F} = q\mathbf{E} = -e\mathcal{E}\hat{\mathbf{x}}$. During a short time interval δt in which the force acts, an electron moves a distance $v_g\delta t$ and the work done by the force is

$$\begin{aligned}\delta w &= F\delta x \\ &= -e\mathcal{E}v_g\delta t \\ &= -\left(\frac{e\mathcal{E}}{\hbar}\right)\left(\frac{dE(k)}{dk}\right)\delta t.\end{aligned} \qquad (64)$$

At the same time, that electron's energy changes by an amount

$$\delta E = \frac{dE}{dk}\delta k. \tag{65}$$

Setting $\delta w = \delta E$, we find

$$\delta k = -\frac{e\mathcal{E}}{\hbar}\delta t. \tag{66}$$

Integrating to get $k(t)$, we have

$$k(t) = k(0) - \frac{e\mathcal{E}}{\hbar}t. \tag{67}$$

The message here is that application of the electric field tends to shift the k values, and hence the energies $E(k)$ of all the electrons in the material. But can this actually happen? It depends on the occupation of the states in the band. If the band is full, any change of state of an electron must result in another electron moving into the vacated state, leaving the electron energy and momentum distribution unaltered. Under these conditions, no current can flow and the material is an electrical insulator. If the band is partially filled, plenty of unoccupied states exist within a small energy range (i.e., within the same band) for these electrons to move into to change their k vectors and energies. The net electron energy and momentum distribution changes and a current flows under the influence of the electric field. This is the signature of electrical conductivity. In the case of a semiconductor, the number of thermally excited electrons in the upper band or holes in the lower band (see Section 11) is very small compared to the number in the metal, and the conductivity is weak.

11 ■ EFFECTIVE MASS

The dispersion relation for a nonrelativistic free particle, one that moves in a region of constant potential, is given by

$$E(k) = \frac{\hbar^2}{2m}k^2. \tag{68}$$

The free electron dispersion relation simply states mathematically that the energy of a free particle comes entirely from its momentum and that there is no potential energy contribution (except perhaps for a constant). This parabolic or quadratic relation between energy and wave vector is characterized by the mass of the particle. Particles with large mass (like protons) are characterized by a parabola with smaller curvature than particles with small mass (like electrons). Now, take another look at the dispersion for the one-dimensional chain of atoms, that is, $E(k) = \alpha + 2\beta\cos(ka)$, which is plotted in Fig. 20 for two different values of β. Notice that near $k = 0$, the band function looks parabolic. Indeed, expand the dispersion relation $E(k)$ for small k to find

$$\begin{aligned} E(k) &= \alpha + 2\beta\cos(ka) \\ &\cong \alpha + 2\beta\left[1 - \tfrac{1}{2}(ka)^2\right] \\ &\cong \alpha + 2\beta - \beta a^2 k^2. \end{aligned} \tag{69}$$

If $\beta < 0$, we see that near the bottom of the band, the energy is parabolic in k and varies according to

$$E - E_{min} = |\beta|a^2k^2. \tag{70}$$

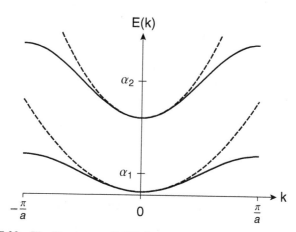

FIGURE 20 The N-square-well $E(k)$ for two values of $\beta < 0$ represented by solid lines, and the parabolic free-particle $E(k)$ represented by dashed lines. At $k = 0$, the effective mass is smaller for the more disperse (wider) upper band.

If we compare Eq. (70) to the free particle dispersion relation, Eq. (68), we see that the electrons in states near the bottom of the band behave like free particles except that $\hbar^2/2m$ has been replaced by $|\beta|a^2$. In other words, the electron behaves as if it had an **effective mass**

$$m^* = \frac{\hbar^2}{2|\beta|a^2}. \tag{71}$$

The denominator of this expression is just the curvature of the band function for small k and the effective mass can be defined more generally for states *anywhere* in the band according to

$$m^* = \hbar^2 \left[\frac{d^2E}{dk^2} \right]^{-1}. \tag{72}$$

By this means, all the effects of the electron's complicated interactions with the crystal lattice have been swept into one parameter, the effective mass. Figure 20 has the free particle dispersion relation with the same curvature at $k = 0$ superimposed on the exact dispersion relation. We see that the upper band has the larger curvature, and hence the smaller effective mass at $k = 0$.

Note the inverse dependence of m^* on β or d^2E/dk^2. This means that the weaker the interactions between atoms (smaller beta), the "heavier" the electron is. Narrow bands (small β) are associated with high effective masses and wide bands (large β) correspond to relatively "light" electrons. This makes sense intuitively: if β is small, the weak interaction or small overlap between atomic wave functions makes it difficult for an electron to move from atom to atom under the influence of an applied electric field, and it behaves as if it has a large mass.

In general, the effective mass changes at different positions in the band, because for any band shape except parabolic, the second derivative of $E(k)$ changes. For states near the top of the band, the effective mass is negative! This means that the acceleration of a particle in an electric field, $a = F/m$, is in the opposite direction to the force. While a negative mass might seem strange, it is perfectly consistent. More detailed texts on semiconductors show that when a band is almost completely full, it is often easier to think in terms of a small number of empty negative-mass electron states that behave like particles with positive electric charges and positive masses, which we call **holes**. So in Fig. 19(c), application of an applied field would cause electrons in the conduction band to move against the field and holes in the valence band to move in the direction of the field. They both result in a current in the same direction, so we add the contributions from the two bands. The number of carriers in each band is the same because the electrons in the upper band originated in the lower band, leaving behind the same number of holes. But in the example of Fig. 20, the response of the holes in the lower band is more sluggish because of the larger effective mass. Therefore, the contribution of the electron current to the total current is larger than the hole current.

12 ■ DIRECT AND INDIRECT BAND GAPS

Semiconductors, particularly Si, are so important in modern technology that it is worthwhile to say a little more about them, although we will leave details to other texts dedicated to the topic. Semiconductors are characterized by an (almost) full valence band and an (almost) empty conduction band. The difference in energy between the *highest energy state in the valence band and the lowest energy state in the conduction band* is called "the **band gap**." The band gap is labeled in Fig. 21. The band gap of Si is 1.11 eV, and that of GaAs, another important semiconductor, is 1.43 eV. Of course, there are always "gaps" between the energies in different bands associated with a particular allowed value of k, but this is not what is meant by "the" band gap.

Another important characteristic of the band gap is whether it is a **direct band gap** or an **indirect band gap**, as illustrated in Fig. 21. The band gap is termed *direct* when the highest energy state in the valence band and the lowest energy state in the conduction band occur at the *same* value of k, and *indirect* when they occur at *different* values of k. The distinction is significant because direct-gap semiconductors absorb and emit light with much higher probability than indirect-gap semiconductors, and this is critical for materials selection in optoelectronic devices like light-emitting diodes (LEDs), light sensors (LEDs operating in reverse), and solar cells.

The reason that direct-gap semiconductors interact more strongly with light is not hard to understand. You probably know how to calculate the probability that an electron makes a transition from one quantum state to another, and that this involves both energy and momentum conservation. The band gaps in semiconductors are of order 1–3 eV, a range that spans the

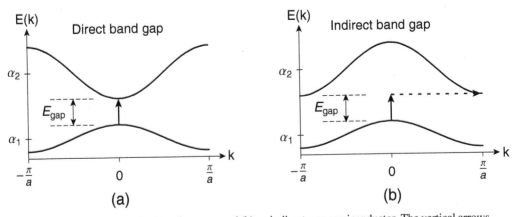

FIGURE 21   Transitions in (a) a direct-gap and (b) an indirect-gap semiconductor. The vertical arrows represent photons and the horizontal arrow in (b) represents a phonon.

energies of visible photons. Such photons then, have sufficient energy to cause electron transitions between bands. In solids, we must also consider the conservation of crystal momentum, represented by $\hbar k$:

$$\hbar k_{e,init} + \hbar k_{photon} = \hbar k_{e,fin}. \tag{73}$$

In a direct transition, the electron's initial and final states have the same value of k. How is this possible if the photon that induces the transition also has momentum? The momentum of an infrared, visible or even ultraviolet photon is extremely small compared with typical electron momenta, so the photon momentum does not change the electron momentum by any significant fraction of the Brillouin zone width. Therefore, the transition is extremely close to being direct (a homework problem quantifies this). It means that only a photon and an electron are necessary for a direct transition to take place. On the other hand, if the transition is indirect, the electron's momentum changes by a significant fraction of the Brillouin zone width, and the photon cannot supply the needed momentum. The necessary momentum comes from another lattice denizen, the **phonon**, or lattice vibration. In other words, the lattice changes its mode of vibration to accommodate the electron transition. In probabilistic terms, it means that three entities must be present at the same place and time (the electron, the photon and the phonon), and this is a far less likely occurrence than a coincidence of just two particles, an electron and a photon. The upshot is that direct transitions are far more likely than indirect transitions.

Now the phonon supplies the necessary momentum for an indirect transition, but it also brings along some energy. However, the phonon energies are rather small compared to the gap energy, so one phonon alone is not sufficient to allow an electron to make an interband transition. As a first approximation, it is the photon that provides the energy and the phonon that provides the momentum for an electron transition across an indirect band gap.

Si is an example of an indirect-gap semiconductor. You can see in Fig. 2 that the valence band maximum occurs at the k-point labeled Γ, while the conduction band minimum occurs at the k point on the line between Γ and X. A phonon and a photon are necessary to facilitate this transition, making it less probable than if the gap were direct. It might seem strange then that Si is the most widely used semiconductor in solar cells! As it happens, Si is the best material we have, despite the indirect-gap problem. Although Si is not as efficient at absorbing photons close to the band gap energy as a direct-gap semiconductor with the same band gap, there is sufficient absorption of photons if the Si is thick enough. Its band gap is the perfect size to capture the photon distribution that comprises the solar spectrum—it is abundant, it is environmentally benign, and we have huge investments in Si-processing technology. All this makes Si the best material currently available for large-scale, economic production of photovoltaic cells. Intense efforts are underway to find other materials that will do the same job more efficiently and more economically. There are some competitors, but Si is still the most widely used photovoltaic material. GaAs is a direct-gap semiconductor. Photovoltaic cells made with GaAs are more efficient than those made with Si and are used for some high-end applications, such as powering equipment in space. They are technologically more difficult to produce than Si, and there are serious concerns about the abundance of Ga and As and the toxicity of the latter.

13 ■ NEW DIRECTIONS—LOW-DIMENSIONAL CARBON

One of the most exciting "new materials" under active research at the present time is an old material—carbon! Carbon, as diamond, has the same structure as silicon, but its wide band gap makes it insulating rather than semiconducting. Carbon, as graphite, has long been used as a lubricant, a reasonable conductor and a handy pencil. Graphite consists of weakly bonded layers of **graphene**, and graphene is a one-atom-thick sheet of C atoms strongly bonded to one another in a honeycomb pattern. It is carbon in this two-dimensional form, as isolated graphene sheets or **carbon nanotubes,** which are rolled-up graphene sheets, that is the topic of intense interest. The band structure of graphene is easy to calculate with the LCAO method, because the interesting part derives from just the C $2p_z$ states that are perpendicular to the graphene plane. The dispersion relation reveals that graphene is a gapless semiconductor—the top of the valence band and the bottom of the conduction band touch at several k points. Moreover, the dispersion relation features a *linear* dependence of $E(k)$ on k at these points. This linear dispersion relation is just like that of a photon (for which $E(k) = \hbar c k$), so graphene is a playground to study relativity! Carbon nanotubes are particularly interesting from the perspective of the material presented in this chapter: nanotubes can be semiconducting or metallic, depending on exactly how the graphene sheet is rolled up. Graphene "ribbons" can also be made semiconducting. The nanometer scale of these fascinating forms of carbon make them textbook examples of quantum phenomena, such as the fractional quantum Hall effect. On the applications front, graphene and carbon nanotubes show promise as high performance transistors, transparent conductors, super-strong fibers, biosensors in cells, cages to store atoms, or nano-pipettes to deliver cellular cargo.

SUMMARY

- The model of a solid as a periodic array of potential energy wells predicts the existence of bands of allowed energies for electrons. This model qualitatively explains solid metals as materials whose electrons partially fill the state of a band, and insulators and semiconductors as materials whose electrons completely fill the band states and have a relatively large band gap between the filled states and the next available empty states. Larger band gaps are characteristic of insulators and smaller band gaps are characteristic of semiconductors.

- Metals are good conductors because electron wave packets under the influence of an electric field may access nearby-energy states and change their momentum. Insulators are poor conductors, because nearby-energy states are occupied by other electrons and no net momentum change can occur. Semiconductors in this model are simply metals (partially filled bands) with very few charge carriers that are generated thermally.

- Electron motion in solids is modeled with the use of a wave packet, a superposition of delocalized Bloch states of different k that peaks at a specific location. This packet moves with a velocity given by the group velocity (velocity of the envelope of the packet), while individual states that comprise the packet move with a different velocity called the phase velocity.

- The interactions of an electron in a solid with the lattice cause its response to external forces to be different than the response of a free electron. This difference is parameterized by the effective mass, which describes the curvature of the $E(k)$ relation. It is especially useful near the maxima and minima of bands, where the dispersion relation is often parabolic, similar to the dispersion relation of a free electron.

- The density of states $g(E)$ is the number of states per unit energy interval. It is useful when it is necessary to quantify the total number of electrons involved in a process, such as optical absorption, or electron transport.

- The band gap in solids may be termed direct or indirect. A direct (indirect) gap occurs when the highest occupied state in an occupied band is at the same (different) k value as (than) the lowest energy state in an empty band. Electrons can absorb photons or emit photons to make a transition across the gap. Such transitions are more efficient in direct-gap semiconductors.

RESOURCES

Activities

Periodic Systems is a course based on this chapter taught at Oregon State University. The course treats both classical and quantum mechanical periodic systems. The website has a description and activities associated with this course:

www.physics.oregonstate.edu/portfolioswiki/courses:home:pphome

Band Structure: Explore wave functions and probability densities of chains of up to 10 square wells or Coulomb potential energy wells. The wells can be adjusted and an electric field can be applied:

http://phet.colorado.edu/en/simulation/band-structure

Quantum Crystal: Explore wave functions and the dispersion relation of several different shapes of potential energy wells:

http://www.falstad.com/qm1dcrystal/

Solid State Physics Simulations (ISBN 0-471-54885-5), by Graham Keeler, Roger Rollins, Steven Spicklemire, and Ian Johnston, is one of nine parts of the Consortium for Upper-Level Physics Software (CUPS) published by Wiley, edited by Maria Dworzecka, Robert Ehrlich, and William Mac-Donald. *Solid State Physics Simulations* has several useful programs that allow you to explore a one-dimensional chain of atoms, band structure, dispersion relations, and the LCAO method applied to small clusters. There is an accompanying text. The series is out of print, but used copies are listed at Amazon.com.

http://physics.gmu.edu/~cups/ss.html

Further Reading

The Kronig-Penney model is discussed in more detail in several well-known Quantum Mechanics texts:
  D. J. Griffiths, *Introduction to Quantum Mechanics,* 2nd ed., Upper Saddle River, NJ: Prentice Hall, 2005.
  R. L. Liboff, *Introductory Quantum Mechanics,* 4th ed., San Francisco: Addison Wesley, 2003.
  A. Goswami, *Quantum Mechanics,* 2nd ed., Dubuque, IA: William C. Brown, 1996.
More advanced references:
  C. Kittel, *Introduction to Solid State Physics,* 8th ed., New York: John Wiley & Sons, Inc., 2005. An introductory text that treats metals, semiconductors, and insulators, and many of the concepts mentioned in this chapter.
  R. F. Pierret, *Semiconductor Device Fundamentals*, Reading, MA: Addison Wesley, 1996. Discusses the details of carrier transport in semiconductors and modern devices.
  A. K. Geim and A. H. MacDonald, "Graphene: Exploring Carbon Flatland," *Phys. Today* **60**(8), 35–41 (2007), http://dx.doi.org/10.1063/1.2774096. Gives a nice introduction to graphene, and explains the linear dispersion relation and the fractional quantum Hall effect.
  C. Dekker, "Carbon Nanotubes as Molecular Quantum Wires," *Phys. Today* **52**(5), 22–28 (1999), http://dx.doi.org/10.1063/1.882658. Talks about measurements to distinguish the difference between semiconducting and metallic carbon nanotubes, and discusses some potential uses.

Periodic Systems: Problem Set

1 Write down the matrix representation of the Hamiltonian within the nearest-neighbor approximation in terms of α and β for a linear chain of three wells, assuming only one atomic state per well. Find the normalized eigenfunctions and eigenvalues. This problem is quite tractable analytically.

2 Write down the matrix representation of the Hamiltonian within the nearest-neighbor approximation in terms of α and β for a linear chain of N wells, assuming only one atomic state per well. Use a computer to find the normalized eigenfunctions and eigenvalues. Start with $N = 3$ to repeat the result from the previous problem, and then increase N. Aficionado-code-writers might like to make N much larger.

3 How would you alter the example presented in Problem 1 to find the molecular states and energies of a linear molecular like carbon dioxide, $O=C=O$, in the nearest neighbor approximation?

4 Derive the dispersion relation $E(k)$ for the Hamiltonian H_B in Fig. 10, which corresponds to the case where there are two states per well, and there is an interaction between the upper state of one well and the lower state of the adjacent well in addition to the interactions between states of the same energy. Assume an N-well chain as in Section 1.2.

5 a) Find the LCAO state that corresponds to $k = \pi/4a$, similar to Eq. (39),

$$
\begin{aligned}
\psi_{\pi/2a}(x) &= \frac{1}{\sqrt{N}} \sum_{n=1}^{N} e^{in\pi/2} \varphi_n(x) \\
&= \frac{1}{\sqrt{N}} \left[\varphi_1(x) + i\varphi_2(x) - \varphi_3(x) - i\varphi_4(x) + \varphi_5(x) + i\varphi_6(x)... \right] \quad (39) \\
&= \frac{1}{\sqrt{N}} \left[\varphi_1(x) - \varphi_3(x) + \varphi_5(x)... \right] + \frac{i}{\sqrt{N}} \left[\varphi_2(x) - \varphi_4(x) + \varphi_6(x)... \right].
\end{aligned}
$$

Sketch the real and imaginary parts of the wave function, and illustrate that the wavelength is $8a$. What is the energy of this state?

b) Pick another allowed value of k within the first Brillouin zone, and repeat.

c) Pick a value of k that differs by $2\pi/a$ from one you have already chosen, and repeat. Discuss your results.

6 Explain why the integral $\int_{E_{min}}^{E_{max}} E g(E) dE$ in Eq. (46),

$$
E_{TOT} = \int_{E_{min}}^{E_{max}} E g(E) dE = N\alpha, \quad (46)
$$

does indeed represent the total energy. Use the density of states expression in Eq. (45),

$$
g(E) = \frac{L}{2\pi\beta a \sin(ka)}, \quad (45)
$$

to show that the integral evaluates to $N\alpha$, despite the infinity in $g(E)$.

7 a) Find the density of states $g(E)$ for the case of the free particle in one dimension.

b) Show that the density of states $g(E)$ for the free particle dispersion relation in two dimensions is a constant (challenge problem).

From Chapter 15 of *Quantum Mechanics: A Paradigms Approach*, First Edition. David H. McIntyre. Copyright © 2012 by Pearson Education, Inc. Published by Pearson Addison-Wesley. All rights reserved.

The companion websites for this text are http://physics.oregonstate.edu/portfolioswiki and http://physics.oregonstate.edu/qmactivities.

8 Find the single bound state energy for an electron in an isolated well of depth $V_0 = 1$ eV and width $b = 0.35$ nm, as discussed in Section 8. Find the matrix elements α and β for a periodic system with well spacing $a = 3b$ and confirm the results given in the text.

9 a) Show that the Kronig-Penney dispersion relation, Eq. (60),

$$\cos(qb)\cos(\kappa(a-b)) - \frac{q^2 + \kappa^2}{2q\kappa}\sin(qb)\sin(\kappa(a-b)) = \cos(ka), \qquad (60)$$

results from Eq. (59),

$$\begin{pmatrix} 1 & 1 & -1 & -1 \\ e^{-iqb} & e^{iqb} & -e^{-ika}e^{-i\kappa(a-b)} & -e^{-ika}e^{i\kappa(a-b)} \\ q & -q & -\kappa & \kappa \\ qe^{-iqb} & -qe^{iqb} & -\kappa e^{-ika}e^{-i\kappa(a-b)} & \kappa e^{-ika}e^{i\kappa(a-b)} \end{pmatrix} \begin{pmatrix} A \\ B \\ C \\ D \end{pmatrix} = 0. \qquad (59)$$

This is a straightforward but long calculation, and it's easy to make mistakes. Be careful, and check each step.

b) Show that Eq. (61),

$$\cos(qb)\cosh(|\kappa|(a-b)) - \frac{q^2 - \kappa^2}{2q\kappa}\sin(qb)\sinh(|\kappa|(a-b)) = \cos(ka), \qquad (61)$$

results from Eq. (60) if κ is imaginary.

10 a) Explore the band structures of C, Si, and Ge, which are all tetrahedrally-bonded solids with the same crystal structure. What trends are evident and how can you explain them?

b) In a given solid, effective masses at the extrema of higher bands tend to be lower than effective masses at the extrema of lower bands. Is there a plausible physical interpretation of this?

11 Explain how a simplistic argument that energy bands in solids are entirely derived from the corresponding atomic states might lead to the false conclusion that Mg (or any alkali earth element) is in an electrical insulator. How do you rationalize the observed metallic behavior within the LCAO model?

12 a) What is the energy of a visible photon? What are the band gaps of important semiconductors? Are visible photon energies in the right range to facilitate electron transitions across the band gap of a typical semiconductor?

b) Show that the momentum of a visible photon is insufficient to facilitate electron indirect transitions across the band gap of a typical semiconductor.

c) Phonons are quantized lattice vibrations. Like photons, they are massless entities, with a characteristic wavelength that determines the momentum, and a characteristic frequency that determines the energy. If the characteristic wavelength of a phonon is roughly the lattice spacing in a solid, and the characteristic frequency is roughly 10^{13} Hz, show that the momentum of a phonon is in the right range to facilitate indirect electron transitions across the band gap of a typical semiconductor, but that the energy is too small.

Modern Applications
of Quantum Mechanics

From Chapter 16 of *Quantum Mechanics: A Paradigms Approach*, First Edition. David H. McIntyre. Copyright © 2012 by Pearson Education, Inc. Published by Pearson Addison-Wesley. All rights reserved.

The companion websites for this text are http://physics.oregonstate.edu/portfolioswiki and http://physics. oregonstate.edu/qmactivities.

Modern Applications
of Quantum Mechanics

Time for some fun! (Not that you weren't having fun before.) You have acquired a tool set for understanding how the microscopic world works. Let's spend this chapter using that tool set to examine two current research topics that are extensions of some of the examples of quantum mechanics that you have studied. Quantum mechanical forces on atoms and quantum information processing both have important connections to Stern-Gerlach spin-1/2 experiments and to resonant atom-light interactions. These new research fields can be considered to be quantum engineering in that we understand the quantum mechanics so well that we are now using it for practical applications. The research is expanding so rapidly that we cannot provide a complete overview in just one chapter. We will focus on a few aspects of these fields. The resources at the end of the chapter provide references for you to learn more.

1 ■ MANIPULATING ATOMS WITH QUANTUM MECHANICAL FORCES

In the last 30 years, physicists have developed a broad collection of quantum mechanical tools to exert forces on atoms. These forces allow us to manipulate the positions and velocities of atoms so well that we can stop atoms and hold them in place for an extended time. We can, therefore, measure them for longer and improve spectroscopic energy measurements that are limited by the energy-time uncertainty principle. For example, the standard of time is based upon a microwave transition between two hyperfine states in the cesium atom and the longer the atom can be observed, the better we can define the second—the basic unit of time. Along the way, researchers have uncovered a host of other fun things to do with mechanical forces, and they have even discovered a new form of matter—the Bose-Einstein condensate. In the following two subsections, we will discuss two examples of quantum mechanical forces.

1.1 ■ Magnetic Trapping

The first example of quantum mechanical forces on atoms is **magnetic trapping**, where we use magnetic fields to confine atoms to a small region of space. Magnetic traps are used to confine atoms at very low temperatures, and have played an important role in Bose-Einstein condensation experiments. To explain how a magnetic trap works, we turn to a Stern-Gerlach experiment. In fact, a magnetic moment experiences a force in a magnetic field gradient. That is a classical argument, but we discover the quantum mechanical underpinnings of the Stern-Gerlach experiment when we discuss the Zeeman effect. The Stern-Gerlach force derives from the potential energy of interaction between the magnetic moment of the atom and the magnetic field:

$$V = -\boldsymbol{\mu}\cdot\mathbf{B}. \tag{1}$$

The force on the atom is the negative gradient of this potential energy: $\mathbf{F} = -\nabla V$. The potential energy of the magnetic moment in the magnetic field is the Zeeman energy we found from perturbation theory, which has the general form

$$V_Z = E_Z^{(1)} = gm\mu_B B. \tag{2}$$

For this discussion, we won't worry about whether the magnetic moment is associated with a spin ($\mathbf{S}$), orbital ($\mathbf{L}$), or total angular momentum ($\mathbf{J}$ or $\mathbf{F}$), so we leave the subscripts off the Landé g-factor and the magnetic quantum number m.

In a typical Stern-Gerlach experiment, the deflection angle of the atom is small (Problem 1). But what if the Stern-Gerlach force were large enough to significantly deflect the atom, say by 90°, or even 180°, and the magnetic field were shaped so that the atom kept on being deflected? Then you could imagine constructing a system that contained the atom and didn't let it escape. That is the essence of a magnetic trap.

To discuss the mechanics of how a magnetic trap works, it is more instructive to use the energy approach rather than the force approach. To trap a particle in general, the potential energy must have a spatial minimum to form a confining well. For example, the generic potential energy well shown in Fig. 1 has a minimum at $x = 0$ and will confine or trap particles that have kinetic energies less than V_{max}. As the particles move, they exchange kinetic for potential energy. Such a potential energy well is no different in principle from the potential energy wells you have already studied—square well, harmonic oscillator, hydrogen atom. We call it a trap when we control the potential energy to confine particles that are otherwise free to move.

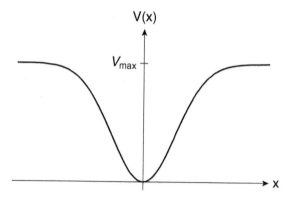

FIGURE 1 Generic potential energy for a particle trap in one dimension. Particles with kinetic energy less than V_{max} are trapped in the vicinity of the origin, where the potential energy is a minimum.

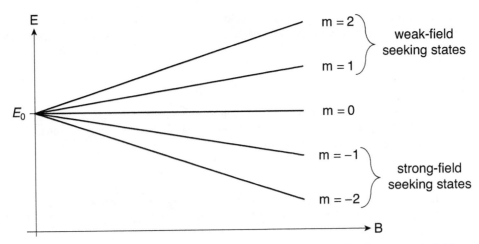

FIGURE 2 Zeeman energy levels. States with positive m are attracted to low magnetic field regions and states with negative m are attracted to high magnetic field regions.

For a magnetic trap, the potential energy that determines the particle motion is the Zeeman energy $V_Z(\mathbf{r}) = g m \mu_B B(\mathbf{r})$. A generic Zeeman energy level diagram is shown in Fig. 2. The force on the atom is the negative gradient of the Zeeman energy, so atomic states with *positive* magnetic quantum number m are attracted toward regions of *low* magnetic field and are called **weak-field seeking states**. Atom states with *negative* m are attracted toward regions of *high* magnetic field and are called **strong-field seeking states**. A local spatial maximum in the magnetic field is not allowed by Maxwell's equations in free space, so a magnetic trap must rely on a local minimum in the magnetic field along with a positive magnetic quantum number m. Hence, a magnetic trap confines atoms in weak-field seeking states and ejects atoms in strong-field seeking states. An atom in a weak-field seeking state has its angular momentum aligned with the field (positive m), so the magnetic moment is aligned against the field.

In a three-dimensional magnetic field, the magnetic field direction is not uniform, especially around the local minimum that forms the trap. The changing field direction would seem to be problematic because the potential energy $V_Z(\mathbf{r}) = g m \mu_B B(\mathbf{r})$ assumes a given quantization axis along which to measure the angular momentum component characterized by the magnetic quantum number m. However, if the magnetic field direction does not change too quickly, then the atom's Larmor precession about the field adiabatically follows the changing field direction and the atom remains in a weak-field seeking state that is forced toward the origin. This condition holds in most magnetic trapping situations (Problem 2). There are some important exceptions, but that is more detail than we need for our brief introduction.

The simplest magnetic field configuration that produces a magnetic trap is a pair of circular coils with opposing currents. This configuration of **anti-Helmholtz coils** is shown in Fig. 3 with its resultant quadrupole magnetic field (normal Helmholtz coils have parallel current directions and produce a nearly uniform field at the center). The magnitude of the magnetic field of anti-Helmholtz coils is zero of the center of the trap and has a spatial dependence

$$B(\mathbf{r}) = A\sqrt{x^2 + y^2 + 4z^2}. \tag{3}$$

This field magnitude increases linearly along any direction from the trap center, but the gradient has different values in different directions because of the factor of 4 in Eq. (3). The field magnitude

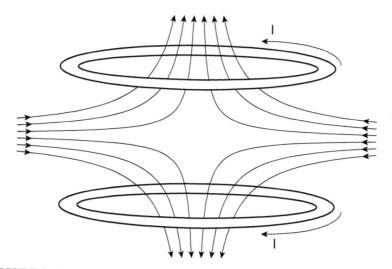

FIGURE 3 The opposing currents in a pair of anti-Helmholtz coils produce a quadrupole magnetic field that traps weak-field seeking states at the center of the coils.

along the *x*-axis is shown in Fig. 4. As noted above, the magnetic field direction shown in Fig. 3 is continuously changing.

For the magnetic trap to be useful, it should have enough potential energy depth to confine atoms with a range of kinetic energies, which is determined by the temperature of the ensemble of atoms. The thermal spread of energies is $E_{thermal} = k_B T$, where we ignore factors of order unity (like π, $1/2$, etc.). The Landé *g*-factor and the magnetic quantum number are of order unity, so the potential energy well depth of a magnetic trap is approximately

$$\Delta V_{trap} = \mu_B B_{max}. \tag{4}$$

A typical magnetic trap has a gradient of 100 Gauss/cm and a trapping region of order 1 cm, giving a maximum field of 100 Gauss (atom trappers use Gauss and cm as their standard units, so we follow

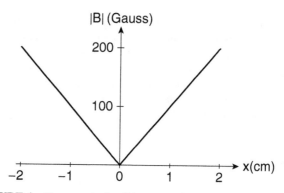

FIGURE 4 The magnitude of the magnetic field in a quadrupole magnetic trap increases linearly from the origin of the trap.

their lead; recall that 1 Gauss $= 10^{-4}$ Tesla). Equating the trap depth and the thermal energy, we estimate the temperature of atoms that can be trapped:

$$
\begin{aligned}
T &= \frac{\Delta V_{trap}}{k_B} = \frac{\mu_B B_{\max}}{k_B} \\[2mm]
&= \frac{(h\,1.4\,\text{MHz}/\text{Gauss})\,(100\,\text{Gauss})}{8.62 \times 10^{-5}\,\text{eV/K}} \\[2mm]
&= \frac{0.58 \times 10^{-6}\,\text{eV}}{8.62 \times 10^{-5}\,\text{eV/K}} \\[2mm]
&= 7\text{mK}.
\end{aligned}
\tag{5}
$$

That is pretty cold! We could use superconducting coils to provide much higher current. That has been done, but the well depth is still only a few Kelvin. So to trap atoms with magnetic fields, we must find a way to reduce the temperature (i.e., the translational motion) of the atoms. The force of the magnetic trap itself cannot cool the atoms because it is a conservative force; atoms in the trap speed up and slow down (only slightly compared to room temperature motion), but the temperature of the ensemble is not reduced. We could use liquid helium to cool the atoms, but that requires expensive cryogenic techniques and cools only into the Kelvin range. A simpler technique, that also allows cooling to the milliKelvin level required for typical magnetic traps, is laser cooling of atoms, which we will discuss in the next section.

The magnetic trap has become an important research tool in atomic physics. A variety of different magnetic field geometries have been designed to optimize the confinement of the atoms, to allow optical access of laser beams to the atoms, or to build an array of traps for quantum computing. The best known application is in experiments to achieve Bose-Einstein condensation. The magnetic trap collects and confines atoms that have been cooled with laser cooling (more below). The atoms are then cooled further by evaporation (like coffee in a mug) in the trap. This slow process takes several seconds, so the ability to trap the atoms is vital. These experiments are done at very low pressure (high vacuum) so that background gas atoms do not collide with trapped atoms and knock them out of the trap.

Finally, it is interesting to note that there are two macroscopic systems that also use magnetic fields to trap objects. There is a toy called a Levitron where a spinning magnet is suspended in air above a magnetic base plate. The magnetic field is similar to the quadrupole field in that there is a region where the field is a minimum. The spinning magnet has its magnetic moment aligned against the magnetic field of the base plate, much like the weak-field seeking states of the atom in the magnetic trap. The strong magnetic field of the base plate tries to flip the spinning magnet over to be aligned with the field, but the torque causes the spinning top to precess about the field, like the Larmor precession of an atom's magnetic moment. The second macroscopic system is the use of strong superconducting magnetic field gradients to float diamagnetic objects, for example, frogs (this was announced in April 1997, but it was not an April Fool's joke). In a diamagnetic material, an applied magnetic field induces a magnetic moment in the material that opposes the applied field, again analogous to the weak-field seeking states above.

1.2 ■ Laser Cooling

Our second example of a quantum mechanical force is the use of lasers to slow down and cool atoms. **Laser cooling** allows us to cool atoms from room temperature or higher down to temperatures below 1 mK—low enough to be easily confined in a magnetic trap.

The force that light exerts on matter is known as **radiation pressure** and comes about because light carries momentum as well as energy. Photons have momentum given by $p = h/\lambda = \hbar k$, where $k = 2\pi/\lambda$ is the wave vector. Consider the absorption of a photon by an atom, whereby the *energy* of the photon causes the electron to be excited to a higher level, and the *angular momentum* of the photon is taken up by the atom according to the selection rules on the atom's angular momentum quantum number. We ignore the role of the *linear momentum* because it is usually quite small. However, the force of a laser on an atom can be quite large if the right conditions are satisfied. To illustrate the conditions required for efficient laser cooling, we use the rubidium atom (Rb) as an example. The relevant parameters for rubidium are shown in Table 1.

When an atom of mass M absorbs a photon, the transfer of momentum from the photon to the atom is

$$\Delta p = M\Delta v = \hbar k. \tag{6}$$

This momentum transfer causes the atom to recoil with a change in velocity of

$$\Delta v = v_r = \frac{\hbar k}{M} = \frac{h}{M\lambda}. \tag{7}$$

For a rubidium atom absorbing a 780 nm resonance photon, the **recoil velocity** v_r is 0.6 cm/s, which is much less than the typical thermal velocity of $v_T = 280$ m/s. So one photon does not impact a rubidium atom significantly, just as one mosquito hitting the windshield does not slow down your car. But if the atom repeatedly absorbs photons, then the net impact can be large. For a thermal rubidium atom to come to rest requires approximately $v_T/v_r \simeq 50{,}000$ recoil kicks. For the atom to absorb this many photons, the atom must return to the same state after each absorption so that it is ready to absorb another laser photon. The best way to achieve this cycle is to start with the atom in the ground state and excite it to the first excited state so that spontaneous emission returns it to the ground state. Hence, laser cooling requires an atom that behaves like a two-level system and a laser wavelength tuned close to resonance with the primary transition in the atom from the ground state of the atom $|g\rangle = |1\rangle$ to the first excited state $|e\rangle = |2\rangle$. Though no atom is truly a two-level system, there are straightforward laser techniques that allow the two-level model to be applicable in laser cooling experiments, and the atom can be cycled through the absorption-emission process enough times for radiation pressure to be effective.

The cycle of laser absorption and subsequent spontaneous emission that is required for laser cooling of an atom is depicted in Fig. 5. The three steps illustrated are: (1) A resonant laser beam is incident on an atom in the ground state of the two-level system. (2) The atom absorbs a photon, which promotes the electron to the excited state and causes the atom to recoil in the direction of the incident laser with momentum change $\Delta \mathbf{p} = \hbar \mathbf{k}$. (3) The excited atom decays back down to the ground state via spontaneous emission of another photon. The spontaneous photon is emitted in a *random* direction, so the recoil kick due to the spontaneously emitted photons averages to zero over many

Table 1   Rubidium Laser Cooling Parameters

Resonance Wavelength	$\lambda = 2\pi c/\omega_{21}$	780 nm
Resonance Linewidth	$\Delta\omega = A_{21}$	$2\pi \times 6$ MHz
Lifetime	$\tau = 1/A_{21}$	27 ns
Mass	M	85 amu $= 1.4 \times 10^{-25}$ kg
Thermal Velocity	$v_T = \sqrt{2k_B T/M}$	280 m/s
Recoil Velocity	$v_r = \hbar k/M$	0.6 cm/s

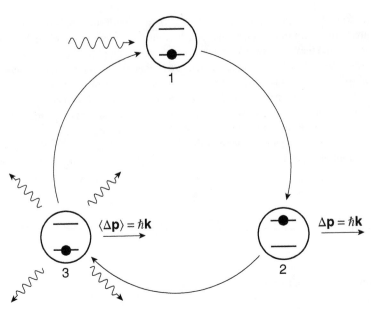

FIGURE 5 The laser cooling cycle: (1) A resonant laser beam is incident on a two-level atom in its ground state. (2) The atom absorbs a photon with the energy going to excite the electron and the momentum causing the atom to recoil. (3) Spontaneous emission produces a photon in a random direction and the atom returns to the ground state.

absorption-emission cycles and the average momentum change per complete absorption-emission cycle is $\langle \Delta \mathbf{p} \rangle_{cycle} = \hbar \mathbf{k}$, due only to the momenta of the absorbed photons. Once the atom returns to the ground state, it is ready to absorb another photon and begin the cycle anew. The average absorption-emission cycle time is at least as long as the spontaneous emission lifetime of the atom, but that is typically nanoseconds, so this process can finish in much less than one second. Assuming that the minimum cycle time is twice the atomic lifetime (e.g., τ to absorb a laser photon and τ to emit a spontaneous photon), the maximum force on the atom is

$$\mathbf{F}_{max} = \frac{d\mathbf{p}}{dt} = \frac{\langle \Delta \mathbf{p} \rangle_{cycle}}{\langle \Delta t \rangle_{min}} = \frac{\hbar \mathbf{k}}{2\tau}. \tag{8}$$

The complete process of photon absorption and emission is called **scattering**. We refer to the force depicted in Fig. 5 as the **scattering force** to distinguish it from other radiation forces. This force is not conservative because the spontaneous emission is an irreversible process. Hence the scattering force differs in a critical way from the magnetic force used to trap atoms described earlier. The good aspect of this is that the non-conservative nature of the scattering force permits cooling, which is not possible with a conservative force. It is important to distinguish slowing from cooling. Individual atoms are *slowed* by the scattering force. *Cooling* requires that we reduce the velocity *spread* of the ensemble of atoms, which we'll explain below.

The typical geometry for laser cooling is a laser beam counterpropagating against an atomic beam, as shown in Fig. 6. The scattering force decelerates the atoms with a maximum acceleration of

$$a_{max} = \frac{F_{max}}{M} = \frac{\hbar k}{2M\tau} = \frac{h}{2M\lambda\tau}. \tag{9}$$

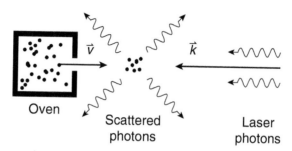

FIGURE 6 An oven with a small opening produces an atomic beam. The photons from a counterpropagating resonant laser beam are scattered and the atoms are slowed.

For example, the deceleration of a rubidium atom is

$$a_{max} = \frac{h}{2M\lambda\tau}$$

$$= \frac{\left(6.626 \times 10^{-34}\,\text{Js}\right)}{2\left(85\,\text{amu} \times 1.66 \times 10^{-27}\,\text{kg/amu}\right)\left(780 \times 10^{-9}\,\text{m}\right)\left(27 \times 10^{-9}\,\text{s}\right)} \tag{10}$$

$$= 1.11 \times 10^5\,\text{m/s}^2 = 1.14 \times 10^4\,g.$$

Each absorbed photon produces a small momentum change of the atom, but the process is repeated so rapidly that the resulting acceleration dominates gravity $\left(g = 9.8\,\text{m/s}^2\right)$ and is sufficient to stop a thermal atom within 1 meter (Problem 3).

So far our description explains only laser slowing or deceleration. Laser cooling requires one additional aspect of the scattering force that we have neglected. The scattering force is *velocity dependent* because of the **Doppler effect** that causes the frequency experienced by a moving atom to be shifted from the laser frequency by an amount proportional to the atomic velocity. The Doppler-shifted angular frequency of a laser beam with wave vector **k** as observed by an atom with velocity **v** is

$$\omega_{Atom} = \omega_{Laser} - \mathbf{k} \cdot \mathbf{v}. \tag{11}$$

An atom moving *toward* the laser source experiences a *blue-shifted* beam (higher frequency, shorter wavelength) and an atom moving *away* from the laser source experiences a *red-shifted* beam (lower frequency, longer wavelength), as shown in Fig. 7. Because the scattering force relies on the

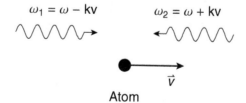

FIGURE 7 Doppler shifts of copropagating and counterpropagating laser beams. The laser photons are produced in the laboratory with angular frequency ω. The moving atom observes these photons shifted up (counterpropagating) or down (copropagating) by kv.

resonance of the laser beam with the atomic transition, the motion of the atom has a strong effect on the strength of the scattering force.

We quantify the velocity dependence of the scattering force by expressing the force as the momentum change per scattering cycle (absorption-emission cycle) divided by the time for each cycle. The cycle time is the inverse of the scattering rate, which is the excitation rate $R_{1\rightarrow2}$. This results in

$$\mathbf{F}_{scatt} = \frac{d\mathbf{p}}{dt} = \frac{\langle\Delta\mathbf{p}\rangle_{cycle}}{\langle\Delta t\rangle_{cycle}}$$
$$= (\text{momentum per scattered photon}) \times (\text{scattered photons per second}) \qquad (12)$$
$$= \hbar\mathbf{k}\,R_{1\rightarrow2}.$$

Substituting Eq. (11) into the scattering rate, we find

$$R_{1\rightarrow2} = 3\frac{I}{c}B_{12}f(\omega_{Atom})$$
$$= 3\frac{I}{c}B_{12}\frac{\dfrac{A_{21}}{2\pi}}{\left(\omega_{Laser} - \omega_{21} - \mathbf{k}\cdot\mathbf{v}\right)^2 + \left(\dfrac{A_{21}}{2}\right)^2}. \qquad (13)$$

The scattering force is then

$$\mathbf{F}_{scatt}(\mathbf{v}) = \hbar\mathbf{k}\frac{A_{21}}{2}\frac{I}{I_0}\frac{\left(\dfrac{A_{21}}{2}\right)^2}{\left(\omega_{Laser} - \omega_{21} - \mathbf{k}\cdot\mathbf{v}\right)^2 + \left(\dfrac{A_{21}}{2}\right)^2}, \qquad (14)$$

where the characteristic intensity is $I_0 = \left(\hbar\omega^3 A_{21}/12\pi c^2\right)$. This expression for the scattering force is valid only for incident laser intensities that satisfy $I \ll I_0$. The valid expression for all intensities is the subject of Problem 4.

The Doppler shift of the laser beam has two main effects: (1) the laser frequency must be tuned away from the resonance frequency ω_{21} to excite moving atoms, and (2) only atoms in a small velocity range experience the radiation pressure. Both of these effects are illustrated in Fig. 8, which shows the Maxwellian velocity distribution of rubidium atoms in a thermal beam $\left(N(v) \propto v^3 e^{-v^2/v_T^2}\right)$ and the velocity-dependent scattering force for a counterpropagating laser that is tuned 450 MHz below the resonance frequency $f_{21} = \omega_{21}/2\pi = c/\lambda_{21}$. For this detuning, the laser beam excites rubidium atoms that are moving toward the laser source at $v = 350$ m/s (Problem 5). The scattering force in Eq. (14) has the same Lorentzian resonance behavior of the excitation rate, with an inherent linewidth $\Delta\omega = A_{21} = 1/\tau$ caused by spontaneous emission. Hence, only atoms in the velocity range $\Delta v = \Delta\omega/k$ about the resonant velocity of 350 m/s experience an appreciable scattering force. For rubidium, the spontaneous emission linewidth is $\Delta f = \Delta\omega/2\pi = 1/2\pi\tau = 6$ MHz in frequency space, yielding a velocity width

$$\Delta v = \frac{\Delta\omega}{k} = \frac{\lambda}{2\pi\tau} = \frac{780\,\text{nm}}{2\pi(27\,\text{ns})} = 4.6\,\text{m/s}, \qquad (15)$$

as indicated in Fig. 8. This width is much smaller than the thermal spread of the atomic beam, so only a small fraction of the atoms in the beam are decelerated by the scattering force (the force is opposite the atomic velocity for a counterpropagating laser beam). For the laser frequency detuning

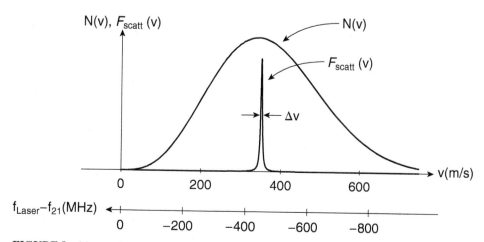

FIGURE 8 Maxwellian velocity distribution of a rubidium atomic beam at 400°C and the magnitude of the scattering force for a laser tuned 450 MHz below resonance. The narrow width of the scattering force arises from the spontaneous emission line width of the resonance transition.

depicted in Fig. 8, the scattering force decelerates atoms with velocities in the approximate range 345–355 m/s. These atoms subsequently move at lower velocities and no longer experience the scattering force, because their new Doppler shift makes the laser photons appear to be off resonance. The scattering force thus alters the velocity distribution as shown in Fig. 9. The number of atoms in the range 345–355 m/s is depleted and the number of atoms in the range below that is augmented.

If our goal is to stop the rubidium atoms in this beam, then we have failed, because the deceleration caused by the scattering force has changed the Doppler shift and taken the atoms away from the initial resonance condition. The solution to this problem is straightforward: we change the laser frequency

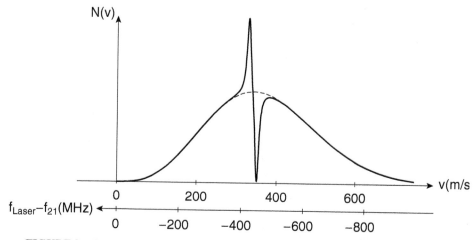

FIGURE 9 Atoms in resonance with the detuned laser beam are slowed, depleting the number of atoms at that velocity and augmenting the number at a slightly lower velocity.

to be in resonance with the previously slowed group of atoms (e.g., from $f_{Laser} - f_{21} = -450$ MHz to $f_{Laser} - f_{21} = -444$ MHz). After this group is slowed and falls out of resonance again, we repeat the laser frequency change. In practice, the laser frequency is continuously swept from the starting point toward the resonance frequency f_{21} to keep the slowing atoms in resonance with the laser beam throughout their journey. This method of compensating for the changing Doppler shift is called **chirped cooling**, in analogy with the changing pitch of a bird's chirp. From the expression for the scattering force in Eq. (14), we see that chirped cooling increases ω_{Laser} to keep the term $(\omega_{Laser} - \omega_{21} + kv) = 0$ as the velocity decreases. The resultant velocity distribution after the frequency chirp is finished is shown in Fig. 10. Atoms from the initial resonant velocity downward are slowed and accumulate near the final resonant velocity of the chirp. The final velocity distribution (at least the part below the initial resonant velocity) is much narrower than the initial distribution, so the atoms have been cooled, not merely decelerated. It is also possible to compensate for the Doppler shift and keep slowing atoms in resonance by altering the atomic frequency ω_{21} by applying either a spatially varying magnetic or electric field that perturbs the atomic energy levels through the Zeeman effect or Stark effect, respectively.

The laser cooling of an atomic beam illustrated in Fig. 10 affects only one of the velocity components. Cooling the complete three-dimensional velocity distribution requires scattering forces in all three directions. This is achieved with a configuration of six laser beams along the positive and negative Cartesian axes, as shown in Fig. 11. This arrangement of laser beams is called **optical molasses** because it strongly damps the atomic motion, just as molasses damps the motion of a spoon dropped into it. At first glance, it might appear that the counterpropagating beams of optical molasses would cancel each other out to give no net force. This is true for an atom at rest, but once again the Doppler shift of moving atoms plays a key role.

In optical molasses, the six laser beams come from the same laser and have the same frequency. The laser is tuned about one line width $\Delta\omega = A_{21}$ below the resonance ω_{21} (red detuning). For a moving atom, the laser beam propagating in the same direction as the atomic velocity is Doppler shifted to lower frequencies, taking it farther from resonance, while the laser beam propagating in the opposite direction is Doppler shifted to higher frequencies, bringing it closer to resonance. Hence, the scattering force from the laser beam counterpropagating to the atom dominates and the atom is slowed

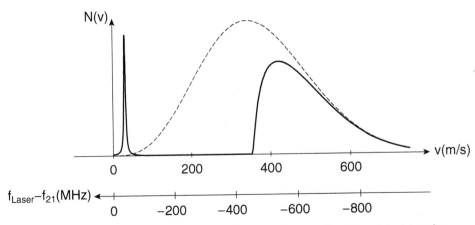

FIGURE 10 In chirped laser cooling, the laser frequency is swept from the original detuning (−450 MHz) toward the resonance frequency and a wide range of atoms are slowed and accumulate near zero velocity.

FIGURE 11 Optical molasses comprises six laser beams along the Cartesian axes.
Atoms at the intersection of the six laser beams are strongly cooled in all three dimensions.

down. The resultant force $\mathbf{F}_{+k\hat{x}}(v) + \mathbf{F}_{-k\hat{x}}(v)$ along one of the axes is shown in Fig. 12. For the laser frequency detuning shown $\left(\omega_{Laser} - \omega_{21} \simeq -A_{21}\right)$, the scattering force is approximately a linear function of velocity for small velocities. The resultant atomic motion in optical molasses is similar to the motion of a particle in a viscous liquid.

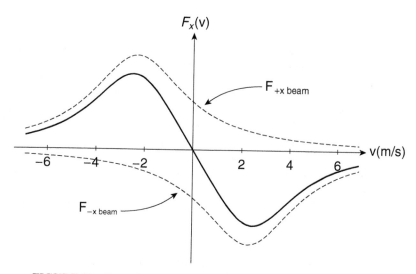

FIGURE 12 Scattering force as a function of velocity in optical molasses.

Comparing the scattering force in Fig. 12 with the Maxwellian velocity distribution in Fig. 8, we note that the range of velocities that are affected by optical molasses is very small. In a typical experiment, laser cooling of an atomic beam is first performed to produce a sample of atoms with low velocity, as in Fig. 10, and then the atoms are further cooled in all three dimensions in optical molasses. Atoms in optical molasses can be cooled to a temperature of approximately $100\,\mu$K, which provides a sample of atoms that is easily confined in a magnetic trap. This temperature limit, called the **Doppler cooling limit**, arises from the balance between the cooling force and heating caused by the random nature of spontaneous emission. The development of these laser cooling techniques resulted in the Nobel Prize for physics in 1997. Laser cooling has been used to improve the precision of atomic clocks, to make precision measurements of gravity, and to create sources of atoms that behave as quantum mechanical waves rather than classical particles. Laser cooling and magnetic trapping were combined in the discovery of Bose-Einstein condensation, which was recognized by the Nobel Prize for physics in 2001.

2 ■ QUANTUM INFORMATION PROCESSING

Our second example of a modern application of quantum mechanics is **quantum information processing**. We live in the information age. Computers, smart phones, personal digital assistants, GPS devices, and more surround us, whether we want them or not. The explosion of information processing systems has been enabled by the continuing miniaturization of electronic circuits. Every year, engineers are able to put more circuits on computer chips. Now that we have entered the nanotechnology phase of the information revolution, we are approaching the physical limitation presented by the atoms that make up the devices. Extrapolation of the miniaturization march would soon have us using individual atoms as memory devices and circuit elements. As we approach the physical size limitation of the atoms themselves, quantum mechanics must play a role in building and using information processing devices. This shift is sure to be a disruptive influence in computing, but it also represents an opportunity to take advantage of unique quantum mechanical aspects of information processing.

The idea that quantum mechanics could be useful in computing stems in part from a talk and a paper by Richard Feynman in the early 1980's. Feynman asked the question: Can a classical computer reliably model a quantum mechanical system? Imagine that we want to model the quantum mechanical time evolution of a system of 50 spin-1/2 particles. The Hilbert space of this 50-particle system has 2^{50} states, so the quantum state vector of the system requires $2^{50} \simeq 10^{15}$ coefficients to describe a general state in the Hilbert space of this system (more details on the numerics later). A 100-particle system would require $2^{100} \simeq 10^{30}$ coefficients and a 300-particle system would require $2^{300} \simeq 10^{90}$ coefficients, which is more than the number of protons in the universe! A computer would have to keep track of all these coefficients in order to properly account for the particle-particle interactions and their effect on the system's Schrödinger time evolution. So it appears impossible to model the dynamics of a modestly-sized multiparticle quantum mechanical system because the Hilbert space is so exponentially large. On the other hand, nature has no trouble managing this large Hilbert space and producing those same dynamics that we are not able to model! This suggests that we let nature, in the form of a quantum mechanical system of 50, 100, or 300 particles, be the computer. We let this **quantum computer** use its own Schrödinger time evolution to calculate what our classical computer cannot.

This conjecture has led to an explosion in the field of quantum information processing with research to uncover the theory of quantum information and to implement some basic experiments to demonstrate the principles. The field is too broad and too deep for us to cover thoroughly here, but here is a taste of some of the possibilities. We'll introduce the idea of quantum bits to store data and quantum gates to manipulate data. These elements are required to make a quantum computer, so we'll briefly discuss some of the quantum algorithms that make a quantum computer attractive. Then finally, we'll discuss how quantum teleportation works.

2.1 ■ Quantum Bits—Qubits

Classical computing relies on binary digits—**bits**—to store information. Each bit has the value 0 or 1, and individual bits are strung together to represent larger binary numbers (for example, 001100101). Each binary number represents an actual number or, through coding, some other piece of information like the letter "A." The job of a classical computer is to store and process bits. Because there are only two possible states for each bit, many of the tasks required in a classical computer are implemented with simple on-off switches.

In quantum information processing, information is stored in **quantum bits**, or **qubits**. A qubit is a quantum system with two possible states, analogous to the 0 and 1 of a classical bit. The canonical qubit system is the spin-1/2 system we know and love, with the spin up state $|+\rangle$ and the spin down state $|-\rangle$ playing the roles of the two binary states. But any two-state quantum system can be used as a qubit. Other common qubit systems include hyperfine levels in atoms and polarization states of photons. To address all of these diverse systems with the same formalism, we refer to the qubit states as $|0\rangle$ and $|1\rangle$, whether the actual states are spin states, atomic states, or photon polarization states. But we will make our discussion concrete when needed by reference to the spin-1/2 system, with the spin up state $|+\rangle$ representing $|0\rangle$ and the spin down state $|-\rangle$ representing $|1\rangle$:

$$\begin{aligned} |0\rangle &= |+\rangle \\ |1\rangle &= |-\rangle. \end{aligned} \tag{16}$$

Superposition states

The key difference between bits and qubits is that qubits can exist in *superposition* states. A general qubit superposition is

$$|\psi\rangle = c_0|0\rangle + c_1|1\rangle \doteq \begin{pmatrix} c_0 \\ c_1 \end{pmatrix}. \tag{17}$$

For this superposition state, the probability that we measure the system to be in the $|0\rangle$ state is

$$\mathcal{P}_0 = |\langle 0|\psi\rangle|^2 = |c_0|^2, \tag{18}$$

and the probability that we measure the system to be in the $|1\rangle$ state is

$$\mathcal{P}_1 = |\langle 1|\psi\rangle|^2 = |c_1|^2. \tag{19}$$

This is in stark contrast to a classical bit, which is either 0 or 1 with 100% probability. If that weren't the case, then our classical computers would not function very well!

The probabilistic nature of quantum mechanics doesn't seem to bode well for the promise of a quantum computer. You would not buy a computer if the salesman told you that it would "probably" get the right answer. But quantum superposition states are more than simple probability mixtures of different possibilities. A quantum superposition state is a *coherent* combination of states that does contain an aspect of certainty that would be lacking in a classical bit that was only "probably" in the one state. For example, the spin state

$$|\psi\rangle = |+\rangle_x = \tfrac{1}{\sqrt{2}}|+\rangle + \tfrac{1}{\sqrt{2}}|-\rangle \tag{20}$$

has 100% probability of being measured to be spin up along the x-axis, even though the probabilities of measuring the spin component on the z-axis are 50/50. So whether we view this state as lacking or having the certainty we expect from our computer depends on our point of view.

Superposition states are at the heart of the power of quantum information processing because the amount of information contained in a quantum system grows *exponentially* with the number of qubits in the system. For example, if we build a system with 2 qubits, labeled A and B, then the basis states of this system are the uncoupled basis states:

$$\begin{aligned}
|00\rangle &= |0\rangle_A|0\rangle_B \\
|01\rangle &= |0\rangle_A|1\rangle_B \\
|10\rangle &= |1\rangle_A|0\rangle_B \\
|11\rangle &= |1\rangle_A|1\rangle_B.
\end{aligned} \tag{21}$$

In this 2-qubit system, a general superposition state is

$$|\psi\rangle = c_{00}|00\rangle + c_{01}|01\rangle + c_{10}|10\rangle + c_{11}|11\rangle. \tag{22}$$

This single 2-qubit state contains $2^2 = 4$ pieces of information—the c_{ij} coefficients. A classical 2-bit state, such as 01, contains just two pieces of information. For an N-qubit system, a single superposition state contains 2^N pieces of information. The classical N-bit system does have 2^N possible states, but any single state contains just N pieces of information.

Though the N-qubit superposition state contains 2^N pieces of information, it is not possible to measure it all. When we measure the state of the system, we destroy much of the information by collapsing the system state vector onto the measured state. For example, if we measure the spin components of the two particles described by Eq. (22), we learn which one of the four basis states the system is in, just as we would for a classical 2-bit system. Even though there are 2^N pieces of information in an N-qubit system, it turns out that we can extract only N pieces of classical information through our measurements. You might ask whether we can call it information if we cannot know it! This question has spawned research into quantum information and how it differs from classical information. The trick of quantum computing is to harness the vast store of information that resides in the superposition state, but is hidden from direct measurement. A number of algorithms have been discovered that access the hidden quantum information by performing operations that affect many or all of the qubits at once. By performing these multiple operations simultaneously, we achieve **quantum parallelism**. You can also perform parallel computing with classical computers, but you do so by buying more computers!

Entangled states

The power of quantum parallelism relies on the phenomenon of *quantum entanglement*. Entangled quantum states are responsible for the "spookiness" of the Einstein-Podolsky-Rosen paradox. The EPR state $|\psi\rangle = \frac{1}{\sqrt{2}}(|+\rangle_1|-\rangle_2 - |-\rangle_1|+\rangle_2)$ is entangled because measurements on one spin are perfectly anti-correlated with measurements on the other spin. The EPR state is a specific example of the set of 2-qubit entangled states known as **Bell states**. In terms of the basis states $|00\rangle$, $|01\rangle$, $|10\rangle$, and $|11\rangle$ of a 2-qubit system, the four Bell states are

$$\begin{aligned}
|\beta_{00}\rangle &= \tfrac{1}{\sqrt{2}}(|00\rangle + |11\rangle) \\
|\beta_{01}\rangle &= \tfrac{1}{\sqrt{2}}(|01\rangle + |10\rangle) \\
|\beta_{10}\rangle &= \tfrac{1}{\sqrt{2}}(|00\rangle - |11\rangle) \\
|\beta_{11}\rangle &= \tfrac{1}{\sqrt{2}}(|01\rangle - |10\rangle).
\end{aligned} \tag{23}$$

The EPR state is the Bell state $|\beta_{11}\rangle$. The Bell states comprise an alternate basis to the uncoupled and coupled bases. In quantum computing, we typically use either the Bell basis or the uncoupled basis, which is called the **computational basis**.

The correlations of measurements on the EPR state, and the Bell states in general, show us that quantum mechanics is a nonlocal theory. Measuring one of the qubits affects the other, possibly distant, qubit instantaneously. Rather than regarding these nonlocal correlations as spooky, we can use them as a resource in quantum information processing. The nonlocal aspect of entangled states is useful because we can act on one part of a system and control another part of the system, and we can measure one part to learn about another part or about the system as a whole. This is how quantum algorithms are able to process the 2^N pieces of information hidden in an N-qubit system. To be useful, the quantum algorithms must be cleverly designed so that the answer we want is contained within the N pieces of classical information available through measurements on the system. It is no use having more information available if we cannot access it after the calculation.

The importance of entangled states is also evident in our argument about the exponential increase in information content of a quantum superposition state. We said that the 2-qubit superposition state $|\psi\rangle$ in Eq. (22) contains $2^2 = 4$ pieces of information and that an N-qubit superposition contains 2^N pieces of information. However, there is a caveat to that statement. It turns out that there are some superposition states that have less information content because they can be expressed as a product of 1-qubit states. An example of such a 2-qubit **product state** is

$$|\psi\rangle = \left(a_0|0\rangle_A + a_1|1\rangle_A\right)\left(b_0|0\rangle_B + b_1|1\rangle_B\right). \tag{24}$$

Product states do not exhibit correlations in measurement and, therefore, they are not entangled states; they behave more like classical states. The 2-qubit state in Eq. (24) contains $2 \times 2 = 4$ pieces of information—the a_i and b_i coefficients. For a general N-qubit system, a superposition state that *is* a product state and so *is not* entangled contains $2 \times N$ pieces of information. Unfortunately, for the 2-qubit examples we have chosen, $2^2 = 4$ and $2 \times 2 = 4$ are the same, so the difference between the 2^N exponential information content of general superposition states (which includes entangled states) and the $2 \times N$ linear information content of non-entangled states is not immediately evident. We'll leave it to you to explore the $N = 3$ case in Problem 8 and distinguish the difference. The take-home message is that access to the power of quantum parallelism requires the use of entangled states.

Quantum computing algorithms are designed to process the hidden information in the large Hilbert space in a way that the desired result is brought out in the measured qubits. Two of the most impressive quantum algorithms are Shor's factorization algorithm and Grover's search algorithm. Factoring a large number into its two prime factors is a difficult task for a classical computer. In 1994, Peter Shor developed a quantum algorithm that finds the prime factors of an integer in a time that is faster than a classical computer by a factor that is exponential in the number of digits of the number being factored. Because of the importance of factoring in encryption, Shor's algorithm has inspired many to try to build a quantum computer. Grover's search algorithm allows a quantum computer to search an unsorted database of N entries in a time proportional to $\sqrt{N}$, compared to a classical computer that requires a time that is proportional to N. Details of these algorithms are available in the resources at the end of the chapter.

Quantum algorithms are not immune to the probabilistic nature of quantum mechanics. If we run the same program twice on a quantum computer, then we might get two different answers. The power of quantum computing is that it can produce answers in many fewer steps than a classical computer. As long as we can easily confirm the answers on a classical computer, then the time advantage overcomes the need to run the program many times. For example, as hard as it is to find prime factors of a large number, it is trivial to check whether the product of the two proposed factors do in fact yield the original number. Likewise, as hard as it is to find a needle in a haystack, it is simple to determine if the object you find is a needle, so confirming the result of a quantum search algorithm is straightforward on a classical computer.

2.2 ■ Quantum Gates

To process information, a classical computer uses **gates** that operate on bits. A few typical classical gates are shown in Fig. 13 along with the truth tables that describe their operation. The *NOT* gate is a 1-bit gate with one input bit and one output bit. The *AND* and *OR* gates are 2-bit gates with two input bits and one output bit. Using a small set of such binary logic gates, albeit a large number of them, classical computers perform a wide range of tasks.

Quantum computers likewise rely on a small set of 1- and 2-qubit gates to perform their tasks. The measurement devices we have encountered throughout this text, like Stern-Gerlach devices, are *not* quantum gates. Rather, quantum gates are devices that alter the relative coefficients in a qubit superposition without destroying the coherence. A 1-qubit gate has an input state $|\psi_{in}\rangle$ and an output state $|\psi_{out}\rangle$, which we write as

$$|\psi_{in}\rangle = c_0|0\rangle + c_1|1\rangle \tag{25}$$

and

$$|\psi_{out}\rangle = c_0'|0\rangle + c_1'|1\rangle. \tag{26}$$

For any general 1-qubit quantum gate, we represent the transformation from input to output states in matrix notation as

$$\begin{pmatrix} c_0' \\ c_1' \end{pmatrix} = \begin{pmatrix} U_{11} & U_{12} \\ U_{21} & U_{22} \end{pmatrix}\begin{pmatrix} c_0 \\ c_1 \end{pmatrix}. \tag{27}$$

The transformation matrix U must be a unitary matrix ($UU^\dagger = \mathbf{1}$) to preserve the coherence of the qubit. The matrix elements of the transformation tell us how the qubit is changed by the gate. For example, a quantum *NOT* gate changes $|0\rangle \rightarrow |1\rangle$ and also $|1\rangle \rightarrow |0\rangle$. The quantum *NOT* gate is a linear operator, so it also changes a superposition $a|0\rangle + b|1\rangle \rightarrow b|0\rangle + a|1\rangle$. The quantum *NOT* gate unitary transformation matrix is

$$U_{NOT} \doteq \begin{pmatrix} 0 & 1 \\ 1 & 0 \end{pmatrix}. \tag{28}$$

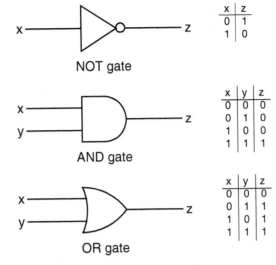

x	z
0	1
1	0

NOT gate

x	y	z
0	0	0
0	1	0
1	0	0
1	1	1

AND gate

x	y	z
0	0	0
0	1	1
1	0	1
1	1	1

OR gate

FIGURE 13 Classical logic gates.

This unitary operator looks similar to the S_x operator for a spin-1/2 system. That is not a coincidence. It turns out that all unitary operators for a spin-1/2 system can be expressed as a linear combination of the four operators comprising the identity matrix **1** and the three spin-1/2 angular momentum component operators, with the factor of $\hbar/2$ removed. These dimensionless matrices are called the **Pauli matrices** and are

$$\sigma_x = \begin{pmatrix} 0 & 1 \\ 1 & 0 \end{pmatrix} \quad \sigma_y = \begin{pmatrix} 0 & -i \\ i & 0 \end{pmatrix} \quad \sigma_z = \begin{pmatrix} 1 & 0 \\ 0 & -1 \end{pmatrix}. \tag{29}$$

The unitary transformation of a spin-1/2 system also has a convenient geometric interpretation as a rotation or a series of rotations of the spin, as affected by the spin precession. For example, the quantum *NOT* gate is performed by a π rotation about the x-axis, as depicted for a state that is initially spin up. Let's now show that this is also true for a general initial state.

Example1 **Quantum *NOT* gate** Show that the spin precession transformation of a general spin state for a π rotation about the x-axis is equivalent to a quantum *NOT* gate.

For the spin to precess about the x-axis, we apply a magnetic field B_0 in the x-direction. The energy states in this applied field are $|\pm\rangle_x$ and the energies are $E_\pm = \pm\hbar\omega_0/2$, where $\omega_0 = eB_0/m_e$ is the Larmor precession frequency. To find how the state vector is changed by the applied magnetic field, we use the Schrödinger time-evolution recipe. The initial general state is

$$|\psi(0)\rangle = c_+|+\rangle + c_-|-\rangle. \tag{30}$$

We must write this state in the energy basis, which is the S_x basis in this case:

$$\begin{aligned}
|\psi(0)\rangle &= \left(|+\rangle_x{}_x\langle+| + |-\rangle_x{}_x\langle-|\right)|\psi(0)\rangle \\
&= c_+\left({}_x\langle+|+\rangle|+\rangle_x + {}_x\langle-|+\rangle|-\rangle_x\right) + c_-\left({}_x\langle+|-\rangle|+\rangle_x + {}_x\langle-|-\rangle|-\rangle_x\right) \\
&= \tfrac{1}{\sqrt{2}}(c_+ + c_-)|+\rangle_x + \tfrac{1}{\sqrt{2}}(c_+ - c_-)|-\rangle_x.
\end{aligned} \tag{31}$$

To find the time-evolved state, we insert the time-dependent phase factor for each energy basis state:

$$\begin{aligned}
|\psi(t)\rangle &= \tfrac{1}{\sqrt{2}}(c_+ + c_-)e^{-iE_+t/\hbar}|+\rangle_x + \tfrac{1}{\sqrt{2}}(c_+ - c_-)e^{-iE_-t/\hbar}|-\rangle_x \\
&= \tfrac{1}{\sqrt{2}}(c_+ + c_-)e^{-i\omega_0 t/2}|+\rangle_x + \tfrac{1}{\sqrt{2}}(c_+ - c_-)e^{+i\omega_0 t/2}|-\rangle_x.
\end{aligned} \tag{32}$$

The angle of spin precession is $\omega_0 t$, so to have a π rotation about the x-axis requires that the field be applied long enough to have $\omega_0 t = \pi$. Thus the state vector after the time evolution is

$$\begin{aligned}
|\psi(t)\rangle &= \tfrac{1}{\sqrt{2}}(c_+ + c_-)e^{-i\pi/2}|+\rangle_x + \tfrac{1}{\sqrt{2}}(c_+ - c_-)e^{+i\pi/2}|-\rangle_x \\
&= \tfrac{-i}{\sqrt{2}}(c_+ + c_-)\tfrac{1}{\sqrt{2}}(|+\rangle + |-\rangle) + \tfrac{i}{\sqrt{2}}(c_+ - c_-)\tfrac{1}{\sqrt{2}}(|+\rangle - |-\rangle) \\
&= -i(c_-|+\rangle + c_+|-\rangle),
\end{aligned} \tag{33}$$

or in matrix notation:

$$\begin{pmatrix} c'_+ \\ c'_- \end{pmatrix} = -i\begin{pmatrix} 0 & 1 \\ 1 & 0 \end{pmatrix}\begin{pmatrix} c_+ \\ c_- \end{pmatrix}. \tag{34}$$

a)

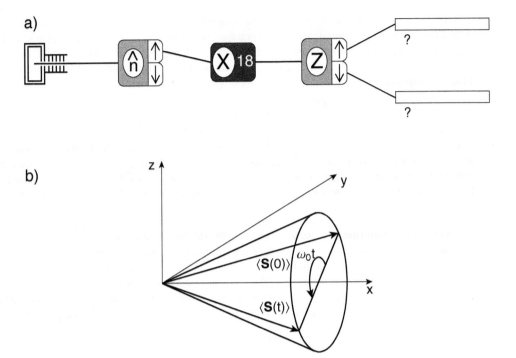

b)

FIGURE 14 (a) A Stern-Gerlach spin precession experiment and (b) the resulting precession of the spin vector around the x-axis for the case of a π rotation.

The overall phase $e^{-i\pi/2} = -i$ does not produce any measurable effects, so we ignore it in defining the quantum NOT gate transformation matrix:

$$U_{NOT} \doteq \begin{pmatrix} 0 & 1 \\ 1 & 0 \end{pmatrix}. \tag{35}$$

A schematic diagram of this spin-precession experiment is shown in Fig. 14. The unitary spin precession is performed by the magnet (box with "X"), while the Stern-Gerlach devices perform measurements, which are nonunitary transformations. (Recall that the number "18" in the magnet box rotates the spin by 180°.)

Rotations due to spin precession about the other Cartesian axes produce two more 1-qubit gates. The quantum Z gate is a π rotation around the z-axis, with a transformation matrix (Problem 10)

$$U_Z \doteq \begin{pmatrix} 1 & 0 \\ 0 & -1 \end{pmatrix} \tag{36}$$

that is equal to the Pauli σ_z matrix. The quantum Y gate is a π rotation around the y-axis, with a transformation matrix (Problem 11)

$$U_Y \doteq \begin{pmatrix} 0 & -i \\ i & 0 \end{pmatrix} \tag{37}$$

that is equal to the Pauli σ_y matrix.

One other important 1-qubit gate is the **Hadamard gate**, with a transformation matrix

$$U_H \doteq \frac{1}{\sqrt{2}} \begin{pmatrix} 1 & 1 \\ 1 & -1 \end{pmatrix}. \tag{38}$$

The Hadamard gate can be made with a π rotation around the z-axis followed by a $\pi/2$ rotation around the y-axis (Problem 12). The Hadamard gate transforms basis states into superposition states:

$$
\begin{aligned}
U_H|0\rangle &= \tfrac{1}{\sqrt{2}}(|0\rangle + |1\rangle) \\
U_H|1\rangle &= \tfrac{1}{\sqrt{2}}(|0\rangle - |1\rangle).
\end{aligned} \tag{39}
$$

Given the importance of superposition states in quantum information processing, this is a useful gate. Note that the symbol "H" is used for the Hadamard gate, and it must not be confused with the Hamiltonian.

Though we have explained the unitary transformations of 1-qubit gates in terms of the precession of a spin-1/2 particle in a magnetic field, these same transformations apply to any two-level system. The physical mechanisms for effecting the transformations are different, but the matrices describing them are the same. For example, pulses of light can transform an atom into a superposition of states to effect a Hadamard gate. Figure 15 depicts a general Stern-Gerlach spin precession experiment (a) using our schematic diagram from the SPINS program and (b) using a simplified schematic used for describing quantum information processing in general. The quantum Z gate performs the U_Z transformation and the quantum X gate (*NOT* gate) performs the $U_{NOT} = U_X$ transformation. The Stern-Gerlach measurement devices are not quantum gates because they do not perform a unitary transformation, so we do not depict them in Fig. 15(b).

The quantum gates we have described so far are all 1-qubit gates, but the power of quantum information processing resides in entangled superposition states, so multiqubit gates are required. It

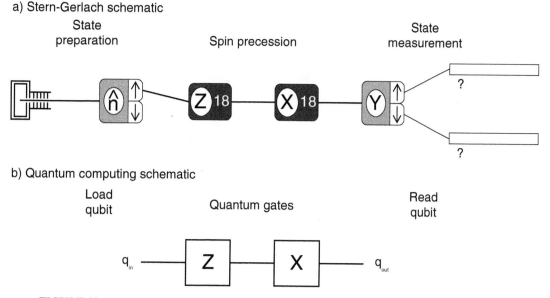

FIGURE 15   (a) A Stern-Gerlach spin precession experiment and (b) the equivalent experiment depicted with quantum gates.

turns out that we can perform all the quantum tasks we need with 1-qubit gates and one type of 2-qubit gate. The 2-qubit gate we need is a **Controlled-NOT gate** (*CNOT* **gate**). A *CNOT* gate has two input qubits, referred to as the *control* and *target* qubits, and two output qubits. The target qubit is negated (by a 1-qubit *NOT* gate) if the control qubit is in state $|1\rangle_C$. If the control qubit is in state $|0\rangle_C$, then the target qubit is unchanged. In both cases, the control qubit is unaltered by the gate. We denote the two-qubit states as $|ij\rangle = |i\rangle_C|j\rangle_T$ and the transformations of the *CNOT* gate are

$$U_{CNOT}|00\rangle = |00\rangle$$
$$U_{CNOT}|01\rangle = |01\rangle$$
$$U_{CNOT}|10\rangle = |11\rangle$$
$$U_{CNOT}|11\rangle = |10\rangle. \tag{40}$$

The transformation matrix of a *CNOT* gate is (Problem 13)

$$U_{CNOT} \doteq \begin{pmatrix} 1 & 0 & 0 & 0 \\ 0 & 1 & 0 & 0 \\ 0 & 0 & 0 & 1 \\ 0 & 0 & 1 & 0 \end{pmatrix}, \tag{41}$$

and the transformation of a general 2-qubit state is

$$U_{CNOT}|\psi\rangle \doteq \begin{pmatrix} 1 & 0 & 0 & 0 \\ 0 & 1 & 0 & 0 \\ 0 & 0 & 0 & 1 \\ 0 & 0 & 1 & 0 \end{pmatrix} \begin{pmatrix} c_{00} \\ c_{01} \\ c_{10} \\ c_{11} \end{pmatrix} = \begin{pmatrix} c'_{00} \\ c'_{01} \\ c'_{10} \\ c'_{11} \end{pmatrix}. \tag{42}$$

A schematic diagram of a *CNOT* gate is shown in Fig. The 1-qubit *NOT* (*X*) gate acts on the target bit based upon the condition of the control bit. The conditional connection is depicted by the vertical line and node connecting the control qubit with the *NOT* gate.

The physical implementation of a *CNOT* gate is more complicated than the 1-qubit gates described above. The conditional connection between the two qubits requires an interaction between the two physical qubits. For example, two spin-1/2 particles can interact through their magnetic moments, causing a coupling of the Larmor precession frequencies.

One of the most important applications of a *CNOT* gate is to make entangled states. To make an entangled 2-qubit state, like an EPR state, we combine a 1-qubit Hadamard gate and a 2-qubit *CNOT* gate, as shown in Fig. 17. The Hadamard gate acts on the input control qubit to place it into a superposition state, then the *CNOT* gate couples the two qubits together to make an entangled state.

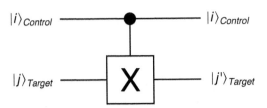

FIGURE 16 A 2-qubit controlled-NOT gate has a 1-qubit *NOT* gate (*X*) on the target qubit, which is conditionally activated based upon the control qubit.

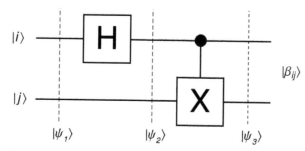

FIGURE 17   Preparation of an entangled Bell state by application of a Hadamard gate (H) and a controlled-NOT gate.

Example 2   Entangled state preparation   Show that the combination of a Hadamard gate and a *CNOT* gate (Fig. 17) acting on the input state $|11\rangle$ produces an entangled Bell state.

The input state of the system is

$$|\psi_1\rangle = |11\rangle = |1\rangle_C|1\rangle_T. \tag{43}$$

The Hadamard gate acts only on the control qubit, with the result

$$|\psi_2\rangle = U_{Had,C}|\psi_1\rangle = (U_{Had,C}|1\rangle_C)|1\rangle_T. \tag{44}$$

The transformation of the single control qubit is

$$
\begin{aligned}
U_{Had,C}|1\rangle_C &\doteq \frac{1}{\sqrt{2}}\begin{pmatrix} 1 & 1 \\ 1 & -1 \end{pmatrix}\begin{pmatrix} 0 \\ 1 \end{pmatrix} \\
&\doteq \frac{1}{\sqrt{2}}\begin{pmatrix} 1 \\ -1 \end{pmatrix} \\
&= \frac{1}{\sqrt{2}}(|0\rangle_C - |1\rangle_C).
\end{aligned} \tag{45}
$$

The resultant state of the 2-qubit system before the *CNOT* gate is

$$|\psi_2\rangle = \frac{1}{\sqrt{2}}(|0\rangle_C - |1\rangle_C)|1\rangle_T = \frac{1}{\sqrt{2}}(|01\rangle - |11\rangle) \doteq \frac{1}{\sqrt{2}}\begin{pmatrix} 0 \\ 1 \\ 0 \\ -1 \end{pmatrix}. \tag{46}$$

The transformation of the *CNOT* gate is

$$|\psi_3\rangle = U_{CNOT}|\psi_2\rangle \doteq \frac{1}{\sqrt{2}}\begin{pmatrix} 1 & 0 & 0 & 0 \\ 0 & 1 & 0 & 0 \\ 0 & 0 & 0 & 1 \\ 0 & 0 & 1 & 0 \end{pmatrix}\begin{pmatrix} 0 \\ 1 \\ 0 \\ -1 \end{pmatrix} = \begin{pmatrix} 0 \\ 1 \\ -1 \\ 0 \end{pmatrix}. \tag{47}$$

The output state is thus

$$|\psi_3\rangle = \frac{1}{\sqrt{2}}(|01\rangle - |10\rangle). \tag{48}$$

This is the entangled Bell state $|\beta_{11}\rangle$ from Eq. (23).

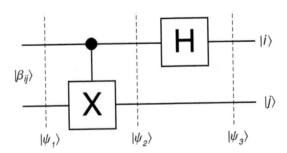

FIGURE 18 Transformation of a Bell state to the computational basis with a *CNOT* gate and a Hadamard gate.

Now we see why we labeled the Bell states as we did. The particular Bell state produced in Example 2 is labeled $|\beta_{11}\rangle$ because we started with the input state $|11\rangle$. The four Bell states are produced by using one of the basis states $|00\rangle, |01\rangle, |10\rangle,$ or $|11\rangle$ as the input into the combined Hadamard and *CNOT* gates (Problem 14).

The beauty of the 2-qubit *CNOT* gate is that it lets us transform between the computational basis and the Bell basis, when combined with the 1-qubit Hadamard gates. If we reverse the order of the Hadamard and *CNOT* gates, as shown in Fig. 18, then Bell states are transformed into computational basis states (Problem 15). Hence, to determine which Bell state a system is in, we perform the transformation in Fig. 18 and then measure the single qubits (e.g., the z-components of the spins). The four possible results $ij = 00, 01, 10, 11$ then correspond to the four Bell states of Eq. (23). This is called a **Bell-state measurement**.

2.3 ■ Quantum Teleportation

Using the tools we have described above, we now illustrate the use of entangled states (quantum spookiness) as a resource. The problem we want to solve is how to transmit information about an unknown quantum state. Imagine that Carol has given Alice a "secret" message in the form of a single qubit that she wants Alice to transmit to Bob. Without giving the qubit directly to Bob, how can Alice convey the information with the highest probability of success? The answer lies in utilizing entangled states, as depicted in Fig. 19. In a nutshell, Alice and Bob share an entangled state of two qubits that was previously prepared and is independent of Carol's secret message qubit. Alice performs a Bell-state measurement on the two-state system comprising Carol's qubit and Alice's half of the entangled state she shares with Bob. Alice than transmits the results of her measurement to Bob who performs a unitary transformation on his half of the entangled state, and voilà, his qubit is in the same state as Carol's secret message. Let's see how this works in detail.

Alice and Bob have previously met and share an entangled state, meaning that each has one of the two qubits of a Bell state, which we assume to be the $|\beta_{00}\rangle$ state. Using explicit subscripts to distinguish the different qubits held by Alice (A), Bob (B), and Carol (C), we denote the entangled state shared by Alice and Bob as

$$|\beta_{00}\rangle_{AB} = \tfrac{1}{\sqrt{2}}(|00\rangle_{AB} + |11\rangle_{AB}) = \tfrac{1}{\sqrt{2}}|0\rangle_A|0\rangle_B + \tfrac{1}{\sqrt{2}}|1\rangle_A|1\rangle_B. \tag{49}$$

The secret qubit that Carol wants Alice to convey to Bob is in a general, unknown superposition state

$$|\psi_{\text{secret}}\rangle_C = \alpha_0|0\rangle_C + \alpha_1|1\rangle_C. \tag{50}$$

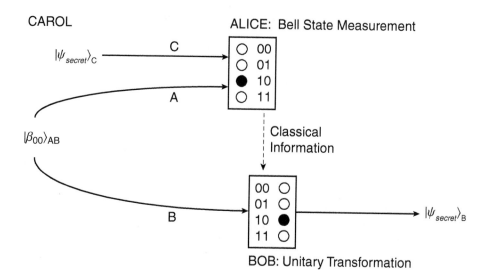

CAROL

$|\psi_{secret}\rangle_C$

ALICE: Bell State Measurement

○ 00
○ 01
● 10
○ 11

C

A

$|\beta_{00}\rangle_{AB}$

Classical
Information

B

00 ○
01 ○
10 ●
11 ○

$|\psi_{secret}\rangle_B$

BOB: Unitary Transformation

FIGURE 19 Quantum teleportation of a secret qubit from Alice to Bob. Alice and Bob share the entangled qubit pair AB. Alice makes a Bell-state measurement upon the AC qubit pair. Alice transmits the result, 10 for example, to Bob, who applies the appropriate unitary transformation (see Table 2) to his qubit B, which is then in the same state as the original secret qubit C.

If Alice had many copies of this state, she could make repeated measurements and determine the coefficients α_0 and α_1 with a statistical uncertainty based on the number of copies. But with only one copy of the state, Alice is hard pressed to make a meaningful measurement of the state and send the secret message to Bob.

Alice's solution is to make a joint measurement on the system comprising the secret qubit C and the single qubit A of the entangled $|\beta_{00}\rangle_{AB}$ state that she shares with Bob. By a joint measurement, we mean that she performs a Bell-state measurement by applying a *CNOT* gate and a Hadamard gate to the A and C qubits to transform to the computational basis (Fig. 18) and then measuring the single qubits. To see why Alice's Bell-state measurement is useful, consider the state vector for the complete three-qubit system

$$|\psi_{ABC}\rangle = |\beta_{00}\rangle_{AB}|\psi_{secret}\rangle_C$$
$$= \left(\tfrac{1}{\sqrt{2}}|0\rangle_A|0\rangle_B + \tfrac{1}{\sqrt{2}}|1\rangle_A|1\rangle_B\right)\left(\alpha_0|0\rangle_C + \alpha_1|1\rangle_C\right) \tag{51}$$
$$= \tfrac{\alpha_0}{\sqrt{2}}|0\rangle_A|0\rangle_B|0\rangle_C + \tfrac{\alpha_0}{\sqrt{2}}|1\rangle_A|1\rangle_B|0\rangle_C + \tfrac{\alpha_1}{\sqrt{2}}|0\rangle_A|0\rangle_B|1\rangle_C + \tfrac{\alpha_1}{\sqrt{2}}|1\rangle_A|1\rangle_B|1\rangle_C.$$

The qubits A and C are not entangled (they have never interacted), but we are free to write the system state vector in terms of the basis of entangled Bell states $|\beta_{ij}\rangle_{AC}$ of those two qubits. Some algebra reveals that the state vector of the system expressed in this way is (Problem 16)

$$|\psi_{ABC}\rangle = \frac{1}{2}\big\{|\beta_{00}\rangle_{AC}\left(\alpha_0|0\rangle_B + \alpha_1|1\rangle_B\right)$$
$$+ |\beta_{01}\rangle_{AC}\left(\alpha_1|0\rangle_B + \alpha_0|1\rangle_B\right)$$
$$+ |\beta_{10}\rangle_{AC}\left(\alpha_0|0\rangle_B - \alpha_1|1\rangle_B\right)$$
$$+ |\beta_{11}\rangle_{AC}\left(\alpha_1|0\rangle_B - \alpha_0|1\rangle_B\right)\big\}. \tag{52}$$

Table 2 Quantum Teleportation of a Secret State from Alice to Bob

Alice measures	Alice transmits	Bob applies	Bob transforms
$|\beta_{00}\rangle$	00	**1**	$\mathbf{1}(\alpha_0|0\rangle_B + \alpha_1|1\rangle_B) = |\psi_{\text{secret}}\rangle_B$
$|\beta_{01}\rangle$	01	U_{NOT}	$U_{NOT}(\alpha_1|0\rangle_B + \alpha_0|1\rangle_B) = |\psi_{\text{secret}}\rangle_B$
$|\beta_{10}\rangle$	10	U_Z	$U_Z(\alpha_0|0\rangle_B - \alpha_1|1\rangle_B) = |\psi_{\text{secret}}\rangle_B$
$|\beta_{11}\rangle$	11	$U_Z U_{NOT}$	$U_Z U_{NOT}(\alpha_1|0\rangle_B - \alpha_0|1\rangle_B) = |\psi_{\text{secret}}\rangle_B$

By expressing the state vector in this Bell basis, we identify a correlation between each Bell state of the qubits A and C and the state of Bob's qubit B, which turns out to be a superposition state with the secret coefficients from Carol! For example, if Alice's Bell-state measurement indicates that the A and C qubits are in the state $|\beta_{00}\rangle_{AC}$, then Bob's qubit B is in the state

$$|\psi\rangle_B = \alpha_0|0\rangle_B + \alpha_1|1\rangle_B. \tag{53}$$

This is exactly the secret state that Carol gave to Alice. There are four possible results of Alice's Bell-state measurement, each with a probability of 25%, indicating that the qubits A and C are indeed not entangled. If Alice measures one of the other Bell states, then she communicates her results to Bob over a classical channel (she calls him on the phone) and tells him to perform a unitary transformation on his qubit to change it to the secret state. The transformations that Bob must perform are indicated in Table 2 (Problem 17).

With this quantum teleportation scheme, Alice has conveyed Carol's secret message to Bob using only a classical information channel, and the prearranged Bell state $|\beta_{00}\rangle_{AB}$. Note that neither Alice nor Bob know what the secret state is. Alice has destroyed all her qubits by measuring them, and her results reveal no information to her about the secret message. Bob has not measured anything yet, but has the secret qubit in his possession as long as he does what Alice tells him to do. More precisely, he has a qubit that is in the same state as Carol's original qubit. The actual physical qubit representing the secret message (e.g., a particle with spin) is still with Alice, or destroyed in detection. Only the quantum information about the state of the secret qubit has been teleported to Bob.

This scheme is made possible by the Bell state that Alice and Bob have set up previously. The correlations inherent in that entangled state allow Alice to tell Bob what quantum gates he must use to transform his half of their Bell state into the secret message. This is one of many examples that demonstrate the utility of entangled quantum states for information processing.

SUMMARY

These two examples have provided a mere taste of the fun you can have with quantum mechanics. Magnetic trapping, laser cooling, and quantum information processing are just a few of the current research topics that employ the quantum mechanics you have learned. If our brief overview has raised more questions than we have answered, then we have at least planted the seed for you to delve deeper into these subjects. As with any research field, there are still more questions to be raised and answers to be discovered. Enjoy!

RESOURCES

Further Reading

These references provide further details on laser cooling and magnetic traps for atoms:

H. J. Metcalf and P. van der Straten, *Laser Cooling and Trapping*, New York: Springer University Press, 1999.

C. J. Foot, *Atomic Physics*, Oxford: Oxford University Press, 2005.

M. Fox, *Quantum Optics: An Introduction*, Oxford: Oxford University Press, 2006.

B. H. Bransden and C. J. Joachain, *Physics of Atoms and Molecules*, 2nd ed., Harlow, England: Prentice Hall, 2003.

C. Wieman, G. Flowers, and S. Gilbert, "Inexpensive laser cooling and trapping experiment for undergraduate laboratories," *Am. J. Phys.* **63**, 317–330 (1995).

P. Gould, "Laser cooling of atoms to the Doppler limit," *Am. J. Phys.* **65**, 1120–1123 (1997).

The Nobel Prize in Physics 1997, Nobelprize.org:

http://nobelprize.org/nobel_prizes/physics/laureates/1997/

These references provide further details on magnetic traps for macroscopic objects:

A. Geim, "Everyone's Magnetism," *Phys. Today* **51**(9), 36–39 (1998).

M. D. Simon, L. O. Heflinger, and S. L. Ridgway, "Spin stabilized magnetic levitation," *Am. J. Phys.* **65**, 286–292 (1997).

M. V. Berry and A. K. Geim, "Of flying frogs and levitrons," *Eur. J. Phys.* **18**, 307–313 (1997).

M. V. Berry, "The Levitron™: an Adiabatic Trap for Spins," *Proc. R. Soc. Lond. A* **452**, 1207–1220 (1996).

T. B. Jones, M. Washizu, and R. Gans, "Simple theory for the Levitron," *J. Appl. Phys.* **82**, 883–888 (1997).

These references provide further details on quantum information processing:

R. P. Feynman, "Simulating Physics with Computers," *Int. J. Theor. Phys.* **21**, 467–488 (1982).

S. M. Barnett, *Quantum Information*, Oxford: Oxford University Press, 2009.

P. Kaye, R. Laflamme, and M. Mosca, *An Introduction to Quantum Computing*, Oxford: Oxford University Press, 2007.

M. A. Nielsen and I. L. Chuang, *Quantum Computation and Quantum Information*, Cambridge: Cambridge University Press, 2000.

Modern Applications of Quantum Mechanics: Problem Set

1 Calculate the angular deflection of a room temperature rubidium atom traveling through the magnetic field gradient of a Stern-Gerlach device. Assume the gradient is $100 \, \text{G/cm} = 1 \, \text{T/m}$ and that the magnetic moment is one Bohr magneton.

2 Show that for an atom in a typical magnetic trap, the magnetic moment adiabatically follows the changing magnetic field direction. That is, show that the Larmor precession frequency is much larger than the frequency of motion in the trap. Estimate the motional frequency by considering the circular motion (radius 1 cm) of a rubidium atom in the trapping potential shown in Fig. 4.

3 Find the distance required to stop a room-temperature rubidium atom with the resonant scattering force. Do the same for a sodium atom.

4 The general expression for the scattering force that is valid for all intensities is

$$F_{scatt} = \hbar k \, \frac{A_{21}}{2} \, \frac{I}{I_0} \, \frac{\left(\dfrac{A_{21}}{2}\right)^2}{\left(\omega_{Laser} - \omega_{21} + kv\right)^2 + \left(\dfrac{A_{21}}{2}\right)^2 \left(1 + \dfrac{I}{I_0}\right)},$$

where I_0 is a characteristic intensity. Show that this force has the same maximum value given by Eq. (8),

$$\mathbf{F}_{max} = \frac{d\mathbf{p}}{dt} = \frac{\langle \Delta \mathbf{p} \rangle_{cycle}}{\langle \Delta t \rangle_{min}} = \frac{\hbar \mathbf{k}}{2\tau}, \tag{8}$$

and state the conditions required to achieve that maximum force. Plot the force as a function of intensity and suggest a name for I_0.

5 Show that rubidium atoms with velocity $v = 350 \, \text{m/s}$ are resonant with a counterpropagating laser with a frequency detuning $f_{Laser} - f_{21} = -450 \, \text{MHz}$.

6 Calculate the maximum chirp rate (frequency change per unit time interval) of a laser used in chirped laser cooling of rubidium atoms.

7 Calculate the linear friction coefficient of optical molasses, (i.e., find the slope of the force curve in Fig. 12 for low velocities).

8 For an N-qubit system, a general superposition state (which includes *entangled* states) contains 2^N pieces of information [see Eq. (22)],

$$|\psi\rangle = c_{00}|00\rangle + c_{01}|01\rangle + c_{10}|10\rangle + c_{11}|11\rangle, \tag{22}$$

and a *product* superposition state (nonentangled) contains $2 \times N$ pieces of information [see Eq. (24)],

$$|\psi\rangle = \left(a_0|0\rangle_A + a_1|1\rangle_A\right)\left(b_0|0\rangle_B + b_1|1\rangle_B\right). \tag{24}$$

Demonstrate this for $N = 3$ and $N = 4$.

From Chapter 16 of *Quantum Mechanics: A Paradigms Approach*, First Edition. David H. McIntyre. Copyright © 2012 by Pearson Education, Inc. Published by Pearson Addison-Wesley. All rights reserved.

The companion websites for this text are http://physics.oregonstate.edu/portfolioswiki and http://physics.oregonstate.edu/qmactivities.

9 Verify the operation of a quantum *NOT* gate by acting on the computational basis states with the unitary matrix U_{NOT}. Demonstrate that the transformation matrix is unitary by showing that the norm of a general superposition state is unchanged by the transformation.

10 Show that the transformation matrix for a π rotation about the z-axis is the Pauli matrix σ_z. (Hint: as in Example 1, ignore an overall phase.)

11 Show that the transformation matrix for a π rotation about the y-axis is the Pauli matrix σ_y. (Hint: as in Example 1, ignore an overall phase.)

12 Show that the Hadamard gate for a spin-1/2 system can be made with a π rotation about the z-axis followed by a $\pi/2$ rotation about the y-axis.

13 Using the transformation equations of the *CNOT* gate in Eq. (40),

$$
\begin{aligned}
U_{CNOT}|00\rangle &= |00\rangle \\
U_{CNOT}|01\rangle &= |01\rangle \\
U_{CNOT}|10\rangle &= |11\rangle \\
U_{CNOT}|11\rangle &= |10\rangle,
\end{aligned}
\tag{40}
$$

derive the transformation matrix in Eq. (41),

$$
U_{CNOT} \doteq \begin{pmatrix} 1 & 0 & 0 & 0 \\ 0 & 1 & 0 & 0 \\ 0 & 0 & 0 & 1 \\ 0 & 0 & 1 & 0 \end{pmatrix}.
\tag{41}
$$

14 Show that the combination of a Hadamard gate and a *CNOT* gate (see Fig. 17) transforms the computational basis states $|00\rangle, |01\rangle$, and $|10\rangle$ into Bell states.

15 Show that the combination of a *CNOT* gate and a Hadamard gate (see Fig. 18) transforms a Bell state into a computational basis state, for each of the possible Bell states.

16 Show that the complete state vector for Alice, Bob, and Carol's qubits can be written as in Eq. (52),

$$
\begin{aligned}
|\psi_{ABC}\rangle = \frac{1}{2}\{ &|\beta_{00}\rangle_{AC} \left(\alpha_0|0\rangle_B + \alpha_1|1\rangle_B\right) \\
+ &|\beta_{01}\rangle_{AC} \left(\alpha_1|0\rangle_B + \alpha_0|1\rangle_B\right) \\
+ &|\beta_{10}\rangle_{AC} \left(\alpha_0|0\rangle_B - \alpha_1|1\rangle_B\right) \\
+ &|\beta_{11}\rangle_{AC} \left(\alpha_1|0\rangle_B - \alpha_0|1\rangle_B\right) \}.
\end{aligned}
\tag{52}
$$

17 Show that the transformations that Alice asks Bob to do (see Table 2) produce the secret state.

APPENDIX

Physical Constants

These values are taken from: "CODATA recommended values of the fundamental physical constants: 2006," P. J. Mohr, B. N. Taylor, and D. B. Newell, *Rev. Mod Phys.* **80**, 633–730 (2008). Experimental uncertainties are shown in parentheses.

Quantity	Symbol	Value
Speed of light in vacuum	c	$299\ 792\ 458$ m/s (*Exact*)
Permeability of free space	μ_0	$4\pi \times 10^{-7}$ N·s^2/C^2 (*Exact*)
Permittivity of free space	$\varepsilon_0 = 1/\mu_0 c^2$	$8.854\ 187\ 817... \times 10^{-12}$ C^2/N·m^2 (*Exact*)
Planck's constant	$\hbar$	$6.582\ 118\ 99\,(16) \times 10^{-16}$ eV·s
		$1.054\ 571\ 628\,(53) \times 10^{-34}$ J·s
	$h = 2\pi\hbar$	$4.135\ 667\ 33\,(10) \times 10^{-15}$ eV·s
		$6.626\ 068\ 96\,(33) \times 10^{-34}$ J·s
Elementary charge	e	$1.602\ 176\ 487\,(40) \times 10^{-19}$ C
Electron mass	m_e	$0.510\ 998\ 910\,(13)$ MeV/c^2
		$9.109\ 382\ 15\,(45) \times 10^{-31}$ kg
Proton mass	m_p	$938.272\ 013\,(23)$ MeV/c^2
		$1.672\ 621\ 637\,(83) \times 10^{-27}$ kg
Fine structure constant	$\alpha = \dfrac{e^2}{4\pi\varepsilon_0\hbar c}$	$\dfrac{1}{137.035\ 999\ 679\,(94)}$
Rydberg constant	$R_\infty = \dfrac{\alpha^2 m_e c}{2h}$	$10\ 973\ 731.568\ 527\,(73)$ m^{-1}
	$R_\infty c$	$3.289\ 841\ 960\ 361\,(22) \times 10^{15}$ Hz
Rydberg energy	$Ryd = R_\infty hc$	$13.605\ 691\ 93\,(34)$ eV
Bohr radius	$a_0 = \dfrac{4\pi\varepsilon_0\hbar^2}{m_e e^2}$	$0.529\ 177\ 208\ 59\,(36) \times 10^{-10}$ m
Bohr magneton	$\mu_B = \dfrac{e\hbar}{2m_e}$	$9.274\ 009\ 15\,(23) \times 10^{-24}$ J/T
	μ_B/h	$1.399\ 624\ 604\,(35)$ MHz/Gauss

The companion websites for this text are http://physics.oregonstate.edu/portfolioswiki and http://physics.oregonstate.edu/qmactivities.

Appendix: Physical Constants

Nuclear magneton	$\mu_N = \dfrac{e\hbar}{2m_p}$	$5.050\,783\,24\,(13) \times 10^{-27}\,\text{J/T}$
Boltzmann constant	k_B	$1.380\,650\,4\,(24) \times 10^{-23}\,\text{J/K}$

Conversion factors

$1\,\text{J} = 10^7\,\text{erg} = 6.24151 \times 10^{18}\,\text{eV}$

$1\,\text{eV} = 1.60218 \times 10^{-19}\,\text{J}$

$1\,\text{eV}$ corresponds to $(E = hf = hc/\lambda = hc\bar{\nu})$

$\quad 2.41799 \times 10^{14}\,\text{Hz}\ (f = E/h)$

$\quad 1239.84\,\text{nm}\ (\lambda = hc/E)$

$\quad 8065.54\,\text{cm}^{-1}\ (\bar{\nu} = E/hc)$

$1\,\text{cm}^{-1}$ corresponds to

$\quad 29.9792458\,\text{GHz}\ (f = c\bar{\nu})$

$\quad 10^7\,\text{nm}\ (\lambda = 1/\bar{\nu})$

$\quad 1.23984 \times 10^{-4}\,\text{eV}\ (E = hc\bar{\nu})$

$hc = 1240\,\text{eV} \cdot \text{nm}$

$1\,\text{amu} = 931.494\,\text{MeV}/\text{c}^2 = 1.66054 \times 10^{-27}\,\text{kg}$

APPENDIX

Integrals

A small collection of useful integrals is listed below. You may already be accustomed to using Maple or Mathematica to do integrals, which is not too different than looking up an integral in this table. But be careful to not become too reliant on the computer. For example, if the computer tells you the answer is zero, then maybe that should have been obvious from examining the symmetry of the integrand.

$$\int \sin mx \sin nx \, dx = \frac{\sin(m-n)x}{2(m-n)} - \frac{\sin(m+n)x}{2(m+n)}, \left(m^2 \neq n^2\right) \tag{1}$$

$$\int \cos mx \cos nx \, dx = \frac{\sin(m-n)x}{2(m-n)} + \frac{\sin(m+n)x}{2(m+n)}, \left(m^2 \neq n^2\right) \tag{2}$$

$$\int \sin mx \cos nx \, dx = -\frac{\cos(m-n)x}{2(m-n)} - \frac{\cos(m+n)x}{2(m+n)}, \left(m^2 \neq n^2\right) \tag{3}$$

$$\int \sin^2 ax \, dx = \frac{1}{2}x - \frac{1}{2a}\sin ax \cos ax \tag{4}$$

$$\int \cos^2 ax \, dx = \frac{1}{2}x + \frac{1}{2a}\sin ax \cos ax \tag{5}$$

$$\int \sin ax \cos ax \, dx = \frac{1}{2a}\sin^2 ax \tag{6}$$

$$\int \sin ax \cos^m ax \, dx = -\frac{\cos^{m+1} ax}{(m+1)a} \tag{7}$$

$$\int \sin^m ax \cos ax \, dx = \frac{\sin^{m+1} ax}{(m+1)a} \tag{8}$$

$$\int x \sin ax \, dx = \frac{1}{a^2}\sin ax - \frac{x}{a}\cos ax \tag{9}$$

$$\int x \cos ax \, dx = \frac{1}{a^2}\cos ax + \frac{x}{a}\sin ax \tag{10}$$

$$\int x^2 \sin ax \, dx = \frac{2x}{a^2}\sin ax - \frac{a^2x^2 - 2}{a^3}\cos ax \tag{11}$$

From Appendix F of *Quantum Mechanics: A Paradigms Approach*, First Edition. David H. McIntyre. Copyright © 2012 by Pearson Education, Inc. Published by Pearson Addison-Wesley. All rights reserved.

The companion websites for this text are http://physics.oregonstate.edu/portfolioswiki and http://physics.oregonstate.edu/qmactivities.

$$\int x^2 \cos ax\, dx = \frac{2x}{a^2}\cos ax + \frac{a^2 x^2 - 2}{a^3}\sin ax \tag{12}$$

$$\int x \sin^2 ax\, dx = \frac{x^2}{4} - \frac{x}{4a}\sin 2ax - \frac{1}{8a^2}\cos 2ax \tag{13}$$

$$\int x \cos^2 ax\, dx = \frac{x^2}{4} + \frac{x}{4a}\sin 2ax + \frac{1}{8a^2}\cos 2ax \tag{14}$$

$$\int x^2 \sin^2 ax\, dx = \frac{x^3}{6} - \left(\frac{x^2}{4a} - \frac{1}{8a^3}\right)\sin 2ax - \frac{x}{4a^2}\cos 2ax \tag{15}$$

$$\int x^2 \cos^2 ax\, dx = \frac{x^3}{6} + \left(\frac{x^2}{4a} - \frac{1}{8a^3}\right)\sin 2ax + \frac{x}{4a^2}\cos 2ax \tag{16}$$

$$\int x e^{-x}\, dx = -x e^{-x} - e^{-x} \tag{17}$$

$$\int x^2 e^{-x}\, dx = -x^2 e^{-x} - 2x e^{-x} - 2e^{-x} \tag{18}$$

$$\int x^3 e^{-x}\, dx = -x^3 e^{-x} - 3x^2 e^{-x} - 6x e^{-x} - 6e^{-x} \tag{19}$$

$$\int x^4 e^{-x}\, dx = -x^4 e^{-x} - 4x^3 e^{-x} - 12x^2 e^{-x} - 24x e^{-x} - 24e^{-x} \tag{20}$$

$$\int_0^\infty x^n e^{-ax}\, dx = \frac{n!}{a^{n+1}} \tag{21}$$

$$\int_0^\infty e^{-a^2 x^2}\, dx = \frac{1}{2a}\sqrt{\pi} \tag{22}$$

$$\int_{-\infty}^\infty e^{-a^2 x^2 + bx}\, dx = \frac{\sqrt{\pi}}{a} e^{b^2/4a^2} \tag{23}$$

$$\int_0^\infty x e^{-x^2}\, dx = \frac{1}{2} \tag{24}$$

$$\int_0^\infty x^2 e^{-x^2}\, dx = \frac{\sqrt{\pi}}{4} \tag{25}$$

$$\int_0^\infty x^{2n} e^{-x^2}\, dx = \sqrt{\pi}\,\frac{(2n)!}{n!}\frac{1}{2^{2n+1}} \tag{26}$$

$$\int_0^\infty x^{2n+1} e^{-x^2}\, dx = \frac{n!}{2} \tag{27}$$

APPENDIX

Matrices

We present some of the basic definitions and properties of matrices necessary to implement the matrix formulation of quantum mechanics. We adopt the Dirac bra-ket notation. We adopt the quantum mechanical viewpoint that matrices are representations of operators or states and so we use the $\doteq$ notation where appropriate to mean "is represented by."

A **matrix** is an ordered array of numbers:

$$A \doteq \begin{pmatrix} A_{11} & A_{12} & A_{13} & \cdots \\ A_{21} & A_{22} & A_{23} & \cdots \\ A_{31} & A_{32} & A_{33} & \cdots \\ \vdots & \vdots & \vdots & \ddots \end{pmatrix}, \tag{1}$$

where the subscript labels the rows and columns:

$$A_{ij} = \text{ Matrix element in the } i^{th} \text{ row and } j^{th} \text{ column.} \tag{2}$$

A **vector** is a special case of a matrix with only one column or row. A **column vector**

$$|a\rangle \doteq \begin{pmatrix} a_1 \\ a_2 \\ a_3 \\ \vdots \end{pmatrix} \tag{3}$$

requires only one subscript to label its elements. A **row vector** has its elements arranged in a row

$$\langle b| \doteq \begin{pmatrix} b_1 & b_2 & b_3 & \cdots \end{pmatrix}. \tag{4}$$

To add matrices, we add the corresponding elements:

$$C_{ij} = A_{ij} + B_{ij}. \tag{5}$$

For example, given the two matrices

$$A \doteq \begin{pmatrix} a & b \\ c & d \end{pmatrix}, \qquad B \doteq \begin{pmatrix} e & f \\ g & h \end{pmatrix}, \tag{6}$$

From Appendix C of *Quantum Mechanics: A Paradigms Approach*, First Edition. David H. McIntyre. Copyright © 2012 by Pearson Education, Inc. Published by Pearson Addison-Wesley. All rights reserved.

The companion websites for this text are http://physics.oregonstate.edu/portfolioswiki and http://physics.oregonstate.edu/qmactivities.

their sum is

$$A + B \doteq \begin{pmatrix} a & b \\ c & d \end{pmatrix} + \begin{pmatrix} e & f \\ g & h \end{pmatrix} = \begin{pmatrix} a+e & b+f \\ c+g & d+h \end{pmatrix}. \tag{7}$$

For addition, the two matrices must have the same size and shape and the result is the same size and shape.

Matrix multiplication is more complicated. If we multiply two matrices A and B to form a third matrix C, then the elements of the matrix C are

$$C_{ij} = \sum_{k=1}^{n} A_{ik} B_{kj}. \tag{8}$$

For example, given the two matrices

$$A \doteq \begin{pmatrix} a & b \\ c & d \end{pmatrix}, \qquad B \doteq \begin{pmatrix} e & f \\ g & h \end{pmatrix}, \tag{9}$$

their product is

$$AB \doteq \begin{pmatrix} a & b \\ c & d \end{pmatrix}\begin{pmatrix} e & f \\ g & h \end{pmatrix} = \begin{pmatrix} ae+bg & af+bh \\ ce+dg & cf+dh \end{pmatrix}. \tag{10}$$

In general, Eq. (8) tells us that to find the matrix element C_{ij} in the ith row and j^{th} column of C, take the ith row of the matrix A and overlay it on top of the jth column of the matrix B. Multiply each pair of overlaid numbers and sum the products. For this to make any sense, the number of elements in a row of A must equal the number of elements in a column of B, which means that the number of columns in A must equal the number of rows in B. Thus, if A is an $\ell \times n$ matrix and B is an $n \times m$ matrix, then the product $C = AB$ is an $\ell \times m$ matrix. Matrix multiplication is not commutative, that is

$$AB \neq BA \tag{11}$$

in general.

The rules of matrix multiplication make it clear that multiplication of a column vector by a matrix yields another column vector

$$A|a\rangle = |b\rangle \tag{12}$$

and multiplication of a row vector and a matrix yields another row vector

$$\langle c|A = \langle d|, \tag{13}$$

but each must occur in the order shown. The product of a row vector and a column vector in the "proper" bra-ket order is an **inner product**

$$\big(\langle b|\big)\big(|a\rangle\big) = \langle b|a\rangle \tag{14}$$

or a **scalar product** because the result is a scalar. For example,

$$\langle b|a\rangle = \begin{pmatrix} r & s & t \end{pmatrix}\begin{pmatrix} u \\ v \\ w \end{pmatrix} = ru + sv + tw. \tag{15}$$

The product of a row vector and a column vector in the "wrong" ket-bra order is an **outer product**

$$\big(|a\rangle\big)\big(\langle b|\big) = |a\rangle\langle b|, \tag{16}$$

which is a matrix. For example,

$$|a\rangle\langle b| \doteq \begin{pmatrix} u \\ v \\ w \end{pmatrix} \begin{pmatrix} r & s & t \end{pmatrix} = \begin{pmatrix} ur & us & ut \\ vr & vs & vt \\ wr & ws & wt \end{pmatrix}. \tag{17}$$

The **transpose** of a matrix is obtained by interchanging rows and columns. In component notation this means that

$$\left(A^T\right)_{ij} = A_{ji}. \tag{18}$$

For example, if the matrix A is

$$A \doteq \begin{pmatrix} a & b \\ c & d \end{pmatrix}, \tag{19}$$

then the transpose A^T is

$$A^T \doteq \begin{pmatrix} a & c \\ b & d \end{pmatrix}. \tag{20}$$

A matrix is called **symmetric** if it is equal to its transpose, $A = A^T$. The transpose of a column vector is a row vector.

The **Hermitian conjugate** (or **adjoint**) of a matrix is obtained by transposing the matrix *and* complex conjugating each element. We denote the Hermitian conjugate with a dagger †. In component notation, the Hermitian conjugate is

$$\left(A^\dagger\right)_{ij} = A_{ji}^*. \tag{21}$$

For example, if the matrix A is

$$A \doteq \begin{pmatrix} a & b \\ c & d \end{pmatrix}, \tag{22}$$

then the Hermitian conjugate $A^\dagger$ is

$$A^\dagger \doteq \begin{pmatrix} a^* & c^* \\ b^* & d^* \end{pmatrix}. \tag{23}$$

A matrix is called **Hermitian** (or **self-adjoint**) if it is equal to its Hermitian conjugate, $A = A^\dagger$. In quantum mechanics, all operators that correspond to physical observables are Hermitian operators.

The **determinant** of a matrix is defined as the sum of the products of the elements of any row (or column) with the cofactors of those elements. The **cofactor** of an element A_{ij} of a matrix is the product of the factor $(-1)^{i+j}$ and the determinant of the submatrix obtained by striking out the row and column containing A_{ij}. For example, the determinant of the 2×2 matrix A in Eq. (22) is

$$\det(A) = \begin{vmatrix} a & b \\ c & d \end{vmatrix} = ad - bc. \tag{24}$$

The determinant of a 3×3 matrix is

$$\det(A) = \begin{vmatrix} a & b & c \\ d & e & f \\ g & h & i \end{vmatrix} = a(-1)^{1+1}\begin{vmatrix} e & f \\ h & i \end{vmatrix} + b(-1)^{1+2}\begin{vmatrix} d & f \\ g & i \end{vmatrix} + c(-1)^{1+3}\begin{vmatrix} d & e \\ g & h \end{vmatrix} \tag{25}$$

$$= a(ei - fh) - b(di - fg) + c(dh - eg).$$

The **eigenvalues** and **eigenvectors** of a matrix are found by solving the eigenvalue problem:

$$A|a\rangle = \lambda|a\rangle, \tag{26}$$

where λ are the eigenvalues and $|a\rangle$ are the eigenvectors. The eigenvalue equation has a solution when the determinant of the coefficients of the homogeneous equations is zero:

$$\det(A - \lambda\mathbf{1}) = 0, \tag{27}$$

that is

$$\det\begin{pmatrix} A_{11} - \lambda & A_{12} & A_{13} & \cdots \\ A_{21} & A_{22} - \lambda & A_{23} & \cdots \\ A_{31} & A_{32} & A_{33} - \lambda & \cdots \\ \vdots & \vdots & \vdots & \ddots \end{pmatrix} = 0. \tag{28}$$

The resulting equation is the **characteristic equation** and its solution yields the eigenvalues of the matrix. For an $n \times n$ matrix, the characteristic equation is an nth order equation and yields n solutions, though some may be **degenerate** or equal. To find the eigenvectors of the matrix, we substitute each eigenvalue in turn into the eigenvalue equation (26) and solve for the corresponding eigenvector.

RESOURCES

Activities

Math Primer Course: A weeklong course that reviews matrix algebra and frames the discussion of matrices in the context of vectors spaces and linear transformations. The course includes several student activities.

www.physics.oregonstate.edu/portfolioswiki/courses:home:prhome

APPENDIX

Waves and Fourier Analysis

1 ■ CLASSICAL WAVES

A classical wave in one dimension is represented by a function $f(x,t)$ that is a solution of the classical wave equation

$$\frac{\partial^2 f(x,t)}{\partial x^2} = \frac{1}{v^2} \frac{\partial^2 f(x,t)}{\partial t^2},$$

(1)

where v is the wave speed. This equation is applicable to water waves, waves on a string, electromagnetic waves, and other types of classical waves. Any function of the form $f(x \pm vt)$ satisfies this equation and represents a wave moving in the positive (for $x - vt$ argument) or negative (for $x + vt$ argument) x direction. The wave equation obeys the linear superposition principle, so any two solutions can be added to form another valid solution. Because of this, we typically focus on the harmonic or sinusoidal solutions and then use the Fourier principle to construct any general solution when needed.

A sinusoidal wave is periodic in space and in time, as shown in Fig. 1, and is characterized by the spatial period, or wavelength, λ, and by the temporal period T. We write the sinusoidal wave as

$$f(x,t) = A \sin\left[2\pi \left(\frac{x}{\lambda} - \frac{t}{T} \right) + \delta \right],$$

(2)

where A and δ are the amplitude and phase constant, respectively, required to produce a general solution to the second-order differential wave equation. It is standard practice to write the sinusoidal wave in a simpler form by using the wave vector k and the angular frequency ω, given by

$$k = \frac{2\pi}{\lambda}$$

$$\omega = \frac{2\pi}{T}.$$

(3)

Thus we get

$$f(x,t) = A \sin(kx - \omega t + \delta).$$

(4)

The velocity of a point of fixed phase on this harmonic wave is found by the condition

$$d(phase) = 0$$

$$d(kx - \omega t + \delta) = 0$$

(5)

$$kdx - \omega dt = 0,$$

The companion websites for this text are http://physics.oregonstate.edu/portfolioswiki and http://physics.oregonstate.edu/qmactivities.

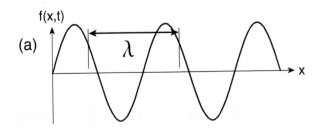

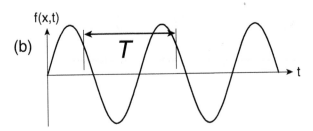

FIGURE 1 A classical wave, showing (a) the wavelength in space and (b) the period in time, for the choice of the phase constant $\delta = 0$.

yielding the **phase velocity**

$$v_{phase} = \left. \frac{dx}{dt} \right|_{fixed\ phase} = \frac{\omega}{k} = \frac{\lambda}{T}. \tag{6}$$

In many cases, the phase velocity is referred to simply as the velocity of the wave.

The relation between the wave vector k and the angular frequency ω

$$\omega = \omega(k) \tag{7}$$

is called the **dispersion relation**. We typically treat the wave vector k as the independent variable. If the (phase) velocity is constant, independent of the wave vector, then we say that there is no dispersion in the system. If the velocity is not constant, then waves with different wave vectors (i.e., different wavelengths) move at different speeds and a general wave composed of different harmonic solutions will disperse as it propagates. In that case, the motion of the superposition or wave packet is characterized by the group velocity

$$v_g = \left. \frac{d\omega(k)}{dk} \right|_{k_0}, \tag{8}$$

where k_0 is the peak of the wave-vector distribution comprising the wave packet. The group velocity is the same as the phase velocity if there is no dispersion.

For mathematical convenience, we often use the complex form of the sinusoidal wave

$$e^{i(kx-\omega t)} = \cos(kx - \omega t) + i \sin(kx - \omega t), \tag{9}$$

noting that we must take the real part at the end of the classical calculation, because we measure only real quantities. Quantum mechanics uses complex numbers, so we focus on the complex form of the classical wave.

2 ◼ FOURIER ANALYSIS

Fourier analysis is the decomposition of a general wave or oscillation into harmonic components. Because we treat the wave vector as the independent variable of a wave, the Fourier decomposition is typically done in terms of wave vectors. A Fourier series is a sum of sinusoidal functions, each of which is a harmonic of some fundamental wave vector or spatial frequency. A Fourier transform is an integral over a continuous distribution of sinusoidal functions.

A Fourier series is appropriate when the system has boundary conditions that limit the allowed wave vectors to a discrete set. For a system where the spatial periodicity is $2L$, the Fourier decomposition of a general periodic function is the series

$$f(x) = \sum_{n=-\infty}^{\infty} c_n e^{ik_n x}, \tag{10}$$

where the allowed wave vectors are

$$k_n = \frac{n\pi}{L}. \tag{11}$$

The expansion coefficients c_n in Eq. (10) are complex. The real version of the Fourier expansion is

$$f(x) = \frac{a_0}{2} + \sum_{n=1}^{\infty}\left[a_n\cos\left(\frac{n\pi x}{L}\right) + b_n\sin\left(\frac{n\pi x}{L}\right)\right]. \tag{12}$$

The expansion coefficients a_n, b_n, c_n are obtained by calculating the overlap integrals (i.e., projections or inner products) of the desired function with the harmonic basis functions

$$a_n = \frac{1}{L}\int_0^{2L} f(x)\cos\left(\frac{n\pi x}{L}\right)dx$$

$$b_n = \frac{1}{L}\int_0^{2L} f(x)\sin\left(\frac{n\pi x}{L}\right)dx \tag{13}$$

$$c_n = \frac{1}{2L}\int_0^{2L} f(x)e^{-ik_n x}dx.$$

A Fourier transform is appropriate when the system has no boundary conditions that limit the allowed wave vectors. In this case, the Fourier decomposition is an integral over a continuum of wave vectors:

$$f(x) = \frac{1}{\sqrt{2\pi}}\int_{-\infty}^{\infty} a(k)e^{ikx}dk, \tag{14}$$

where the expansion function $a(k)$ is complex. To obtain the expansion function $a(k)$ for a given spatial function $f(x)$ requires the inverse Fourier transform

$$a(k) = \frac{1}{\sqrt{2\pi}}\int_{-\infty}^{\infty} f(x)e^{-ikx}dx, \tag{15}$$

which is a projection of the spatial function $f(x)$ onto the harmonic basis functions $e^{ikx}/\sqrt{2\pi}$. The basis functions are orthogonal and normalized in the Dirac sense, which means their projections onto each other are Dirac delta functions

$$\frac{1}{2\pi}\int_{-\infty}^{\infty} e^{ik'x}e^{-ikx}dx = \delta(k - k')$$

$$\frac{1}{2\pi}\int_{-\infty}^{\infty} e^{ikx'}e^{-ikx}dk = \delta(x - x'), \tag{16}$$

whether viewed in the position representation or the wave-vector representation.

Appendix: Waves and Fourier Analysis

Some typical Fourier transform pairs are shown in Fig. 2 and are listed here (without proper scale factors):

$$f(x) = e^{ik_0 x} \quad \Longleftrightarrow \quad a(k) = \delta(k - k_0)$$
sinusoid   delta function

$$f(x) = e^{ik_0 x} e^{-x^2/2\sigma^2} \quad \Longleftrightarrow \quad a(k) = e^{-\sigma^2(k-k_0)^2/2}$$
Gaussian   Gaussian

$$f(x) = e^{ik_0 x} e^{-|x|/\sigma} \quad \Longleftrightarrow \quad a(k) = \frac{1}{1 + \sigma^2(k - k_0)^2}$$
exponential   Lorentzian

(17)

$$f(x) = e^{ik_0 x}; |x| < \sigma \quad \Longleftrightarrow \quad a(k) = \frac{\sin\{\sigma(k - k_0)\}}{\sigma(k - k_0)}.$$
square pulse   sinc

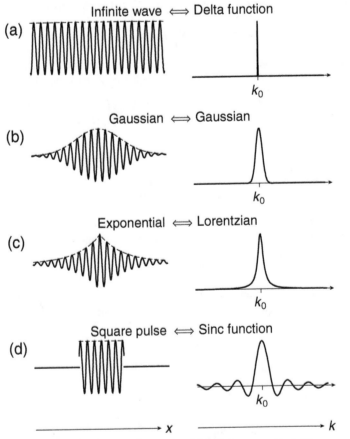

FIGURE 2 Fourier transform pairs: (a) Infinite wave ⇔ delta function, (b) Gaussian ⇔ Gaussian, (c) exponential ⇔ Lorentzian, (d) square pulse ⇔ sinc function.

In each case, $a(k)$ and $f(x)$ are Fourier transforms of each other following Eqs. (14) and (15). In Fig. 2, only the real part of the function $f(x)$ is plotted and each wave has a central wavelength $\lambda_0 = 2\pi/k_0$.

The spatial extent Δx of a function $f(x)$ and the width Δk of the Fourier transform $a(k)$ in wave-vector space are inversely related through the uncertainty relation

$$\Delta k \Delta x \geq 1. \tag{18}$$

This relation tells us that if want to make a wave that is confined to a small region of space, we need to use a wide range of wave vectors. In quantum mechanics, this concept is the Heisenberg uncertainty relation. To describe a wave $f(x,t)$, we replace x with $x - vt$ in the Fourier decomposition of the function $f(x)$, as long as there is no dispersion. This means that the wave retains its initial shape as it moves. When a system has dispersion, this replacement is no longer valid. The different speeds of the different wave-vector components of the superposition $f(x,t)$ cause the shape of the wave to change as it propagates. The expansion function $a(k)$ remains the same and the time dependent wave is represented by

$$f(x,t) = \frac{1}{\sqrt{2\pi}} \int_{-\infty}^{\infty} a(k) e^{i(kx - \omega(k)t)} dk. \tag{19}$$

We must recalculate the integral at each time to learn how the wave shape evolves.

Parseval's theorem says that the power is the same whether calculated in position space or wave-vector space:

$$\int_{-\infty}^{\infty} |f(x)|^2 dx = \int_{-\infty}^{\infty} |a(k)|^2 dk. \tag{20}$$

3 ■ QUANTUM MECHANICS

In quantum mechanics, we describe systems using momentum as the variable rather than wave vector, but the Fourier ideas are similar. Converting from wave-vector space to momentum space requires some care with the units:

$$f(x) = \frac{1}{\sqrt{2\pi}} \int_{-\infty}^{\infty} a(k) e^{ikx} dk = \frac{1}{\sqrt{2\pi}} \int_{-\infty}^{\infty} a(p/\hbar) e^{i(p/\hbar)x} d(p/\hbar)$$
$$= \frac{1}{\sqrt{2\pi\hbar}} \int_{-\infty}^{\infty} \frac{1}{\sqrt{\hbar}} a(p/\hbar) e^{i(p/\hbar)x} dp. \tag{21}$$

This tells us that the amplitudes in wave-vector space and momentum space are related by

$$\phi(p) = \frac{1}{\sqrt{\hbar}} a(k = p/\hbar). \tag{22}$$

Hence, we arrive at the quantum mechanical version of the Fourier transform that connects wave functions in position space and momentum space:

$$\psi(x) = \frac{1}{\sqrt{2\pi\hbar}} \int_{-\infty}^{\infty} \phi(p) e^{ipx/\hbar} dp, \tag{23}$$

$$\phi(p) = \frac{1}{\sqrt{2\pi\hbar}} \int_{-\infty}^{\infty} \psi(x) e^{-ipx/\hbar} dx. \tag{24}$$

Parseval's theorem applied to quantum mechanics says that the probability normalization condition is the same whether calculated in position space or momentum space:

$$1 = \int_{-\infty}^{\infty} |\psi(x)|^2 \, dx = \int_{-\infty}^{\infty} |\phi(p)|^2 \, dp. \tag{25}$$

The Heisenberg uncertainty relation relates the spatial extent Δx of a probability density $|\psi(x)|^2$ and the width Δp of the momentum space probability distribution $|\phi(p)|^2$ in a manner analogous to Eq. (18):

$$\Delta p \Delta x \geq \frac{\hbar}{2}. \tag{26}$$

This relation tells us that if want to make a wave function that is confined to a small region of space, then we must use a wide range of momenta. Hence, we cannot speak of a quantum mechanical system with a well-defined position and a well-defined momentum.

APPENDIX

Separation of Variables

The **separation of variables** procedure permits us to simplify a *partial* differential equation by separating out the dependence on the different independent variables and creating multiple *ordinary* differential equations. To illustrate the method, we apply a six-step process to the classical wave equation to show how the time dependence of the wave function can be found through a separate ordinary differential equation. The scalar wave equation is:

$$\nabla^2 u(\mathbf{r}, t) - \frac{1}{v^2} \frac{\partial^2 u(\mathbf{r}, t)}{\partial t^2} = 0, \tag{1}$$

where v is the wave speed.

To separate the time dependence from the spatial dependence, the six steps are:

Step 1: Write the partial differential equation in an appropriate coordinate system. For the wave equation, we choose Cartesian coordinates (this is not crucial in this example because we are separating only the time dependence):

$$\frac{\partial^2 u}{\partial x^2} + \frac{\partial^2 u}{\partial y^2} + \frac{\partial^2 u}{\partial z^2} - \frac{1}{v^2} \frac{\partial^2 u}{\partial t^2} = 0. \tag{2}$$

Step 2: *Assume* that the solution $u(x, y, z, t)$ can be written as the product of functions, at least one of which depends on only one variable, in this case t. The other function(s) must not depend at all on this variable, that is, assume

$$u(x, y, z, t) = S(x, y, z) T(t). \tag{3}$$

Plug this assumed solution into the partial differential equation Eq. (2). Because of the special form for $u(x, y, z, t)$, the partial derivatives each act on only one of the functions in $u(x, y, z, t)$.

$$T(t) \frac{\partial^2 S(x, y, z)}{\partial x^2} + T(t) \frac{\partial^2 S(x, y, z)}{\partial y^2} + T(t) \frac{\partial^2 S(x, y, z)}{\partial z^2} - \frac{1}{v^2} S(x, y, z) \frac{d^2 T(t)}{dt^2} = 0. \tag{4}$$

Any partial derivatives that act only on a function of a single variable may be rewritten as total derivatives.

Step 3: Divide by $u(x, y, z, t)$ in the form of Eq. (3):

$$\frac{1}{S(x, y, z)} \left\{ \frac{\partial^2 S(x, y, z)}{\partial x^2} + \frac{\partial^2 S(x, y, z)}{\partial y^2} + \frac{\partial^2 S(x, y, z)}{\partial z^2} \right\} - \frac{1}{v^2} \frac{1}{T(t)} \frac{d^2 T(t)}{dt^2} = 0. \tag{5}$$

From Appendix E of *Quantum Mechanics: A Paradigms Approach*, First Edition. David H. McIntyre. Copyright © 2012 by Pearson Education, Inc. Published by Pearson Addison-Wesley. All rights reserved.

The companion websites for this text are http://physics.oregonstate.edu/portfolioswiki and http://physics.oregonstate.edu/qmactivities.

Appendix: Separation of Variables

Step 4: Isolate *all* of the dependence on the chosen separation variable (*t*) on one side of the equation. Do as much algebra as you need to do to achieve this. In our example, this is straightforward:

$$\frac{1}{S(x,y,z)}\left\{\frac{\partial^2 S(x,y,z)}{\partial x^2} + \frac{\partial^2 S(x,y,z)}{\partial y^2} + \frac{\partial^2 S(x,y,z)}{\partial z^2}\right\} = \frac{1}{v^2}\frac{1}{T(t)}\frac{d^2 T(t)}{dt^2}. \tag{6}$$

$$\underbrace{\qquad\qquad\qquad\qquad\qquad\qquad}_{\text{function of space only}} \qquad \underbrace{\qquad\qquad\qquad}_{\text{function of time only}}$$

Step 5: Now imagine changing the isolated variable *t* by a small amount. In principle, the right-hand side of Eq. (6) could change as *t* changes, but nothing on the left-hand side would because there is no time dependence. Therefore, if the equation is to be true for all values of *t*, the particular combination of *t* dependence on the right-hand side must be constant. We call this constant $-k^2$ (because we already know what the answer is):

$$\frac{1}{S(x,y,z)}\left\{\frac{\partial^2 S(x,y,z)}{\partial x^2} + \frac{\partial^2 S(x,y,z)}{\partial y^2} + \frac{\partial^2 S(x,y,z)}{\partial z^2}\right\} = \frac{1}{v^2}\frac{1}{T(t)}\frac{d^2 T(t)}{dt^2} = -k^2. \tag{7}$$

In this way we have broken our original partial differential equation up into a pair of equations, one of which is an ordinary differential equation involving only *t*, the other is a partial differential equation involving only the three spatial variables:

$$\frac{1}{S(x,y,z)}\left\{\frac{\partial^2 S(x,y,z)}{\partial x^2} + \frac{\partial^2 S(x,y,z)}{\partial y^2} + \frac{\partial^2 S(x,y,z)}{\partial z^2}\right\} = -k^2, \tag{8}$$

$$\frac{1}{v^2}\frac{1}{T(t)}\frac{d^2 T(t)}{dt^2} = -k^2. \tag{9}$$

The separation constant $-k^2$ appears in both equations.

Step 6: Write each equation in standard form by multiplying each equation by its unknown function to clear it from the denominator:

$$\frac{\partial^2 S(x,y,z)}{\partial x^2} + \frac{\partial^2 S(x,y,z)}{\partial y^2} + \frac{\partial^2 S(x,y,z)}{\partial z^2} = -k^2 S(x,y,z), \tag{10}$$

$$\frac{1}{v^2}\frac{d^2 T(t)}{dt^2} = -k^2 T(t). \tag{11}$$

We have now separated the time dependence from the spatial dependence. Equation (11) is an ordinary differential equation for the time dependent part $T(t)$ of the complete wave function $u(x,y,z,t) = S(x,y,z)T(t)$. Equation (10) is still a partial differential equation for the space dependent part $S(x,y,z)$ of the complete wave function $u(x,y,z,t) = S(x,y,z)T(t)$. The six steps of this procedure can be applied again to separate the different spatial parts of $S(x,y,z)$ into three separate ordinary differential equations.

APPENDIX

Complex Numbers

Complex numbers are a critical component of the mathematics of quantum mechanics, so we provide a brief review here. Complex numbers are an extension of the real numbers to include an additional imaginary part. The **imaginary number** i is the square root of -1:

$$i = \sqrt{-1}. \tag{1}$$

A complex number has a **real part** and **imaginary part** and is written as

$$z = a + ib, \tag{2}$$

where this form assumes that a and b are real values. We refer to a as the *real part of z* and b as the *imaginary part of z*, and denote them as

$$a = \text{Re}(z)$$
$$b = \text{Im}(z). \tag{3}$$

When we add two complex numbers together, we must keep the real and imaginary parts separate:

$$z_1 + z_2 = (a_1 + ib_1) + (a_2 + ib_2) = (a_1 + a_2) + i(b_1 + b_2). \tag{4}$$

This makes it clear that the real and imaginary parts are the "apples and oranges" that you are often told not to mix together. In fact, a complex number contains two independent pieces of information, much like the components of a vector. We even represent a complex number in a similar way, as shown in Fig. 1.

Visualization of complex numbers in this "complex plane" can be very powerful. The horizontal axis in Fig. 1 corresponds to the real part of a complex number and the vertical axis corresponds to the imaginary part. Expressing the complex number as $z = a + ib$ corresponds to using the Cartesian representation. Figure 1 also suggests that a polar representation is useful and that the radius r and the angle θ could also characterize a complex number.

How do we connect the Cartesian and polar representations mathematically? Consider the exponential of a complex number. The Taylor series expansion of a complex exponential is

$$e^{i\theta} = 1 + (i\theta) + \frac{1}{2!}(i\theta)^2 + \frac{1}{3!}(i\theta)^3 + \frac{1}{4!}(i\theta)^4 + \frac{1}{5!}(i\theta)^5 + \dots. \tag{5}$$

Evaluating the powers of the imaginary number i results in half of the terms of the expansion being real (the even powers) and half being imaginary (the odd powers). Moreover, alternating signs arise from $i^2 = -1$ and $i^4 = +1$, yielding

$$e^{i\theta} = \left(1 - \frac{1}{2!}\theta^2 + \frac{1}{4!}\theta^4 - \dots\right) + i\left(\theta - \frac{1}{3!}\theta^3 + \frac{1}{5!}\theta^5 + \dots\right). \tag{6}$$

The companion websites for this text are http://physics.oregonstate.edu/portfolioswiki and http://physics.oregonstate.edu/qmactivities.

Appendix: Complex Numbers

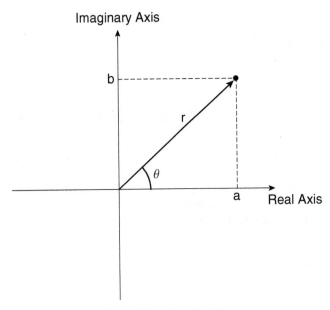

FIGURE 1 Complex plane.

The bracketed terms are the Taylor series expansion for the cosine and sine functions, giving the famous **Euler's formula**:

$$\boxed{e^{i\theta} = \cos\theta + i\sin\theta}. \tag{7}$$

Using Euler's formula, the polar representation of a point in the complex plane is

$$z = re^{i\theta} = r\cos\theta + ir\sin\theta, \tag{8}$$

as depicted in Fig. 1. We refer to r as the **modulus** or **magnitude** and θ as the **phase** or **argument**. We connect the Cartesian and polar viewpoints by equating the real and imaginary parts of Eqs. (2) and (8), giving

$$\begin{aligned} a &= r\cos\theta \\ b &= r\sin\theta, \end{aligned} \tag{9}$$

which agrees with trigonometry. The inverse relations are

$$\begin{aligned} r &= \sqrt{a^2 + b^2} \\ \theta &= \tan^{-1}\left(\frac{b}{a}\right). \end{aligned} \tag{10}$$

Care must be exercised when finding the polar angle because the inverse tangent function is multi-valued. However, the real and imaginary parts of a complex number separately determine the cosine and sine of the polar angle, so the correct quadrant is determined by using Eq. (10) in conjunction with Eq. (9). You should practice converting numbers between Cartesian and polar forms, and use whichever form is most convenient. For example, the complex number i is one unit along the imaginary axis in the Cartesian form. In the polar form, i is the number 1 rotated by $\pi/2$ from the real axis, thus $i = e^{i\pi/2}$. Likewise, the complex number -1 is one unit along the negative real axis in Cartesian form. In polar form, -1 has magnitude 1 and is rotated (has phase) π from the real axis, thus $-1 = e^{i\pi}$.

The polar representation of complex numbers makes multiplication and division easy:

$$z_1 z_2 = r_1 e^{i\theta_1} r_2 e^{i\theta_2} = r_1 r_2 e^{i(\theta_1+\theta_2)}$$

$$\frac{z_1}{z_2} = \frac{r_1 e^{i\theta_1}}{r_2 e^{i\theta_2}} = \frac{r_1}{r_2} e^{i(\theta_1-\theta_2)}. \tag{11}$$

Addition and subtraction are easier in the Cartesian representation [Eq. (4)].

Complex numbers have a unique operation known as complex conjugation, which is defined by changing $i \rightarrow -i$. We say that z^* is the **complex conjugate** of z:

$$z^* = a - ib = re^{-i\theta}. \tag{12}$$

In the complex plane, this operator corresponds to reflection through the real axis. A complex number multiplied by its own complex conjugate yields the square of its modulus or magnitude:

$$|z|^2 = zz^* = (a+ib)(a-ib) = a^2 + b^2$$

$$= (re^{i\theta})(re^{-i\theta}) = r^2, \tag{13}$$

sometimes called the **complex square**. The resultant modulus from Eq. (13) agrees with the geometric result in Eq. (10). The complex square is also a handy device to express a complex fraction in standard Cartesian form. For example, multiplying the numerator and denominator by the complex conjugate of the denominator places all the imaginary numbers in the numerator:

$$w = \frac{1}{a+ib} = \left(\frac{1}{a+ib}\right)\left(\frac{a-ib}{a-ib}\right) = \frac{a-ib}{a^2+b^2}$$

$$= \frac{a}{a^2+b^2} - i\frac{b}{a^2+b^2}. \tag{14}$$

This is standard form with

$$\text{Re}(w) = \frac{a}{a^2+b^2}$$

$$\text{Im}(w) = \frac{b}{a^2+b^2}. \tag{15}$$

A particularly useful case is $a = 0, b = 1$, which gives $1/i = -i$.

Complex notation can also be used to make trigonometric manipulations much easier, even when complex numbers are not really needed. Euler's formula can be inverted to express trigonometric functions in terms of complex exponentials

$$\cos\theta = \frac{e^{i\theta} + e^{-i\theta}}{2}$$

$$\sin\theta = \frac{e^{i\theta} - e^{-i\theta}}{2i} \tag{16}$$

that are very handy. For example, consider the trigonometric identity

$$\sin(a+b) = \sin a \cos b + \cos a \sin b. \tag{17}$$

It can be derived using Eq. (16):

$$\sin(a+b) = \frac{e^{i(a+b)} - e^{-i(a+b)}}{2i}$$

$$= \frac{e^{ia}e^{ib} - e^{-ia}e^{-ib}}{2i}$$

$$= \frac{1}{2i}\left\{(\cos a + i\sin a)(\cos b + i\sin b) - (\cos a - i\sin a)(\cos b - i\sin b)\right\} \quad (18)$$

$$= \frac{1}{2i}\left\{2i\sin a\cos b + 2i\cos a\sin b\right\}$$

$$= \sin a\cos b + \cos a\sin b.$$

That is a useful trick when you can't find your trigonometry book!

APPENDIX

Probability

Quantum mechanics is inherently a probabilistic theory, so we present here a brief review of some important concepts in probability theory. We distinguish between discrete probabilities, encountered in spin measurements, and continuous probabilities, encountered in position measurements.

1 ■ DISCRETE PROBABILITY DISTRIBUTION

Imagine collecting together all the grades that students received in your English class last term. You find that the students received 8 A's, 14 B's, 7 C's and 1 D. Though these are not random events, you could still ask, what is the **probability** of receiving an A? A classmate received an A grade $n_A = 8$ times out of the 30 total students, so the probability is the ratio

$$\mathcal{P}_A = \frac{n_A}{n_A + n_B + n_C + n_D} = \frac{8}{30}. \tag{1}$$

You calculate all four probabilities and represent them in a histogram, such as shown in Fig. 1. This set of probabilities is a **discrete probability distribution**. In this case, the distribution has been determined by experiment. In some cases, such as throwing dice, the probability distribution can be calculated theoretically and compared to experiment.

In the general case, we label the possible results (e.g., grades) x_i, and if there are N possible results that can occur, then the probability of any one result is

$$\mathcal{P}_{x_i} = \frac{n_{x_i}}{\sum_{i=1}^{N} n_{x_i}}. \tag{2}$$

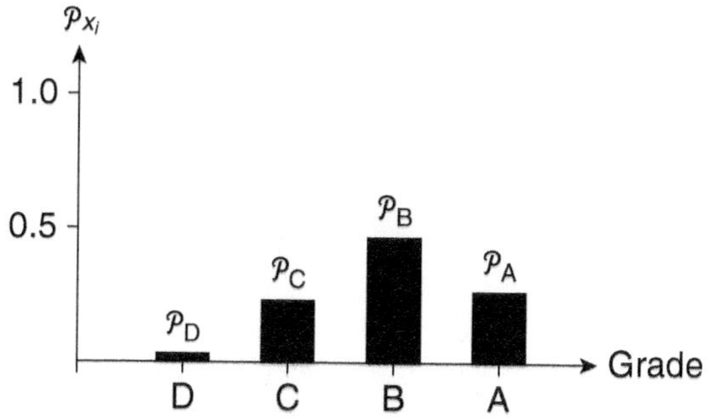

FIGURE 1 The histogram of grades received in an English class.

From Appendix A of *Quantum Mechanics: A Paradigms Approach*, First Edition. David H. McIntyre. Copyright © 2012 by Pearson Education, Inc. Published by Pearson Addison-Wesley. All rights reserved.

The companion websites for this text are http://physics.oregonstate.edu/portfolioswiki and http://physics.oregonstate.edu/qmactivities.

Appendix: Probability

The sum of the individual probabilities must be one because you are certain to get some result. The general statement of this condition is

$$\sum_{i=1}^{N} \mathcal{P}_{x_i} = 1. \tag{3}$$

Of course, the most obvious use of the grade probability distribution is for calculating a grade point average (GPA). Given the standard assignment of grade points $A = 4$, etc., the class GPA is

$$GPA = \frac{4n_A + 3n_B + 2n_C + 1n_D}{n_A + n_B + n_C + n_D} \tag{4}$$

$$= 4\mathcal{P}_A + \mathcal{P}3\mathcal{P}_B + 2\mathcal{P}_C + 1\mathcal{P}_D.$$

In the general case, we calculate the **average** or **mean** of the possible results using

$$\boxed{\langle x \rangle = \sum_{i=1}^{N} x_i \, \mathcal{P}_{x_i}}, \tag{5}$$

where we use the angled brackets $\langle \rangle$ to denote the average. In quantum mechanics, the average is referred to as the **expectation value**, which is a bit misleading because it is not the value you *expect* to get. In fact, the expectation value is in general *not* one of the possible results. The class GPA may be 3.14, but no student received that value as a grade.

We also quantify probability distributions by the spread of the distribution. The most used measure of the spread is the **standard deviation** σ, defined as the square root of the average of the squares of the deviations from the average! Once more, slowly: (1) find the deviation of each result x_i from the average value $\langle x \rangle$; (2) square the deviations (to avoid negative values); (3) average all possible squared deviations, weighted by the probabilities of each result, as in Eq. (5); and (4) take the square root. This is also called the **root-mean-square deviation**, or **rms deviation**. Mathematically, the standard deviation is

$$\sigma = \sqrt{\langle (x - \langle x \rangle)^2 \rangle} = \sqrt{\sum_{i=1}^{N} (x_i - \langle x \rangle)^2 \mathcal{P}_{x_i}}. \tag{6}$$

The **variance** σ^2 is the square of the standard deviation.

There is a useful shortcut for evaluating the standard deviation of a probability distribution. Consider the variance:

$$\sigma^2 = \langle (x - \langle x \rangle)^2 \rangle = \sum_{i=1}^{N} (x_i - \langle x \rangle)^2 \mathcal{P}_{x_i}. \tag{7}$$

Expand the square

$$\sigma^2 = \sum_{i=1}^{N} \left(x_i^2 - 2x_i \langle x \rangle + \langle x \rangle^2 \right) \mathcal{P}_{x_i}$$

$$= \sum_{i=1}^{N} x_i^2 \mathcal{P}_{x_i} - \sum_{i=1}^{N} 2x_i \langle x \rangle \mathcal{P}_{x_i} + \sum_{i=1}^{N} \langle x \rangle^2 \mathcal{P}_{x_i} \tag{8}$$

$$= \sum_{i=1}^{N} x_i^2 \mathcal{P}_{x_i} - 2\langle x \rangle \sum_{i=1}^{N} x_i \mathcal{P}_{x_i} + \langle x \rangle^2 \sum_{i=1}^{N} \mathcal{P}_{x_i}$$

and use the definition of the average in Eq. (5) and the normalization condition in Eq. (3) to get

$$\sigma^2 = \langle x^2 \rangle - 2\langle x \rangle \langle x \rangle + \langle x \rangle^2$$
$$= \langle x^2 \rangle - \langle x \rangle^2. \tag{9}$$

So the variance is also the difference between the average of the squares and the square of the average, where the average of the squares of the possible results is

$$\langle x^2 \rangle = \sum_{i=1}^{N} x_i^2 \mathcal{P}_{x_i}. \tag{10}$$

Note that the square $\langle x \rangle^2$ of the average and the average $\langle x^2 \rangle$ of the squares are not generally equal. In fact, Eq. (9) implies that the $\langle x \rangle^2 = \langle x^2 \rangle$ only if the variance is zero, which happens only if there is no spread in the distribution, that is, there is only one possible result. Using Eq. (9), we write the standard deviation as

$$\boxed{\sigma = \sqrt{\langle x^2 \rangle - \langle x \rangle^2}}. \tag{11}$$

In quantum mechanics, we use the standard deviation for the uncertainty, and we use the symbol Δx or Δp or ΔS_z instead of σ.

2 ■ CONTINUOUS PROBABILITY DISTRIBUTION

If the possible results of an experiment form a continuum rather than a discrete set, then we must modify some of the definitions from the last section. Rather than speaking of a probability for a specific result, we must speak of the probability for a range of results within some interval. For example, if you were a product tester and were charged with specifying how long the battery lasts on a laptop computer, then you might make a series of measurements of the time it takes for the laptop to drain the battery. Time is a continuum, but if you made measurements to the nearest minute, then the histogram of probability results would have bins of 1 minute on the time axis, as indicated in Fig. 2(a) where we use the nontraditional convention of labeling time with x to follow our notation in the last section. For small enough intervals, you would expect that the probability $\mathcal{P}_{x_i < x < x_i + \Delta x}$ of obtaining a result within

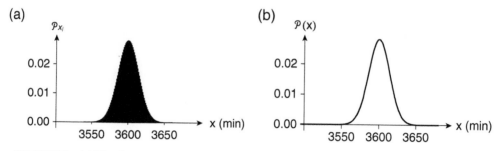

FIGURE 2   (a) The discrete probability distribution of battery lifetimes expressed as a histogram, and (b) the continuous probability distribution of lifetimes expressed as a function.

the time interval $x_i < x < x_i + \Delta x$ is proportional to the width of the interval and to a factor telling you the likelihood of results in that interval. We express this as

$$\mathcal{P}_{x_i < x < x_i + \Delta x} = \mathcal{P}(x_i) \Delta x, \tag{12}$$

where $\mathcal{P}(x_i)$ is the likelihood factor. Because the probability $\mathcal{P}_{x_i < x < x_i + \Delta x}$ is a dimensionless number and Δx has dimensions (x could be time, height, velocity, etc.), the likelihood factor $\mathcal{P}(x_i)$ must have dimensions of $1/x$. We call this the **probability density** $\mathcal{P}(x)$ because it is the probability per unit time (or height or velocity, etc.). We distinguish the probability density from a probability by denoting it as a function rather a subscripted value. The probability density is a **continuous probability distribution**, in contrast to the discrete probability distribution in the previous section. For the battery experiment, the continuous probability distribution is shown in Fig. 2(b).

For a continuous probability distribution, the condition that the sum of the individual probabilities must be one becomes an integral

$$\int_{-\infty}^{\infty} \mathcal{P}(x)\, dx = 1. \tag{13}$$

The average or expectation value is

$$\boxed{\langle x \rangle = \int_{-\infty}^{\infty} x \mathcal{P}(x)\, dx} \tag{14}$$

and the expectation value of any other function of the measurement variable is

$$\langle f(x) \rangle = \int_{-\infty}^{\infty} f(x) \mathcal{P}(x)\, dx. \tag{15}$$

The standard deviation is still defined by Eq. (11)

$$\sigma = \sqrt{\langle x^2 \rangle - \langle x \rangle^2}, \tag{16}$$

with the new definition of the average in Eq. (14).

Useful Definitions and Equations

State vector, wave function:
$$|\psi\rangle \doteq \psi(x) = \langle x|\psi\rangle$$

Normalization:
$$\langle\psi|\psi\rangle = \int_{-\infty}^{\infty} |\psi(x)|^2\, dx = 1$$

Measurement probability:
$$\mathcal{P}_{a_n} = |\langle a_n|\psi\rangle|^2 = \left|\int_{-\infty}^{\infty} \varphi_{a_n}^*(x)\psi(x)\,dx\right|^2$$

Expectation value:
$$\langle A\rangle = \langle\psi|A|\psi\rangle = \sum_n a_n \mathcal{P}_{a_n}$$

Probability density:
$$\mathcal{P}(x) = |\psi(x)|^2$$

Position probability:
$$\mathcal{P}_{a<x<b} = \int_a^b |\psi(x)|^2\, dx$$

Position representation:
$$\hat{x} \doteq x, \qquad \hat{p} \doteq -i\hbar\frac{d}{dx}$$

Energy eigenvalue equation:
$$H|E_n\rangle = E_n|E_n\rangle, \qquad H\varphi_n(x) = E_n\varphi_n(x)$$

Orthogonality:
$$\langle E_n|E_m\rangle = \int_{-\infty}^{\infty} \varphi_n^*(x)\varphi_m(x)\,dx = \delta_{nm}$$

Completeness:
$$|\psi\rangle = \sum_n c_n|E_n\rangle, \qquad \psi(x) = \sum_n c_n\varphi_n(x)$$

The companion websites for this text are http://physics.oregonstate.edu/portfolioswiki and http://physics.oregonstate.edu/qmactivities.

Useful Definitions and Equations

Schrödinger equation:
$$i\hbar\frac{d}{dt}|\psi(t)\rangle = H(t)|\psi(t)\rangle$$

Schrödinger time evolution:
$$|\psi(t)\rangle = \sum_n c_n e^{-iE_n t/\hbar}|E_n\rangle$$

Position-momentum commutator:
$$[\hat{x}, \hat{p}] = i\hbar$$

Momentum space wave function:
$$\phi(p) = \langle p|\psi\rangle = \frac{1}{\sqrt{2\pi\hbar}}\int_{-\infty}^{\infty}\psi(x)e^{-ipx/\hbar}dx$$

Momentum eigenstate:
$$|p\rangle \doteq \varphi_p(x) = \frac{1}{\sqrt{2\pi\hbar}}e^{ipx/\hbar}$$

de Broglie wavelength:
$$\lambda_{deBroglie} = \frac{h}{p}$$

Heisenberg uncertainty relation:
$$\Delta x \Delta p \geq \frac{\hbar}{2}$$

Perturbation corrections:
$$E_n^{(1)} = H'_{nn} = \langle n^{(0)}|H'|n^{(0)}\rangle$$
$$E_n^{(2)} = \sum_{m\neq n}\frac{|\langle n^{(0)}|H'|m^{(0)}\rangle|^2}{\left(E_n^{(0)} - E_m^{(0)}\right)}$$

Transition probability:
$$\mathcal{P}_{i\rightarrow f}(t) = \frac{1}{\hbar^2}\left|\int_0^t \langle f|H'(t')|i\rangle e^{i(E_f - E_i)t'/\hbar}dt'\right|^2$$

Spin and Angular Momentum Relations

Spin eigenvalue equations:
$$S_z|+\rangle = \frac{\hbar}{2}|+\rangle, \quad S_z|-\rangle = -\frac{\hbar}{2}|-\rangle$$

Spin-1/2 eigenstates:
$$|+\rangle \doteq \begin{pmatrix} 1 \\ 0 \end{pmatrix} \quad |+\rangle_x \doteq \frac{1}{\sqrt{2}}\begin{pmatrix} 1 \\ 1 \end{pmatrix} \quad |+\rangle_y \doteq \frac{1}{\sqrt{2}}\begin{pmatrix} 1 \\ i \end{pmatrix}$$
$$|-\rangle \doteq \begin{pmatrix} 0 \\ 1 \end{pmatrix} \quad |-\rangle_x \doteq \frac{1}{\sqrt{2}}\begin{pmatrix} 1 \\ -1 \end{pmatrix} \quad |-\rangle_y \doteq \frac{1}{\sqrt{2}}\begin{pmatrix} 1 \\ -i \end{pmatrix}$$

Spin-1/2 matrices:
$$S_x \doteq \frac{\hbar}{2}\begin{pmatrix} 0 & 1 \\ 1 & 0 \end{pmatrix} \quad\quad S_y \doteq \frac{\hbar}{2}\begin{pmatrix} 0 & -i \\ i & 0 \end{pmatrix}$$
$$S_z \doteq \frac{\hbar}{2}\begin{pmatrix} 1 & 0 \\ 0 & -1 \end{pmatrix} \quad\quad \mathbf{S}^2 \doteq \frac{3\hbar^2}{4}\begin{pmatrix} 1 & 0 \\ 0 & 1 \end{pmatrix}$$

Spin-1 matrices:
$$S_x \doteq \frac{\hbar}{\sqrt{2}}\begin{pmatrix} 0 & 1 & 0 \\ 1 & 0 & 1 \\ 0 & 1 & 0 \end{pmatrix} \quad\quad S_y \doteq \frac{\hbar}{\sqrt{2}}\begin{pmatrix} 0 & -i & 0 \\ i & 0 & -i \\ 0 & i & 0 \end{pmatrix}$$
$$S_z \doteq \hbar\begin{pmatrix} 1 & 0 & 0 \\ 0 & 0 & 0 \\ 0 & 0 & -1 \end{pmatrix} \quad\quad \mathbf{S}^2 \doteq 2\hbar^2\begin{pmatrix} 1 & 0 & 0 \\ 0 & 1 & 0 \\ 0 & 0 & 1 \end{pmatrix}$$

Angular momentum:
$$\mathbf{J}^2|jm_j\rangle = j(j+1)\hbar^2|jm_j\rangle$$
$$J_z|jm_j\rangle = m_j\hbar|jm_j\rangle$$
$$J_{\pm}|jm_j\rangle = \hbar\left[j(j+1) - m_j(m_j \pm 1)\right]^{1/2}|j, m_j \pm 1\rangle$$

Orbital angular momentum:
$$\mathbf{L}^2 Y_\ell^m(\theta,\phi) = \ell(\ell+1)\hbar^2 Y_\ell^m(\theta,\phi), \quad\quad \ell = 0,1,2,3,\ldots$$
$$L_z Y_\ell^m(\theta,\phi) = m\hbar Y_\ell^m(\theta,\phi), \quad\quad m = -\ell,\ldots,\ell$$

Angular momentum commutators:
$$[J_x, J_y] = i\hbar J_z, \quad [J_y, J_z] = i\hbar J_x, \quad [J_z, J_x] = i\hbar J_y$$
$$[\mathbf{J}^2, J_x] = [\mathbf{J}^2, J_y] = [\mathbf{J}^2, J_z] = 0$$

From *Quantum Mechanics: A Paradigms Approach*, First Edition. David H. McIntyre. Copyright © 2012 by Pearson Education, Inc. Published by Pearson Addison-Wesley. All rights reserved.

The companion websites for this text are http://physics.oregonstate.edu/portfolioswiki and http://physics.oregonstate.edu/qmactivities.

Bound State Systems

Infinite square well:
$$E_n = \frac{n^2\pi^2\hbar^2}{2mL^2}, \quad n = 1,2,3,\ldots$$

$$\varphi_n(x) = \sqrt{\frac{2}{L}}\sin\frac{n\pi x}{L}$$

Hydrogen atom:
$$E_n = -\frac{1}{n^2}\frac{m}{2\hbar^2}\left(\frac{e^2}{4\pi\varepsilon_0}\right)^2 = -\frac{1}{n^2}\frac{1}{2}\alpha^2 mc^2 = -\frac{1}{n^2}13.6\,\text{eV}$$

Harmonic oscillator:
$$E_n = \hbar\omega\left(n + \frac{1}{2}\right), \quad n = 0,1,2,3,\ldots$$

$$a = \sqrt{\frac{m\omega}{2\hbar}}\left(\hat{x} + i\frac{\hat{p}}{m\omega}\right)$$

$$a^\dagger = \sqrt{\frac{m\omega}{2\hbar}}\left(\hat{x} - i\frac{\hat{p}}{m\omega}\right)$$

$$a|n\rangle = \sqrt{n}|n-1\rangle$$

$$a^\dagger|n\rangle = \sqrt{n+1}|n+1\rangle$$

Fundamental Constants

Planck's constant:
$$\hbar = 6.582 \times 10^{-16}\,\text{eVs}$$

Speed of light:
$$c = 299\,792\,458\,\text{m/s}$$

Electron mass:
$$m_e c^2 = 511\,\text{keV}$$

Proton mass:
$$m_p c^2 = 938\,\text{MeV}$$

Fine-structure constant:
$$\alpha = \frac{e^2}{4\pi\varepsilon_0\hbar c} \cong \frac{1}{137}$$

Bohr radius:
$$a_0 = 0.0529\,\text{nm}$$

Bohr magneton:
$$\frac{\mu_B}{h} = 1.40\,\text{MHz/Gauss}$$

Preface

This text is designed to introduce undergraduates at the junior and senior levels to quantum mechanics. The text is an outgrowth of the new physics major curriculum developed by the Paradigms in Physics program at Oregon State University. This new curriculum distributes material from the subdisciplines throughout the two upper-division years and provides students with a more gradual transition between introductory and advanced levels. We have also incorporated and developed modern pedagogical strategies to help improve student learning. This text covers the quantum mechanical aspects of our curriculum in a way that can also be used in traditional curricula, but that still preserves the advantages of the Paradigms approach to the ordering of materials and the use of student engagement activities.

PARADIGMS PROGRAM

The Paradigms project began in 1997, when the Department of Physics at Oregon State University began an extensive revision of the upper-division physics major. In an effort to encourage students to draw connections between the subdisciplines of physics, the structure of the Paradigms has been crafted to mimic the organization of expert physics knowledge. Students are presented with a model of how physicists organize their understanding of physical phenomena and problem solving. Each of the nine short junior-year Paradigms courses focuses on a specific paradigm or class of physics problems that serves as the centerpiece of the course and on which different tools and skills are built. In the senior year, students resume a more traditional curriculum, taking six capstone courses in the traditional disciplines. This curriculum incorporates a diverse set of student activities that allow students to stay actively engaged in the classroom and to work together in constructing their understanding of physics. Computer resources are used frequently to help students visualize the systems they are studying.

CONTENT AND APPROACH

Quantum mechanics is integrated into four of the junior-year Paradigms courses and one senior-year capstone course at Oregon State University. This text includes all the quantum mechanics topics covered in those five courses. We adopt a "spins-first" approach by introducing quantum mechanics through the analysis of sequential Stern-Gerlach spin measurements. This approach is based upon previous presentations of spin systems by Feynman, Leighton, and Sands; Cohen-Tannoudji, Diu, and Laloe; Sakurai; and Townsend. The aim of the spins-first approach is twofold: (1) To immediately immerse students in the inherently **quantum** mechanical aspects of physics by focusing on simple measurements that have no classical explanation, and (2) To give students early and extensive experience with the **mechanics** of quantum mechanics in the forms of Dirac and matrix notation.

The companion websites for this text are http://physics.oregonstate.edu/portfolioswiki and http://physics.oregonstate.edu/qmactivities.

The simplicity of the spin-1/2 and spin-1 systems allows the students to focus on these new features, which run counter to classical mechanics.

The first three chapters of this text deal exclusively with spin systems and extensions to general two- and three-state quantum mechanical systems. The basic postulates of quantum mechanics are illustrated through their manifestation in the Stern-Gerlach experiments. After these three chapters, students have the tools to tackle any quantum mechanical problem presented in Dirac or matrix notation. After a brief interlude into quantum spookiness (the EPR Paradox and Schrödinger's cat), we tackle the traditional wave function aspects of quantum mechanics. We present several quantum systems—a particle in a box, on a ring, on a sphere, the hydrogen atom, and the harmonic oscillator—and emphasize their common features and their connections to the basic postulates. The differential equations of angular momentum and the hydrogen atom radial problem are solved in detail to expose students to the rigor of series solutions, though we stress that these are again eigenvalue equations, no different in principle from the spin eigenvalue equations. Whenever possible, we continue the use of Dirac notation and matrix notation learned in the spin chapters, emphasizing the importance of fluency in multiple representations. We build upon the spins-first approach by using the spin-1/2 example to introduce perturbation theory, the addition of angular momentum, and identical particles.

USAGE

At Oregon State University, the content of this text is taught in five courses as shown below.

Junior-Year Paradigms Courses			
Spin and Quantum Measurement	**Waves**	**Central Forces**	**Period Systems**
1. Stern-Gerlach Experiments 2. Operators and Measurement 3. Schrödinger Time Evolution 4. Quantum Spookiness	*Mechanical waves and EM waves* 5. Quantized Energies: Particle in a Box 6. Unbound States	*Planetary orbits* 7. Angular Momentum 8. Hydrogen Atom	*Coupled Oscillations* 15. Periodic Systems
Senior-Year Quantum Mechanics Capstone Course			
9. Harmonic Oscillator 10. Perturbation Theory	11. Hyperfine Structure and the Addition of Angular Momentum 12. Perturbation of Hydrogen	13. Identical Particles 14. Time-Dependent Perturbation Theory	16. Modern Applications

For a traditional curriculum, the content of this text would cover a full-year course, either two semesters or three quarters. A proposed weekly outline for two 15-week semesters or three 10-week quarters is shown below.

Week	Chapter	Topics
1	1	Stern-Gerlach experiment, Quantum State Vectors, Bra-ket notation
2	1	Matrix notation, General Quantum Systems
3	2	Operators, Measurement, Commuting Observables
4	2	Uncertainty Principle, $\mathbf{S}^2$ Operator, Spin-1 System
5	3	Schrödinger Equation, Time Evolution
6	3	Spin Precession, Neutrino Oscillations, Magnetic Resonance
7	4	EPR Paradox, Bell's Inequalities, Schrödinger's Cat
8	5	Energy Eigenvalue Equation, Wave Function
9	5	One-Dimensional Potentials, Finite Well, Infinite Well
10	6	Free Particle, Wave Packets, Momentum Space
11	6	Uncertainty Principle, Barriers
12	7	Three-Dimensional Energy Eigenvalue Equation, Separation of Variables
13	7	Angular Momentum, Motion on a Ring and Sphere, Spherical Harmonics
14	8	Hydrogen Atom, Radial Equation, Energy Eigenvalues
15	8	Hydrogen Wave Functions, Spectroscopy
16	9	1-D Harmonic Oscillator, Operator Approach, Energy Spectrum
17	9	Harmonic Oscillator Wave Functions, Matrix Representation
18	9	Momentum Space Wave Functions, Time Dependence, Molecular Vibrations
19	10	Time-Independent Perturbation Theory: Nondegenerate, Degenerate
20	10	Perturbation Examples: Harmonic Oscillator, Stark Effect in Hydrogen
21	11	Hyperfine Structure, Coupled Basis
22	11	Addition of Angular Momenta, Clebsch-Gordan Coefficients
23	12	Hydrogen Atom: Fine Structure, Spin-Orbit, Zeeman Effect
24	13	Identical Particles, Symmetrization, Helium Atom
25	14	Time-Dependent Perturbation Theory, Harmonic Perturbation
26	14	Radiation, Selection Rules
27	15	Periodic Potentials, Bloch's Theorem
28	15	Dispersion Relation, Density of States, Semiconductors
29	16	Modern Applications of Quantum Mechanics, Laser Cooling and Trapping
30	16	Quantum Information Processing

AUDIENCE AND EXPECTED BACKGROUND

The intended audience is junior and senior physics majors, who are expected to have taken intermediate-level courses in modern physics and linear algebra. No other upper-level physics or mathematics courses are required. For our own students, we review matrix algebra in a seven contact hour "preface" course that precedes the Paradigms courses that teach quantum mechanics. The material for that preface course is in Appendix C. The material in Appendix B summarizes an earlier Paradigms course on oscillations, and the material in Appendix D summarizes the classical wave part of the Paradigms course on waves.

STUDENT ACTIVITIES AND WEBSITE

Student engagement activities are an integral part of the Paradigms curriculum. All of the activities that we have developed are freely available on our wiki website:

http://physics.oregonstate.edu/portfolioswiki

The wiki contains a wealth of information about the Paradigms project, the courses we teach, and the materials we have developed. Details about individual activities include descriptions, student handouts, instructor's guides, advice about how to use active engagement strategies, videos of classroom practice, narratives of classroom activities, and comments from users—both internal and external to Oregon State University. This is a dynamic website that is continually updated as we develop new activities and improve existing ones. We encourage you to visit the website and join the community. E-mail us with corrections, additions, and suggestions.

Each of the quantum mechanics activities that we use in our five courses is referenced in the resource section at the end of the appropriate chapter in the text. The quantum mechanics activities are collected within the wiki website with a direct link:

www.physics.oregonstate.edu/qmactivities

These activities include different types of activities such as computer-based activities, group activities, and class response activities. The most extensive activity is a computer simulation of Stern-Gerlach experiments. This SPINS software is a full-featured, menu-driven application that allows students to simulate successive Stern-Gerlach measurements and explore incompatible observables, eigenstate expansions, interference, and quantum dynamics. The use of the SPINS software facilitates our spins-first approach. The beauty of the simulation is that students steeped in classical physics perform a foundational quantum experiment and learn the most fascinating and counterintuitive aspects of quantum mechanics at an early stage.

ACKNOWLEDGMENTS

This work is the product of a broad and energetic community of educators and students within the Paradigms in Physics program. I thank all of our students for their hard work, insights, and innumerable suggestions. My colleagues Corinne Manogue and Janet Tate have developed some of the courses upon which this text is based. They have worked with me throughout the writing of this text and I am indebted to them for their valuable contributions. I gratefully acknowedge my fellow faculty who have developed and taught in the new curriculum: Dedra Demaree, Tevian Dray, Tomasz Giebultowicz, Elizabeth Gire, William Hetherington, Henri Jansen, Kenneth Krane, Yun-Shik Lee, Victor Madsen, Ethan Minot, Oksana Ostroverkhova, David Roundy, Philip Siemens, Albert Stetz, William

Warren, and Allen Wasserman. I would also like to acknowledge the important contributions of early teaching assistants Kerry Browne, Jason Janesky, Cheryl Klipp, Katherine Meyer, Steve Sahyun, and Emily Townsend—their expertise, dedication, and enthusiasm were above and beyond the call of duty. The many subsequent teaching assistants have also been enthusiastic and valued contributors. I also thank those who have contributed in various ways to the development of activities: Mario Belloni, Tim Budd, Wolfgang Christian, Paco Esquembre, Lichun Jia, and Shannon Mayer. I particularly thank Daniel Schroeder for sharing his original SPINS software. I acknowledge useful and constructive feedback from Jeffrey Dunham, Joshua Folk, Rubin Landau, Edward (Joe) Redish, Joseph Rothberg, Homeyra Sadaghiani, Daniel Schroeder, Chandralekha Singh, and Daniel Styer. The Paradigms advisory committee has also provided valuable feedback and I acknowledge David Griffiths, Bruce Mason, William McCallum, Harriett Platsek, and Michael Wittmann for their help. I am grateful to the successive Physics Department chairs, Kenneth Krane and Henri Jansen, and Deans Fred Horne and Sherman Bloomer at Oregon State University for their endorsement of the Paradigms project.

This material is based on work supported by the National Science Foundation under Grant Nos. 9653250, 0231194, and 0618877. Any opinions, findings, and conclusions or recommendations expressed in this material are those of the authors and do not necessarily reflect the views of the National Science Foundation. I thank Duncan McBride and Jack Hehn for their encouragement and support of our endeavor.

Jim Smith at Addison Wesley has been enthusiastic about this project from the early stages. Peter Alston has navigated me through the editorial process with skill and patience. I am grateful to them and also to Katie Conley, Steven Le, and the rest of the staff at Addison Wesley for their work to produce this text.

David H. McIntyre
Corvallis, Oregon
November 2011

Index

Page references followed by "f" indicate illustrated figures or photographs; followed by "t" indicates a table.

A

A ring, 234-240, 242-243, 252, 255, 261-262, 519, 604-605
Absolute zero, 457
Absorption, 95-97, 103-104, 198, 279-280, 489-490, 495-496, 503, 510, 539-540, 551-552, 554
  of hydrogen, 103, 279, 503
  of light, 279-280
Acceleration, 147-148, 208, 422, 537, 552-553
  angular, 422, 553
  average, 552
actinides, 472
Action, 40, 74, 107, 161-162, 171, 175, 303-305, 331, 388, 391, 397, 399, 409-410, 419, 447
Action at a distance, 162
Addition, 11, 54, 88, 184, 305, 328, 340, 343, 375, 383-407, 409-412, 422, 428, 430, 441, 447-448, 466, 501-502, 524, 543, 580, 593, 604-605
Air, 32, 200, 204, 550
Allowed transitions, 280, 502
Alpha decay, 173
Amplitude, 10, 15, 18, 22, 47-48, 51, 95, 108-110, 112-113, 121, 123, 143, 145-147, 150, 178-180, 196-198, 209, 241, 290-291, 298, 489-490, 504, 583
Analyzer, 4-9, 16-18, 24, 44-45, 49-52, 61, 64, 67, 70, 100, 427, 438, 443
Angular frequency, 74-77, 80, 95, 494, 553, 583-584
Angular momentum, 2-3, 59, 61, 64, 70, 80-81, 88, 91, 162, 217-262, 263-268, 270-271, 275-276, 280-281, 283, 292, 295, 364, 383-388, 390, 393-395, 397, 399-402, 405-406, 418, 421-425, 427-429, 431-432, 437, 439, 448, 467, 470, 501-502, 547-548, 551, 563, 601, 604-605
  conservation of, 88, 162, 226, 280, 502
  of hydrogen, 281, 384-385, 393, 405-406, 418, 421-425, 427-429, 431-432, 437, 439, 604
  of particle, 88, 162
  orbital, 2-3, 227-230, 233-235, 237, 239-240, 247, 255, 257, 261, 264, 267, 364, 383-387, 394, 405, 418, 422-425, 427-428, 431, 437, 470, 501, 547, 601
  quantization of, 3
  rotational, 252-253, 266
  spin, 2-3, 59, 61, 64, 70, 80-81, 88, 91, 162, 227-230, 237, 239, 247, 249, 280, 364, 383-387, 390, 393-395, 397, 399-401, 405-406, 418, 421-425, 427-428, 432, 439, 448, 467, 470, 502, 547, 563, 601, 604-605
  transfer of, 551
Angular momentum quantum number, 64, 228, 247, 255, 257, 270-271, 275-276, 281, 386, 394, 406, 423-424, 551
annihilation, 306, 425
Antineutrino, 88-89
Antinodes, 131, 147, 287, 310
Area, 2, 289, 499-500, 520
astronomy, 393
Atom interferometers, 208
Atomic beam, 3, 5, 552-556, 558
Atomic clock, 393
Atomic motion, 556-557
Atomic number, 470
atomic orbitals, 474, 511
Atomic physics, 3, 30, 98, 200, 505, 550, 571
  lasers, 550
Atomic structure, 463
  Pauli exclusion principle, 463

atoms, 1, 4-9, 18-20, 34, 50-53, 61, 96, 98, 103, 141, 168-169, 204-206, 230, 253, 270, 279-280, 282, 284, 291, 327, 405, 446, 448-449, 459, 470-471, 473, 477-478, 483, 492-500, 511, 513, 515, 517-520, 530-531, 534-537, 539-541, 546, 548-550, 552-559, 571, 573
  atomic number, 470
  bonding, 270, 291, 477-478, 515
  characteristics of, 517
  electrons, 204-206, 279, 327, 405, 446, 448, 459, 470, 473, 477-478, 511, 534-537, 540
  elements, 280, 500, 511, 530, 534, 558
  isotopes, 449
  neutrons, 205-206, 448
  periodic table, 446, 470-471, 473, 478
  properties of, 1, 280
  protons, 446, 448, 473, 536, 558
  size of, 492, 500
  structure of, 103, 204, 470, 478, 492, 511, 531, 540
  valence electrons, 459, 534
AU, 472, 591
Axon, 169

B

Balmer series, 279
Band gap, 143, 538-540
bar, 12, 88
bases, 89, 177, 179, 251, 366, 383, 397, 399-402, 406, 411, 429, 434, 446, 561
Beam, 1-6, 8, 19-20, 32-34, 51, 68-70, 96, 100, 142, 201-202, 206, 211, 213-214, 427, 483, 491, 499, 551-558
  spread, 3, 491, 552, 554
  width, 213-214, 491, 499, 554-556
Beta decay, 88, 294
Binding energy, 418
biology, 91
Blackbody, 493-496
Blackbody radiation, 493-496
Bohr model, 279
Bohr radius, 277, 281, 287-288, 292, 293-294, 392, 423-424, 464, 500, 575, 602
Boltzmann constant, 576
Bose-Einstein condensate, 546
boson, 449, 452, 454, 457, 460-461
Bosons, 448-449, 451-462, 470, 478, 479-480
Bound states, 116, 125, 127, 131, 143, 146, 150, 153, 156, 193-194, 214, 270-271, 278, 511, 532
Boundary conditions, 118-119, 124-126, 145, 152, 195-197, 199, 236, 247, 253, 518, 522, 524, 585
broadening, 493
Buckyballs, 206

C

Calculations, 18, 23, 29-30, 31, 39, 49, 68, 99, 135, 149, 167, 228-229, 276, 289, 300, 318, 367, 416, 434, 442, 478, 514, 522
Cancellation, 10
capillaries, 458
Carbon, 230, 257, 405, 539-541, 543
  forms of, 540
Carbon atom, 230, 257
Carrier wave, 182, 186-187
carriers, 535, 538, 540
Cartesian coordinates, 222, 224, 294-295, 589
cells, 538-540
Center of mass, 220, 222, 253
  motion of, 220, 222
central force, 226, 230
Central maximum, 189
changes, 8, 42, 89, 143, 199, 208, 244, 253, 325, 328, 332, 336, 349, 393, 399-400, 457, 459, 483-484, 504, 511, 536-537, 539, 562, 590
  physical, 199, 253
Charge carriers, 540
Charge distribution, 3

continuous, 3
  symmetric, 3
Charged particles, 2, 462
Charges, 371, 537
  like, 537
  opposite, 537
chemistry, 3, 91, 446, 459, 470, 511
  elements, 511
Chips, 558
Circuits, 558
Classical physics, 11, 52, 103, 192, 446, 606
classical wave, 15, 120, 179, 198, 207, 583-584, 589, 606
Classically forbidden regions, 116-117
clocks, 558
clouds, 291
  molecular, 291
  probability, 291
Clusters, 541
Coherence, 169, 562
Coils, 548-550
collision, 372
Collisions, 498, 500
Color, 4, 8, 103, 242, 257, 285
colors, 143, 187
community, 606
Commutators, 67, 226, 601
Complex numbers, 10-11, 22, 110, 256, 584, 591-594
Components of, 8, 18, 25, 61, 69-70, 75, 162, 168, 226, 238, 386, 560, 568, 587, 591
Computers, 23, 166, 285, 287, 522, 558-560, 562, 571
Concrete, 13, 559
Condensation, 458-459, 478, 546, 550, 558
Conduction, 142-143, 535, 537-540
  electrical, 535
  model of, 540
Conduction band, 142-143, 535, 537-540
Conductivity, 458, 536
  electrical, 536
  thermal, 458
Conductor, 539
Conductors, 540
  isolated, 540
  semiconductors, 540
conjunction, 592
conservation, 88-89, 106, 162, 187, 208, 226, 280, 502, 538-539
  of angular momentum, 88, 162, 226, 280, 502
  of energy, 88, 106
  of momentum, 187, 208
Conservation laws, 88
Conservation of angular momentum, 88, 162, 226, 280, 502
Conservation of energy, 88, 106
Conservation of momentum, 187, 208
Constructive interference, 181
Coordinate, 25, 42, 82, 84, 122, 129, 219-220, 222, 225, 230-231, 233, 244, 263, 371, 589
coordinates, 129, 221-222, 224-225, 230-231, 234, 247, 264-267, 270, 294-295, 371-372, 450, 463, 589
Copper, 473
Correlation, 162-163, 462, 534, 570
Cosmology, 88
Coulomb, 213, 218-219, 270-271, 277-279, 292, 327, 370, 383, 426, 462-463, 466, 468-469, 473, 475-476, 478, 481, 512, 541
Couples, 406, 425, 566
Covalent bond, 477
crests, 535
Crystal lattice, 537
Crystals, 142, 204
Current, 2, 200, 204, 210, 215, 407, 421, 535-536, 538, 546, 548, 550, 570
  magnetic field of, 548, 550
Current density, 407
Current loops, 2

currents, 204, 548-549
    surface, 204

D

De Broglie wavelength, 175, 206, 208, 458, 600
Decay, 88, 101, 125, 129-132, 146-147, 149-150, 162, 164, 173, 196, 200-201, 294, 467, 469, 495-498, 502-503, 508, 510
    exponential, 125, 130, 147, 149-150, 497-498
    nuclear, 88, 173, 294
    rate, 495-498, 502, 508, 510
Decay constant, 130, 132, 147, 201
Deceleration, 553, 555
degeneracy, 57, 176, 238-239, 252, 255, 279, 295, 343, 360-362, 372, 374, 392, 395, 415, 424-425, 427-428, 430, 434, 437, 439, 462, 467, 470-471, 480-481, 515
degrees, 219
Degrees of freedom, 219
delta, 26, 131, 134-135, 157, 177-178, 190-191, 313, 379, 491-493, 585-586
Deltas, 316
Density, 110-111, 113-114, 121, 141, 150, 156, 176-177, 184, 186-187, 206-207, 211, 213, 240-242, 256-257, 262, 266, 285-287, 292, 294, 310-311, 315, 318-326, 330, 331, 353, 385, 407, 450, 453-454, 457-458, 475-476, 479-480, 492, 494-496, 498, 504, 508, 511-512, 523-524, 526-528, 540, 543, 588, 598, 599, 605
    average, 184, 320-321, 494, 598
    critical, 458, 523
    infinite, 121, 141, 150, 156, 177, 211, 213, 266, 310, 325, 453-454, 457-458, 479-480, 508, 511, 524, 605
Density wave, 241
deposition, 142
Derivative, 92, 107, 117, 129, 145, 149, 157, 187, 192, 196-197, 202, 235, 237, 245, 249, 272, 297-298, 307, 318, 532, 537
desert, 416
Destructive interference, 180, 186, 189
detector, 1-2, 89-90, 101, 171, 442
Detectors, 7, 171
Deuterium, 294, 411, 442-443, 449
Deuteron, 411, 442, 449
development, 103, 414, 425, 518, 558, 607
Diamond, 230-231, 539
differentiation, 220, 249
Diffraction, 10, 204-206
    double slit, 10
    electron diffraction, 204
    single slit, 10
    single-slit, 10, 205
Diode, 142-143
    laser, 143
Diodes, 103, 200, 538
Dipole, 76, 81, 96, 132, 290-291, 294, 324, 330, 371-372, 375, 379-380, 384, 393, 421, 492-493, 500-504, 509
Dipole moment, 81, 290-291, 294, 371-372, 375, 379, 493
Dipoles, 384-385, 393
direction, 1-5, 8, 12, 14, 18, 25, 36-37, 43-44, 59, 67, 70, 76, 78-86, 91, 99-100, 162-165, 171-172, 174-175, 179, 204, 238-239, 241, 244, 252, 279, 290-291, 337-338, 340, 347, 349, 356, 371, 375, 378, 385-386, 393, 421, 502, 537-538, 548-549, 551-552, 556, 563, 573, 583
Dispersion, 187, 517, 519-522, 526-528, 530-531, 533, 535-537, 540-541, 543-544, 584, 587, 605
Displacement, 297, 333, 371
Distance, 90, 101, 162, 226, 285, 513, 535, 573
    angular, 162, 226, 573
distortion, 325, 534
Disturbance, 9, 65, 161
DNA, 204
Doppler cooling, 558
Doppler effect, 553
Doppler shift, 554-556
Doppler shifts, 553
Double-slit interference, 10, 205-206
    Interference fringes, 10, 205-206
Dynamics, 218, 558, 606

E

Earth, 2, 88, 101, 218, 544
    angular momentum of, 2
    measuring, 101
EER, 371
Efficiency, 499-500
Einstein A and B coefficients, 496, 500
Einstein, Albert, 161
Electric dipole, 96, 132, 290-291, 294, 371-372, 375, 379-380, 393, 492-493, 500-504
Electric field, 10, 96, 205-206, 291, 370-371, 375, 380, 414, 420, 492-493, 501, 535-537, 540-541, 556
Electric fields, 208, 535
Electromagnetic fields, 483, 497
Electromagnetic waves, 583
Electromagnetism, 88
Electron, 3, 88-90, 101, 111, 121, 124, 141, 143, 156, 162, 204, 211, 213, 215, 218, 230, 257, 270-271, 276-277, 279, 281, 285-287, 289-292, 293-294, 327, 363-364, 366, 371, 378, 383-385, 389-390, 393-394, 405-406, 409-411, 414, 416-418, 420-422, 424-426, 428, 433, 442, 446, 449, 451, 463-467, 469-470, 473-478, 481, 501, 510, 511, 513-514, 520, 523, 528, 530, 533-540, 544, 551-552, 575, 602
    production of, 539
    spin of, 426, 449, 463
Electron cloud, 285, 290-291
Electron current, 538
Electron diffraction, 204
electron neutrino, 88-90
Electron spin, 3, 389-390, 406, 414, 416, 418, 426, 428, 433
Electron transitions, 279, 539
electron transport, 511, 540
Electrons, 3, 88-89, 104, 143, 167, 204-206, 213-214, 279, 327, 405, 411-412, 446-448, 454, 459, 463-470, 472-473, 476-478, 481, 511, 533-538, 540
    acceleration of, 537
    atomic structure and, 463
    conduction, 143, 535, 537-538, 540
    de Broglie wavelength, 206
    energy levels of, 470
    energy of, 89, 213-214, 279, 464, 466-468, 535-536
    magnetic moment of, 3
    mass of, 536
    nature of, 204, 206
    orbits, 470
    sea of, 459
    spin of, 463
    valence, 143, 459, 477, 534-535, 538, 540
    velocity of, 535, 540
Element, 14, 39, 48, 53, 78, 97, 106, 113, 132, 140, 163, 224-225, 280, 284-285, 317, 324, 340, 343, 346, 354-355, 369, 373, 384, 393, 419, 423, 429, 431, 435, 456, 459-460, 487, 490, 493, 500-501, 511, 518, 528, 530, 532, 544, 579-581
elements, 38-40, 46, 67, 77, 140, 161, 163, 280, 287, 315-317, 324, 340-341, 344, 348, 350, 352-353, 355-357, 365-368, 372-373, 380, 384-385, 389-390, 395, 419-420, 423, 426, 429-432, 434-436, 441, 456, 463, 467, 472, 500-502, 511, 514, 516, 528, 530, 534, 544, 558, 562, 579-581
emission, 95-97, 103-104, 252, 278-280, 294, 489-490, 495-498, 502, 504, 508, 510, 551-552, 554-555, 558
    spontaneous, 495-498, 502, 504, 508, 510, 551-552, 554-555, 558
    stimulated, 490, 495, 498
Emission line, 555
emission lines, 252, 279
Emission spectrum, 104, 278
Energy, 1, 28, 33, 46, 72-79, 81, 83-92, 94-97, 99, 101, 103-110, 113-136, 138-153, 155-159, 173-176, 181, 183-184, 192-196, 198-201, 203-204, 208-209, 211, 213-215, 218-220, 222-225, 230-231, 234-240, 243-244, 252-253, 255-256, 258-261, 263, 265, 267, 270-272, 275-280, 282-287, 290-292, 294-295, 297-308, 310-319, 321-322, 324-325, 327-329, 331-334, 336-353, 355-361, 363-372, 374-375, 377-381, 383, 385, 387-388, 392-393, 397-398, 405, 411, 414-439, 441-442, 446, 450-453, 456-457,
459-471, 473-475, 477-478, 480-481, 483-486, 489-499, 503-504, 507-508, 511-518, 520-524, 526-536, 538-541, 543-544, 546-552, 556, 563, 575, 599, 605
    binding, 121, 277, 418, 466, 511
    bond, 253, 327-328, 334, 475, 477
    chemical, 142, 348, 358
    conservation of, 88, 106, 208, 280, 539
    conservation of energy, 88, 106
    dark, 1
    electrostatic, 291, 468
    internal, 91, 279, 383, 405, 414, 420
    kinetic, 106, 116, 125, 130, 145, 150, 208, 211, 213-215, 220, 235, 252, 294, 299, 303, 364, 370, 414, 417-418, 426, 473, 513, 528, 547, 549
    kinetic energy, 106, 116, 125, 130, 145, 150, 208, 211, 213-215, 235, 252, 294, 364, 418, 426, 473, 513, 528, 547
    of photon, 552
    of photons, 96-97, 103, 425, 495, 498-499, 539
    potential, 1, 76, 106, 108, 114-117, 119-120, 122-132, 142-152, 155-157, 159, 173-174, 192-196, 198-201, 203-204, 208-209, 213-215, 218-220, 222-224, 234-236, 238, 244, 261, 270-271, 276, 278-279, 286, 295, 297-300, 303-304, 307, 310, 321, 325, 327-328, 332-334, 336-337, 347, 352, 356, 364, 370-371, 378-380, 414, 417-418, 427, 450, 453, 456, 459, 462-463, 466, 468-469, 473, 475, 480-481, 508, 511-514, 522-523, 526, 528-533, 536, 540-541, 547-549
    potential energy, 1, 76, 106, 108, 114-117, 119-120, 122-132, 142-144, 150-152, 157, 173-174, 192-196, 201, 204, 208-209, 213-215, 218-220, 222, 224, 234-236, 244, 261, 270-271, 276, 278, 295, 336-337, 347, 352, 356, 364, 370-371, 379-380, 414, 418, 427, 450, 453, 456, 459, 462-463, 466, 468-469, 473, 475, 511, 513, 523, 528-529, 533, 536, 540-541, 547-549
    quantization of, 124, 143, 174
    relativistic, 88-90, 414, 418-420, 422-425, 434-435, 439, 441-442
    relativity and, 279
    rest, 89, 277, 361, 416, 418, 465, 551, 556
    rotational, 94, 252-253, 328-329
    solar, 88, 90, 538-539
    thermal, 457, 494-496, 535, 549-551
    transfer of, 551
    transformation of, 366-367, 563
    transitions, 91, 94-95, 97, 103-104, 132, 252, 279-280, 305, 317, 324, 328-329, 358, 415, 425, 459, 469, 483, 495-496, 503-504, 538-540, 544
    uncertainty principle, 192-193, 211, 213, 218, 367, 535, 546, 605
    vacuum, 204, 306, 425, 497-498, 550, 575
    work, 91, 117, 173, 175, 204, 215, 220, 287, 316, 343-344, 367, 425, 429, 436, 441, 446, 478, 527, 533, 535
    zero-point, 304, 306, 328
Energy bands, 521-522, 526
Energy density, 494-496, 504
Energy diagrams, 469
Energy gap, 522, 526, 535
Energy levels, 95-97, 103-105, 119, 132, 143, 193, 200, 219, 239, 252-253, 276-279, 283, 285-286, 295, 336-337, 344, 356, 363-364, 366, 368-369, 371, 378, 380, 383, 387, 414-417, 419, 424-425, 427, 435, 439, 457, 459, 465, 469-470, 483, 492, 494, 504, 513, 531, 548, 556
    of hydrogen atom, 439
environment, 3, 91, 169, 206, 348
EQ, 3-4, 13-14, 17, 19, 22-24, 26, 29, 31, 39-40, 47, 53, 55-56, 67-68, 73-79, 85, 88, 90, 93-94, 96-97, 99, 106-107, 109-122, 125-127, 133-137, 139, 147-149, 155-158, 162, 164, 166, 168-169, 172, 174-176, 178-179, 182-187, 189, 192-193, 203-204, 206-207, 212, 214, 221-225, 228, 230-231, 233-235, 237-241, 243-250, 252-253, 255, 263, 265-266, 271-277, 279, 281, 283-285, 289-290, 293-294, 297, 299-304, 307-310, 312-319, 321, 323-325, 331-333, 337-340, 342-346, 348-349, 351-355, 357, 359-363,

366-367, 369-370, 372-373, 375, 377-379,
384-385, 388-392, 394-399, 403, 409-412,
415-416, 418, 420, 422-424, 426, 429-430,
432-433, 435-438, 441-442, 447, 451-454,
456-457, 459-461, 464-468, 474-476,
479-481, 484-498, 500-502, 507-509,
515-524, 526-528, 530-533, 537, 543-544,
548, 554, 556, 560-561, 567-568, 573-574,
580-581, 585, 588, 589-590, 592-594,
596-598
Equation of motion, 80, 517
Equations, 12, 37, 40-42, 61, 64-65, 67, 70, 77, 92-94,
101, 108, 118, 126-128, 135, 144-149, 156,
158-159, 194-197, 201-202, 213, 223, 227,
230-231, 233-234, 253, 255, 261, 263,
270-271, 283, 308, 316, 344, 346, 348-349,
360, 363, 377, 386, 388-390, 405, 407,
409-410, 485, 507, 516, 519, 532, 548, 574,
582, 589-590, 599-600, 601, 604
Equations of motion, 148
Equilibrium, 253, 297, 328, 334, 494-496
mechanical, 297
one-dimensional, 297
rotational, 253, 328
thermal, 494-496
thermal equilibrium, 494-496
eV, 3, 33, 104, 143, 211, 214-215, 271, 278, 280, 328,
415, 442, 467, 475, 477, 481, 503, 512, 528,
535, 538, 550, 602
Evaporation, 550
Events, 30, 52, 595
evolution, 28, 71-98, 99-101, 103, 133, 135-136, 141,
153, 155, 174, 180-181, 183, 210, 219, 241,
262, 290-291, 299, 315, 321-323, 325, 330,
333, 484-485, 558, 563, 600, 604-605
excitation, 489-491, 493-494, 498-500, 504, 554
excited state, 121, 137-138, 156, 159, 281, 290-291,
364, 452, 454-455, 458, 460-462, 467-468,
483, 493, 495, 497, 504, 520-521, 551
Excited states, 104, 168, 372, 452-453, 462, 467, 469,
478, 490, 493, 496-497
Exclusion principle, 446, 448, 454, 459, 463, 470, 478,
511, 534
exercise, 42
Expansion, 73-74, 133-136, 138, 183, 254, 256,
259-260, 262, 267-268, 273-275, 290, 297,
313-314, 316, 333, 340, 342-344, 351, 397,
402-403, 406, 418, 429, 441, 484-486, 507,
585, 587, 591-592
Experiment, 1-10, 15-19, 24, 27-28, 30, 33, 49-53, 56,
58-59, 61-62, 64, 70, 78, 81, 84, 100, 105,
109, 153, 161-163, 166-169, 196-197,
205-207, 210, 305, 425, 427, 447, 483, 490,
546-547, 558, 564-565, 571, 595, 597-598,
605-606
Exponential decay, 147, 150
Exponential function, 274, 518
exponential growth, 149
External forces, 222, 540
Eye, 146, 208

F

fact, 7-9, 18, 47, 57-58, 107, 113, 176, 220, 222, 253,
256, 301, 303, 360, 394-395, 397, 406, 422,
446, 517-518, 527, 535, 546, 561, 591,
596-597
Fermi, Enrico, 88
fermion, 449, 452, 457, 462
Fermions, 448-449, 451-462, 464, 470, 478, 479-481
Feynman, Richard, 168, 170, 558
Fields, 11, 91, 95, 205, 208, 279, 306, 338-340, 383,
414, 420, 428, 434, 437-439, 443, 483, 494,
497-498, 535, 546, 550
fringe, 208
gravitational, 208
Film, 199
interference, 199
Filters, 4
color, 4
Final velocity, 556
flowers, 571
Flux, 197
focus, 1, 6, 11, 15, 98, 179, 196, 219, 234, 276, 336,
349, 383, 504, 516, 546, 583-584, 604
forbidden transition, 97, 132
Force, 1-3, 27, 88, 106, 116, 124, 218, 222, 226, 230,
265, 274, 297, 324, 383, 427, 429, 456, 535,
537, 547-548, 550-558, 573
conservative, 550, 552

electric, 324, 383, 535, 537, 556
external, 222, 427
external forces, 222
fictitious, 222
friction, 573
identifying, 218
magnetic, 1-3, 88, 383, 427, 547-548, 550, 552,
556, 558, 573
magnetic force, 552
measuring, 27
net, 551, 556
normal, 427, 548
nuclear force, 88
restoring, 297, 324
resultant, 548, 556-557
superposition of, 535
types, 88
work, 429, 535
Forces, 28, 88, 106, 222, 226, 540, 546, 552, 556, 604
Fourier analysis, 583-588
Fourier series, 180, 182-183, 189, 248, 260, 585
Fourier transform, 179, 183-185, 189-191, 209, 486,
498, 585-587
discrete, 183-185, 189, 585
Frequency, 74-77, 80-81, 85-86, 91, 95-96, 100, 104,
138, 141, 200, 241, 290, 298-299, 301, 305,
324, 337-339, 347-348, 356-357, 364, 370,
393, 424, 483, 486-491, 493-495, 498-499,
502, 504, 508, 510, 544, 553-557, 563, 573,
583-585
angular, 74-77, 80-81, 91, 95, 241, 298-299, 364,
393, 424, 494, 502, 553, 563, 573,
583-584
Doppler effect, 553
fundamental, 585
natural, 510
period of, 490
resonance, 91, 95-96, 200, 348, 483, 487, 489-491,
499, 554-556
wave, 96, 138, 200, 241, 290, 299, 324, 347, 393,
424, 553, 583-585
Friction, 573
Fringes, 10, 199, 205-206, 208, 325
Front, 199, 540
Fundamental forces, 88
Fundamental particles, 385, 446, 478

G

g, 3, 7, 12-13, 40-41, 52, 58, 64, 76, 90, 96, 110,
162-163, 169-170, 185-186, 196, 211-212,
226, 257, 267, 273-275, 279, 281, 292,
315-317, 343-346, 354, 360-362, 405, 407,
426-428, 430, 432-434, 439, 470, 474-476,
481, 491, 512-514, 516, 521-522, 526-527,
540, 543, 547, 549, 552-553, 556, 568,
570-571, 573, 575, 579-582, 595
galaxy, 393
active, 393
radio, 393
gaps, 511, 521, 533, 538, 540, 544
Gas, 166, 494, 534, 550
Gases, 459, 472
Geiger counter, 166-167
General theory of relativity, 208
Geometry, 12, 403, 528, 552
Glass, 187, 198-200
GPS, 558
Graph, 109, 512, 533
Graphite, 539
Gravity, 88, 553, 558
quantum, 553, 558
solar, 88
theory of, 558
ground state, 104, 119, 121-122, 131, 145, 156, 159,
213, 272, 279, 281, 285-290, 293-294, 336,
353, 364, 369, 371-372, 377-379, 384-385,
389, 392-394, 397-398, 405-407, 416, 425,
437-438, 451-454, 457-460, 464-470,
474-477, 483, 495, 497, 502, 520-521, 524,
534, 551-552
Ground states, 457-458, 464, 474, 514
Group velocity, 176, 182-183, 186-188, 535, 540, 584
GUT, 167

H

HA, 73, 99, 135, 302-303, 521
Hall effect, 540-541
Harmonic wave, 182, 583

Harmonics, 243-244, 253-259, 261-262, 267-268, 270,
287-288, 292, 324, 372, 501-502, 605
heart, 7, 48, 175, 208, 516, 560
Heat, 458
Heisenberg uncertainty principle, 188-189, 192-193,
535
Helium, 206, 294, 446, 458, 463-470, 473, 476, 478,
481, 550, 605
thermal conductivity, 458
helium atom, 446, 463-465, 469-470, 473, 476, 605
helium-3, 294
Hermite polynomials, 309
hour, 166, 606
Hydrogen, 103-105, 213, 218-220, 222-224, 230-232,
235, 243, 250, 253, 261, 266, 269-292,
293-295, 297, 299-300, 306, 310, 328, 330,
348, 370-372, 374, 378, 380, 383-385, 389,
392-394, 405-407, 410-411, 413-439,
441-443, 446, 449, 463, 465, 467, 470,
473-478, 481, 483, 502-503, 508-509, 511,
520, 534, 547, 602, 604-605
absorption, 103-104, 279-280, 503
angular momentum of, 393-394, 405, 502
emission spectrum, 104, 278
energy levels of, 103, 105, 219, 253, 283, 285, 380,
414, 439, 470
isotopes, 449
metallic, 534
spectrum of, 103-104, 278-279, 292, 414, 439, 470
stationary states of, 483
wave functions of, 270, 282-284, 292, 475
Hydrogen atom, 103, 213, 218-220, 222-224, 230-232,
235, 243, 250, 261, 269-292, 293-295, 330,
370-372, 383-384, 414, 416-417, 422,
425-426, 439, 463, 475, 483, 502, 511, 520,
547, 602, 604-605
mass, 213, 220, 222-224, 231, 235, 243, 276-277,
279, 281, 295, 384, 416, 426, 475, 602
hydrogen chloride, 253
Hydrogen ion, 477-478
Hypothesis, 206
Hz, 393, 544, 575-576

I

Image, 204
imaging, 91, 204
magnetic resonance, 91
Index of refraction, 168, 187
dispersion, 187
Inertia, 235, 244, 253, 266, 328
Initial conditions, 149
Insulators, 533-534, 540-541
Intensity, 10, 15, 205-207, 499, 504, 554, 573
of light, 205-206
Interaction, 1, 88-89, 96-97, 101, 169, 196, 220, 223,
277, 280, 292, 324, 364, 372, 383-385, 389,
394, 407, 411, 414, 416-418, 420-422,
424-429, 434, 437, 439, 441-442, 446,
456-457, 459-460, 462-463, 466, 468, 475,
480, 483, 490, 492-493, 498-500, 504, 511,
518, 520-521, 531, 537, 543, 547, 566
interactions, 91, 96, 103, 196, 279, 437, 459, 466,
468, 481, 483, 489, 492, 497, 500, 505, 537,
540, 543, 546, 558
Interference, 10, 51-52, 167-169, 180-181, 186, 189,
199, 204-208, 210, 325, 606
constructive, 180-181
constructive interference, 181
destructive, 180-181, 186, 189
destructive interference, 180, 186, 189
double slit, 10
mathematics of, 167
of light, 205-206
Interference fringes, 10, 199, 205-206, 208
Interferometer, 70, 205, 208
interferometers, 208
atom, 208
Interferometry, 204-205
Inverse relation, 189
Ion, 294, 466, 474-478, 534
Ionization, 276, 465-467
Ionization limit, 276
Isotope, 294, 411, 442
Isotopes, 3, 449

K

Kinetic energy, 106, 116, 125, 130, 145, 150, 208, 211,
213-215, 235, 252, 294, 364, 418, 426, 473,

513, 528, 547
and momentum, 106, 211
equation for, 145, 513
momentum and, 211, 213
rotational, 252
rotational kinetic energy, 252

L

lanthanides, 472
Laplacian operator, 225
Laser, 96, 103, 132, 143, 187, 204, 439, 483, 491,
    493, 498-500, 505, 550-558, 570-571, 573,
    605
    applications, 491, 550-558, 570-571, 573, 605
    operation, 132
Laser beam, 96, 483, 491, 499, 551-556
Laser beams, 483, 550, 553, 556-557
Laser Cooling, 204, 550-553, 556, 558, 570-571, 605
Laser light, 132, 499
Lasers, 124, 142-143, 492, 550
    applications of, 492, 550
    semiconductor diode laser, 143
lattice, 142, 230-231, 518, 523, 532, 534, 537,
    539-540, 544
law, 72, 106, 147, 165, 297-298, 421, 495
Lead, 11, 31, 43, 56, 75, 92, 127, 152, 167, 180, 193,
    197, 352-353, 377, 424, 459, 483, 512, 544,
    550
    density, 353, 512
lepton, 89
Leptons, 88
life, 301, 370
Lifetime, 88, 467, 469, 490, 492-493, 495, 497-498,
    502, 504, 508, 510, 551-552
lift, 437, 439
Light, 10, 46, 51-52, 83, 90-91, 96-97, 101, 109, 121,
    132, 141, 143, 163, 197-200, 204-208, 272,
    279-280, 306, 315, 330, 418, 425, 469, 483,
    492-494, 497-500, 505, 537-538, 546, 551,
    565, 575, 602
    absorption of, 198, 279-280, 551
    coherent, 51-52, 330, 493
    diffraction, 10, 204-206
    dispersion, 537
    double-slit interference, 10, 205-206
    emission of, 96, 498, 551
    energy of, 200, 279, 418, 425, 497-498, 551
    frequencies of, 96
    interference, 10, 51-52, 199, 204-208
    laser light, 132, 499
    nature of, 51-52, 121, 198, 204, 206
    polarization, 492, 494
    polarization of, 492
    power of, 565
    prism, 200
    properties of, 91, 121, 280
    quanta, 306
    radiation and, 493-494
    scattering, 198, 208
    speed of, 90, 418, 575, 602
    visible, 492
    visible light, 492
    wave properties of, 121
Light waves, 10
Light-emitting diodes (LEDs), 538
Limit, 53, 79, 120, 129, 157, 249, 272, 274, 276, 287,
    320, 327, 364, 379, 384, 389, 425, 442, 467,
    477, 491, 497, 502, 507, 526, 558, 571, 585
Linear dispersion, 540-541
Linear momentum, 162, 551
Linear polarization, 503
Linear superposition, 11, 583
Linewidth, 551, 554
Liquid, 449, 458, 550, 557
Liquids, 270
Load, 565
Loop, 2, 421
Lyman series, 279

M

Macroscopic systems, 167, 550
magnetic dipole moment, 81
Magnetic dipoles, 384-385, 393
Magnetic field, 1-4, 64, 76-86, 88, 91-96, 98, 103, 279,
    337-338, 341, 347-348, 356, 358, 363-364,
    366, 378, 384, 418, 420-421, 423, 425-428,
    434-439, 459, 487, 547-550, 563, 565
Magnetic fields, 11, 279, 338, 340, 383, 414, 420, 428,

494, 546, 550
Magnetic force, 552
Magnetic quantum number, 64, 228, 237, 249,
    252-253, 276, 347, 364, 386-387, 394-395,
    406, 419, 422, 426-427, 438-439, 547-549
Magnetic resonance imaging, 91
Magnetic resonance imaging (MRI), 91
Magnetism, 534, 571
Magnets, 100
magnitude, 3, 13, 47, 59, 82, 91, 95, 168, 220-221,
    358, 369, 371, 384, 386, 388, 393, 409,
    416-417, 428, 438, 442, 463, 466, 522,
    548-549, 555, 592-593
Mass, 3, 80, 88-90, 117, 150, 213, 220-224, 226, 231,
    234-235, 243-244, 253, 263, 265-266,
    276-277, 279, 281, 295, 297, 327, 332, 384,
    416, 418-419, 426, 442, 475, 479-480,
    507-508, 510, 535-538, 540, 551, 575, 602
    atomic, 3, 279, 475, 535, 537
    center of, 220, 222, 226, 253
    conservation of, 88, 226
    measuring, 90, 150, 480
Mathematics, 1, 4-5, 11, 23, 27, 36, 116, 167-168, 219,
    306, 374, 591, 606
Matter, 1, 13, 57, 96, 109, 116, 179, 195, 206, 305,
    370, 393, 399, 446, 458, 483, 497, 524, 546,
    551
    nature of, 206
    normal, 13
    properties of, 1
Matter waves, 206
    de Broglie wavelength, 206
Measurement, 4-5, 8, 10-11, 14-20, 22, 25-29, 31-34,
    35-66, 67-70, 72, 75, 78, 82, 87, 99-100,
    103, 105, 108-110, 155, 161-164, 166-169,
    188, 197, 205, 208, 213, 229, 239-241,
    255-256, 260, 263-265, 267-268, 279, 295,
    314-315, 322, 324, 332, 427-428, 439, 448,
    497, 523, 560-562, 565, 568-570, 598, 599,
    604-605
    uncertainties, 5, 58-60, 68, 155, 188
Mechanical energy, 106
    conservation of, 106
    conservation of energy, 106
    kinetic energy, 106
Mechanical interaction, 498
Mechanical waves, 558, 604
Mechanics, 1, 4-5, 7-8, 10-15, 25, 27-28, 30, 31,
    35-36, 38, 42, 46, 48-49, 52-53, 56, 59, 65,
    67, 69, 71-72, 75, 97, 99, 103, 106, 110, 121,
    133, 142, 155, 161, 163, 165-169, 171, 173,
    175, 178, 180, 184, 192-193, 204-206, 208,
    211, 217-220, 226, 263, 269-270, 293, 297,
    299-300, 303, 306, 311, 315, 321, 324, 329,
    331, 335-336, 363, 377, 383, 409, 413-414,
    418, 420, 424, 441, 445-446, 448, 457, 459,
    479, 483, 488, 496, 507, 511, 541, 543,
    545-571, 573-574, 575, 577, 579, 581,
    583-584, 587-588, 589, 591, 595-597, 599,
    601, 603-606
Mesons, 448
Metals, 215, 472-473, 533-534, 540-541
    alkali, 534
    transition, 472-473, 540
    valence band, 540
metric, 454
Microscope, 204, 215
    resolution, 204
minute, 597
Mirrors, 168
mixtures, 521, 559
Mks units, 2
model, 49, 60-61, 68, 82, 87-88, 90, 96, 103, 116, 124,
    141, 153, 180, 182, 207, 253, 279, 290-291,
    297, 375, 425-428, 456, 471, 483, 493-496,
    511, 513, 517, 520-522, 528, 531-534,
    540-541, 544, 551, 558, 603
Models, 88, 253, 279, 427
Modes, 120, 189, 212, 496, 498
Molecular beam, 142
Molecule, 211, 230, 253, 266, 327-329, 473-478, 481,
    501, 511, 515, 523, 533-534
    kinetic energy, 211, 473
molecules, 103, 204-206, 210, 243, 270, 327-328,
    478, 483, 533, 571
    polar, 243, 270
    splitting of, 483
Moment, 1-3, 19, 46, 73, 77, 80-81, 86, 91-92, 99-100,
    110, 112, 192, 235-236, 244, 253, 266, 276,

290-291, 294, 328, 337, 347, 356, 364,
    371-372, 375, 379, 383-385, 395, 397, 418,
    420-421, 423, 426-428, 433, 438, 443, 450,
    493, 517, 547-548, 550, 573
Moment of inertia, 235, 244, 253
Momentum, 2-3, 46, 59, 61, 64, 70, 80-81, 88, 90-91,
    106-107, 113, 139, 142, 152, 155, 157, 162,
    175-194, 208-209, 211-213, 217-262,
    263-268, 270-271, 275-276, 280-281, 283,
    292, 295, 299-300, 304, 311, 317-321,
    324-325, 332-333, 364, 383-388, 390,
    393-395, 397, 399-402, 405-406, 409-412,
    418, 421-425, 427-429, 431-432, 437, 439,
    448, 450, 467, 470, 501-502, 512, 520,
    535-536, 538-540, 544, 547-548, 551-554,
    563, 587-588, 600, 601, 604-605
    angular, 2-3, 59, 61, 64, 70, 80-81, 88, 91, 162,
        217-262, 263-268, 270-271, 275-276,
        280-281, 283, 292, 295, 299, 364,
        383-388, 390, 393-395, 397, 399-402,
        405-406, 409-412, 418, 421-425,
        427-429, 431-432, 437, 439, 448, 467,
        470, 501-502, 547-548, 551, 553, 563,
        601, 604-605
    angular momentum, 2-3, 59, 61, 64, 70, 80-81, 88,
        91, 162, 217-262, 263-268, 270-271,
        275-276, 280-281, 283, 292, 295, 364,
        383-388, 390, 393-395, 397, 399-402,
        405-406, 418, 421-425, 427-429,
        431-432, 437, 439, 448, 467, 470,
        501-502, 547-548, 551, 563, 601,
        604-605
    center of mass, 220, 222, 253
    components, 3, 59, 61, 70, 80, 162, 180-181, 187,
        189, 226-227, 238, 240, 386, 424, 587
    conservation laws, 88
    conservation of, 88, 106, 162, 187, 208, 226, 280,
        502, 539
    conservation of angular momentum, 88, 162, 226,
        280, 502
    decreasing, 190
    increasing, 183, 188, 242
    kinetic energy and, 106, 208, 418
    linear, 162, 242, 262, 268, 324, 399, 437, 439, 535,
        540, 551, 563
    linear momentum, 162, 551
    relativistic, 88, 90, 418, 422-425, 439, 448
    relativistic momentum, 90
    total, 106, 232, 235, 261, 268, 299, 394-395, 397,
        399-401, 405-406, 410-412, 422-424,
        428, 431, 448, 538, 540, 547
Moon, 169
Motion, 2, 72, 80, 103, 106, 115-116, 141, 148,
    173-175, 180, 182, 187, 193, 196, 198, 204,
    209, 212, 220-224, 226, 231, 234, 243,
    252-253, 270, 285, 297-298, 327-328, 364,
    383, 385, 420, 424, 426, 446, 474-475, 517,
    535, 540, 548, 550, 554, 556-557, 573, 584,
    605
    acceleration, 148
    atomic, 204, 270, 285, 474-475, 517, 535, 548,
        550, 554, 556-557
    in one dimension, 106, 535
    natural, 204, 243
    net force, 556
    projectile, 196
    proper, 180
    radial, 231, 234, 270, 420, 605
    rotational, 252-253, 328
    speed, 2, 174, 198, 550
    translational, 550
    translational motion, 550
    unbound, 116, 173-175, 180, 182, 187, 193, 196,
        198, 204, 209, 212
    uniform, 80, 328, 548
    velocity, 148, 174-175, 182, 187, 221, 535, 540,
        554, 556-557, 573, 584
    vibrational, 253, 328
    wave, 116, 148, 173-175, 180, 182, 187, 193, 196,
        198, 204, 209, 212, 220, 222-224, 234,
        243, 270, 285, 420, 424, 474-475, 517,
        535, 540, 584, 605
    zero-point, 328
MRI, 91
Multiplication, 23, 38, 47, 74, 107, 113, 192, 580, 593
Muon, 88-90, 101, 294
Muons, 88-89

N

nanotechnology, 558
Navigation, 208
Negative charges, 371
net force, 556
neutrino, 88-90, 98, 101, 605
    electron, 88-90, 101
    solar, 88, 90
    tau, 88
Neutrino oscillations, 88-90, 98, 605
Neutrinos, 88-90, 101
Neutron, 88, 294, 411, 442, 449
Neutrons, 3, 205-206, 294, 448
    spin angular momentum of, 448
Nitrogen, 378
noble gases, 472
node, 566
Nodes, 121, 131, 287, 310, 524
normal, 13, 426-428, 517, 534, 548
Normalization, 11-12, 14, 21, 26, 33, 42, 110-112,
        120-121, 126, 130, 132, 145, 150, 152, 156,
        174, 177-178, 184-185, 196, 212, 224,
        236-237, 241, 245-247, 259, 266, 268, 274,
        281, 283-284, 288, 293, 308-309, 312-314,
        330, 331-332, 341, 349, 388, 451, 523, 588,
        597, 599
Nuclear force, 88
Nuclear magnetic resonance (nmr), 91
Nuclear reactors, 88
Nuclear spin, 383, 414, 420, 439
nuclei, 91, 103, 213, 243, 291, 327-328, 348, 473-475,
        477
    atomic, 474-475, 477
Nucleons, 294
Nucleus, 91, 166-168, 213, 270-271, 276, 285-288,
        293-294, 347-348, 356, 358, 371, 378, 383,
        405, 411, 424, 442, 449, 463, 466, 470, 477
    beta decay, 294
    properties of, 91
    radius of, 287-288, 293-294
    total angular momentum of, 405

O
opposition, 161
Optical molasses, 556-558
Optics, 10, 51, 187, 199-200, 203, 205-206, 210, 330,
        505, 571
orbital angular momentum, 2-3, 227-230, 233-235,
        237, 239-240, 247, 255, 257, 261, 364,
        384-387, 394, 405, 418, 422-424, 427-428,
        431, 437, 501, 601
Orbital motion, 364, 383, 420, 426
orbits, 218, 470, 604
Oscillation, 90, 94-95, 100, 121, 141, 323, 330, 424,
        490, 585
    neutrinos, 90
Oscillations, 11, 88-90, 95-96, 98, 101, 490, 604-606
    amplitude of, 95
    angular frequency, 95
    driven, 606
    lifetime of, 88, 490
    neutrino, 88-90, 98, 101, 605
    resonance and, 98
    solar, 88, 90
Oscillators, 297-298, 306, 517
Oxygen, 211
oxygen molecule, 211

P
parabola, 297-298, 327, 536
paradigm, 28, 603
Particle model, 207
Particle physics, 88
Particles, 1-2, 4, 32-33, 61, 68-70, 88-90, 100, 103,
        116, 121, 129, 161-166, 173, 181, 187, 196,
        198, 202, 204-207, 209-210, 211, 213-214,
        218-220, 222, 226, 297, 306, 385, 389-390,
        394-395, 397-401, 407, 410, 412, 445-478,
        479-481, 536-537, 539, 547, 558, 560, 566,
        604-605
    angular momentum of, 2, 394, 397, 448
    system of, 165, 218, 220, 390, 394, 397, 400, 407,
        446-450, 454-461, 457-461, 475, 478,
        558
    wave-particle duality, 121, 173, 205, 207
Paschen series, 279
Path, 9, 50-52, 206-208, 235
Pauli exclusion principle, 446, 448, 454, 459, 463,
        470, 478, 511, 534

Pauli, Wolfgang, 88
pc, 90, 448, 500, 595
Period, 141, 236, 323, 421, 490, 517, 530, 583-584,
        604
    of wave, 517
Periodic table, 3, 446, 463, 470-473, 478
    groups, 473
periodicity, 236, 238, 520, 530, 585
Permeability, 575
Permittivity, 575
Phase, 14, 18, 20-21, 24-25, 31-32, 47, 52, 74-75,
        78-79, 81, 85, 87, 97, 112, 119-120, 133,
        167-169, 174-176, 181-183, 186-189, 208,
        212, 224, 241, 290-291, 298, 308, 321-322,
        349, 447, 458, 484, 522, 524, 535, 540, 558,
        563-564, 574, 583-584, 592-593
Phase constant, 583-584
Phase difference, 168, 189
Phase velocity, 174-176, 182-183, 186-188, 535, 540,
        584
phases, 18, 32, 52, 75, 110, 189, 241, 325
Phonon, 538-539, 544
Photon, 103-104, 121, 207-208, 279-280, 491, 499,
        502-503, 539-540, 544, 551-553, 559
    energy of, 279, 551
    radiation pressure and, 551
Photons, 88, 96-97, 103-104, 143, 168-169, 206-207,
        306, 425, 448, 495, 497-499, 509, 538-540,
        544, 551-555, 559
    absorption of, 539, 551
    emission of, 96, 103, 495, 498, 551
    energy of, 425, 497-498, 551
    wavelength of, 143
Photovoltaic cells, 539
physical change, 78
Physical constants, 575-576
Physical optics, 199
    interference, 199
physical properties, 161
Physical quantity, 4
physical state, 4, 119, 448
physics, 1, 3, 7-8, 10-12, 29-30, 31, 35, 52, 66, 67,
        71-72, 74, 88, 90-91, 98, 99, 103, 148, 153,
        155, 161, 171, 173-174, 192, 200, 204, 210,
        211, 217-218, 223, 226, 236, 247, 261, 263,
        269, 279, 292, 293, 297-298, 330, 331, 335,
        374, 377, 383, 407, 409, 413-414, 425,
        438-439, 441, 445-446, 459, 473, 478, 479,
        483, 505, 507, 511, 541, 543, 545, 550, 558,
        571, 573, 575, 577, 579, 582, 583, 589, 591,
        595, 599, 601, 603, 606-607
Pi, 162
Pi meson, 162
Pitch, 556
Plane, 5, 18, 70, 83, 100, 143, 163, 234-235, 285-287,
        294, 540, 591-593
Polar, 43, 78-79, 234, 243-244, 249-251, 256-259,
        261, 265, 270, 274, 276, 371, 591-593
Polarization, 492, 494, 501, 503, 559
    linear polarization, 503
population, 164, 495, 497, 508
Position, 46, 106-107, 109-114, 122, 124, 129,
        139-142, 148, 150, 152, 155-156, 173, 175,
        177-179, 186-193, 205, 209, 211-213, 218,
        220-226, 230, 234, 236-237, 241, 243-244,
        263, 267, 271, 281, 285, 287-289, 293-294,
        299-300, 303-304, 311-312, 315, 317-325,
        332, 371, 387, 412, 420-422, 450, 456-457,
        464, 474, 480, 501, 523, 529, 531, 585,
        587-588, 595, 599-600
Position vector, 220, 222
Positron, 89, 162, 294, 411
Potential, 1, 76, 106, 108, 114-117, 119-120, 122-132,
        142-152, 155-157, 159, 173-174, 192-201,
        203-204, 208-209, 213-215, 218-220,
        222-224, 233-236, 238, 244, 261, 270-271,
        276, 278-279, 286, 295, 297-300, 303-304,
        307, 310, 321, 325, 327-328, 332-334,
        336-337, 347, 352, 356, 364, 370-371,
        378-380, 414, 417-418, 427, 450, 453, 456,
        458-459, 462-463, 466, 468-469, 473, 475,
        479-481, 501, 508, 510, 511-514, 522-523,
        526, 528-533, 536, 540-541, 547-549, 573
    calculation of, 142, 149, 528
Potential difference, 529
Potential energy, 1, 76, 106, 108, 114-117, 119-120,
        122-132, 142-144, 150-152, 157, 173-174,
        192-196, 201, 204, 208-209, 213-215,
        218-220, 222, 224, 234-236, 244, 261,

270-271, 276, 278, 295, 336-337, 347, 352,
        356, 364, 370-371, 379-380, 414, 418, 427,
        450, 453, 456, 459, 462-463, 466, 468-469,
        473, 475, 511, 513, 523, 528-529, 533, 536,
        540-541, 547-549
    calculating, 224, 456
    chemical, 142
    elastic, 116
    electric, 132, 208, 370-371, 379-380, 414, 536,
        540-541
    electrical, 536
    gravitational, 208
    zero of, 76, 194, 276, 548
Potential wells, 143, 146, 150, 159, 173, 193, 198, 370
Power, 36, 72, 246-247, 259, 273-274, 285, 299, 306,
        322, 338-339, 341, 343, 377, 508, 560-561,
        565, 587
    of light, 565
Precession, 61, 76, 79-82, 84-87, 91, 93-95, 98, 99,
        330, 422, 548, 550, 563-566, 573, 605
Pressure, 550-551, 554
    radiation, 551, 554
    thermal, 550-551, 554
Princeton University, 153
Principal quantum number, 275-276, 281, 292
Principal quantum number n, 275-276, 281, 292
Prism, 200
Probability, 5, 7-10, 14-15, 17-19, 21, 23, 25-26,
        28-29, 31, 33, 45, 48-54, 62-63, 69-70,
        74-75, 78-79, 81-82, 84-90, 94-97, 99-101,
        105, 108-115, 121-123, 129, 131-132,
        134-135, 141, 143, 145, 150, 152, 155-157,
        162, 164-166, 168, 171, 176-179, 184-187,
        192, 197-198, 202-204, 206-207, 211,
        213-215, 218, 229-230, 237, 239-243,
        255-257, 259, 262, 265-268, 272, 280,
        285-292, 293-294, 308, 310-311, 314-315,
        318-326, 330, 331-332, 349, 353, 385, 424,
        448, 450, 453-455, 457-458, 460, 469,
        475-476, 479-480, 483, 486-491, 496,
        499-500, 504, 507-509, 514, 521, 523-524,
        530, 535, 538, 541, 559-560, 568, 570, 588,
        595-598, 599-600
Probability density, 110-111, 113-114, 121, 141, 150,
        156, 176-177, 184, 186-187, 206, 211, 213,
        240-242, 256-257, 262, 285-287, 292, 294,
        353, 385, 450, 453-454, 457-458, 475,
        523-524, 588, 598, 599
probe, 168, 205
products, 11-13, 22, 28, 31, 47, 53, 56, 75, 162, 261,
        270, 402, 406, 501, 580-581, 585
projectile, 52, 196
Projection, 3, 12, 28, 46-50, 52, 65, 70, 108-110, 112,
        133, 163, 178-179, 188, 207, 239, 257,
        312-313, 315, 386, 402, 431-433, 456, 502,
        585
Proportionality, 179, 193, 308, 431-432
Proton, 88, 211, 218, 222, 230, 270-271, 294,
        383-385, 389, 393-394, 406, 409-411,
        420-421, 425-426, 442, 446, 449, 451, 465,
        473-478, 575, 602
Protons, 3, 294, 446, 448, 473-476, 536, 558
    mass of, 536
    spin angular momentum of, 448

Q
Quadratic relation, 536
Quanta, 305-306
Quantization, 3, 116, 118-120, 124, 143, 174, 194,
        196, 247, 275, 292, 548
    atomic, 3, 143, 292, 548
    of energy, 119, 124, 196
Quantized, 25, 28, 64, 103-153, 155-159, 173-174,
        196, 219, 228, 230, 270, 276, 425, 498, 544,
        604
Quantum computers, 166, 562
quantum mechanical tunneling, 200, 202, 204
Quantum mechanics, 1, 4-5, 7-8, 10-15, 25, 27-28, 30,
        31, 35-36, 38, 42, 46, 48-49, 52-53, 56, 59,
        65, 67, 71-72, 75, 97, 99, 103, 106, 110, 121,
        133, 142, 155, 161, 163, 165-167, 169, 171,
        173, 175, 178, 180, 184, 192-193, 204-206,
        208, 211, 217-218, 220, 226, 263, 269, 293,
        297, 331, 335-336, 363, 377, 383, 409,
        413-414, 418, 420, 424, 441, 445-446, 448,
        459, 479, 483, 488, 507, 511, 541, 543,
        545-571, 573-574, 575, 577, 579, 581,
        583-584, 587-588, 589, 591, 595-597, 599,
        601, 603-606

electron spin, 414, 418
fundamental particles, 446
history of, 1, 30, 218
Pauli exclusion principle, 446, 448, 459, 511
semiconductors, 142, 541, 605
tunneling, 173, 204
wave functions, 11, 173, 175, 184, 192-193, 208,
211, 220, 293, 414, 420, 511, 541, 587,
605
Quantum number, 64, 89, 118-119, 228, 236-237, 240,
247, 249, 252-253, 255, 257, 270-271,
275-276, 281, 292, 343, 347, 364, 386-387,
394-396, 399, 406, 419, 422-424, 426-427,
429, 438-439, 469-470, 547-549, 551
angular momentum quantum number, 64, 228, 247,
255, 257, 270-271, 275-276, 281, 386,
394, 406, 423-424, 551
magnetic, 64, 228, 237, 249, 252-253, 276, 347,
364, 386-387, 394-396, 399, 406, 419,
422-423, 426-427, 438-439, 547-549
magnetic quantum number, 64, 228, 237, 249,
252-253, 276, 347, 364, 386-387,
394-395, 406, 419, 422, 426-427,
438-439, 547-549
orbital, 228, 237, 240, 247, 255, 257, 364, 386-387,
394, 422-424, 426-427, 470, 547
principal, 275-276, 281, 292
principal quantum number, 275-276, 281, 292
spin, 64, 89, 228, 237, 247, 249, 343, 347, 364,
386-387, 394-395, 399, 406, 419,
422-424, 426-427, 439, 469-470, 547
quantum state, 4, 6, 10-11, 14, 18, 21-22, 30, 36,
48-49, 64-65, 97, 105, 107-110, 133, 150,
162, 166-167, 171, 179, 207, 222, 349, 389,
446, 448-449, 464, 478, 483-484, 492, 538,
558, 568, 605
quantum tunneling, 200, 210
Quantum well devices, 142
lasers, 142
Quark, 384

R
RA, 472
rad, 510
Radial motion, 270
Radial wave functions, 270, 281-283, 286, 292
Radiation, 141, 213, 290, 493-498, 551-552, 554, 605
beta, 213
blackbody, 493-496
defined, 495, 498
distribution of, 141, 554
electromagnetic, 141, 494-495, 497-498
environmental, 498
particle, 141, 213, 605
thermal, 494-496, 551, 554
Radiation pressure, 551, 554
radio astronomy, 393
radioactive decay, 129, 200
Radius, 2, 127, 129, 234, 243, 250, 256-257, 265-266,
271, 277, 281, 286-289, 292, 293-294, 392,
423-424, 464, 500, 573, 575, 591, 602
Rainbow, 143
Randomness, 30, 61, 162
ranges, 245, 276
Rate equation, 496-497
Reaction, 88
Recoil, 551-552
recombination, 8, 231
reduction, 48, 330
Reflection, 198-199, 202-203, 209, 214, 222, 308,
474, 593
Reflection coefficient, 198, 202, 214
Refraction, 168, 187
waves, 187
Relative motion, 220, 222-224, 231
Relative velocity, 221
Relativistic kinetic energy, 418
Relativity, 166, 208, 213, 279, 416, 418, 540
energy and, 208, 418
general, 166, 208
general theory of, 208
measurements, 166, 279
momentum and, 213
special, 279
speed of light, 418
theory of, 208
research, 49, 166, 539, 546, 550, 558, 560, 570
applied, 550
basic, 546, 558

Resolution, 204, 207, 292, 424, 441-442
angular, 292, 424
microscope, 204
Resonance, 91, 95-96, 98, 101, 103, 200, 209, 348,
358, 483, 487, 489-491, 499-500, 551,
554-556, 605
spin-orbit, 605
Resonance frequency, 91, 554, 556
Resonance peak, 491
Rest energy, 418
Rest mass, 277, 416, 418
Resultant, 6, 10, 149, 180, 209, 235, 292, 309, 338,
346, 352, 354-355, 364-366, 368-369, 372,
392, 401, 418, 420, 422, 426, 430, 461, 463,
492, 548, 556-557, 567, 593
Resultant vector, 10, 346, 354-355
Ring system, 238
Rotation, 42, 94, 208, 238, 328, 396, 563-565, 574
molecular, 328
Rotational kinetic energy, 252
Rotational motion, 253
moment of inertia, 253
Rydberg constant, 279, 575

S
Scalar product, 11-12, 422, 580
Scalars, 13
Scale factor, 185
science, 153, 607
physics, 153, 607
Screening, 470-471, 473
second, 5-10, 12-13, 15-16, 18-19, 24, 33, 41, 44-46,
49-52, 56-57, 61, 68-70, 72, 82, 85, 97, 100,
106, 117, 125-126, 129, 138, 140, 143,
147-148, 168, 178, 182, 206, 241, 245-246,
264, 272, 279, 298, 311, 317, 319, 339-340,
342-343, 349, 352-353, 355-360, 365,
367-370, 372, 375, 378-380, 384, 389, 402,
418, 420, 447, 461, 463, 466-468, 472, 487,
489, 493, 495, 517, 520-521, 537, 546, 550,
552, 558, 583
selection rule, 252, 280, 469, 502
Selection rules, 97, 132, 280, 403, 469, 487, 500-502,
504, 551, 605
Semiconductor devices, 142
Semiconductor diode, 143
Semiconductors, 142, 521, 533, 537-538, 540-541,
544, 605
shell, 276, 405, 470, 534
silicon, 512, 534, 539
Silver, 1, 3, 76, 363
Sinc function, 491-492, 586
Single-slit diffraction, 10, 205
Singularity, 424
Sinusoidal wave, 194, 583-584
Sinusoidal waves, 174, 179-180, 212
Sodium, 103, 347-348, 356, 358, 534, 573
solar neutrino, 88, 90
problem, 88, 90
Solar neutrino problem, 88
Solar neutrinos, 88
Solids, 103, 270, 459, 511, 518, 520-521, 533-534,
539-540, 544
energy bands, 521
molecules, 103, 270, 533
solutions, 41, 76, 83, 93, 105, 115, 117-118, 124-126,
128-130, 132-133, 141, 143-147, 149-150,
153, 158, 174, 194-197, 200-202, 234-236,
238, 243-247, 249, 253, 261, 272-274, 281,
297, 299, 319, 328, 336-337, 340-343, 363,
365, 371, 375, 450-451, 463, 483, 513, 517,
532-533, 582, 583-584, 604
basic, 253, 604
Sound, 535
Sound waves, 535
Space, 1, 4, 10-11, 13-14, 22-23, 40, 70, 89, 106, 109,
112-113, 116, 118, 136, 150, 177, 179-180,
183-186, 188-192, 204, 209, 211-212, 238,
285, 318-321, 325, 333, 340, 344, 367,
371-372, 384, 389-390, 396, 447, 451, 456,
462, 478, 486, 489, 514, 518, 520, 522, 526,
535, 539, 546, 548, 554, 558, 561, 575,
583-584, 587-588, 590, 600, 605
at, 1, 10-11, 22, 70, 116, 118, 136, 150, 177, 180,
183-184, 186, 188-189, 191, 209, 211,
238, 285, 321, 325, 340, 344, 371, 447,
478, 486, 489, 518, 520, 535, 539, 546,
548, 554, 561, 584, 587
Spatial frequency, 241, 585

Specific heat, 458
Spectra, 277, 300, 328, 386, 446
electromagnetic, 277
schematic, 328
Spectral line, 104
Spectroscopy, 97, 103, 105, 292, 305, 348, 383, 414,
439, 459, 505, 605
spectrum, 101, 103-105, 109, 111, 119, 121-123, 196,
238, 243, 252, 275-276, 278-279, 292, 299,
302-303, 305-306, 310, 328, 334, 337,
364-365, 386, 388, 393, 401, 414, 439,
469-470, 508, 511, 521, 531, 533-534, 539,
605
absorption, 103-104, 279, 539
emission, 103-104, 252, 278-279, 508
Speed, 2, 90, 100, 174, 176, 198, 211, 418, 421, 550,
575, 583, 589, 602
kinetic energy and, 418
of light, 90, 418, 575, 602
wave, 174, 176, 198, 211, 583, 589
Speed of light, 90, 418, 575, 602
relativity, 418
Spherical symmetry, 243, 279, 371
spin, 2-12, 14-19, 21-25, 28-30, 31-34, 36-37, 39,
42-47, 49, 51-53, 58-66, 67-70, 73, 76-82,
84-92, 94-96, 98, 99-101, 103, 105-106,
108-110, 132, 161-165, 167, 171, 188, 207,
227-230, 237, 239, 247, 249, 279-280, 315,
330, 337-341, 343, 347, 349, 356, 364, 378,
383-387, 389-390, 392-395, 397-401,
405-407, 409-412, 414, 416, 418-428,
432-435, 439, 441-442, 446-465, 467,
469-470, 476-478, 479-481, 483, 487, 490,
502, 509, 534, 546-547, 558-560, 563-566,
570-571, 574, 595, 601, 603-605
of electron, 534
Spin quantum number, 64, 469
Spin-1/2 particle, 7, 77, 81, 86, 88, 91, 167, 337, 383,
565
Spontaneous emission, 495-498, 502, 504, 551-552,
554-555, 558
SS, 541
Standard deviation, 53-56, 184, 188, 596-598
Standard model, 88
Standing waves, 120
stars, 88
neutron, 88
Stationary states, 74, 79, 483, 495-496
Steel, 153
Stern-Gerlach experiment, 1-5, 28, 30, 61, 64,
546-547, 605
Stimulated emission, 490, 495
Stress, 110, 604
strong nuclear force, 88
Subshell, 470-472
Subtraction, 593
succession, 6-7, 9, 55
Sun, 2, 88, 90, 101, 161, 218
oscillations, 88, 90, 101
physical properties of, 161
Sunlight, 10, 206
Superconductivity, 343, 534
Superposition, 11, 19-21, 29, 34, 51-52, 74-75, 85, 94,
97, 101, 133, 135, 138-141, 157, 161,
166-169, 176, 178-183, 186, 209, 239-242,
254, 256, 260, 290-291, 294-295, 314,
322-326, 330, 375, 392, 447, 515, 522, 530,
535, 540, 559-562, 565-566, 568, 570,
573-574, 583-584, 587
of wave, 135, 180, 587
quantum computers, 166, 562
Superposition principle, 583
Symmetry, 97, 122, 126, 132, 156, 243, 253, 259, 279,
310, 318, 371-372, 380, 448-449, 454, 457,
459, 474, 478, 479, 502, 514, 523, 530, 577
System, 4-5, 7-8, 10-13, 15-17, 20, 24-28, 32-33,
36-37, 39-40, 42, 44, 46, 48-49, 53-54, 56,
60-64, 66, 67-70, 72-78, 80-82, 84, 88-89,
91, 94-98, 99-101, 103-106, 108, 113,
116-117, 119, 121-122, 129, 133-136, 139,
157, 161-162, 164-165, 168-169, 171, 175,
211, 218-224, 226, 228, 231, 234, 238-240,
243, 253, 259, 263-264, 270, 290-291,
297-299, 303, 306, 310, 322, 324, 332-334,
336-337, 339, 341, 343-344, 347, 356, 358,
360, 363, 366-367, 371-372, 375, 377-381,
389-390, 394, 397, 400, 406-407, 409-412,
426, 446-455, 457-464, 466-467, 469, 473,
475, 478, 479-481, 483-491, 493, 496-497,

502, 507, 513-516, 520-521, 523, 525-526,
528, 531, 533-534, 544, 547, 550-551,
558-561, 563, 565, 567-569, 573-574,
584-585, 587-588, 589, 605
Systems, 10, 23, 25, 27-29, 44, 52-53, 61, 64-65, 73,
81, 88, 90-91, 97, 103, 111, 115, 118, 124,
133, 141-142, 150, 153, 166-167, 176, 196,
228, 294, 297, 299, 304, 306, 310, 329, 332,
360, 367, 446-449, 457-458, 467, 473, 478,
483, 511-541, 543-544, 550, 558-559, 587,
602, 603-605
  energy of, 133, 294, 467, 513-514, 521, 526,
    528-530, 535-536
  isolated, 513, 515, 528-529, 531, 540, 544
  ordered, 23, 61

T
taste, 109, 558, 570
technology, 142, 166, 210, 538-539
Temperature, 211, 457-459, 494-495, 535, 549-550,
558, 573
  absolute, 457
  blackbody radiation and, 494
  energy and, 459
  specific heat and, 458
Theoretical model, 103
Theory, 1, 7, 10, 36, 49, 52, 72, 88, 97, 132, 145, 161,
163-164, 166, 169, 197, 205, 208, 218, 299,
330, 335-375, 377-381, 383-384, 388-389,
392-393, 398, 414, 419, 422-424, 426,
429-431, 434, 436, 459, 467, 483-505,
507-510, 515, 547, 558, 561, 571, 595,
604-605
Theory of relativity, 208
Thermal conductivity, 458
thermal energy, 457, 535, 550
  absolute zero, 457
  temperature, 457, 535, 550
Thermal equilibrium, 494-496
Thermodynamics, 457
Thermonuclear reactions, 88
Time, 8, 27-28, 53, 61, 68, 71-98, 99-101, 103, 106,
124, 132-136, 139, 141-142, 145, 148, 153,
155, 163-164, 167, 174, 176, 180-181,
183-185, 187-189, 204, 210, 211-212,
219-220, 241-243, 262, 266, 290-291, 295,
299, 309, 315, 321-326, 330, 332-333, 400,
469, 483-505, 507-510, 517-518, 528,
535-536, 539, 546, 552, 554, 558, 561, 563,
573, 583-584, 587, 589-590, 597-598, 600,
604-605
  beginning of, 95
  equation of, 80, 517
  measurement of, 27-28, 68, 75, 155, 163, 295, 497
  Planck, 496
  uncertainty principle, 188-189, 211, 535, 546, 605
Time constant, 487-488
Torque, 80-81, 226, 393-394, 550
  sign, 393
Total angular momentum, 394-395, 397, 399-400,
405-406, 422-423, 431, 547
Total energy, 28, 72, 76, 97, 106, 417, 528
touch, 204, 540
Trajectory, 192
Transistors, 540
transition metals, 472-473
Transitions, 91, 94-95, 97, 103-104, 132, 252,
279-280, 305, 317, 324, 328-329, 358, 403,
415, 425, 459, 469, 483, 495-496, 500,
502-504, 509, 538-540, 544
  allowed, 97, 103, 132, 252, 280, 328, 403, 415,
    459, 500, 502-503, 509, 538, 540
  vibrational, 328-329
translation, 111, 113
Translational motion, 550
Transmission, 197-200, 202-203, 214-215
Transmission coefficient, 197-198
Trigonometric functions, 174, 501, 593
trigonometry, 592, 594
tritium, 294
troughs, 535
Tunneling current, 215
Turning point, 150

U
Uncertainty, 56, 58-59, 65, 157, 184-185, 188-189,
192-193, 209, 211-213, 218, 304, 320-321,
325, 331, 367, 491, 497, 535, 546, 569,

587-588, 597, 600, 605
Uncertainty principle, 58-59, 65, 188-189, 192-193,
211, 213, 218, 320, 367, 535, 546, 605
Unit vectors, 11-13, 23, 38, 61
Unit volume, 494
Units, 2, 521, 549, 587
universe, 90, 393, 446, 558
Uranium, 103, 294
Uranium-238, 294
UT, 138-139, 581

V
Vacuum, 204, 306, 425, 497-498, 550, 575
Valence band, 142-143, 535, 538-540
valence electrons, 459, 534
valence shell, 534
vapor, 142
variation, 8, 347, 356, 492
Vector, 8, 10-14, 18-19, 21-23, 26, 31-32, 36, 40, 43,
48-49, 59-61, 65, 68, 74, 79-82, 84, 87, 89,
92-93, 100-101, 108-112, 117-121, 125, 130,
133-135, 143-144, 150, 155, 167, 171,
174-175, 179, 187, 201, 205, 207, 212, 220,
222, 239, 313, 315-316, 346, 348-349,
354-355, 357-360, 386, 389-390, 421, 431,
448-452, 460, 464-465, 478, 484, 492, 494,
501, 503, 513, 517-518, 526, 530, 536, 551,
553, 558, 560, 563-564, 569-570, 574,
579-581, 583-585, 587, 591, 599
Vectors, 10-13, 15, 23, 25, 30, 31, 36-38, 61, 64, 73,
97, 106, 118-119, 132, 144-145, 171, 195,
315-316, 341, 349, 356, 361, 389, 400, 406,
449, 451-452, 462, 464, 536, 582, 584-585,
587, 605
  component, 10, 12, 15, 31, 36, 61, 64, 97, 171, 349
  components of, 25, 61, 587
  decomposition of, 585, 587
  force, 106
  magnitude of, 13
  position, 106, 315, 464, 585, 587
  properties of, 11-12
  resultant, 10
  unit, 11-13, 23, 38, 61, 64, 315-316
  velocity, 584
  zero, 61, 97, 118, 132, 144, 361, 451-452, 464, 582
Velocity, 148, 174-176, 182-183, 186-188, 221,
417-418, 421, 535, 540, 551-558, 573,
583-584, 598
  average, 552, 598
  momentum and, 175-176
  relative, 221
  relative velocity, 221
  signs of, 174
  wave, 148, 174-176, 182-183, 186-188, 535, 540,
    551, 553, 583-584
Vibrational motion, 253
vibrations, 327-328, 544, 605
Viscosity, 458
Visible light, 492
Voltage, 204, 215
Volts, 213
Volume, 8, 30, 224-225, 284-285, 450, 494, 520,
526-527
  unit volume, 494

W
walking, 211
Water, 199, 583
watts, 499
Wave equation, 583, 589
Wave function, 11, 107-114, 116-122, 124-127,
129-133, 135-139, 143-150, 152-153,
155-157, 167, 173-176, 178-181, 183-186,
189-191, 194-197, 199-200, 202-203, 206,
208-209, 211, 213, 218, 222-225, 230,
234-237, 240-241, 243-244, 254-255,
257-261, 270, 272, 274-276, 281, 283-288,
290-291, 293, 318, 347, 352, 372, 375, 379,
389, 392-393, 424, 450-454, 457, 460-464,
474-475, 520, 523-526, 528-532, 588,
589-590, 599-600, 604-605
  boundary conditions, 118-119, 124-126, 145, 152,
    195-197, 199, 236, 524
  drawing, 147
  energy and, 149, 199, 203, 208, 291
  normalization of, 178, 184, 224
  radial wave functions, 270, 281, 283, 286
Wave functions, 11, 107, 113, 118-120, 122-123,

127-132, 143, 147, 149, 153, 157, 159,
173-175, 177, 184, 190, 192-195, 208-210,
211, 220, 223-224, 230, 240, 243, 245, 254,
256-257, 261, 270, 272, 274, 281-284,
286-287, 290, 292, 293, 306, 372, 403, 414,
419-420, 452-453, 456, 464, 474-476, 511,
513-515, 518-519, 521, 523-526, 530-531,
537, 541, 587, 605
Wave packets, 177, 180, 190, 210, 540, 605
Waveform, 333
Wavelength, 104, 120-121, 130-131, 143-147,
175-176, 180, 182, 190, 199-200, 205-206,
208-209, 279-280, 294, 393, 442, 458, 492,
500, 511, 520, 524-526, 530, 535, 543-544,
551, 553, 583-584, 587, 600
  of electrons, 143, 535
  rest, 551
Wavelengths, 105, 120, 143, 180, 190, 199, 211, 459,
584
  of sinusoidal waves, 180
Wave-particle duality, 121, 173, 175, 180, 190, 205,
207
Waves, 10, 120-121, 174, 179-180, 182, 186-187,
189, 196-197, 199, 203, 205-206, 212, 535,
558, 583-588, 604, 606
  amplitude, 10, 121, 179-180, 196-197, 583
  electromagnetic, 583
  electron, 121, 535
  frequency, 583-585
  intensity, 10, 205-206
  interference, 10, 180, 186, 189, 199, 205-206, 606
  mathematical description, 10
  motion, 174, 180, 182, 187, 196, 212, 535, 584
  motion of, 180, 182, 187, 196, 212, 535, 584
  phase of, 558
  refraction, 187
  sound, 535
  sound waves, 535
  speed, 174, 583
  standing waves, 120
  transverse, 205
  types of, 583, 606
  wavelength, 120-121, 180, 182, 199, 205-206, 535,
    583-584, 587
weak force, 88
Weak interaction, 88-89, 537
week, 604-605
Weight, 165
Wires, 143, 541
Work, 7, 40, 91, 117, 173, 175, 187, 204, 215, 220,
228, 247, 287, 316, 343-344, 367, 399, 425,
429, 436, 441, 446, 478, 527, 533, 535, 603,
606-607
  sign of, 175

X
x-axis, 5-7, 16, 18-19, 24, 45, 79, 82, 450, 549, 560,
563-564

Y
y-axis, 5, 24-25, 100, 564-565, 574
year, 558, 603-604

Z
Zeeman effect, 414, 420, 424-428, 434, 436-437, 547,
556, 605
Zeeman splitting, 439
zero, 24, 48, 51, 54, 56, 61, 76, 82, 84, 87, 97,
116-118, 120-121, 129-130, 132, 135-136,
140, 144, 147, 149, 155, 173, 177, 186, 194,
196, 198-199, 202-203, 226-227, 234-236,
243-244, 246, 254, 259, 273-276, 297-298,
304, 306, 310, 314, 317-318, 321, 324,
327-328, 337, 340, 346, 351, 353-354,
359-361, 365-366, 368, 372-373, 378-380,
384, 390, 393, 418, 423, 437, 451-452, 454,
457-458, 464-465, 476-477, 479, 481,
488-489, 496, 500-502, 516, 520, 528, 531,
533, 535, 548, 551, 556, 577, 582, 597
  absolute, 198, 276, 310, 457
  of potential energy, 76, 194, 276, 533
zero-point energy, 304
zinc, 473